A & P
TECHNICIAN
POWERPLANT
TEXTBOOK

2nd Edition

International Standard Book Number 0-89100-396-7
For sale by: IAP, Inc., A Hawks Industries Company
Mail To: P.O. Box 10000, Casper, WY 82602-1000
Ship To: 7383 6WN Road, Casper, WY 82604-1835
(800) 443-9250 ❖ (307) 266-3838 ❖ FAX: (307) 472-5106
WCB0592 Printed in the USA

Library of Congress Cataloging-in-Publication Data

A & P technician powerplant textbook -- 2nd ed.
  p. cm.
Includes index
"Order number EA-ITP-P2."
ISBN 0-89100-396-7 (pbk.)
  1. Airplanes--Motors--Maintenance and repair. I. IAP, Inc.
II. Title: A and P technician powerplant textbook.
TL701.5.A17 1992
629.134'353--dc20

92-3012
CIP

Preface

Certified Aviation Maintenance Technician Schools all operate under individual Federal Aviation Administration approvals, and all have in their approved curriculum enough information to satisfy the FAA that anyone completing their course will meet the knowledge requirements for certification as a technician.

Realizing the need for updated information, presented in a format that is in keeping with the latest developments in education technology, IAP, Inc., is offering an Integrated Training Program (ITP) that presents basic information needed for technician certification, in a form that will provide a good foundation in aviation maintenance knowledge. The ITP training manuals, workbooks, study guides, and audiovisuals are designed to follow the FAA written examinations and are written to the level required for the FAR Part 147 schools.

All of this material can be used by an individual preparing for certification on his own, or by schools preparing groups of individuals for certification under FAR Part 65.

One of the most basic premises of aviation maintenance is that all operations must be carried out according to FAA-approved data, and all information of a specific nature furnished by the manufacturer of an aircraft, powerplant, or component must be followed in detail. These training manuals are, of necessity, general in nature and cover a wide scope of aircraft, powerplants, and components. Because of this, it must be understood that they should *never* be allowed to take precedence over specific information furnished by the manufacturer.

The authors and publishers of this Integrated Training Program wish to express our appreciation to the various manufacturers, Aviation Maintenance Technician Schools, and FAA personnel who have aided our efforts to provide this coordinated training material to meet the challenge of better training for aviation maintenance technicians.

Table of Contents

Chapter IV   Engine Maintenance And Operation   4-1

Chapter I
Reciprocating Engines

The lack of a practical propulsion system has been the limiting factor in the development of mechanical devices throughout our history. Leonardo daVinci conceived a flying machine, the aerial screw, in 1483, but with no means of propulsion it was never developed.

The first patent for a heat engine was taken out by John Barber in England in 1791; this was a turbine engine. The first piston engine that could be considered practical was built by Etienne Lenoir in France in 1860. The next major breakthrough in piston engines came in 1876 when Dr. Nikolaus Otto developed the four-stroke, five-event cycle. It is this operating cycle which is used for modern piston-type aircraft engines.

A. Comparison Of Aircraft Powerplants

For an aircraft to remain in level unaccelerated flight, a thrust must be provided that is equal to and opposite in direction to the aircraft drag. This thrust, or propulsive force, is provided by a suitable type of heat engine.

All heat engines have in common the ability to convert heat energy into mechanical energy, by the flow of some fluid mass (the fuel/air mixture) through the engine. In all cases, the heat energy is released at a point in the cycle where the pressure is high, relative to the atmosphere.

The propulsive force is obtained by the displacement of a working fluid (not necessarily the same fluid used within the engine) in a direction opposite to that in which the airplane is propelled. This is an application of Newton's third law of motion. Air is the principle fluid used for propulsion in every type of powerplant except the rocket, in which the by-products of combustion are accelerated and displaced.

The propellers of aircraft powered by reciprocating or turboprop engines accelerate a large mass of air through a small velocity change. The fluid (air) used for the propulsive force is a different quantity than that used within the engine to produce the mechanical energy. Turbofan and turbo-jet engines ac-

celerate a smaller quantity of air through a large velocity change. Turbojet engines use the same working fluid for propulsive force that is used within the engine.

B. Types Of Reciprocating Engines

Many types of reciprocating engines have been designed since the Wright Brothers first used their four-cylinder in-line engine to make aviation history. Reciprocating engines may be classified according to cylinder arrangement with respect to the crankshaft (in-line, V-type, radial, and opposed) or according to the method of cooling (liquid-cooled or air-cooled).

Actually, all engines are cooled by transferring the excess heat to the surrounding air. In air-cooled engines, this heat transfer is direct from the cylinders to the air. In liquid-cooled engines, the heat is transferred from the cylinders to the coolant, which is then sent through tubing and cooled within a radiator placed in the airstream. Most aircraft engines are air-cooled.

1. Radial Engines

The radial engine consists of a row, or rows, of cylinders arranged radially about a central crankcase. Radial engines have appeared in two forms, the rotary-radial and the static-radial.

During World War I the rotary-radial engine was used by all of the warring nations. It produced the greatest horsepower for its weight. The cylinders of this engine mount radially around a small crankcase and rotate with the propeller. Fins cut into the outside of the cylinders provide all of the cooling needed as the engine spins around. The torque and gyro effect of this large rotating mass made the aircraft somewhat difficult to control. This difficulty, coupled with problems with carburetion, lubrication, and exhaust systems limited the development of the rotary-radial.

In the late 1920's the Wright Aeronautical Corporation, with the encouragement of the U.S. Navy, developed a series of five-, seven-, and nine-cylinder static radial engines that revolutionized aviation. The reliability of these

Figure 1-1. Rotary-radial engines were popular on both sides during World War I. They produced more power for their weight than any other engine configuration at that time.

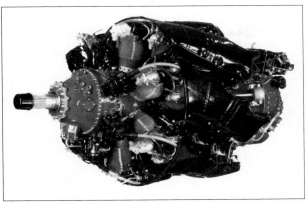

Figure 1-2. The radial engine provides the greatest power for its weight, but its large frontal area makes it difficult to streamline.

engines was far greater than that of any other powerplant up to this time. The radial engine made possible the long distance flights in which Lindbergh and others awoke the world to the realization that the airplane was a practical means of travel.

The radial engine was manufactured with as few as three cylinders and as many as 28 but, it was in the higher horsepower applications that the radial engine proved most useful. Radial engines were produced by the thousands and powered most of our military and airline aircraft until the advent of the turbine engine for these high power applications.

2. In-Line Engines

An in-line engine generally has an even number of cylinders, although some three-cylinder engines have been constructed. This engine may be either liquid-cooled or air cooled and has only one crankshaft, which is located either above or below the cylinders. If the engine is designed to operate with the cylinders below the crankshaft, it is called an inverted engine.

The in-line engine has a small frontal area and is better adapted to streamlining. When mounted with the cylinders in an inverted position, it offers the added advantage of a shorter landing gear and greater pilot visibility. The in-line engine has a higher weight-to-horsepower ratio than most other engines. With increase in engine size, the air cooled in-line type offers additional handicaps to proper cooling; therefore, this type of engine is, to a large degree, confined to low- and medium-horsepower engines used in light aircraft.

3. V-Type Engines

In the V-type engines, the cylinders are arranged in two in-line banks generally set 60° apart. Most of the engines have 8 or 12 cylinders, which are either liquid-cooled or air cooled. The V-12 engines developed in the World War II era represent some of the highest horsepowers achieved with reciprocating engines, and are likely today to be found only on restored military and racing aircraft.

4. Opposed

The opposed-type engine has two banks of cylinders directly opposite each other with a crankshaft in the center. The pistons of both

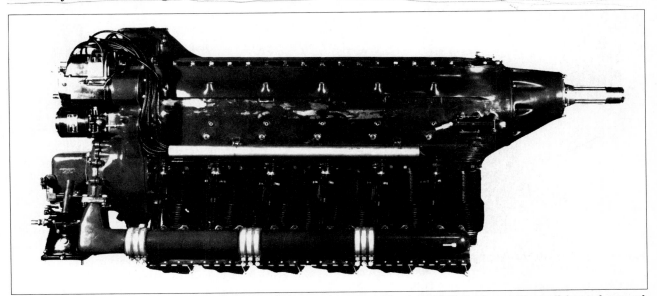

Figure 1-3. The in-line engine was favored for fast airplanes during the 1930's because it small frontal area allowed good streamlining.

cylinder banks are connected to the single crankshaft. Liquid-cooled and air cooled versions are currently being produced. It can be mounted in either a vertical or horizontal position.

The radial engine has the disadvantage of a large frontal area which produces a great amount of drag, and as airplane speed increased, the need to reduce this drag has become of increasing importance. The in-line engine has little frontal area and thus little drag, but its weight is its disadvantage. The V-type engine is a good compromise between weight and frontal area, but air cooling is difficult. The horizontally-opposed air cooled engine is such a good combination of low weight, small frontal area, and ease of cooling that it has become the standard con-

Figure 1-4. V-type engines offer a good compromise between weight for horsepower ratio and small frontal area. They are, however, difficult to cool.

Figure 1-5. The horizontally opposed engine is the main type of reciprocating engine being produced today. It provides the best balance between weight for horsepower and low frontal area, while being easy to cool with air.

figuration, and today, virtually all production of reciprocating engine-powered aircraft use this type of engine.

C. Principles Of Energy Transformation—Reciprocating Engines

The aircraft engine is a form of heat engine, in which the chemical energy in the fuel is converted into heat energy, which is in turn converted into mechanical energy. There are basically two types of engines that use heat to convert chemical energy into mechanical energy. They are the external combustion and the internal combustion engine.

A steam engine is an example of an external combustion engine. Fuel burned in a boiler heats water and changes it into steam. This steam is then carried into the engine where it either forces pistons to move and turn a crankshaft or, spins a turbine.

External combustion engines are quite inefficient with regard to the amount of fuel they convert into work. This is offset somewhat since they can operate on fuels that are available at low cost (anything that burns). This leaves the external combustion engine a viable alternative for such jobs as electrical powerplants.

Internal combustion engines are more selective in the fuels they can burn, but even they have a relatively wide latitude. Some commercial engines burn liquified petroleum gases such as butane or propane, and some burn natural gas. Diesel fuel and turbine fuels are used as well as many grades of gasoline, and alcohol fuels.

Aircraft engines are a rather specialized form of internal combustion engine because of their demand for light weight along with maximum reliability. The fuels that are allowed for use in aviation reciprocating engines must be tested under almost every conceivable condition and approved both by the engine manufacturer and the Federal Aviation Administration.

Regardless of the type of internal combustion engine, the process of releasing the energy from the fuel and converting it into work is essentially the same. Liquid fuel is measured out and converted into a fuel vapor. This vapor is mixed with the correct amount of air to provide the most combustible mixture. Then this mixture is compressed and heated until it ignites. When the mixture burns, it releases its energy and causes that portion of the air that does not enter into the combustion process to expand.

Remember that air is composed of approximately 21% oxygen and 78% nitrogen. Nitrogen is an inert gas that does not enter into the combustion process, but does expand when heated. The expanding gas is used to push down on a piston in the reciprocating engine or to spin the turbine in a gas-turbine engine.

All internal combustion engines, therefore, have a certain sequence of events that must take place to convert the chemical energy in the fuel into mechanical energy and work.

(1) Intake: Fuel and air must be taken into the engine.

(2) Compression: The air or fuel-air mixture must be compressed.

(3) Ignition: The combustible mixture must be ignited.

(4) Power: The burning gases expand and produce work.

(5) Exhaust: The burned gases must then be scavenged and released to the atmosphere.

1. Energy Transformation Cycles

There are two operating cycles in general use for reciprocating engines: (1) The two-stroke cycle, and (2) the four-stroke cycle. At the present time the two-stroke cycle is not being used on type-certified aircraft and will only be dealt with briefly.

a. Two-Stroke Cycle Reciprocating Engines

The extreme simplicity and light weight of a two-stroke cycle engine make it useful for such applications as chain saws, lawn mowers, and other small displacement engines. For aviation application, the inefficiency of this form of engine has limited its use.

The same five events occur in each operating cycle of this engine, and all five occur in two strokes of the piston (one complete crankshaft revolution). In figure 1-6 we see the way this engine works. In view A of the illustration the piston is moving up, and two events are occurring simultaneously. The fuel/air charge in the cylinder is being compressed by the piston, and the upward movement of the piston is drawing a fresh fuel/air charge into the crankcase through a check valve. A few degrees before the piston reaches top dead center, ignition occurs and the piston will begin its downward travel on the power stroke.

This downward movement of the piston (view B) will begin to compress the fuel/air charge in the crankcase. The piston first uncovers the exhaust port and the spent gases begin to exit the cylinder. With further travel (as seen in view C) the intake port is uncovered and the fuel/air mixture from the crankcase is allowed to flow into the cylinder, displacing the exhaust gases.

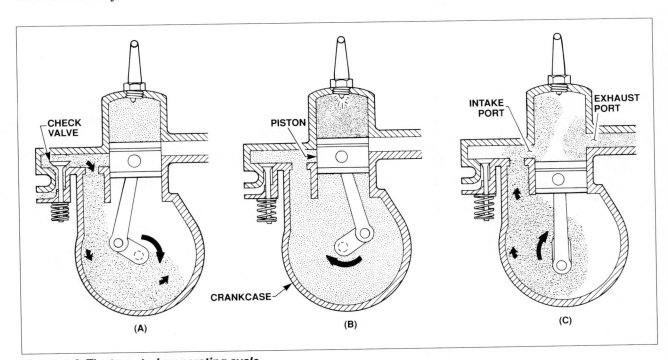

Figure 1-6. The two-stroke operating cycle.

As the piston begins its upward stroke, the intake port will be covered, and then the exhaust port. The fuel/air mixture in the cylinder is compressed and a new fuel/air charge is drawn into the crankcase, completing the cycle.

It is easy to see that efficiency is lost when the fuel/air charge is free to mix with the exhaust gases and exit through the exhaust port, and with the cylinder firing on each revolution, cooling is made more difficult.

b. Four-Stroke Cycle Reciprocating Engines

The Otto cycle of energy release is the most widely used operating cycle for aircraft reciprocating engines. This is classified as a constant volume cycle because the burning fuel inside the cylinder increases the pressure with almost no change in volume.

In the following discussion of the four-stroke cycle engine operation, it should be realized that

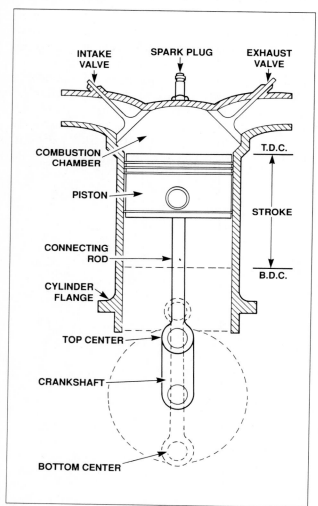

Figure 1-7. Components and terminology of engine operation.

the timing of the ignition and the valve events will vary considerably in different engines. Many factors influence the timing of a specific engine, and it is most important that the engine manufacturer's recommendations in this respect be followed in maintenance and overhaul.

The timing of the valve and ignition events is always specified in degrees of crankshaft travel. In the following paragraphs, the timing of each event is specified in terms of degrees of crankshaft travel on the stroke during which each event occurs. It should be remembered that a certain amount of travel is required to open a valve fully; therefore, the specified timing represents the start of opening rather than the full-open position of the valve.

Figure 1-7 illustrates the various engine components of a four-stroke cycle engine, and presents the principle terms used to indicate engine operation.

1) Intake Stroke

During the intake stroke, the piston is pulled downward in the cylinder by the rotation of the crankshaft. This reduces the pressure in the cylinder and causes air under atmospheric pressure to flow through the carburetor, which meters the correct amount of fuel. The fuel/air mixture passes through the intake pipe and intake valve into the cylinder. The quantity or weight of the fuel/air mixture depends upon the degree of throttle opening.

The intake valve is opened considerably before the piston reaches top dead center on the exhaust stroke, in order to induce a greater quantity of the fuel/air charge into the cylinder and thus increase horsepower. The distance the valve may be opened before top dead center, however, is limited by several factors, such as the possibility that hot gases remaining in the cylinder from the previous cycle may flash back into the intake pipe and the induction system.

In all high-power aircraft engines, both the intake and the exhaust valve are off the valve seats at top dead center at the start of the intake stroke. As mentioned above, the intake valve opens before top dead center on the exhaust stroke (valve lead), and the closing of the exhaust valve is delayed considerably after the piston has passed top dead center and has started the intake stroke (valve lag). This timing is called valve overlap and is designed to aid in cooling the cylinder internally by circulating the cool incoming fuel/air mixture, to increase the amount of fuel/air mixture induced into the cylinder, and to aid in scavenging the by-products of combustion.

The intake valve is timed to close about 50° to 75° past bottom dead center on the compression stroke depending upon the specific engine, to allow the momentum of the incoming gases to charge the cylinder more completely. Because of the comparatively large volume of the cylinder above the position when the piston is near bottom dead center, the slight upward travel of the piston during this time does not have a great effect on the incoming flow of gases.

2) Compression Stroke

After the intake valve is closed, the continued upward travel of the piston compresses the fuel/air mixture to obtain the desired burning and expansion characteristics.

The charge is ignited by means of an electric spark as the piston approaches top dead center. The time of ignition will vary from 20° to 35° before top dead center, depending upon the requirements of the specific engine, to ensure complete combustion of the charge by the time the piston is slightly past the top dead center position.

Many factors affect ignition timing, and the engine manufacturer has expended considerable time, research and testing to determine the best setting. All engines incorporate devices for adjusting the ignition timing, and it is most important that the ignition be timed according to the engine manufacturer's recommendations.

3) Power Stroke

As the piston moves through the top dead center position at the end of the compression stroke and starts down on the power stroke, it is pushed downward by the rapid expansion of the burning gases within the cylinder head with a force that can exceed 15 tons. The temperature of these burning gases may be as high as 3,000° or 4,000° F.

The pressure exerted on the piston by the burning gases is changed to rotary motion by the crankshaft. This rotary movement is transmitted to the propeller shaft to drive the propeller. As the burning gases are expanded, the temperature drops to within safe limits before the exhaust gases flow out through the exhaust port.

The timing of the exhaust valve opening is determined by, among other considerations, the desirability of using as much of the expansive force as possible and of scavenging the cylinder as completely and rapidly as possible. The valve is opened considerably before bottom dead center on the power stroke, while there is still some pressure in the cylinder. This timing is used so that the pressure can force the gases out of the exhaust port as soon as possible. This process frees the cylinder of waste heat after the desired expansion has been obtained and avoids overheating the cylinder and piston. Scavenging is also an important consideration as any exhaust products remaining in the cylinder will dilute the incoming fuel/air charge at the start of the next cycle.

4) Exhaust Stroke

As the piston travels through bottom dead center at the completion of the power stroke and starts upward on the exhaust stroke, it will begin to push the burned exhaust gases out the exhaust port. The speed of the exhaust gases leaving the cylinder creates a low pressure in the cylinder. This low or reduced pressure speeds the flow of the fresh fuel/air charge into the cylinder as the intake valve is beginning to open.

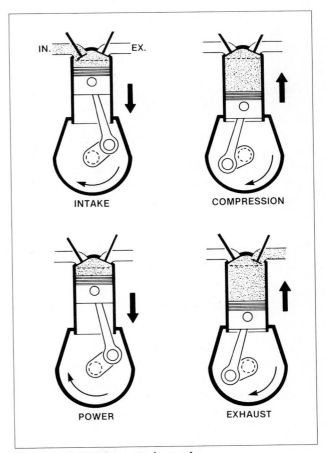

Figure 1-8. The four-stroke cycle.

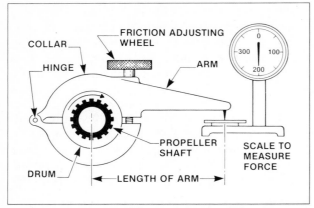

Figure 1-9. The basic principle of operation of a prony brake to measure the torque produced by an engine.

The intake valve opening is timed to occur at 8° to 55° before top dead center on the exhaust stroke.

2. Work-Power Considerations

All aircraft engines are rated according to their ability to do work and produce power. This section presents an explanation of work and power and how they are calculated. Also discussed are the various efficiencies that govern the power output of a reciprocating engine.

a. Work

Work is accomplished when a force moves through a specific distance. In the English system of measurement, work is expressed in foot-pounds and in the metric system, in meter-kilograms. Work, measured in foot-pounds, is the product of the force in pounds times the distance through which the force acts, measured in feet, and may be found by the formula:

$$\text{WORK} = \text{FORCE} \times \text{DISTANCE}$$

When one pound of mass is raised one foot, one foot-pound of work is accomplished.

b. Power

Time is not considered in the determination of the amount of work that has been done, but does become part of the formula when we wish to calculate power. Power is the rate of doing work, and it may be expressed in foot-pounds of work done in one minute or in one second.

$$\text{POWER} = \frac{\text{FORCE} \times \text{DISTANCE}}{\text{TIME}}$$

c. Horsepower

James Watt, the inventor of the steam engine, found that an English dray horse could do, for a reasonable period of time, about 33,000 foot-pounds of work in one minute, and from his observations came the term "horsepower," which has been standardized as 33,000 foot-pounds of work per minute, or 550 foot-pounds per second. In electrical power, there is a relationship between the watt and the horsepower. One horsepower is equal to 746 watts, or one kilowatt (1,000 watts) is equal to 1.34 horsepower.

a) Brake Horsepower

The actual amount of power delivered to the propeller shaft of a reciprocating engine is called the brake horsepower and it derives its name from the method by which it was measured. In the early days of reciprocating engine technology, power was measured by clamping a brake around the output shaft of an engine and measuring the force exerted on an arm at the speed the measurement was being taken (see figure 1-9). The measuring device was called a prony brake; thus the name—brake horsepower. Today, the same type of measurement is made using a dynomometer, but here the engine drives either an electrical generator or a fluid pump. The output of the generator or pump is forced to perform work, and the amount of work done in a given time is used to calculate the power the engine is producing. A modern dynamometer is shown in figure 1-10.

b) Friction Horsepower

Pistons slide back and forth in the cylinders, and air is pulled into the engine and then compressed. This requires power, as does the movement of all of the rotating machinery such as the gears and each of the accessories. All of the power used to drive the engine is lumped into one measurement called friction horsepower. This may be measured by driving the engine with a calibrated motor and measuring the amount of power actually needed to turn the engine at each speed.

c) Indicated Horsepower

The power delivered to the propeller plus the power used to drive the engine (brake horsepower + friction horsepower) is the total power developed in the cylinders. This total power is called the indicated horsepower. Brake horsepower, as we have seen, may be measured by a mechanical device on the shaft, but since friction horsepower is involved, indicated horsepower cannot be measured directly. It may, however, be calculated by the formula:

$$IHP = \frac{PLANK}{33,000}$$

P stands for the Indicated Mean Effective Pressure, the IMEP, and is the average pressure inside the cylinder during the power stroke. Originally this was measured by an instrument called an indicator (thus its name), but modern technology allows us to use an electrical pressure transducer which is far more accurate and convenient to use. IMEP is expressed in pounds per square inch.

A is the area of the piston head in square inches, and since P is measured in pounds per square inch and A is in square inches, the product of P and A gives us the amount of force in pounds that acts on the piston.

L is the length of the stroke in feet. P × A gives the pounds of force acting on the piston, and L, the distance through which this force acts during each power stroke. So P × A × L gives the number of foot-pounds of work done on each power stroke.

N is the number of power strokes per minute for each cylinder. This is found for a four-stroke cycle engine by dividing the RPM by two, since there is only one power stroke for each two revolutions.

$$N = \frac{RPM}{2}$$

K is the number of cylinders in the engine.

The product of PLANK gives the number of foot-pounds of work done each minute by the engine, and since one horsepower is equal to 33,000 foot-pounds of work per minute, dividing PLANK by 33,000 we can find the indicated horsepower.

To check our understanding of this formula, let's compute the indicated horsepower for a six-cylinder aircraft engine that has a bore of five inches, and a stroke of five inches. It is turning at 2750 RPM and has a measured IMEP of 125 pounds per square inch.

P = 125 psi
L = 5/12 foot
A = 0.7854 × 5² = 19.63 sq. in.
N = 2750 ÷ 2 = 1375
K = 6

$$IHP = \frac{125 \times \dfrac{5}{12} \times 19.63 \times 1375 \times 6}{33,000}$$

= 255.60 indicated horsepower

d. Factors Affecting Power

As we have seen in our examination of engine power, a number of factors can affect the power produced by a reciprocating engine. There are a several conditions which can affect each of the terms in our PLANK formula, and ultimately the horsepower of the engine.

a) Thermal Efficiency

The thermal efficiency of an engine is the ratio of the amount of heat energy converted into useful work, to the heat energy contained in the fuel. Simply stated, it is the ratio of the power out, to the power in. If two engines produce the same amount of horsepower, but one burns less fuel than the other, the engine using the least fuel converts a greater portion of the available energy into useful work and therefore has the higher thermal efficiency.

Thermal efficiency may be found by the formula:

$$TE = \frac{HP \times 33,000}{F \times 20,000 \times 778}$$

The horsepower, HP, used in this formula may be either brake or indicated horsepower, depending upon the type of thermal efficiency you want. If BHP is used, the result will be brake thermal efficiency, and if IHP is used you will get indicated thermal efficiency.

Figure 1-10. The output of modern engines may be measured using a dynomometer such as this one.

9

The constant 33,000 is the number of foot-pounds of work per minute in one horsepower. Horsepower times 33,000 gives the foot-pounds of work done in one minute. This is the output.

F is equal to the number of pounds of fuel consumed by the engine in one minute, and for aviation gasoline which nominally weighs six pounds per gallon, F is found by multiplying the gallons per hour by six and dividing this by 60. This is the same as dividing the pounds of fuel burned per hour by the number of minutes in one hour.

The constant 20,000 is the nominal heat energy content of aviation gasoline. Each pound contains 20,000 BTU of heat energy.

The constant 778 is the number of foot-pounds of work each BTU is capable of doing.

The product of $F \times 20,000 \times 778$ is the number of foot-pounds of work the fuel burned is capable of producing, and this is therefore the input.

Let's check our understanding of the thermal efficiency formula by finding the thermal efficiency of an engine that produces 150 brake horsepower while burning 14.0 gallons of aviation gasoline per hour.

$$TE = \frac{150 \times 33,000}{(14 \times 6) \div 60 \times 20,000 \times 778} = 22.7\%$$

By using this formula, we see that reciprocating engines are extremely inefficient with regard to the energy they use. The low percentage found in this example is for a popular engine developing its maximum rated horsepower, but even at an efficient cruise speed, these engines seldom convert more than one-third of the fuel they burn into useful work.

b) Volumetric Efficiency

Reciprocating engines are air-breathing and require a maximum amount of air in the cylinder to release the most energy from the fuel. Volumetric efficiency is the ratio of the amount of air the engine takes into the cylinder to the total displacement of the piston.

For this to be meaningful, the density of the air in the cylinder must be converted to standard density by correcting the temperature and pressure of the air to standard conditions of 59° F (or 15° C) and 14.69 psi (or 29.92 inches of mercury).

If an engine draws in a volume of charge at this density, exactly equal to the piston displacement, the volumetric efficiency will be 100%. The volumetric efficiency of a normally aspirated engine is always less than 100%. This is because of the friction of the induction system walls and the bends in the intake tubing which will restrict the amount of air that can flow into the cylinder during the time that the intake valve is open. Supercharged engines, on the other hand, compress the air before it enters the cylinders, and they may have volumetric efficiencies greater than 100%. Volumetric efficiency is found by the formula:

$$VE = \frac{VOLUME\ OF\ CHARGE}{PISTON\ DISPLACEMENT}$$

Anything that decreases the mass of air entering the cylinder during the intake stroke will decrease the volumetric efficiency. Some of the typical factors that affect volumetric efficiency of a non-supercharged engine are:

Part throttle operation—This restricts the amount of air that can flow into the cylinders.

Long intake pipes of small diameter—The friction increases directly as the length of the intake pipes and inversely as their cross-sectional area.

Sharp bends in the induction system—The air is slowed down each time it turns a corner, and the slower the air, the less will get into the cylinders.

Carburetor air temperature too high—As the temperature increases, the density of the air decreases, and there will be fewer pounds of air taken into the cylinder.

Cylinder head temperature too high—This also lowers the density of the air in the cylinders and provides fewer pounds of air for the same volume.

Incomplete scavenging—The incoming fuel/air mixture will be diluted with exhaust gases, and there will be less fresh charge drawn into the cylinder.

Improper valve timing—If the intake valve is not open long enough to draw a complete charge of fuel-air mixture into the cylinder, the volumetric efficiency will be low.

c) Mechanical Efficiency

Mechanical efficiency is the ratio of brake horsepower to indicated horsepower. It shows the percentage of power developed in the cylinders that actually reaches the propeller shaft. Aircraft engines are usually quite efficient mechanically and it is not unusual for ninety percent of the indicated horsepower to be converted into brake horsepower.

d) Piston Displacement

Piston displacement is the product of the area of the piston, the length of the stroke, and the number of cylinders. Since the amount of work done by the expanding gases is determined by these factors, it is evident that the piston displacement is of major importance in power computations. Increasing either the bore of the cylinder or the stroke of the piston will increase the piston displacement. The formula for piston displacement is:

$$PD = A \times L \times N$$

A is the area of the piston head in square inches
L is the length of the stroke inches
N is the number of cylinders

e) Compression Ratio

The ratio of the volume of the cylinder with the piston at the bottom of the stroke to the volume with the piston at the top of the stroke is called the compression ratio of the engine. This ratio will determine, to a great extent, the amount of heat energy in the fuel/air mixture that can be converted into useful work.

Engines with high compression ratios allow the fuel/air mixture to release its energy rapidly and produce the maximum pressure inside the cylinder just as the piston starts down on the power stroke.

The practical limit of compression ratio is determined by the fuel used. When the compressed fuel/air mixture is ignited, the flame front moves across the piston head, heating and further compressing the charge in front of it. A point is reached, called the critical pressure and temperature of the mixture, where it no longer burns and releases its energy evenly, but rather explodes. This almost instantaneous release of energy is called detonation, and it creates such a high pressure and temperature inside the cylinder that severe damage to the engine may result.

All aircraft engines have a published minimum grade of fuel that must be used. This fuel grade is critical to the safe operation of the engine, free

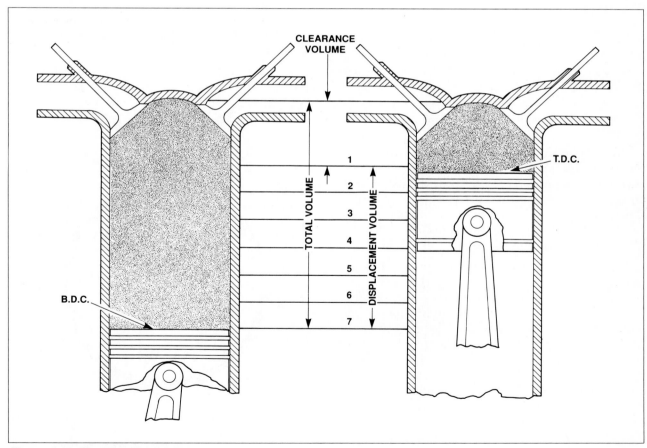

Figure 1-11. Compression ratio.

from detonation. Aircraft must never be operated using a fuel of a lower grade than that specified.

The pressure generated within the cylinder is important, as it must always be kept below the critical pressure of the fuel/air mixture. This cylinder pressure is determined by both the compression ratio of the engine and the pressure of the fuel/air mixture when it enters the cylinder.

The pilot has no direct way of measuring cylinder pressure, but the manifold air pressure (MAP) gauge does sample the absolute pressure at the intake manifold. This pressure, normally measured in inches of mercury, is related to engine r.p.m. to get an indication of the power being produced by the engine.

f) Ignition Timing

It is of extreme importance that the maximum pressure within the cylinder be reached shortly after the piston passes its top dead center position and starts down on the power stroke. For this to occur, the mixture must be ignited quite a way before the piston reaches top center. This is usually somewhere around thirty degrees before top center on the compression stroke.

Automobile engines have a variable timing device on their distributor that changes the amount of spark advance as the engine operating conditions change, but aircraft engines employ fixed timing. This setting is, of necessity, a compromise between the timing required to give good performance for takeoff and that needed for cruise.

When the engine is started, it rotates so slowly that a spark occurring at the proper time for high speed operation would cause kickback and possible damage to the starter. To prevent this, the spark is retarded for starting, using any of several devices that will be discussed at length when we study ignition systems.

If ignition occurs too early, the engine will lose power because the maximum cylinder pressure will be reached while the piston is still moving upward and the force of the expanding gases will oppose the rotational inertia of the engine. But, on the other hand, if it occurs too late, there will be a more serious loss of power; since the cylinder volume is increasing as the gases expand, the effect of the push will be lost. Also, late ignition does not allow enough time for all of the fuel/air mixture to burn before the exhaust valve opens, and these burning gases, forced out past the exhaust valve, increase its temperature and will damage the engine by overheating.

The excess heat in the cylinder from late timing gives rise to a problem known as preignition. The burning gases leaving the cylinder may cause local overheating of the valve edges or carbon particles within the cylinder. When these particles glow from the heat, they may ignite the fuel/air mixture while it is being compressed and cause, in effect, extremely early timing. This timing may be so early that the mixture will reach its critical pressure before the piston reaches top center and, detonation will occur.

g) Engine Speed

The amount of power produced by an aircraft engine is determined by the cylinder pressure, the area of the piston, the distance the piston moves on each stroke, and the number of times this movement occurs in one minute.

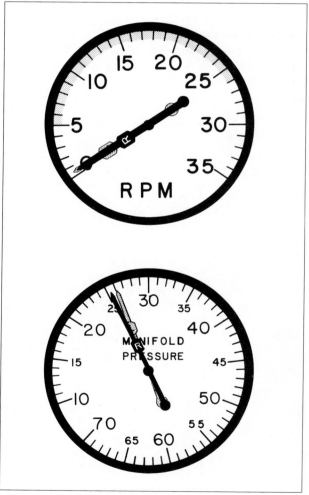

Figure 1-12. The tachometer and manifold pressure gauge give the pilot the information needed to determine the amount of power the engine is developing.

In simplest terms the faster an engine runs, the more power it will produce. This does, however, have certain limitations. We have already discussed the problems associated with detonation, but what about design considerations. The maximum speed at which an aircraft engine can be designed to turn will be limited by the speed of the propeller tips. In order to efficiently produce thrust, the tip speed of a propeller blade must not exceed the speed of sound.

As we can see in figure 1-13, the velocity of a propeller increases as the distance from the hub increases. To increase the amount of power produced by an engine by increasing its speed, we must either use a shorter propeller or introduce propeller reduction gearing. These gears will enable the engine to turn at a higher speed (and produce more power) while the propeller rotates at a low speed where it will operate more efficiently.

h) Specific Fuel Consumption

While not actually a measure of the power itself, specific fuel consumption is an important measure for comparing the efficiencies of engines. The number of pounds of fuel burned per hour to produce one horsepower, either indicated or brake, is known as the specific fuel consumption of the engine. For most practical purposes, brake horsepower is used, and this gives us brake specific fuel consumption, BSFC.

Figure 1-14 illustrates the way specific fuel consumption varies with the RPM of the engine. Since brake horsepower depends upon engine speed, below 2400 RPM the engine is not developing as much power as it is capable of for the amount of fuel it is using. Above 2400 RPM, the amount of power needed to drive the engine, the friction horsepower, increases and the brake horsepower decreases. From this curve, we can see that the most efficient operating speed for this particular engine is around 2400 RPM. At this speed, the engine requires about 0.51 pounds of fuel per hour for each horsepower it produces. At full throttle, because of the additional power required to turn the engine itself, the power requirements have gone up to 0.59 pounds per horsepower, per hour.

3. Distribution Of Power

When we consider the amount of power that is available in aviation gasoline compared to the amount of power that is actually delivered to the propeller shaft, we can easily see that an aircraft engine is an inefficient machine. A typical engine

may develop 200 brake horsepower when burning 14 gallons of fuel per hour, but when this amount of aviation gasoline is burned in one hour, it releases enough heat energy to produce 667 horsepower. About 33 horsepower is used just to turn the engine and compress the air in the cylinders, and an equivalent of about 434

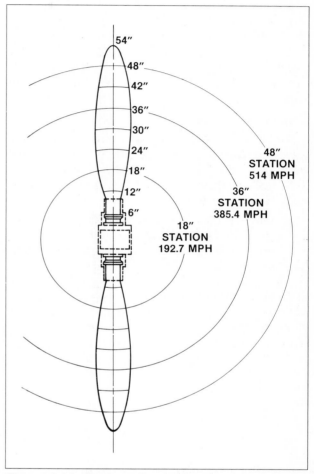

Figure 1-13. Comparative velocities at three blade stations of a typical propeller.

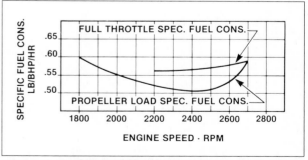

Figure 1-14. The relationship between brake specific fuel consumption and engine RPM.

horsepower is lost to the air through the cooling and exhaust systems. Anything that can be done to minimize these losses will increase the efficiency of the engine.

Even when power is delivered to the propeller shaft, we do not have what we really need because for an airplane to be pulled through the air or a helicopter lifted, we must convert the torque produced by the engine into thrust by the propeller or rotor. Torque is a force that acts perpendicular to the axis of rotation of the propeller, and thrusts acts parallel to this axis. A propeller converts about 90% of the torque it receives into thrust, and is limited by the maximum tip speed and by the inefficiency of the blade near the root.

4. Power Curves

The engine manufacturer produces a set of power curves for each engine built. These charts show the power the engine will develop for each RPM and give the specific fuel consumption for each power setting.

In figure 1-16 we have a typical power curve for a popular four-cylinder aircraft engine. You will notice that there are two power curves and two specific fuel consumption curves that meet at the normal rated power. The upper curve shows the maximum amount of power the engine will produce with a wide open throttle on a dynomometer. You can tell that under these conditions the engine will produce 160 horsepower at 2400 RPM, and a maximum of 168 horse-

power at 2700 RPM. The lower power curve is the propeller load curve and when an engine is equipped with the recommended propeller, it will produce 118 horsepower at 2400 RPM and its normal rated 168 horsepower at 2700 RPM. At 2700 RPM, the throttle will be wide open.

There are also two specific fuel consumption curves, the upper for full throttle operation and the lower for propeller load conditions. At 2400 RPM, the propeller load specific fuel consumption curve shows the BSFC to be 0.51 and since the engine is developing 118 horsepower, it is consuming 118 × 0.51 or 60.18 pounds of fuel per hour. Aviation gasoline has a nominal weight of six pounds per gallon, and so the engine is burning 10.03 gallons of gasoline per hour.

At full throttle, the engine has a BSFC of 0.59 and develops 168 horsepower. At this power it is burning 16.52 gallons of fuel per hour.

D. Reciprocating Engine Design And Construction

Although it may not be the most efficient method of transforming heat energy provided by gasoline into mechanical energy, the reciprocating engine is quite a marvelous machine. It has taken aircraft from Kitty Hawk to a safe and reliable means of global transportation.

1. Comparison Of Powerplants

All engines must meet certain general requirements of efficiency, economy, and reliability. Besides being economical in fuel consumption, an aircraft engine must be economical (the cost of original procurement and the cost of maintenance) and it must meet exacting requirements of efficiency, and have a low weight per horsepower ratio. It must be capable of sustained high-power output with no sacrifice in reliability; it must also have the durability to operate for long periods of time between overhauls. It needs to be as compact as possible, yet have easy accessibility for maintenance. It is required to be as vibration free as possible and be able to cover a wide range of power output at various speeds and altitudes.

These requirements dictate the use of ignition systems that will deliver the firing impulse to the spark plugs or igniter plugs at the proper time in all kinds of weather and under other adverse conditions. Fuel-metering devices are needed that will deliver fuel in the correct proportion to the air ingested by the engine regardless of the altitude, or type of weather in which the engine

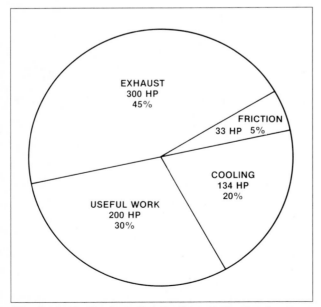

Figure 1-15. Typical distribution of the heat energy released in an aircraft engine.

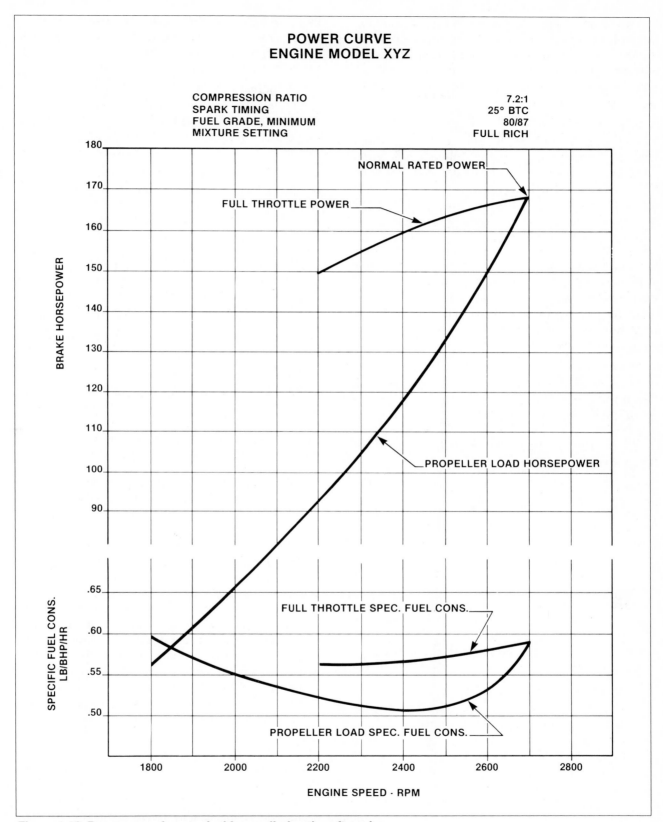

Figure 1-16. Power curve for a typical four-cylinder aircraft engine.

is operated. The engine needs a type of oil system that delivers oil under the proper pressure to all of the operating parts of the engine when it is running. Also, it must have a system of damping units to damp out the vibrations of the engine when it is operating.

a. Power And Weight

This has been one of the areas in which aircraft reciprocating engines have made great strides, but also an area in which they are woefully inferior to turbine engines. Some of the first aircraft engines weighed, including all of their vital accessories, almost 16 pounds for every horsepower they produced. By the end of the 1930's the weight of the larger engines was down to about one pound per horsepower, but two to four pounds per horsepower was more typical for the smaller engines. Today, the four- or six-cylinder engines that power most of the general aviation fleet weigh between one and a half and two pounds per horsepower.

b. Fuel Economy

The need for reliability, compactness, and low weight per horsepower has encouraged engine manufacturers to improve their designs, but the increase in the price of aviation fuel has had perhaps a greater impact on engine development than any other factor in recent years.

In the past we have been content to enrich the fuel/air mixture and use the excess fuel to cool the engine during times of high power output. But today with fuel costing so much, and very little prospect of its ever costing less, engine manufacturers are conducting basic research into ways of recovering some of the power we lose in our inefficient engines. Cylinders are being designed to allow for higher operating temperatures, and turbochargers are installed to use part of the energy that would otherwise be wasted to compress the induction air before it enters the cylinders.

c. Durability And Reliability

Durability relates to the amount of service life you should be able to expect from the engine. A measure of durability, the TBO, or time between overhauls, has been established by the engine manufacturer to give us a benchmark from which we can estimate the life expectancy of an engine. This time, given in hours, is a recommendation for the maximum amount of time the engine should be operated between major overhauls. It presumes the engine is being operated in favorable conditions and is always given the maintenance recommended by the manufacturer. There is no guarantee that the engine will run for its full TBO without needing an overhaul, but it is the best measure of durability we have.

Reliability is the ability of an engine to consistently live up to the manufacturer's specifications. It must be designed, built, and maintained in such a way that chances of it failing are minimized.

Before an engine is granted a Type Certificate it must prove its reliability by an endurance run witnessed by the Federal Aviation Administration in which it is operated for 85 hours at maximum continuous power, 15 hours at takeoff power, and 50 hours at high cruise power. After this amount of running, the engine is disassembled and it must show no signs of abnormal wear nor any indication of impending failure.

Put simply, durability is the time between overhauls and reliability is the time between failures.

d. Operational Flexibility

This demands that an aircraft engine operate efficiently at both idle and cruise RPM, and it must never hesitate when full power is applied for takeoff. It must operate well at sea level conditions and be capable of being adjusted to provide the needed power at any altitude the aircraft will fly. The engine must be designed so that rain, dust, sand, heat, and vibration will have a minimal damaging effect.

2. Crankcase Sections

The foundation of an engine is the crankcase. It contains the bearings in which the crankshaft revolves. Besides supporting itself, the crankcase must provide a tight enclosure for the lubricating oil and must support various external and internal mechanisms of the engine. It also provides support for attachment of the cylinder assemblies, and the powerplant to the aircraft. It must be sufficiently rigid and strong to prevent misalignment of the crankshaft and its bearings. Cast or forged aluminum alloy is generally used for crankcase construction because it is light and strong.

The crankcase is subjected to many variations of vibrational and other forces. Since the cylinders are fastened to the crankcase, the tremendous expansion forces tend to pull the cylinder off the crankcase. The unbalanced centrifugal and inertia forces of the crankshaft acting through the main bearings subject the

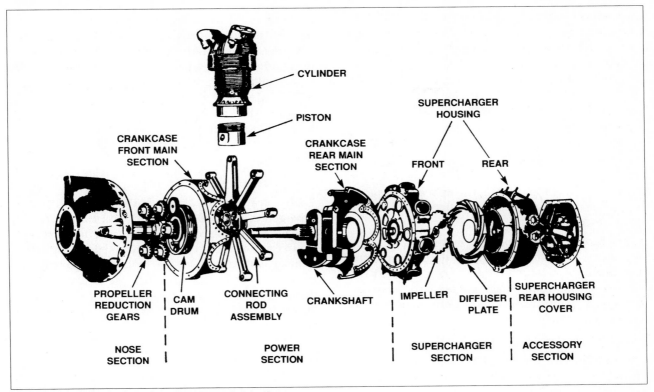

Figure 1-17. Major components of a radial engine.

crankcase to bending moments which change continuously in direction and magnitude. The crankcase must have sufficient stiffness to withstand these bending moments without objectionable deflections. If the engine is equipped with a propeller reduction gear, the front or drive end will be subjected to additional forces.

In addition to the thrust force developed by the propeller under high-power output, there are severe centrifugal and gyroscopic forces applied to the crankcase due to sudden changes in the direction of flight, such as those occurring during maneuvers of the airplane. Gyroscopic forces are, of course, particularly severe when a heavy propeller is installed.

a. Radial Engine Crankcases

The engine shown in figure 1-17 is a single-row, nine-cylinder radial engine of relatively simple construction, having a one-piece nose and a two-section main crankcase. We will examine each major section individually.

1) Nose Section

The shape of the nose section varies considerably. In general, it is either tapered or round in order to place the metal under tension or com-

pression instead of shear stresses. A tapered nose section is used quite frequently on direct drive, low-powered engines, because extra space is not required to house the propeller reduction gear. It is usually cast of either aluminum alloy or magnesium since the low power developed and the use of a lightweight propeller do not require the more expensive forged nose sections.

2) Power Section

This portion of the engine is often called the power section, because it is here that the reciprocating motion of the piston is converted to rotary motion of the crankshaft.

Because of the tremendous loads and forces from the crankshaft assembly and the tendency of the cylinders to pull the crankcase apart, especially in the extreme conditions when a high-powered engine is detonated, the main crankcase section must be very well designed and constructed.

On engines equipped with a two-piece master rod and a solid type crankshaft, the main or power crankcase section may be solid, usually of aluminum alloy. The front end of this section is open when the diaphragm plate in which the front main bearing is mounted is removed. The split main section (aluminum or magnesium) may be slightly more expensive, but permits better control over the quality of casting or forging. The split main section is generally a necessity when a solid master rod and a split-type crankshaft are used.

The machined surfaces on which the cylinders are mounted are called cylinder pads. They are provided with a suitable means of retaining or fastening the cylinders to the crankcase. The general practice in securing the cylinder flange to the pad is to mount studs in threaded holes in the crankcase.

The inner portion of the cylinder pads are sometimes chamfered or tapered to permit the installation of a large rubber O-ring around the cylinder skirt, which effectively seals the joint between the cylinder and the crankcase pads against oil leakage.

3) Diffuser Section

The diffuser or supercharger section generally is cast of aluminum alloy, although in a few cases, the lighter magnesium is used. The diffuser aids in complete vaporization of the fuel/air mixture and even distribution to the cylinders.

Because of the elongation and contraction of the cylinders, the intake pipes which carry the mixture from the diffuser chamber through the intake valve ports are arranged to provide a slip joint which must be leakproof. The atmospheric pressure on the outside of the case on an unsupercharged engine will be higher than on the inside, especially when the engine is operating at idling speed. If the engine is equipped with a supercharger and operating at full throttle, the pressure will be considerably higher on the inside than on the outside of the case. Any leakage in the slip joint will result in an incorrect fuel/air mixture at certain operating speeds.

4) Accessory Section

The accessory (rear) section usually is of cast construction and may be either aluminum alloy, which is used most widely, or magnesium. On some engines, it is cast in one piece and provided with means for mounting accessories, such as magnetos, carburetors, and fuel, oil, and vacuum pumps, and starter, generator, etc. Other adaptations consist of an aluminum alloy casting and a separate cast magnesium cover plate on which the accessory mounts are arranged.

Accessory drive shafts are mounted in suitable bronze bushings located in the diffuser and rear sections. These shafts extend into the rear section and are fitted with suitable gears from which power takeoffs or drive arrangements are carried out to the accessory mounting pads. In this manner, the various gear ratios can be arranged to give the proper drive speed to magneto, pump, and other accessories to obtain correct timing or functioning.

5) Accessory Gear Trains

Gear trains, containing both spur- and bevel-type gears, are used in the different types of engines for driving components and accessories. Spur-type gears are generally used to drive the heavier loaded accessories or those requiring the least play or backlash in the gear train. Bevel gears permit angular location of short stub shafts leading to the various accessory mounting pads.

On low-powered engines, the accessory gear trains are usually simple arrangements. Many of these engines use synthetic rubber or spring couplings to protect the magneto and generator gear trains from excessive loads.

b. Opposed Engine Crankcases

The crankcase of horizontally opposed engines are made of two halves of cast aluminum alloy that have been manufactured either by sand casting or by a method using permanent molds. Crankcases made by the permanent mold process are denser than those made by sand casting, and the metal is somewhat thinner.

The crankcase is approximately cylindrical, with areas machined to serve as a base to which the cylinders are attached by means of studs secured in the crankcase, and through bolts. These accurately machined surfaces are frequently referred to as cylinder pads.

The crankshaft is carried in a position parallel to the longitudinal axis of the crankcase, and is generally supported by a main bearing between each throw. The crankshaft main bearings must be supported rigidly in the crankcase. This is usually accomplished by means of transverse webs in the crankcase, one for each main bearing. The webs form an integral part of the structure and, in addition to supporting the main bearings, add to the strength of the engine case.

The crankcase halves split vertically and are held together with studs and through bolts at the crankshaft bearings, and with smaller bolts and nuts around the outside of the case. Since the supply of oil in most of the modern horizontally opposed engines is carried inside of the crankcase, provisions are made to seal the crankcase to prevent its leaking.

The two halves of the crankcase must not only be permanently sealed against oil leakage, but the seal must not interfere with the tight fit of the bearings. Most crankcase halves are sealed with a very thin coating of a non-hardening gasket compound applied to the surface. A fine silk thread is imbedded in the compound, extending the full length of the case. When the assembled crankshaft and camshaft are installed in the crankcase, and the halves are bolted together with the proper torque, the gasket material and the silk thread form an effective oil seal without interfering with the bearing fit.

c. Engine Mounts

On radial engines, mounting lugs may be spaced about the periphery of the diffuser section to attach the engine assembly to the engine mount or framework provided for attaching the powerplant to the fuselage of single-engine aircraft or to the wing nacelle structure of a multi-engine aircraft. The mounting lugs may be either integral with the diffuser section or detachable, as in the case of flexible or dynamic engine mounts.

Engine mounting provisions may be an integral part of the crankcase of an opposed-type engine, or may be a bolt-on addition. Generally speaking, the lower horsepower engines will use mount brackets that are cast into the crankcase, and the higher powered engines will use mount legs that are bolted to the crankcase.

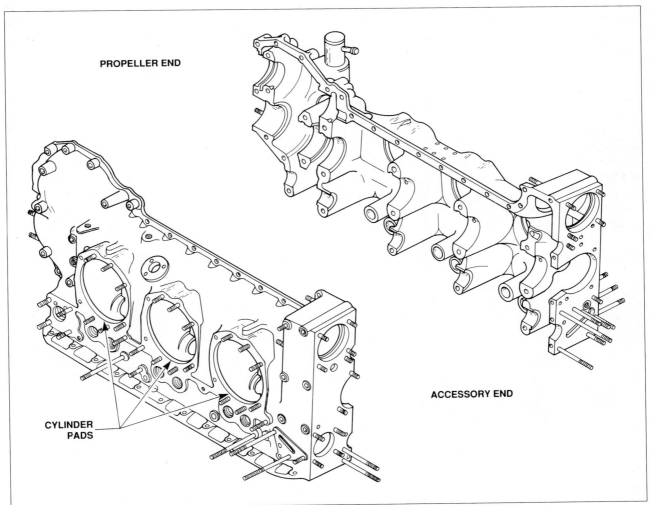

PROPELLER END

ACCESSORY END

CYLINDER PADS

Figure 1-18. A crankcase used for a horizontally opposed engine, incorporating spur-type propeller reduction gearing.

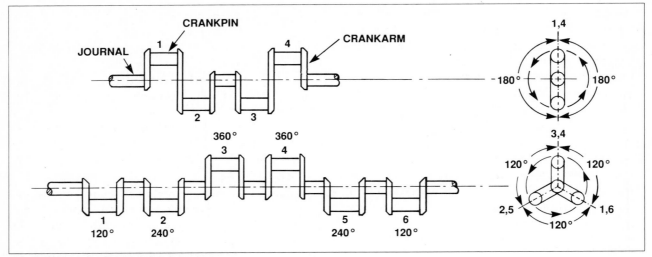

Figure 1-19. Types of solid crankshafts.

On any engine, the mounting arrangement supports the entire powerplant including the propeller, and therefore is designed to provide ample strength for rapid maneuvers or other loadings.

3. Engine Parts

As you have already discovered, there are a number of configurations of engines that have had their place in aircraft development, and each of these utilize their own unique construction features. Because the static-radial and the horizontally opposed engines represent the vast majority of reciprocating engines used on aircraft in the last fifty years, we center our discussion on the design features for each of them, and take only a cursory look at other engine types.

a. Crankshafts

The crankshaft is the backbone of the reciprocating engine. It is subjected to most of the forces developed by the engine. Its main purpose is to transform the reciprocating motion of the piston and connecting rod into rotary motion to turn the propeller. The crankshaft, as the name implies, is a shaft composed of one or more cranks located at specified points along its length. The cranks, or throws, are formed by forging offsets into a shaft before it is machined. Since crankshafts must be very strong, they generally are forged from a very strong alloy, such as chromium-nickel molybdenum steel.

A crankshaft may be of single-piece or multi-piece construction. Figure 1-19 shows two repre-

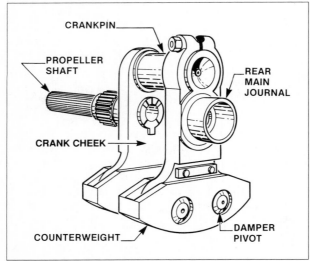

Figure 1-20. Crankshaft for a single-throw radial engine.

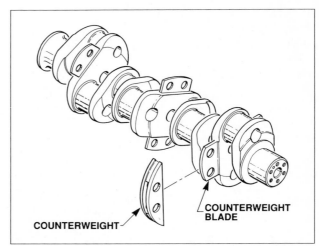

Figure 1-21. Movable counterweights serve as dynamic dampers to reduce the torsional vibrations in an aircraft engine.

sentative types of solid crankshafts used in aircraft engines. The four-throw construction may be used either on four-cylinder horizontal opposed or four-cylinder in-line engines. The six-throw shaft is used on six-cylinder in-line engines, 12-cylinder V-type engines, and six-cylinder opposed-type engines.

Crankshafts of radial engines may be the single-throw, two-throw, or four-throw type, depending on whether the engine is the single-row, twin-row, or four-row type. A single-throw radial engine crankshaft is shown in figure 1-20.

No matter how many throws it may have, each crankshaft has three main parts—a journal, crankpin, and crank cheek. Counterweights and dampers, although not a true part of the crankshaft, are usually attached to it to reduce engine vibration.

The journal is supported by, and rotates in, a main bearing. It serves as the center of rotation of the crankshaft. It is surface-hardened to reduce wear.

The crankpin is the section to which the connecting rod is attached. It is off-center from the main journals and is often called a throw. Two crank cheeks and a crankpin make a throw. When a force is applied to the crankpin in any direction other than parallel or perpendicular to and through the center line of the crankshaft, it will cause the crankshaft to rotate. The outer surface is hardened by nitriding to increase its resistance to wear and to provide the required bearing surface. The crankpin is usually hollow. This reduces the total weight of the crankshaft and provides a passage for the transfer of lubricating oil. The hollow crankpin also serves as a chamber for collecting sludge, carbon deposits, and other foreign material. Centrifugal force throws these substances to the outside of the chamber and thus keeps them from reaching the connecting-rod bearing surface. On some engines, a passage is drilled in the crank cheek to allow oil from the hollow crankshaft to be sprayed on the cylinder walls.

The crank cheek connects the crankpin to the main journal. In some designs, the cheek extends beyond the journal and carries a counterweight to balance the crankshaft. The crank cheek must be of sturdy construction to obtain the required rigidity between the crankpin and the journal.

In all cases, the type of crankshaft and the number of crankpins must correspond with the cylinder arrangement of the engine. The position of the cranks on the crankshaft in relation to the other cranks of the same shaft is expressed in degrees.

The simplest crankshaft is the single-throw or 360° type. This type is used on a single-row radial engine. It can be constructed in one or two pieces. Two main bearings (one on each end) are provided when this type of crankshaft is used.

1) Crankshaft Balance

Excessive vibration in an engine not only results in fatigue failure of the metal structures, but also causes the moving parts to wear rapidly. In some instances, excessive vibration is caused by a crankshaft which is not balanced. Crankshafts are balanced for static balance and dynamic balance.

A crankshaft is statically balanced when the weight of the entire assembly of crankpins, crank cheeks, and counterweights is balanced around the axis of rotation. When testing the crankshaft for static balance, it is placed on two knife edges. If the shaft tends to turn toward any one position during the test, it is out of static balance.

A crankshaft is dynamically balanced when all the forces created by the crankshaft rotation and

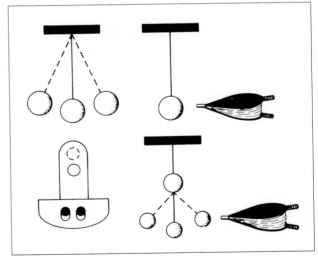

Figure 1-22. Operating principle of a dynamic damper. The crankshaft of an aircraft engine behaves as a pendulum and has a resonant frequency. Power impulses supplied to the pendulum at its resonant frequency cause a maximum amplitude of deflection. A weight placed on the pendulum in such a way that it is free to oscillate, will change the resonant frequency of the pendulum, and the power impulses will cause less amplitude of vibrations.

power impulses are balanced within themselves so that little or no vibration is produced when the engine is operating. To reduce vibration to a minimum during engine operation, dynamic dampers are incorporated on the crankshaft.

2) Dynamic Dampers

A dynamic damper is merely a pendulum which is so fastened to the crankshaft that it is free to move in a small arc. It is incorporated in the counterweight assembly. Some crankshafts utilize two or more of these assemblies, each being attached to a different crank cheek. The distance the pendulum moves and its vibrating frequency correspond to the frequency of the power impulses of the engine. When the vibration frequency of the crankshaft occurs, the pen-dulum oscillates out of time with the crankshaft vibration, thus reducing vibration to a minimum.

The construction of the dynamic damper used in one engine consists of a movable slotted-steel counterweight attached to the crank cheek. Two spool-shaped steel pins extend into the slot and pass through oversized holes in the counterweight and crank cheek. The difference in diameter between the pins and the holes provides a pendulum effect. An analogy of the functioning of a dynamic damper is shown in figure 1-22.

b. Connecting Rods

The connecting rod is the link which transmits forces between the piston and the crankshaft. Connecting rods must be strong enough to

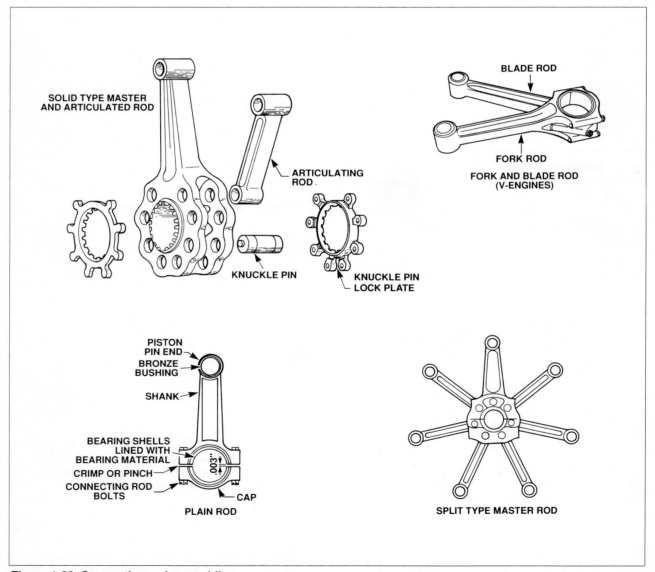

Figure 1-23. Connecting rod assemblies.

remain rigid under a load and yet be light enough to reduce the inertia forces which are produced when the rod and piston stop, change direction, and start again at the end of each stroke.

There are three types of connecting-rod assemblies: (1) the plain-type connecting rod, (2) the fork-and-blade connecting rod, and (3) the master-and-articulated-rod assembly (see figure 1-23).

1) Plain Rods

Plain-type connecting rods are used in in-line and opposed engines. The end of the connecting rod that attaches to the piston is fitted with a pressed-in bushing in which the wrist pin floats. The big end, or the end of the rod attached to the crankpin, is fitted with a cap and a two-piece bearing. The bearing cap is held on the end of the rod by bolts or studs. To maintain proper fit and balance, connecting rods should always be replaced in the same cylinder and in the same relative position.

2) Master And Articulating Rod Assembly

The master-and-articulated rod assembly is commonly used in radial engines. In a radial engine the piston in one cylinder in each row is connected to the crankshaft by a master rod. All other pistons in the row are connected to the master rod by an articulated rod. The articulated rods are constructed of forged steel alloy in either the I- or H-shape, denoting the cross-sectional shape. Bronze bushings are pressed into

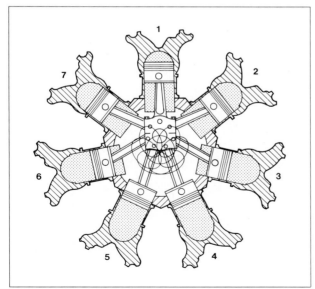

Figure 1-24. Elliptical travel path of knuckle pins in an articulated rod assembly.

the bores in each end of the articulated rod to provide knuckle-pin and piston-pin bearings.

The master rod serves as the connecting link between the piston pin and the crankpin. The crankpin end, or the "big end", contains the crankpin or master rod bearing. Flanges around the big end provide for the attachment of the articulated rods. The articulated rods are attached to the master rod by knuckle pins, which are pressed into holes in the master rod flanges during assembly. A plain bearing, usually called a piston-pin bushing, is installed in the piston end of the master rod to receive the piston pin.

When a crankshaft of the split-spline or split-clamp type is employed, a one-piece master rod is used. The master and articulated rods are assembled and then installed on the crankpin; the crankshaft sections are then joined together. In engines that use the one-piece type of crankshaft, the big end of the master rod is split, as is the master rod bearing. The main part of the master rod is installed on the crankpin; then the bearing cap is set in place and bolted to the master rod.

The centers of the knuckle pins do not coincide with the center of the crankpin. Thus, while the crankpin center describes a true circle for each revolution of the crankshaft, the centers of the knuckle pins describe an elliptical path (see figure 1-24).

The elliptical paths are symmetrical about a center line through the master rod cylinder. It can be seen that the major diameters of the ellipses are not the same. Thus, the link rods will have varying degrees of angularity relative to the center of the crank throw.

Because of the varying angularity of the link rods and the elliptical motion of the knuckle pins, all pistons do not move an equal amount in each cylinder for a given number of degrees of crankshaft rotation. This variation in piston position between cylinders can have considerable effect on engine operation. To minimize the effect of these factors on valve and ignition timing, the knuckle pin holes in the master rod flange are not equi-distant from the center of the crankpin, thereby off-setting to an extent the effect of the link rod angularity.

3) Knuckle Pins

The knuckle pins are of solid construction except for the oil passages drilled in the pins, which lubricate the knuckle-pin bushings. These pins may be installed by pressing them into holes in the master rod flanges so that they are prevented from turning in the master rod. Knuckle pins may also be installed with a loose fit so that they can turn in the master rod flange holes, and also turn in the articulating rod bushings. These are called "full floating" knuckle pins. In either type of installation, a lock plate on each side retains the knuckle pins and prevents a lateral movement of it.

4) Fork And Blade Rod Assembly

The fork-and-blade rod assembly is used primarily in V-type engines. The forked rod is split at the crankpin end to allow space for the blade rod to fit between the prongs. A single two-piece bearing is used on the crankshaft end of the rod.

c. Pistons

The piston in a reciprocating engine is a cylindrical device that moves back and forth within the cylinder and acts as a moveable wall for the combustion chamber. As the piston moves down in the cylinder, it creates a low pressure area and draws in the fuel/air mixture. Then, as it moves upward, it compresses the charge, ignition occurs, and the expanding gases force the piston downward. This force is transmitted to the crankshaft through the connecting rod. On the return path upward, the piston forces the exhaust gases from the cylinder.

1) Piston Construction

The majority of aircraft engine pistons are machined from aluminum alloy forgings. Grooves are machined in the outside surface of the piston to receive the piston rings, and cooling fins are provided on the inside of the piston for greater heat transfer to the engine oil.

Pistons may be either the trunk type or the slipper type; both are shown in figure 1-25. Slipper type pistons are not used in modern high-powered engines because they do not provide adequate strength or wear resistance. The top face of the piston, or head, may be machined to prevent interference with the valves.

As many as six grooves may be machined around the piston to accommodate the compression rings and oil rings. (see figure 1-25). The compression rings are installed in the three uppermost grooves; the oil control rings are in-

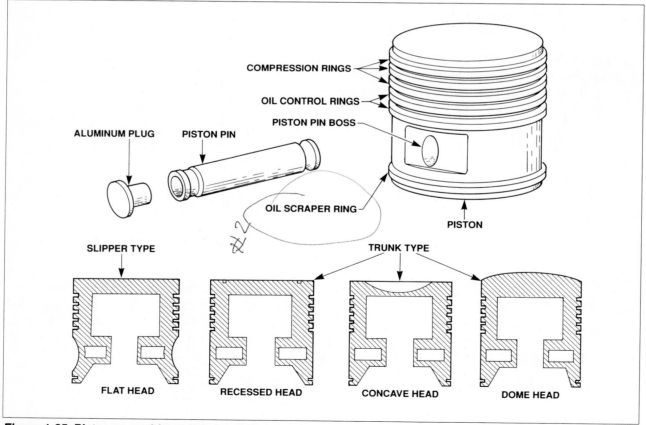

Figure 1-25. Piston assembly and types of pistons.

stalled immediately above the piston pin. This piston is usually drilled at the oil control ring grooves to allow surplus oil scraped from the cylinder walls by the oil control rings to pass back into the crankcase. An oil scraper ring is installed at the base of the piston wall or skirt to prevent excessive oil consumption. The portions of the piston walls that lie between each pair of ring grooves are called the ring lands.

In addition to acting as a guide for the piston head, the piston skirt incorporates the piston-pin bosses. The piston-pin bosses are of heavy construction to enable the heavy load on the piston head to be transferred to the piston pin.

2) Piston Pins

The piston pin joins the piston to the connecting rod. It is machined in the form of a tube from a nickel-steel alloy forging, case-hardened and ground. The piston pin is sometimes called a wrist pin because of the similarity between the relative motions of the piston and the articulated rod and that of the human arm.

The piston pin used in modern aircraft engines is the full-floating type, so called because the pin is free to rotate in both the piston and in the connecting rod piston-pin bearing.

The piston pin must be held in place to prevent the pin ends from scoring the cylinder walls. In earlier engines, spring coils were installed in grooves in the piston-pin bores at either end of the pin. The current practice is to install a plug of relatively soft aluminum in the pin ends to provide a good bearing surface against the cylinder walls.

3) Piston Rings

The piston rings prevent leakage of gas pressure from the combustion chamber and reduce to a minimum the seepage of oil into the combustion chamber. The rings fit into the piston grooves but spring out to press against the cylinder walls; when properly lubricated, the rings form an effective gas seal.

a) Piston Ring Construction

Most piston rings are made of high-grade cast iron. After the rings are made, they are ground to the cross section desired. They are then split so that they can be slipped over the outside of the piston and into the ring grooves. Since their purpose is to seal the clearance between the piston and the cylinder wall, they must fit the cylinder wall snugly enough to provide a gas-tight fit; they must exert equal pressure at all points on

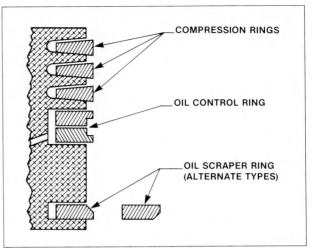

Figure 1-26. Typical piston rings fitted to an aircraft engine piston.

the cylinder wall, and they must make a gas-tight fit against the sides of the ring grooves.

Gray cast iron is most often used in making piston rings. However, many other materials have been tried. In some engines, chrome-plated mild steel piston rings are used in the top compression ring groove because these rings can better withstand the high temperatures present at this point.

b) Compression Ring

The purpose of the compression rings is to prevent the escape of gas past the piston during engine operation. They are placed in the ring grooves immediately below the piston head. The number of compression rings used on each piston is determined by the type of engine and its design, although most aircraft engines use two compression rings plus one or more oil control rings.

The cross section of the ring is either rectangular or wedge shaped with a tapered face. The tapered face presents a narrow bearing edge to the cylinder wall which helps to reduce friction and provide better sealing.

c) Oil Control Ring

Oil control rings are placed in the grooves immediately below the compression rings and above the piston pin bores. There may be one or more oil control rings per piston; two rings may be installed in the same groove, or they may be installed in separate grooves. Oil control rings regulate the thickness of the oil film on the cylinder wall. If too much oil enters the combustion chamber, it will burn and leave a thick coating of carbon on the combustion chamber walls, the piston head, the spark plugs, and the valve heads. This carbon can cause the valves and piston rings to stick if it enters the ring grooves or valve guides. In addition, the carbon can cause spark plug misfiring as well as detonation, preignition, or excessive oil consumption. To allow the surplus oil to return to the crankcase, holes are drilled in the piston ring grooves or in the lands next to these grooves.

d) Oil Scraper Ring

The oil scraper ring usually has a beveled face and is installed in the groove at the bottom of the piston skirt. The ring is installed with the scraping edge away from the piston head or in the reverse position, depending upon cylinder position and the engine series. In the reverse position, the scraper ring retains the surplus oil above the ring on the upward piston stroke, and this oil is returned to the crankcase by the oil control rings on the downward stroke. It is very important that these rings be installed in accordance with the manufacturer's instructions.

d. Cylinders

Power in an engine is developed in the cylinder. The cylinder provides a combustion chamber where the burning and expansion of gases takes place, and it houses the piston and connecting rod.

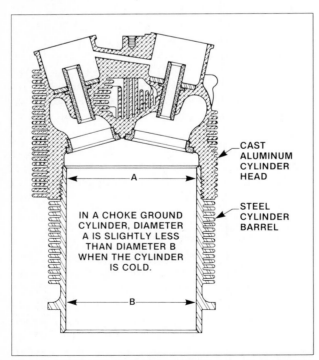

IN A CHOKE GROUND CYLINDER, DIAMETER A IS SLIGHTLY LESS THAN DIAMETER B WHEN THE CYLINDER IS COLD.

CAST ALUMINUM CYLINDER HEAD

STEEL CYLINDER BARREL

Figure 1-27. Construction details of an air-cooled aircraft engine cylinder.

There are four major factors that need to be considered in the design and construction of the cylinder assembly. They are:

(1) It must be strong enough to withstand the internal pressures developed during engine operation.

(2) It must be constructed of a lightweight metal to keep down engine weight.

(3) It must have good heat-conducting properties for efficient cooling.

(4) It must be comparatively easy and inexpensive to manufacture, inspect, and maintain.

Some of the earliest two- and four-cylinder horizontally opposed engines had the cylinder barrels cast as part of the crankcase halves and used removable cylinder heads. Almost all of the modern engines use individual cylinders with permanently attached heads.

The cylinder used in the air-cooled engine is the overhead valve type shown in figure 1-27. Each cylinder is an assembly of two major parts: (1) the cylinder head, and (2) the cylinder barrel. At assembly, the cylinder head is expanded by heating and then screwed down on the cylinder barrel which has been chilled. When the head cools and contracts, and the barrel warms up and expands, a gas-tight joint results.

1) Cylinder Heads

The purpose of the cylinder head is to provide a place for combustion of the fuel/air mixture, and to give the cylinder more heat conductivity for adequate cooling. The fuel/air mixture is ignited by the spark in the combustion chamber and commences burning as the piston travels toward top dead center on the compression stroke. The ignited charge is rapidly expanding at this time, and pressure is increasing so that as the piston travels through the top dead center position, it is driven downward on the power stroke. The intake and exhaust valve ports are located in the cylinder head along with the spark plugs and the intake and exhaust valve actuating mechanisms.

The cylinder head of an air-cooled engine is generally made of aluminum alloy, because aluminum is a good conductor of heat and is light weight. Cylinder heads are forged or die-cast for greater strength. The inner shape of a cylinder may be flat, semi-spherical, or peaked, in the form of a house roof. The semi-spherical type has proved more satisfactory because it is stronger and aids in a more rapid and thorough scavenging of the exhaust gases.

Cooling fins are cast into the cylinder head to aid in transferring the heat from the cylinder head to the cooling airstream. Because of the difference in temperature in the various sections of the cylinder head, it is necessary to provide more cooling-fin area on some sections than on others. The exhaust valve region is the hottest part of the internal surface; therefore, more fin area is provided around the outside of the cylinder in this area.

After casting, the spark plug bushings, valve guides, rocker arm bushings, and valve seats are installed in the cylinder head. Spark plug openings may be fitted with bronze or steel bushings that are shrunk and screwed into the openings. Stainless steel Heli-Coil spark plug inserts are used on most engines of current manufacture. Bronze or steel valve guides are usually shrunk or screwed into drilled openings in the cylinder head to provide guides for the valve stems. These are generally located at an angle to the center line of the cylinder. The valve seats are circular rings of hardened metal which protect the relatively soft metal of the cylinder head from the hammering action of the valves and from the exhaust gases.

2) Cylinder Barrels

In general, the cylinder barrel in which the piston operates must be made of a high-strength material, usually steel. It must be as light as possible, yet have the proper characteristics for operating under high temperatures. It must be made of a good bearing material and have high tensile strength.

A high-strength chrome molybdenum steel barrel is machined from a forged blank, with a skirt which projects into the crankcase and a mounting flange to attach the cylinder to the crankcase. Thin cooling fins are machined into the exterior cylinder wall and threads are cut at the top of the barrel so that it can be screwed into the head.

The bore of the cylinder may be ground so that the diameter at the top portion of the barrel is slightly smaller than the diameter of the main part of the barrel. This is called a choke bore cylinder. The reason for this difference in diameters is that the upper end screws solidly into the cast aluminum cylinder head and the heat that concentrates in the head will cause the upper end of the cylinder barrel to expand more than the rest of the barrel. With a choke bore, this expansion will straighten the bore so that, at

normal operating temperatures, the diameter is uniform throughout the part of the cylinder in which the piston moves.

The piston rings continually rub up and down inside the cylinder, and to increase the life of the cylinder barrel, some cylinder walls are hardened. There are two commonly used methods of providing a hard wearing surface: chrome plating and nitriding.

a) Chrome-Plated Barrels

Chromium is a hard, natural element, which has a high melting point, high heat conductivity, and a very low coefficient of friction. Because of its hardness and high coefficient of friction, a thin coating of chromium is sometimes applied by electroplating to the inside of aircraft cylinder barrels.

Chromium has a natural tendency to form surface cracks, and after the plating process is completed, current is then sent through the plating solution in the reverse direction for a controlled period of time. This will cause these tiny surface cracks open up and form a network of interconnecting cracks that hold lubricating oil on the cylinder wall.

Chromed cylinders have many advantages over both plain steel and nitrided cylinders. They are less susceptible to rusting or corrosion, both because of the natural corrosion resistance of chromium and because oil adheres to the chromed cylinder walls better than it does to plain steel. Chromium is much harder than steel, and so it wears less.

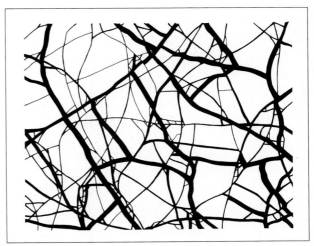

Figure 1-28. A reproduction of a photomicrograph of the tiny cracks in the chrome-plated wall of an aircraft engine cylinder.

When cylinders have worn beyond their usable limits, they may be chrome plated back to their original size. Cylinders that have been chrome plated will be identified by a band of orange paint around their base, or by a stripe of orange paint on certain of their cooling fins.

b) Nitrided Barrels

Case hardening is a process in which the surface of steel is changed by the infusion of some hardening agent. It differs from plating in that no material is deposited on the surface, but there is actually a change in the surface of the material itself. Nitriding does not require quenching, and so it does not warp the cylinders as other forms of case hardening might do.

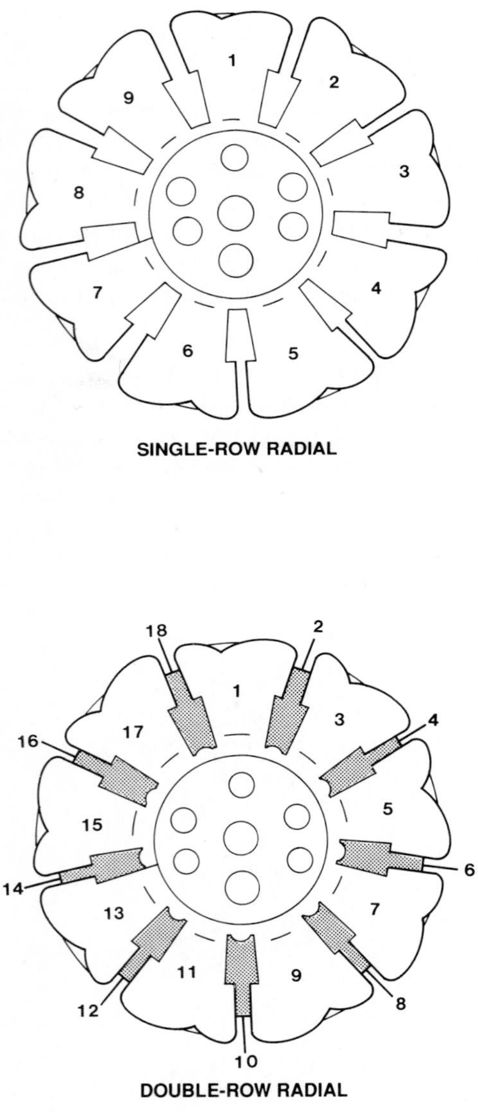

After the cylinder barrel has been ground to the required size and smoothness, it is placed in a furnace or retort, in an atmosphere of ammonia gas. The length of time the barrel is kept in the retort and the temperature are both carefully controlled and, in the nitriding process, the ammonia gas breaks down, or disassociates, into nitrogen and hydrogen. The steel in the cylinder barrel has a small percentage of aluminum as an alloying agent, and the nitrogen combines with the aluminum to form aluminum nitrides, the hard, wear-resistant surface we want.

Since nitriding is not a plating or a coating, it causes a dimensional growth of only about two to four ten thousandths of an inch. The hardened layer varies in depth to about 0.020 inch, and gradually decreases in hardness from the surface inward, until it corresponds to that of the metal itself. After the nitriding process is completed, the cylinder walls are honed to a micro-smooth finish.

One of the problems with a nitrided surface is its susceptibility to corrosion and rust. Nitrided cylinder walls must be kept covered with oil, and if an engine is left out of service for any period of time, the cylinder walls should be coated with a sticky preservative oil.

Nitrided cylinders are identified by a band of blue paint around their base, or by certain fins being painted blue.

c. Cylinder Numbering

Occasionally it is necessary to refer to the left or right side of the engine, or to a particular cylinder. Therefore, it is necessary to know the engine directions and how cylinders on an engine are numbered.

The propeller shaft end of the engine is always the front end, and the accessory end is the rear end, regardless of how the engine is mounted in an aircraft. When referring to the right side or the left side of an engine, always assume you are viewing it from the rear or accessory end. As seen from this position, crankshaft rotation is referred to as either clockwise or counterclockwise.

1) Single-Row Radial Engines

Radial engine cylinders are numbered clockwise as viewed from the accessory end. In-line and V-type engine cylinders are usually numbered from the rear. In V-type engines, the

SINGLE-ROW RADIAL

DOUBLE-ROW RADIAL

Figure 1-29. Cylinder numbering on radial engines.

cylinder banks are known as the right bank and the left bank, as viewed from the accessory end.

Single-row radial engine cylinders are numbered clockwise when viewed from the rear end. Cylinder No. 1 is the top cylinder.

2) Double-Row Radial Engines

In double-row radial engines, the same system is used, in that the No. 1 cylinder is the top one of the rear row. No. 2 cylinder is the first one clockwise from No. 1, but No. 2 is in the front row. No. 3 cylinder is the next one clockwise to

No. 2, but is in the rear row. Thus, all odd-numbered cylinders are in the rear row, and all even-numbered cylinders are in the front row. Figure 1-29 illustrates the cylinder numbering for single- and double-row radial engines.

3) Opposed

Teledyne-Continental and Avco-Lycoming both make four- and six-cylinder horizontally opposed engines that operate in exactly the same way, but the cylinder numbering method used by the two manufacturers differ. Because the method on numbering differs, the firing orders differ, but the actual firing impulses are the same. Figure 1-30 shows the cylinder numbering for engines built by both manufacturers. You can see that both manufacturers start numbering on the right side but that Continental engines have the No. 1 cylinder at the rear, and Lycoming locates the No. 1 at the front of the engine.

4) Firing Order

The firing order of an engine is the sequence in which the power event occurs in the different cylinders. The firing order is designed to provide for balance and to eliminate vibration to the greatest extent possible.

On a single-row radial engine, first, all the odd numbered cylinders fire in numerical succession, then the even-numbered cylinders fire in numerical succession. The firing order of a nine-cylinder radial engine is 1-3-5-7-9-2-4-6-8.

On a double-row radial engine, the firing order is somewhat complicated. The firing order is arranged with the firing impulse occurring in a cylinder in one row and then in a cylinder in the other row; therefore two cylinders in the same row never fire in succession.

A handy way to remember the firing order of an 18-cylinder radial engine is to start with number one and add 11 when you can, and when you cannot add 11, subtract 7. Just keep all of the numbers between one and 18. You can do the same thing for a 14-cylinder engine by adding nine and subtracting five.

The fact that Lycoming and Continental engines number their cylinders differently gives us two sets of firing orders, but if you will trace out the firing impulses, you will see that the two engines are the same. Carefully follow the arrows in each of the firing order diagrams (figure 1-31) and you can see that the patterns are exactly the same, even if the numbers are different.

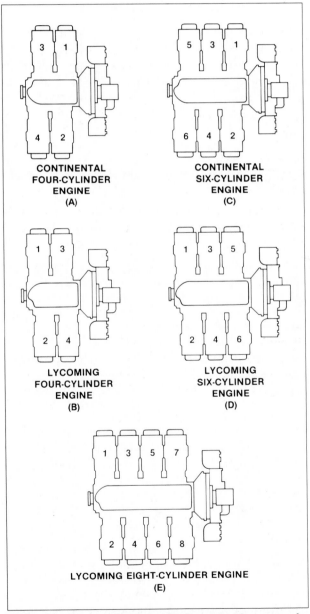

Figure 1-30. Cylinder arrangement for popular horizontally opposed aircraft engines.

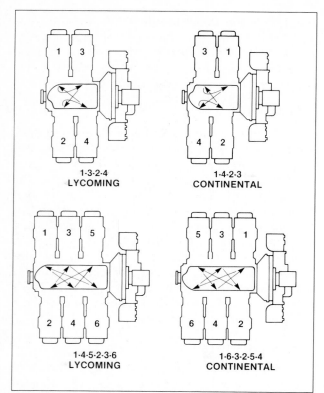

Figure 1-31. Firing orders of horizontally opposed engines.

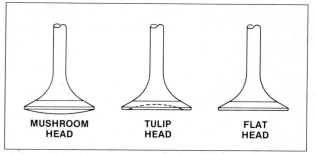

Figure 1-32. Typical head shapes for poppet valves used in aircraft engines.

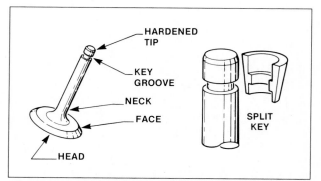

Figure 1-33. Typical poppet-type valve for an aircraft engine.

f. Valves

The fuel/air mixture enters the cylinders through the intake valve ports, and burned gases are expelled through the exhaust valve ports. The head of each valve opens and closes these cylinder ports. The valves used in aircraft engines are the conventional poppet type. The valves are also typed by their shape and may be called either mushroom or tulip because of their resemblance to the shape of these plants. Figure 1-32 illustrates common head shapes.

1) Construction

The valves in the cylinders of an aircraft engine are subject to high temperatures, corrosion, and operating stresses, and the metal used in their manufacture must be able to resist all of these attritional factors.

Because intake valves operate at lower temperatures than exhaust valves, they may be made of chrome, nickel, or tungsten steel, but the exhaust valves are usually made of some of the more exotic metals such as inconel, silicon-chromium or cobalt-chromium alloys.

The face of the valve is ground to form a seal against the valve seat in the cylinder head when the valve is closed. The face is usually ground to an angle of 30, 45, or 60 degrees, with the manufacturer specifying the angle that will give the best airflow efficiency and sealing.

Valve faces are often made more durable by the application of a material called Stellite, an alloy of cobalt and chromium. About 1/16-inch of this alloy is welded to the valve face and is then ground to the correct angle. Stellite is resistant to high temperatures and corrosion, and it also withstands the shock and wear associated with valve operation.

The valve stem is surface hardened so it will act as a pilot for the valve head as it rides up and down in the valve guide that is installed in the cylinder head for that purpose. The tip of the stem is hardened to withstand the hammering of the valve rocker arm as it opens the valve, and a groove is machined around the valve stem near the tip for the split key which holds the valve spring retaining washer in place.

Some exhaust valves stems are hollow and are partially filled with metallic sodium. The sodium melts at approximately 208° F, and the up and down motion of the valve circulates the liquid sodium so that it can carry heat from the valve head into the stem where it can be dissipated through the valve guide into the cylinder head and then out to the air through the cooling fins. In this way the operating temperature of the valve can be reduced by as much as 300 to 400 degrees Fahrenheit.

2) Valve Seats

The valve operates in the hot environment of the inside of the cylinder head and is continually exposed to a pounding action. Because of this,

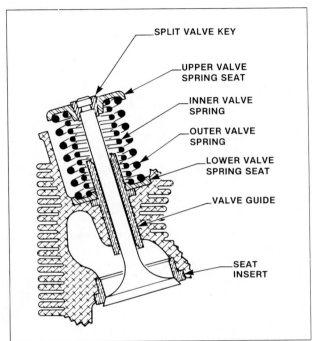

Figure 1-34. Method of securing a poppet valve in an aircraft cylinder.

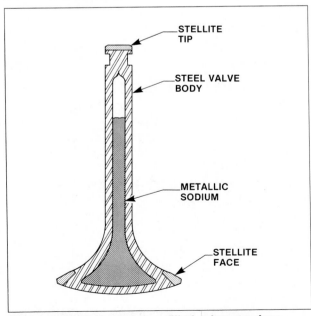

Figure 1-35. Hollow sodium-filled exhaust valves.

an extremely durable seat must be installed in the soft aluminum cylinder head. Rings of aluminum, bronze, or steel are machined with an outside diameter about 0.010 to 0.015 inch larger than the hole into which they are to fit, and are installed into the cylinder head with a shrink fit. The seating surface is ground to the proper angle using equipment that will assure its concentricity with the valve guide.

g. Valve Operating Mechanisms

For a reciprocating engine to operate properly, each valve must open at the proper time, stay open for the required length of time, and close at the proper time. This timing of the valves is controlled by the valve operating mechanism.

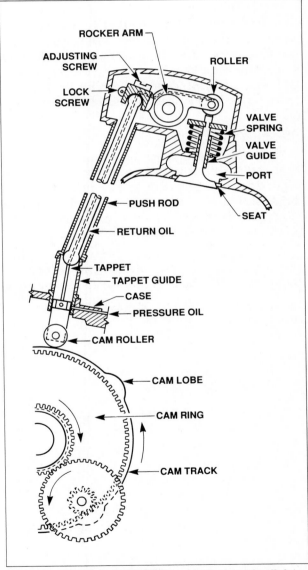

Figure 1-36. Valve-operating mechanism (radial engine).

The valve-operating mechanism consists of a cam ring or camshaft equipped with lobes, which work against a cam follower. Figure 1-36 shows the components of a valve operating mechanism. The cam follower, in turn, pushes a push rod, which, in turn, actuates a rocker arm which opens the valve. Springs, which slip over the stem of the valves and which are held in place by the valve spring retaining washer and stem key, close each valve and push the valve mechanism in the opposite direction when the cam roller or follower rolls along a low section of the cam ring.

The valve lift (distance that the valve is lifted off its seat) and the valve duration (length of time the valve is held open) are both determined by the shape of the cam lobes.

Typical cam lobes are illustrated in figure 1-37. The portion of the lobe that gently starts the valve operating mechanism moving is called a ramp, or step. The ramp is machined on each side of the cam lobe to permit the rocker arm to be eased into contact with the valve tip and thus reduce the shock load which otherwise would occur.

1) Cam Ring

The valve mechanism of a radial engine is operated by one or two cam rings, depending upon the number of rows of cylinders. In a single-row radial engine one ring with a double cam track is used. One track operates the intake valves; the other, the exhaust valves.

The cam ring is a circular piece of steel with a series of cams or lobes and the space between them (on which the cam rollers ride) is known as

5 Cylinders		7 Cylinders		9 Cylinders		Direction Of Rotation
Number Of Lobes	Speed	Number Of Lobes	Speed	Number Of Lobes	Speed	
3	1/6	4	1/8	5	1/10	With Crankshaft
2	1/4	3	1/6	4	1/8	Opposite Crankshaft

Figure 1-38. Radial engines, cam ring table.

the cam track. As the cam ring revolves, the lobes cause the cam roller to raise the tappet in the tappet guide, thereby transmitting the force through the push rod and rocker arm to open the valve.

The cam ring is mounted concentrically with the crankshaft and is driven by the crankshaft at a reduced rate of speed through the cam intermediate drive gear assembly. The timing of the valve events is determined by the spacing of the lobes and the speed and direction at which the cam ring is driven in relation to the speed and direction of the crankshaft.

The method of driving the cam varies on the different makes of engines. The cam ring can be designed with teeth on either the inside or the outside of its periphery. If the reduction gear meshes with the teeth on the outside of the ring, the cam will turn in the direction of rotation of the crankshaft. If the ring is driven from the inside, the cam will turn in the opposite direction from the crankshaft.

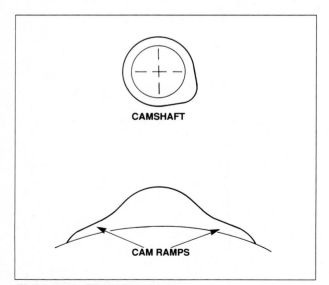

Figure 1-37. Typical cam lobes.

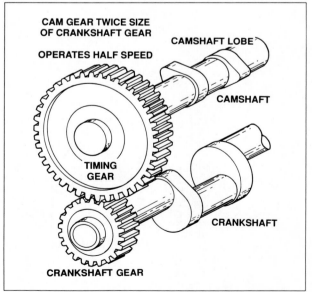

Figure 1-39. Cam drive mechanism for opposed-type aircraft engines.

A study of figure 1-38 will show that a four-lobe cam may be used in either a seven-cylinder or nine-cylinder engine. On a seven-cylinder engine it will rotate in the same direction as the crankshaft, on the nine-cylinder, opposite crankshaft rotation. A formula that sometimes is used in figuring cam speed is: cam ring speed = ½ divided by the number of lobes on either cam track.

One-half is the speed at which the cam would operate if it were equipped with a single lobe for each valve. It is divided by the number of lobes, which will determine how much the speed will have to be reduced.

2) Camshaft

The valve mechanism of an opposed engine is operated by a camshaft. The camshaft is driven by a gear that mates with another gear attached to the crankshaft (see figure 1-39). The camshaft always rotates at one-half the crankshaft speed. As the camshaft revolves, the lobes cause the tappet assemblies to rise in the tappet guide, transmitting the force through the push rod and rocker arm to open the valve.

3) Tappet Assemblies

The tappet assemblies, also called valve lifters or cam followers, ride between the cam and the pushrod. There are two types used: solid lifters and hydraulically operated lifters.

a) Solid

Radial engines and some of the smaller horizontally opposed engines use a solid valve lifter that rides in holes machined in the crankcase, with their large end riding on the lobes of the cam. The spherical end of the push-rod rides in a machined socket in the lifter, and holes drilled in the lifter allow oil from the oil pressure gallery of the engine to flow through the lifter and lubricate the valve mechanism in the rocker box.

The aluminum alloy cylinder heads expand much more than the pushrods, and as the engine gets hot, the valve mechanism in the cylinder head actually moves away from the crankcase. This causes the clearance between the rocker arm and the valve stem to open up. Engines with solid valve lifters must have some means of adjusting the clearance in the valve train, as the mechanism between the cam and the valve is called. To do this, the rocker arm is fitted with an adjustment screw in the end in which the pushrod rides. The engine specifications list the clearance that must be set between the rocker arm and the valve stem. This clearance is measured with a thickness gauge, and the adjustment made with the adjusting screw. After the proper clearance is set, a locknut is tightened to prevent engine vibration from changing the setting.

b) Hydraulic

Most modern horizontally opposed engines are equipped with hydraulic valve lifters. These units are correctly called zero-lash lifters because they maintain zero clearance in the valve train.

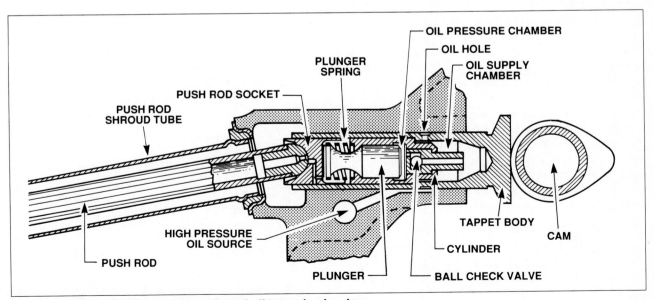

Figure 1-40. Hydraulic valve lifter using a ball-type check valve.

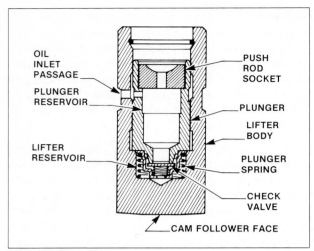

Figure 1-41. Hydraulic valve lifter using a disk-type check valve.

The hydraulic lifters automatically adjust the valve clearance each time the valve is opened, and in this way, it compensates for any dimensional changes that are caused by the expansion of the cylinder head. A typical hydraulic lifter is shown in figure 1-40.

When the engine valve is closed, the face of the tappet body (cam follower) is on the base circle or back of the cam, as shown in figure 1-40. The light plunger spring lifts the hydraulic plunger so that its outer end contacts the push rod socket, exerting a light pressure against it, thus eliminating any clearance in the valve linkage. As the plunger moves outward, the ball check valve moves off its seat. Oil from the supply chamber, which is directly connected with the engine lubrication system, flows in and fills the chamber. As the camshaft rotates, the cam pushes the tappet body and the hydraulic lifter cylinder outward. This action forces the ball check valve onto its seat; thus, the body of oil trapped in the pressure chamber acts as a cushion. During the interval when the engine valve is off its seat, a predetermined leakage occurs between the plunger and cylinder bore which compensates for any expansion or contraction in the valve train. Immediately after the engine valve closes, the amount of oil required to fill the pressure chamber flows in from the supply chamber, preparing for another cycle of operation.

h. Push Rods

Hollow steel or aluminum alloy tubes, with polished ball-type ends pressed in, transmit the movement of the cam follower to the rocker arm. The pushrods are surrounded by a thin sheet of

metal shroud tube. Oil for lubricating the valve mechanism flows under pressure from the engine oil gallery up through the hollow pushrod. Depending upon the type of engine, this oil drains out of the rocker box back into the crankcase through the pushrod shroud tubes or through external drain tubes.

i. Rocker Arms

The rocker arms transmit the lifting force from the cams to the valves. Rocker arms are normally made of forged steel. These assemblies are supported on plain, roller, or ball bearings, or a combination of these and pivot on the rocker shaft. Generally one end of the arm bears against the push rod and the other against the valve stem.

j. Bearings

A bearing is any surface which supports, or is supported by, another surface. A good bearing must be composed of material that is strong enough to withstand the pressure imposed on it and should permit the other surface to move with a minimum of friction and wear. The parts must be held in position with very close tolerances to provide efficient and quiet operation, yet allow freedom of motion. To accomplish this, and at the same time reduce friction of moving parts so that power loss is not excessive, lubricated bearings of many types are used. Bearings are required to take radial loads, thrust loads, or a combination of the two.

There are two ways in which bearing surfaces move in relation to each other. One is by the sliding movement of one metal against the other,

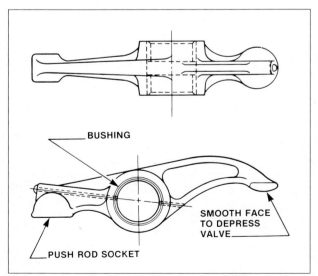

Figure 1-42. Rocker arm for a horizontally opposed engine using hydraulic valve lifters.

and the second is for one surface to roll over the other. The three different types of bearings in general use are plain, roller, and ball (see figure 1-43).

1) Plain

Plain bearings are generally used for the crankshaft, cam ring, camshaft, connecting rods, and the accessory drive shaft bearings. Such bearings are usually subjected to radial loads only, although some have been designed to take thrust loads.

Plain bearings are usually made of nonferrous metals, such as silver, bronze, aluminum, and various alloys of copper, tin, or lead. Master rod or crankpin bearings in some engines are thin shells of steel, plated with silver on both the inside and the outside surfaces and with lead-tin plated over the silver on the inside surface only. Smaller bearings, such as those used to support various shafts in the accessory section, are called bushings. Porous Oilite bushings are widely used in this instance. They are impregnated with oil so that the heat of friction brings the oil to the bearing surface during engine operation.

2) Ball

A ball bearing assembly consists of grooved inner and outer races, one or more sets of balls, and, in bearings designed for disassembly, a bearing retainer. They are used for supercharger impeller shaft bearings and rocker arm bearings in some engines. Special deep-groove ball bearings are used in some aircraft engines to transmit propeller thrust to the engine nose section.

3) Roller

Roller bearings are made in many types and shapes, but the two types generally used in the aircraft engine are the straight roller and the tapered roller bearings. Straight roller bearings are used where the bearing is subjected to radial loads only. In tapered roller bearings, the inner- and outer-race bearing surfaces are cone shaped. Such bearings will withstand both radial and thrust loads. Straight roller bearings are used in high-power aircraft engines for the crankshaft main bearings. They are also used in other applications where radial loads are high.

4. Propeller Reduction Gearing

The power produced by an aircraft engine is determined by the pressure that acts on the pis-

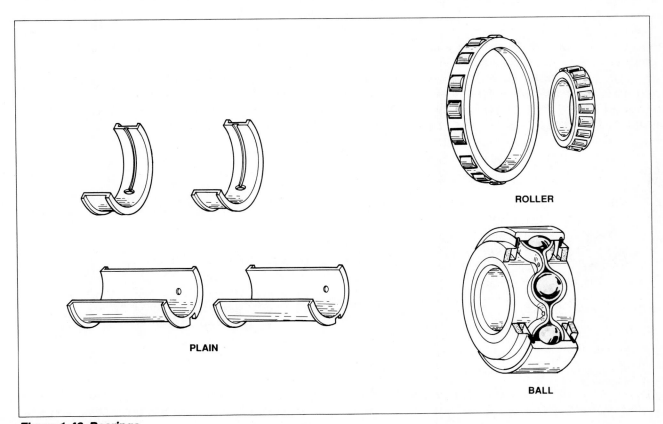

Figure 1-43. Bearings.

ton during each power stroke and the number of power strokes per minute. The faster the engine turns, the more power it produces. We are limited in an aircraft engine, however, by the tip speed of the propeller. As the propeller speed increases, its efficiency drops off.

To get the needed power and at the same time maintain a reasonable propeller tip speed, engine manufacturers have built propeller reduction gear systems into certain high-powered engines. This gearing naturally uses some of the power from the engine and it adds to the weight, but the gain in power more than compensates for the losses.

The simplest type of reduction gearing uses a spur gear attached to the engine crankshaft, mating with a larger spur gear on the propeller shaft. This type of gearing requires a very strong crankcase to withstand the force put into it by the propeller, as it acts like a gyroscope.

One method of overcoming some of the problems of the simple spur gear arrangement has been the use of an internal-tooth driven gear with an external-tooth drive gear. This arrangement keeps the propeller shaft pretty much in line with the crankshaft, and it allows the propeller to turn in the same direction as the engine.

Torsional vibration problems are compounded when an engine is geared. In addition to the counterweights on the crankshaft, some of the popular engines use a quill shaft to further reduce these vibrations. One end of the quill shaft, as we see in figure 1-46, is splined into the front end of the crankshaft. The opposite end is

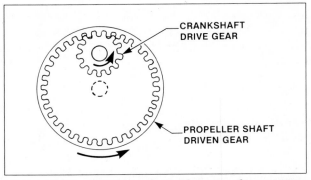

Figure 1-45. Propeller reduction gearing system using an external spur gear driving an internal gear attached to the propeller shaft.

splined into the front end of the propeller shaft. With this arrangement, the propeller drive gear is driven through the quill shaft that flexes torsionally enough to absorb some of the shocks.

Planetary gears are used in some engines to keep the propeller shaft in line with the crankshaft. Power is transmitted from the crankshaft to the propeller with a minimum of weight and space and the direction of rotation of the propeller is the same as that of the engine. This type of reduction gear arrangement is used on some horizontally opposed engines, as well as for radial and turboprop engines.

The planetary system uses a sun gear that is rigidly attached to the nose section of the engine and the crankshaft drives a bell, or ring, gear. Turning between the bell gear and the sun gear is a series of small planetary gears that mount on a spider arrangement to which the propeller shaft is attached. When the crankshaft turns the

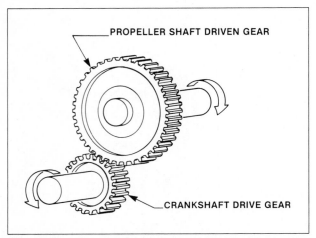

Figure 1-44. External spur gear-type propeller reduction gearing system.

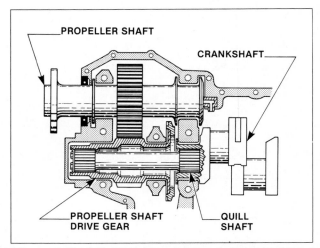

Figure 1-46. A quill shaft used to minimize torsional vibration between the propeller shaft and the crankshaft.

bell gear, it rotates the planetary gears around the sun gear and the spider drives the propeller at a reduction rate that is found by the formula:

$$\text{GEAR RATION} = \frac{\text{TEETH ON BELL GEAR} + \text{TEETH ON SUN GEAR}}{\text{TEETH ON BELL GEAR}}$$

You will notice that neither the number of teeth on the planetary gears nor the number of planetary gears attached to the spider enter into the computation for gear reduction.

If there are 72 teeth on the bell gear and 36 on the sun gear, the propeller turns at a ratio of 1.5 to 1; but this is most generally spoken of as a three-to-two reduction. The crankshaft turns three revolutions for two of the propeller shaft.

5. Propeller Shafts

The method of attaching the propeller to the crankshaft of an aircraft engine has undergone evolutionary changes, as has almost everything else in the engine. Propeller shafts may be one of three major types; tapered, splined, or flanged. Tapered shafts are identified by taper numbers. Splined and flanged shafts are identified by SAE numbers.

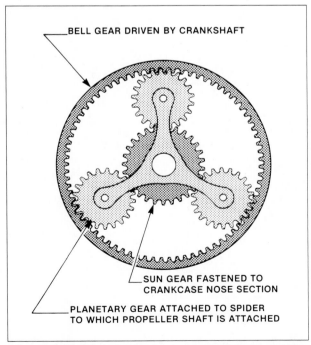

BELL GEAR DRIVEN BY CRANKSHAFT

SUN GEAR FASTENED TO CRANKCASE NOSE SECTION

PLANETARY GEAR ATTACHED TO SPIDER TO WHICH PROPELLER SHAFT IS ATTACHED

Figure 1-47. Planetary gear type propeller reduction gear system.

a. Tapered

Most of the early engines had a tapered propeller shaft, and the wooden propellers used on these engines were mounted in a steel hub that was installed on the tapered shaft. This hub was held in place by a propeller retaining nut that was part of the hub. The retaining nut could back out against a snap ring inside the hub to pull the hub loose from the shaft and remove the propeller assembly. A keyway cut in both the tapered shaft and inside the hub, held a steel key to prevent the propeller assembly from rotating on the shaft.

b. Splined

As the power produced by the engines increased, so did the strength of the propeller attachment. The propeller shaft in many high-powered engines is splined, using standard SAE splines. Most splined shafts have a master spline that is as wide as two splines and the slot between them. This wide spline assures that the propeller will be positioned on the engine with a correct relationship between the propeller and the crankshaft counterweights. This assures the smoothest engine operation.

c. Flanged

Flanged propeller shafts are used on medium- or low-powered reciprocating and turboprop engines. The propeller shaft has a flange forged on the front end to which the propeller is attached with a series of bolts and nuts. In most installations, the nuts are in the form of bushings pressed into the flange.

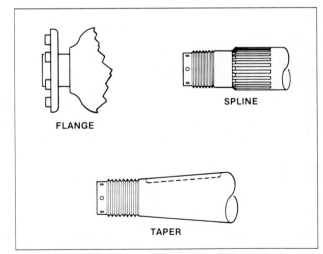

FLANGE

SPLINE

TAPER

Figure 1-48. Types of propeller attachments.

6. Engine Identification

Military engines used descriptive identification numbers far earlier than civilian engines, but today most manufacturers use pretty much the same system for engine identification numbers.

The first letters designate the cylinder arrangement and the basic configuration of the engine.

O - Horizontally opposed engine

R - Radial engine

I - In-line engine

V - V-type engine

T - Turbocharged

I - Fuel injected

S - Supercharged

G - Geared nose section (propeller reduction gearing)

L - Left-hand rotation (for multi-engine installations)

H - Horizontal mounting (for helicopters)

V - Vertical mounting (for helicopters)

A - Modified for acrobatics.

The numbers indicate the piston displacement of the engine in cubic inches.

The last letters indicate the model differences of the basic engine. You must check with the manufacturer specification sheets to correctly interpret these letters, as their meaning will differ between manufacturers.

An example of a couple of engine designations:

LIO-360-C

L - Left hand rotation

I - Fuel injected

O - Horizontally opposed

360 - 360 cubic inch displacement

C - Model C

GTSIO-520-F

G - Geared nose section

TS - Turbo-supercharged

I - Fuel injected

O - Horizontally opposed

520 - 520 cubic inch displacement

F - Model F

Chapter II
Turbine Engines

A. Turbine Engine Development

Jet propulsion is a practical application of Newton's third law of motion (for every action, there is an equal and opposite reaction). This is a method of propulsion that uses the reaction produced by the acceleration of a fluid through an orifice or nozzle to move an object forward. This is, in itself, nothing new or revolutionary. In nature, the squid propels itself through the water by a type of jet propulsion. It takes water into its body, and then, using its muscles, adds energy to the water and expels it in the form of a jet to force itself forward through the water.

As early as 250 B.C., the Greek writer and mathematician Hero devised an application of reaction principle called the aeolipile. This was little more than a curiosity, but evidenced the interest in reaction principles. Men have tried to apply this reaction principle to mechanical designs for centuries, but it is only in the last half of the twentieth century that successful applications for aircraft use were developed.

1. History Of Jet Propulsion

The real history of jet propulsion for aircraft begins in the 20th century. Dr. Sanford Moss, in 1900, published a thesis on gas turbines. Later, as an engineer for the General Electric Company, Moss would be instrumental in the development of the turbo-supercharger. Research done by Dr. Moss influenced Englishman Frank Whittle in the development of what was to become the first successful turbojet engine.

In 1930, Dr. Whittle was granted his first patent for the jet engine, but it was eleven years before this engine completed its first flight. The engine developed by Whittle was a pure reaction type engine and was, in May of 1941, installed and flown in a Gloster model E28/39 aircraft.

Figure 2-2. Hero's aeolipile, conceived more than 200 years before Christ, proved that power by reaction was possible.

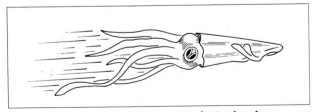

Figure 2-1. Many developments in technology were made by watching nature in action. The squid propels itself through the water by jet reaction in much the same way a turbojet engine propels an aircraft.

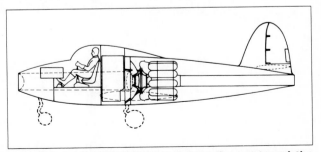

Figure 2-3. The Whittle turbojet engine powered the Gloster E 28/39 that flew in 1941.

The engine produced about one thousand pounds of thrust and propelled the aircraft at a speed in excess of 400 miles per hour.

While Whittle was developing the gas turbine engine in England, a German engineer, Hans Von Ohain, working with the Heinkle company, produced a jet engine that provided 1,100 pounds of thrust. This engine was used to power the Heinkle He-178 that made a successful flight

Figure 2-4. The German Heinkle He-178, flown on August 27, 1939, was the first jet aircraft.

Figure 2-5. The Bell XP-59, which first flew in 1942, was the first American designed and built jet propelled airplane.

on August 27, 1939, to become recognized as the first practical flight by a jet propelled aircraft.

In the United States, research in jet propulsion lagged because all of our efforts were being directed toward the development and production of high powered reciprocating engines. In 1941, the General Electric Company of Schenectady, New York, was given a contract to research and develop a gas turbine engine. G.E. was chosen for this important project because of their extensive experience, both in turbines used for electrical power generation, and in the production of turbo-superchargers.

The result of the contract with General Electric was the GE-1A engine, a centrifugal-compressor type engine that produced about 1,650 pounds of thrust. Two of these engines were used to power the Bell XP-59 which was first flown in October of 1942. The "Airacomet" was successful in proving the concept of jet powered flight, but was never used in combat due to its limited flight time of 30 minutes.

2. Types Of Turbine Engines

The reaction principle has been applied to several propulsive devices used in aviation, past and present. All produce thrust in the same manner, by accelerating a mass of air within the engine. These engines are: the rocket, the ramjet, the pulsejet, and the gas turbine. We will limit our discussion here to the gas turbine engine, as

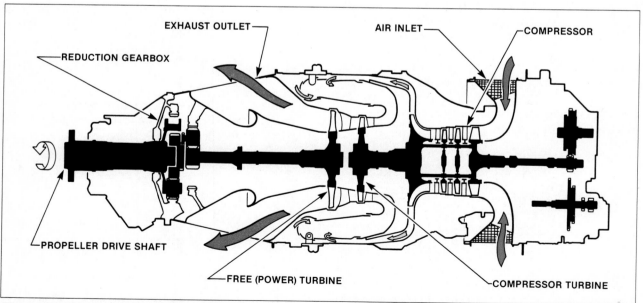

Figure 2-6. The Pratt and Whitney of Canada PT6 turboprop engine is a popular example of a free-turbine engine that has been adapted to both turboprop and turboshaft applications.

it has been applied to supplying the primary thrust on commercially produced aircraft.

The gas turbine principle can be applied to aircraft propulsion in one of two manners. We can use the engine to produce torque and then incorporate a device such as a propeller or helicopter rotor to convert this torque into thrust, or we can use the engine to produce thrust directly.

a. Torque Producing Engines—Turboshaft And Turboprop

A gas turbine engine that delivers power through a shaft to operate something other than a propeller is referred to as a turboshaft engine. These are widely used in such industrial applications as electrical power generating plants and surface transportation systems. In aviation, turboshaft engines are used to power many modern helicopters.

The turboshaft power takeoff may be coupled to, and driven directly by, the turbine that drives the compressor, but it is more likely to be driven by a turbine of its own. Engines using a separate turbine for power takeoff are called free-turbine engines.

A free-turbine engine has two major sections, the gas generator and the free turbine section. The function of the gas generator is to produce the required energy to drive the free turbine system, and it extracts about two-thirds of the energy available from the combustion process.

A turboprop engine is similar in design to a turboshaft engine except that it uses a reduction gear system to drive the propeller.

The propeller may be driven from the gas generator turbine, or it may use its own free turbine in the same way as the turboshaft engine. The free turbine arrangement allows the propeller driven turbine to seek its optimum speed while the compressor turbine operates at the best speed for the compressor efficiency.

b. Thrust Producing Engines—Turbojet And Turbofan

A modern turbojet engine produces its thrust from the acceleration of the flow of hot gases. Air enters the engine inlet and flows into the compressor where its pressure is increased. Fuel is added in the combustor where it is ignited and burns, expanding the gases. As the expanded gases flow out through the turbine where part of their energy is given up to spin the turbine which drives the compressor, energy that remains in the gases as they leave the tail pipe produces the reaction we know as thrust.

A turbofan engine consists basically of a multi-bladed ducted propeller driven by a gas turbine engine. Turbofans were developed to provide a compromise between the best features of the turbojet and the turboprop. The turbofan has turbojet-type cruise speed capability, yet retains some of the short-field takeoff capability of a turboprop.

There are several fan configurations. The fan can be bolted directly to the compressor and rotate at the same speed, or it can be connected through a reduction gear system to the compressor. The fan on some engines is driven by a separate turbine and rotates independently of

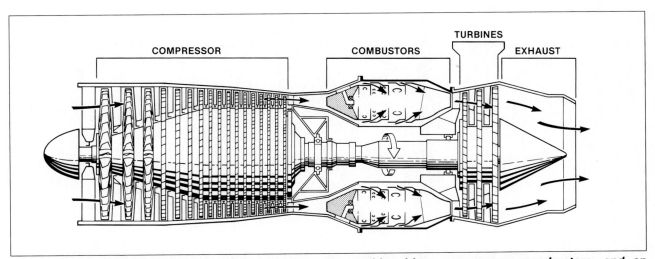

Figure 2-7. The modern turbojet engine consists of a turbine-driven compressor, combustors, and an aerodynamically shaped exhaust duct through which the expanded gases exit at a high velocity.

41

the compressor, and in some engines the fan is mounted in the turbine section as an extension of the turbine blades. An engine with the fan in the turbine section is called an aft-fan engine, and those with the fan in front are called forward-fan engines. The aft-fan configuration is not a popular design today because the fan does not contribute to the compressor pressure ratio.

Turbofans in civil aircraft are generally divided into three classifications, based on by-pass ratio: low bypass (1:1), medium bypass (2 or 3:1), and high bypass (4:1 or greater).

In a low by-pass engine, the fan and compressor section utilize approximately the same mass airflow, but the fan discharge will generally be slightly greater than that of the compressor. The fan discharge air may be ducted directly overboard from a short fan duct, or it may pass along the entire length of the engine in what is called a long fan duct. In either case the end of the duct has a converging discharge nozzle to produce a velocity increase and reactive thrust.

A medium, or intermediate, by-pass engine has an airflow by-pass ratio of between 2:1 and 3:1, and has a thrust ratio that is approximately the same as its by-pass ratio. The fan used on these engines has a larger diameter than that on a low by-pass engine of comparable power. The fan diameter is determined by both the by-pass ratio and the thrust output of the fan compared with the thrust obtained from the core engine.

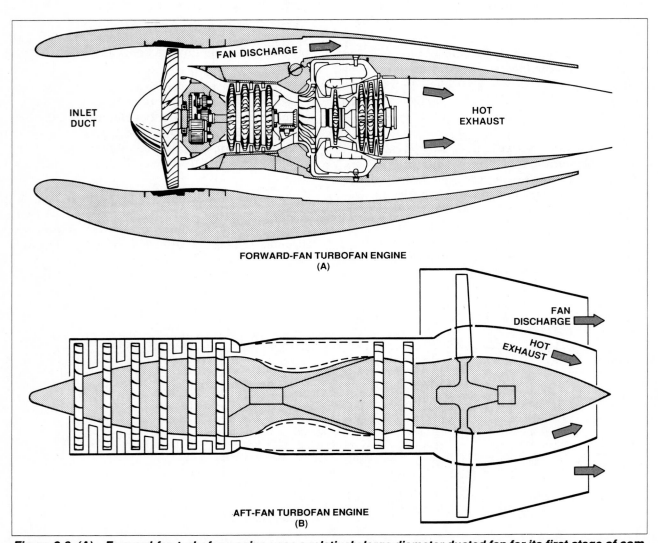

INLET DUCT

FAN DISCHARGE

HOT EXHAUST

FORWARD-FAN TURBOFAN ENGINE
(A)

FAN DISCHARGE

HOT EXHAUST

AFT-FAN TURBOFAN ENGINE
(B)

Figure 2-8. (A)—Forward-fan turbofan engine uses a relatively large diameter ducted fan for its first stage of compression. The forward fan produces thrust and provides additional air to the first stage of the low-pressure compressor. (B)—The aft-fan turbofan engine has its fan blades on the aft turbine.

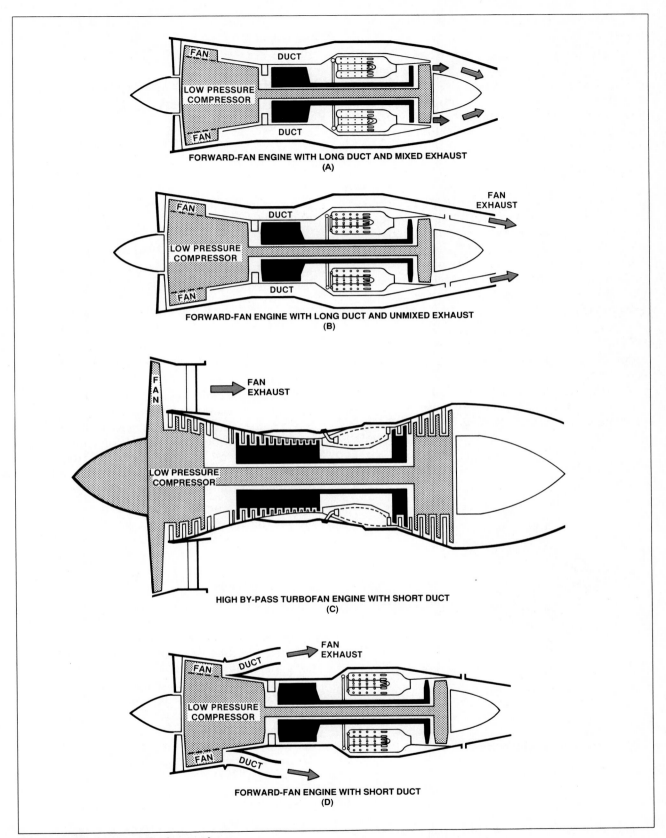

Figure 2-9. Types of turbofan engines.

43

This latter ratio is often called the cold-stream to hot-stream ratio.

A high by-pass turbofan engine has a fan ratio of 4:1 or greater, and has an even wider diameter fan in order to move more air. The Pratt and Whitney JT9D engine used on some current jumbo-jet aircraft has a by-pass ratio of 5:1 with 80% of the thrust provided by the fan, and only 20% by the core engine.

c. Unducted Fan Engines

One recent development that shows much promise is the Ultra High Bypass (UHB) Propfan, or Unducted Fan engine (UDF). This design has been made possible by new material development in titanium, light-weight stainless steel, and composite materials. This will be the most fuel conscious gas turbine in service, surpassing the high by-pass turbofan in fuel economy by 15% to 20%.

The propfan's required high by-pass ratio of 30:1 will come from single or dual 12- to 15-foot diameter propellers with higher tip speeds than propellers now in use. Projections at the time of this writing are for 10,000 to 15,000 horsepower. The new propfan is expected to power a 150-200 passenger size aircraft at speeds up to 0.8 Mach. Additional designs include encasing the propfan

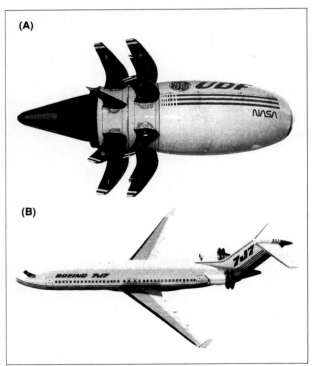

Figure 2-10. Rear propfan (UDF) engine with counter-rotating blades.

in a conventional cowl-type inlet to achieve speeds of Mach 0.9. These engines will be known as "ducted UHB" engines.

B. Principles Of Energy Transformation—Turbine Engines

The gas turbine engine is a type of heat engine that uses air as a working fluid to produce thrust. It converts the heat energy provided by the jet fuel to mechanical energy to drive the turbopropeller, or to kinetic energy in the form of a high velocity jet.

1. Energy Transformation Cycle

The Brayton cycle describes the events that take place in a turbine engine as the fuel releases its energy. When energy is added, the air remains at a relatively constant pressure, but its velocity is increased which increases the velocity of the air as it leaves the engine. The Brayton cycle is known as a constant pressure cycle.

The events occurring in the turbine engine are basically the same as those that occur in a piston engine—intake, compression, combustion, and exhaust. The difference being that in a turbine engine all events are occurring simultaneously, in sections of the engine specially designed for that single function.

In a piston engine, power is produced on only one of the four strokes. The gas turbine engine power event occurs continuously. This allows a greater amount of fuel to be burned in a shorter time, producing a greater power output for a given size of engine.

The four continuous events shown on the pressure-volume graph of figure 2-12 are: intake, compression, expansion, and exhaust. The air entering the inlet duct of the engine is at essentially ambient pressure. The portion of the curve between A and B shows that the air pressure rises from ambient as the compressor does work on the air, it increases its pressure and decreases its volume. When energy is added to the air from the fuel burned in the combustors, the pressure remains relatively constant, but you will notice that the volume increases greatly. It is because of this characteristic that the Brayton cycle is called the constant pressure cycle.

When the heated air leaves the combustion chamber, it passes through the turbine where the pressure drops, but its volume continues to

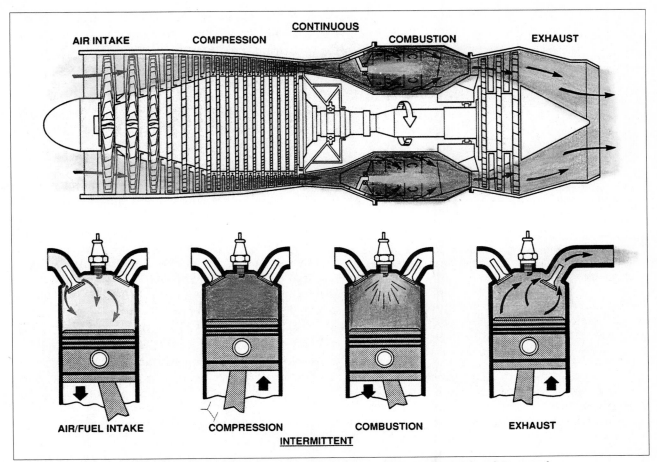

Figure 2-11. A comparison between the working cycle of a gas turbine engine and a piston engine.

increase as we see in the section of the curve between points C and D. The burning gases have heated the air and expanded it greatly, and since there is little opposition to the flow of these expanding gases as they leave the engine, they are accelerated greatly. Some of the energy is extracted from the exiting gases by the turbine and is used to drive the compressor and the various engine accessories.

2. Producing Thrust

Before we examine the manner in which turbine engines transform heat energy into thrust we will review a few pertinent principles of physics. We will examine here a few relationships that should be in the front of your mind when beginning to study the principles of turbine engine operation.

a. Changes In Velocity And Pressure

Bernoulli's principle deals with pressure and velocity in moving fluid, and is based on the fact that air acts as an incompressible fluid when it

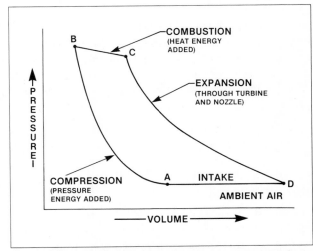

Figure 2-12. The Brayton cycle on a pressure-volume diagram.

flows as a subsonic rate. The principle is stated as follows: When a fluid or gas is supplied at a constant flow rate through a duct, the sum of the pressure (potential) energy and velocity (kinetic)

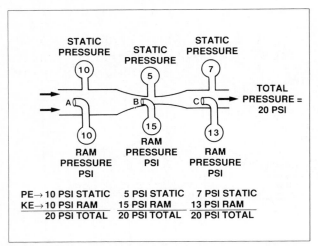

PE→ 10 PSI STATIC	5 PSI STATIC	7 PSI STATIC
KE→ 10 PSI RAM	15 PSI RAM	13 PSI RAM
20 PSI TOTAL	20 PSI TOTAL	20 PSI TOTAL

Figure 2-13. The total pressure in the airstream remains constant as it passes through the narrow passage.

energy is constant. Another way of putting this is: If pressure increases, velocity decreases proportionally or, if pressure decreases, velocity increases proportionally.

To understand Bernoulli's principle, consider the air flowing through a duct has both potential and kinetic energy. This may also be thought of as static pressure and pressure caused by velocity (ram). When this air flows through a section of the duct that has a divergent, or widening, shape, its kinetic energy (velocity) will decrease as the air spreads out radially. Since, by definition, the total energy remains constant, the mass flow rate of the air will be unchanged. The potential energy (pressure) must increase in proportion to the decrease in kinetic energy. If we measure the static pressure inside the duct, we will find that the pressure in the straight portion of the duct is lower than in the divergent portion.

If the duct converges, or becomes smaller, an airstream at a constant flow rate must speed up. The kinetic energy of the airstream increases and its potential energy, as seen by the static pressure, decreases.

The total pressure of an airstream is the sum of the static pressure plus the ram pressure (velocity). In figure 2-13 we see that the flow rate as measured by the total pressure is constant throughout the duct. At point B, the area is the smallest and the velocity is the greatest. The ram pressure is highest but the static pressure is the lowest. At point C, the duct has diverged, and the ram pressure has decreased. Notice that at all three locations, the total pressure is the same.

b. Relationship Between Pressure, Volume And Temperature

During the operation of the turbine engine the air will both receive and give up heat, producing changes in its pressure, volume and temperature. These changes may be explained using the gas laws described by Charles and Boyle. These relationships may be simply illustrated by the diagrams in figure 2-14.

c. Thrust Calculations

Thrust is produced by a turbojet engine as air is taken into the engine and expanded by adding energy from burning fuel. The expanded gases are accelerated as they leave the engine, and it is this change in the velocity of the air between the time it enters the engine and the time it leaves that produces the thrust. This relationship can be applied to the formula used to express Newton's second law of motion.

Newton's second law deals with acceleration and is the one that explains, to a great extent, the thrust produced within a turbine engine. The acceleration produced with a mass by the addition of a given force is directly proportional to the force and is inversely proportional to the mass. This is expressed by the formula: $F = M \times A$.

When building on this formula to calculate the thrust of a turbine engine, the value for F will be the thrust produced, in pounds, the mass used in the thrust formula will be the mass airflow through the engine, and will be expressed using the symbol M_s, and the acceleration will be expressed by the difference between the velocity of the air at the inlet of the engine and that of the exhaust. Assembling the basic thrust formula we have:

$$F = M_S \frac{(V_2 - V_1)}{g}$$

1) Gross Thrust

Gross thrust, represented by the symbol F_g, is the thrust produced when the engine is not in motion. The acceleration of the gas within the engine is the difference in velocity between the air in the inlet duct, and the air as it leaves the exhaust nozzle. In this case, where the engine is not in motion, the velocity at the inlet (V_1) will always be zero.

Let's see the way this formula works: assume that there is a business jet airplane on the runway with the engine producing takeoff power. However, the airplane has not yet begun to roll. There is 50 pounds of air per second moving through the engine; this is M_S. Since the airplane is not yet moving, V_1 is zero, but the exhaust velocity, V_2, is 1,300 feet per second.

$$F_g = M_S \frac{(V_2 - V_1)}{g} \qquad F_g = 50 \frac{(1,300 - 0)}{32.2}$$

$$= 2018.6 \text{ lbs. thrust}$$

2) Net Thrust

When an aircraft is flying, its inlet air has an initial momentum and the velocity change across the engine will be greatly reduced.

We can consider the same airplane whose gross thrust we have just computed as flying at 500 miles per hour (734 feet per second). Its net thrust can be calculated using the basic formula, as follows:

$$F_N = M_S \frac{(V_2 - V_1)}{g} \qquad F_N = 50 \frac{(1,300 - 734)}{32.2}$$

$$= 50 \frac{566}{32.2}$$

$$= 878.9 \text{ lbs. thrust}$$

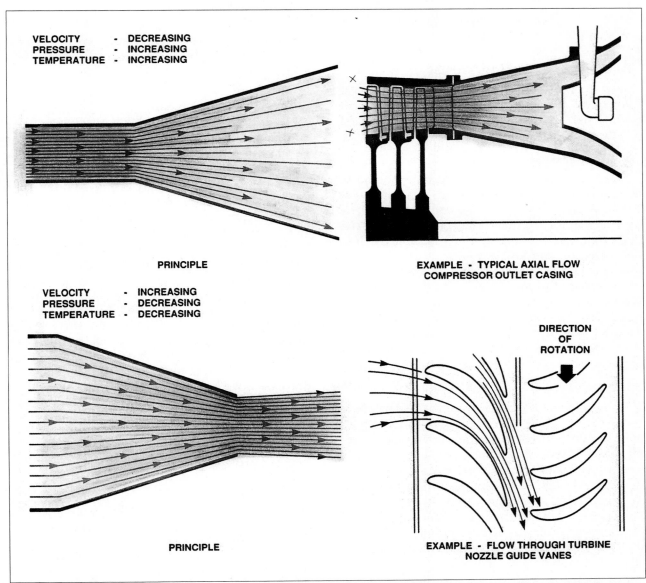

VELOCITY   - DECREASING
PRESSURE   - INCREASING
TEMPERATURE - INCREASING

PRINCIPLE

EXAMPLE - TYPICAL AXIAL FLOW
COMPRESSOR OUTLET CASING

VELOCITY   - INCREASING
PRESSURE   - DECREASING
TEMPERATURE - DECREASING

PRINCIPLE

DIRECTION
OF
ROTATION

EXAMPLE - FLOW THROUGH TURBINE
NOZZLE GUIDE VANES

Figure 2-14. Relationship between pressure, volume, and temperature as it may be applied to turbine engine operation.

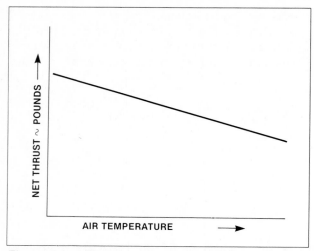

Figure 2-15. Effects of air temperature on the thrust produced by a turbine engine.

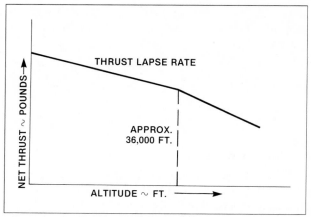

Figure 2-16. Effect of altitude on the thrust produced by a turbine engine.

3. Factors Affecting Thrust

As with the reciprocating engine, there are a number of factors, environmental, design and operational, that will affect the thrust produced by a turbine engine.

a. Temperature

The thrust produced by a turbine engine is determined, as we have just seen, by the mass of the air flowing through it. The temperature of the air entering the engine will affect its density. The hotter the air, the less dense it is, and the less mass the air has for its volume. Less thrust is produced when the inlet air is heated. All calculations of thrust made by engine manufacturers are based on standard temperature conditions of 59 degrees Fahrenheit or 15 degrees Celsius, and all performance calculations must be adjusted for non-standard temperatures.

b. Altitude

The atmosphere that surrounds the earth is a compressible fluid whose density is varied by both the pressure of the air and its temperature. Air under standard conditions at sea level has a pressure of 14.69 pounds per square inch, and this pressure decreases as the altitude increases. At 20,000 feet it is down to 6.75 psi, and at 30,000 feet it has dropped to 4.36 psi, and it continues to drop at a relatively uniform rate. As the pressure of the air decreases so does its density.

The temperature of the air also drops with an increase in altitude from its standard sea level condition. As the temperature drops the air be-comes more dense. The decrease in density caused by dropping pressure more than overcomes the increase caused by lowering the temperature.

At around 36,000 feet, an interesting thing happens. The temperature of the air stabilizes at -69.7 degrees Fahrenheit (-56.5° C) and above this altitude, the air no longer has the help of the dropping temperatures to increase its density. At this altitude, the air density begins to drop more rapidly with altitude. Because of this, long-range jet aircraft find 36,000 feet an optimum altitude to fly. Below this altitude, the dense air creates more aerodynamic drag, and above this altitude the rapidly dropping density decreases engine thrust output.

c. Airspeed

If we remember, the formula for thrust uses the acceleration of the mass of air through the engine, $(V_2 - V_1)$. As the speed of the airplane, V_1, increases, the amount of thrust produced decreases. We see this in the downward slope of the thrust curve in figure 2-17 that shows the effect of velocity. But there is a compensating effect caused by the air being rammed into the inlet duct as the aircraft moves through the air. This is known as the ram effect. You will notice that this line is not straight, but steepens as the airspeed increases. When we combine the loss from acceleration with the gain from ram, we have the net effect of airspeed on thrust. We see this in the resultant curve.

d. Engine RPM

Engine RPM has a non-linear effect on the thrust produced by an engine. At low RPM the thrust is low, but as the RPM increases, the

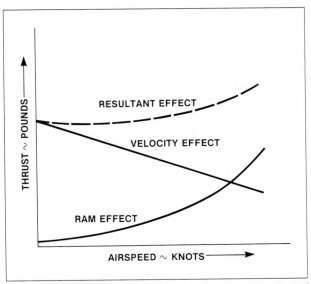

Figure 2-17. Effect of airspeed on the thrust produced by a gas turbine engine.

aerodynamic effect of the compressor moves a greater mass of air through the engine and as the mass airflow increases, so does the thrust.

There is a limit to the engine RPM, however, and this limit is imposed by the aerodynamics of the compressor. As the tips of the compressor blades reach the speed of sound, Mach 1 or slightly higher, their efficiency drops off. The design of the compressor is such that the blades are not operated at such a speed that the airflow over them is not allowed to get into a severe shock stall condition. This accounts for the relatively slow rotational speed of some of the large diameter compressors such as the fan section of the Pratt and Whitney JT9D which turns at 3,000 RPM, and the very high rotational speeds of some of the small diameter turbine engines whose compressor speeds may be upward of 50,000 RPM.

e. Fan Efficiency

The turbofan engine has replaced the turbojet in most airliners and is now doing the same in many business jet airplanes. This is happening because the turbofan is much more fuel efficient and quiet. If a turbojet and a turbofan engine have the same rated thrust, the turbofan will burn less fuel because of the greater propulsive efficiency of the turbofan.

C. Turbine Engine Design And Construction

In a reciprocating engine the functions of intake, compression, combustion, and exhaust all take place in the same combustion chamber; consequently, each must have exclusive occupancy of the chamber during its respective part of the combustion cycle. A significant feature of the gas turbine engine however, is that a separate section is devoted to each function, and all functions are performed simultaneously, without interruption.

A typical gas turbine engine consists of:

(1) An air inlet.

(2) Compressor section.

(3) Combustion section.

(4) Turbine section.

(5) Exhaust section.

(6) Accessory section.

(7) The systems necessary for starting, lubrication, fuel supply, and auxiliary purposes, such as anti-icing, cooling, and pressurization.

The major components of all turbine engines are basically the same; however, the nomenclature of component parts of various engines currently in use will vary slightly due to the difference in each manufacturer's terminology. These differences are reflected in the applicable maintenance manuals.

1. Engine Entrance Ducts

The air entrance, or inlet duct, is normally considered to be a part of the airframe rather than part of the engine. Nevertheless it is usually identified as engine station 1. Understanding the function of the inlet duct and its importance to engine performance make it a necessary part of any discussion on gas turbine engine design and construction.

a. Subsonic Inlets

The inlet duct used on multi-engine subsonic aircraft, such as we find in the business and commercial jet aircraft fleet, is a fixed geometry duct whose diameter progressively increases from front to back (diverges), as we see in figure 2-18. A diverging duct is sometimes called an inlet diffuser because of the effect it has on the pressure of the air entering the engine. As air enters the inlet at ambient pressure it begins to diffuse, or spread out, and by the time it arrives at the inlet to the compressor its pressure is slightly higher than ambient. Usually the air diffuses in the front portion of the duct and then it progresses along at a fairly constant pressure past the engine inlet guide vanes and into the

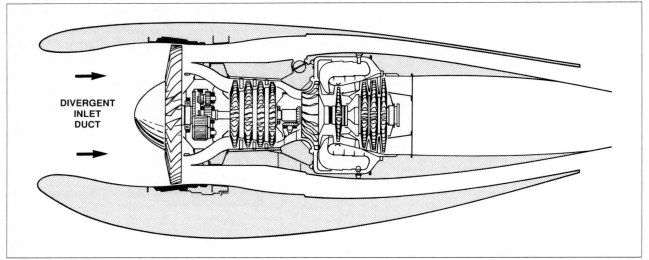

Figure 2-18. The subsonic air inlet forms a divergent duct to increase the pressure of the air as it enters the fan or compressor.

compressor. This allows the engine to receive the air with less turbulence and, at a more uniform pressure.

This added pressure contributes significantly to the mass airflow when the aircraft reaches its design cruising speed. At this speed, the compressor reaches its optimum aerodynamic design point and produces the most compression for the best fuel economy. It is at this design cruise speed that the inlet, the compressor, the combustor, the turbine, and the exhaust duct are designed to match each other as a unit. If any section mismatches any other because of damage, contamination, or ambient conditions, the engine performance will be affected.

The inlet for a turbofan is similar in design to that for a turbojet except that it discharges only a portion of the air into the engine, the remainder passes through the fan.

b. Ram Pressure Recovery

When a turbine engine is operated on the ground there is a negative pressure at the inlet because of the high velocity of the airflow. But, as the aircraft moves forward in flight, air rams into the inlet duct and causes a rise in pressure. This ram pressure rise cancels the pressure drop inside the duct and, at a certain speed, the inlet pressure returns to ambient. This is know as ram recovery. Ram recovery is said to occur above about 160 miles per hour on most aircraft. From this point, pressure continues to increase with aircraft speed and the engine takes ad-

vantage of the increasing pressure at the inlet to create thrust with less expenditure of fuel.

c. Supersonic Inlets

A convergent-divergent (fixed or variable) inlet duct is required on all aircraft traveling as supersonic speeds. Generally aircraft incorporate a variable geometry duct which may be adjusted to operate efficiently at speeds above and below Mach 1.

This type of inlet is used to slow the airflow to subsonic speeds at the face of the compressor. Subsonic airflow to the compressor is required if the rotating airfoils are to remain free of shock wave accumulation, which would be detrimental to the compression process.

In order to vary the geometry, or shape, of the inlet, a moveable retractor is often employed to form a convergent-divergent (C-D) shape of variable proportion. The C-D shaped duct becomes necessary in reducing supersonic airflow to subsonic speeds. At this point it is important to

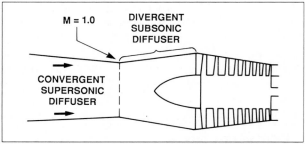

Figure 2-19. Supersonic convergent-divergent inlet (fixed geometry).

remember that at subsonic flow rates, air flowing in a duct acts as an incompressible fluid, but at supersonic flow rates air is compressed to the point of creating the familiar shock wave phenomenon.

One useful aspect of shock waves is that airflow passing through the high pressure shock region slows down. The supersonic inlet shown in figure 2-19 provides us a means of creating a shock wave at the throat of the inlet. Air flowing through the shock wave at the throat will be slowed to about Mach 0.8 and, in the divergent subsonic diffuser section will have its velocity reduced even further (to about Mach 0.5) and its pressure increased.

This controlled formation of the shock wave allows us to take advantage of its effect on air velocity. If, however, the shock wave is not controlled, it may give high duct loss in pressure and airflow and will set up a vibrating condition in the inlet duct called inlet buzz. This is a situation where a shock wave forms, and is alternately swallowed, and then expelled at the inlet of the duct.

Figure 2-20A shows a variable-geometry inlet duct in its high cruise shock wave condition and it also shows a moveable spike which acts to

create more C-D effect when in its forward position.

In view B of the same figure, we see a movable wedge which provides a similar function of convergence, divergence, and shock wave formation. It also has a spill valve to dump unwanted ram air overboard at high speed. Many high performance aircraft have an excess of mass airflow at cruising speeds.

View C shows another popular supersonic inlet, this time with a movable plug. In very high speed flight, the inlet may receive too much air due to ram effect. This inlet restricts airflow as well as controls shock formation by slowing the airflow to subsonic speed before it enters the engine.

d. Bellmouth Inlets

Bellmouth inlets are converging in shape, and found on helicopters and other slower moving aircraft which generally fly below ram-recovery speed. This type of inlet produces a great deal of drag, but this is outweighed by their high degree of aerodynamic efficiency.

When turbine engines are calibrated in test stands, they use a bellmouth fitted with an anti-ingestion screen. Duct loss is so slight with this

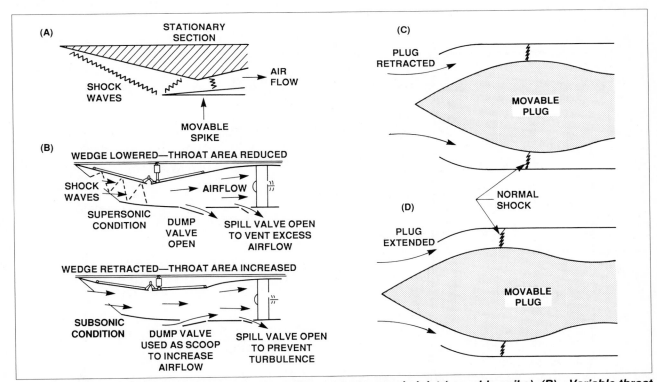

Figure 2-20. (A)—Variable-geometry convergent-divergent supersonic inlet (movable spike). (B)—Variable throat area inlet. (C)—Movable plug insert.

design that it is considered to be zero. Engine performance data is collected when the engine is fitted with a bellmouth compressor inlet.

e. Inlet Screens

The use of compressor inlet screens is usually limited to rotorcraft, turboprop, and ground tur-

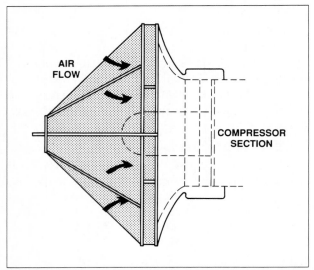

Figure 2-21. Bellmouth compressor inlet (with screen).

bine installations. Inlet screens are seldom used on high mass airflow engines because icing and screen failures have caused so many maintenance problems.

Some aircraft are fitted with sand or ice separators, many of which are removable and only used when operating conditions require them. In the sand separator in figure 2-22, inlet suction causes sand particles and other small debris to be deflected by a centrifugal effect into the sediment trap.

Another type of separator is illustrated in figure 2-23. This unit incorporates a movable vane which can be extended into the inlet airstream. This causes a sudden turn in the engine inlet air, and sand or ice particles continue out undeflected because of their greater momentum. The moveable vane in this installation is operated by the pilot through a control handle in the cockpit.

f. Engine Inlet Vortex Dissipater

Some gas turbine engine inlets have a tendency to form a vortex between the ground and the flight inlet. The suction creating the vortex is strong enough to lift water and debris such as sand, small stones, nuts, bolts, etc., from the

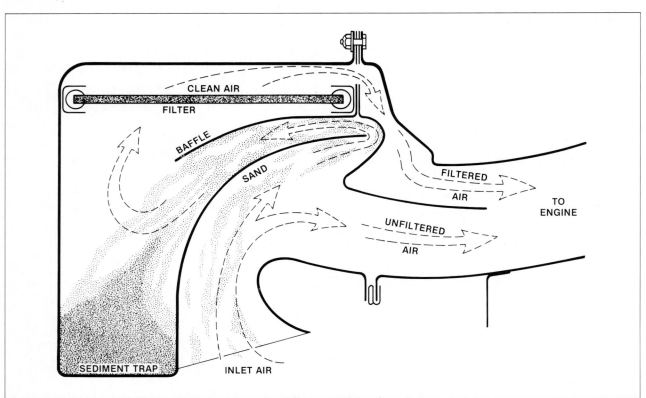

Figure 2-22. Sand and dust separator used on turbine powered helicopters.

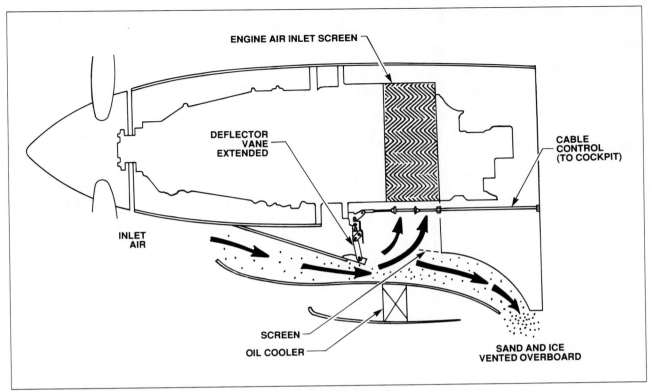

Figure 2-23. Sand and ice separator installed on a turboprop aircraft.

ground and direct it into the engine. This may result in foreign object damage (FOD) to the compressor section of the engine. This is especially true on wing pod installed engines that are mounted with very little ground clearance, as seen on many of the newer high-bypass turbofan powered aircraft. To alleviate this problem, a "vortex dissipater" (also known as a "blow-away jet") is installed.

To dissipate the vortex, a small jet of compressor discharge air is directed to the ground under the inlet, from a discharge nozzle located in the lower part of the engine flight cowl. This is illustrated in figure 2-24. The system is generally activated by a landing gear switch which opens a valve in the line between the engine compressor bleed port and the dissipater nozzle whenever the engine is operating and weight is on the main landing gear.

2. Accessory Section

The accessory section of the gas turbine engine has several functions. The primary function is to provide space for the mounting of accessories necessary for operation and control of the engine. Generally, it also includes accessories concerned with the aircraft, such as electric

generators and fluid power pumps. Secondary functions include acting as an oil reservoir and/or oil sump, and housing the accessory drive gears and reduction gears.

The gearbox is placed so that the envelope size of the engine can be kept to a minimum (figure 2-25). Some engines may place the accessory gearbox at the waist of the engine as seen in view A of the figure. Other main gearbox locations are

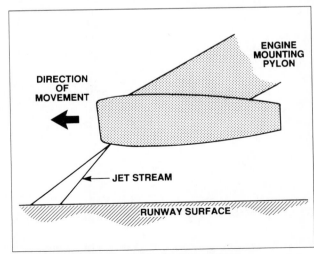

Figure 2-24. Vortex dissipater operation.

the front or rear of the engine if the inlet or exhaust locations will permit. This is a particularly desirable design because it appears to allow for the narrowest engine diameter and lowest drag configuration (view B of figure 2-25). In a few rare instances, the main gearbox can be found at the top of the engine in the area of the compressor.

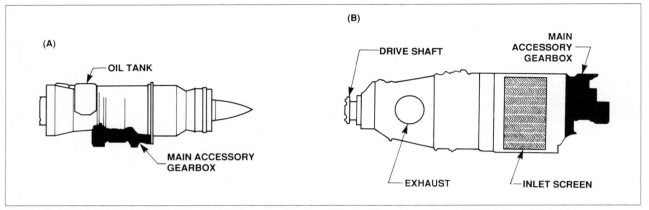

Figure 2-25. (A)—Accesory gearbox location, 6 o'clock position. (B)—Accessory gearbox location, rear.

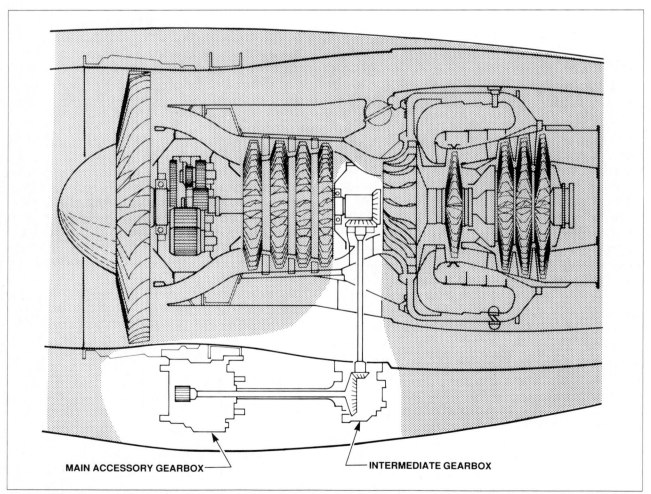

Figure 2-26. Some turbine engines have the accessory section mounted on its waist and drive by a radial shaft through an intermediate gear box.

The power to drive the accessories is typically taken from a rotating engine shaft, via an internal gearbox, through (in some installations) an intermediate gear box, to an external gearbox which will distribute the power to each accessory drive pad. The accessory system on a large high by-pass engine may take upwards to 500 horsepower from the engine. The accessory drive train and gearboxes may be seen in figure 2-26.

3. Compressor Section

The compressor section of the turbojet engine has many functions. Its primary function is to supply air in sufficient quantity to satisfy the requirements of the combustion burners. Specifically, to fulfill its purpose, the compressor must increase the pressure of the mass of air received from the air inlet duct and then discharge it to the burners in the quantity and pressures required.

Compressors may be identified by the direction of airflow through them. The two basic types include centrifugal flow and axial flow, and one or both may be used in the same engine.

a. Centrifugal Flow Compressors

The centrifugal compressor, sometimes referred to as a radial outflow compressor, is the oldest of the designs, and is still in use today. Many of the smaller flight engines as well as a majority of the gas turbine auxiliary power units use this design.

A centrifugal compressor performs its duties by receiving the air at its center and accelerating it outward by centrifugal force. The air is then expelled into a divergent duct called a diffuser, where it will trade velocity for pressure energy.

Centrifugal compressors consist basically of an impeller rotor, a diffuser, and a manifold. The impeller is a forged disk with integral blades, and can be either single- or double-sided. The diffuser acts as a divergent duct in which the air spreads out, slows down, and increases in static pressure. The compressor manifold distributes the air in a smooth flow to the combustion section.

These basic design components may be utilized to build centrifugal flow compressors having a single-or double-sided impeller and occasionally a two-stage compressor using single-sided impellers.

A single-stage, dual-sided impeller allows a high mass airflow from a small diameter engine. This design does not, however, receive the full

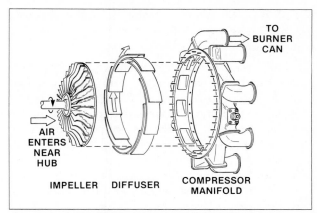

Figure 2-27. Centrifugal compressor components.

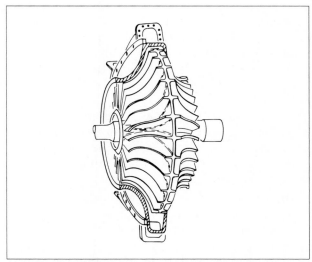

Figure 2-28. Single-stage, dual-sided centrifugal compressor.

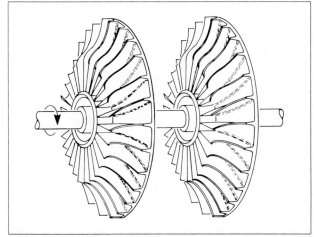

Figure 2-29. Two-stage, single-sided centrifugal compressor.

benefit from ram effect because of the corners the air must turn as it enters and leaves the compressor.

Compression ratios attainable are about the same for both the single- and double-sided centrifugal compressors. To obtain higher compression ratios, more than one stage of compression can be used, but the use of more than two stages of single-entry compressors is considered impractical. The energy lost in the airflow as it slows down to make the turns from one impeller to the next, the added weight, and the amount of power needed to drive the compressor all seem to offset the benefits of additional stages.

Recent developments in centrifugal compressors have produced compression ratios as high as 15:1. In the past, pressures this high could be obtained only with axial flow compressors. Centrifugal flow compressors are shorter than axial flow compressors and, because of their spoke-like design, they can accelerate air faster and immediately diffuse it in the direction of flow.

Tip speeds of centrifugal compressors may reach as high as Mach 1.3, but the pressure within the compressor casing prevents airflow separation and provides a high transfer of energy into the airflow.

The advantages of centrifugal compressors are:

(1) High pressure rise per stage—compression ratios up to 15:1 possible.

(2) Good efficiency over a wide rotational speed range, idle to approximately Mach 1.3 tip speed at takeoff RPM.

(3) Simplicity of manufacture and relatively low cost.

(4) Low weight.

(5) Low starting power requirements.

Disadvantages of a centrifugal compressor include:

(1) Large frontal area for a given airflow.

(2) More than two stages are not practical.

b. Axial Flow Compressors And Fans

The axial flow compressor has two main elements, a rotor and a stator. The rotor has blades fixed on a spindle. These blades impel air rearward in the same manner as a propeller because of their angle and airfoil contour. The stator vanes act as diffusers at each stage, partially converting high velocity to pressure. Each consecutive pair of rotor blades and stator vanes constitutes a pressure stage.

The number of stages is determined by the amount of air and total pressure rise required. Unlike the centrifugal compressor with very high compression ratios, the axial flow compressor can only provide a pressure rise of about 1.25 per stage. The desired compression ratio must be obtained by adding more stages to the compressor. The greater the number of stages, the higher the compression ratio. The diagram shown in figure 2-30 shows the changes in pressure and velocity as air flows through the axial compressor.

From the front to the rear of the compressor section, the space between the rotor shaft and the stator casing gradually becomes smaller. This is evidenced by each stage of blades and vanes being smaller than the one in front. This is necessary to maintain a near constant axial velocity of the air as the density increases with compression.

There are several advantages of the axial flow compressor. They are:

(1) High peak efficiencies from ram, created by its straight-through design.

(2) High peak pressures attainable by addition of compression stages.

(3) Small frontal area and resulting low drag.

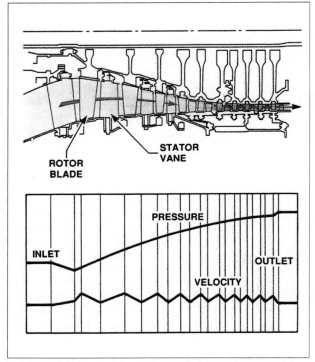

Figure 2-30. Pressure and velocity changes in an axial-flow compressor.

2-18   56

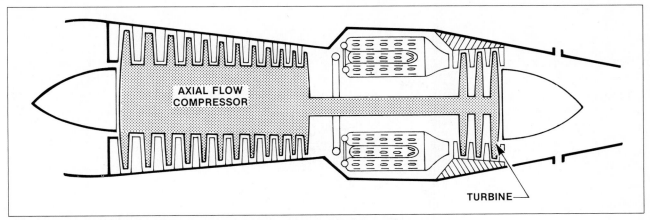

Figure 2-31. A single-spool axial flow compressor is used in this engine.

The disadvantages of the axial flow compressor are:

(1) Difficulty of manufacture, and high cost.

(2) Relatively high weight.

(3) High starting power requirements.

(4) Low pressure rise per stage, approximately 1.25:1.

1) Multiple-Spool Compressors

A single-spool compressor has only one rotating mass. The compressor, shaft, and turbines all rotate together as a single unit. This arrangement is illustrated in figure 2-31.

As additional stages are added to an axial-flow compressor, certain design and operational problems develop. Dual- and triple-spool compressors were developed for the operational flexibility they provide to the engine in the form of high compression ratios, quick acceleration, and better control of compressor stall characteristics. This flexibility is not possible with single-spool compressors.

Figure 2-32 shows a dual-spool engine. The turbine shafts attach to their respective compressors by fitting coaxially, one within the other. The front compressor is referred to as the low pressure, low speed, or N_1 compressor. Its turbine is referred to in the same manner. The rear compressor is called the high pressure, high speed, or N_2 compressor.

Triple-spool designs may be used on some high by-pass turbofan engines. The rotor arrangement we see in figure 2-33 is such that the fan is referred to as the N_1, or low speed compressor, the compressor next in line is called the N_2, or intermediate compressor, and the innermost compressor is the high pressure, or N_3 compressor.

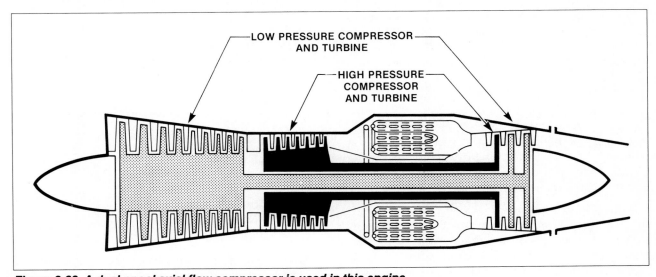

Figure 2-32. A dual-spool axial flow compressor is used in this engine.

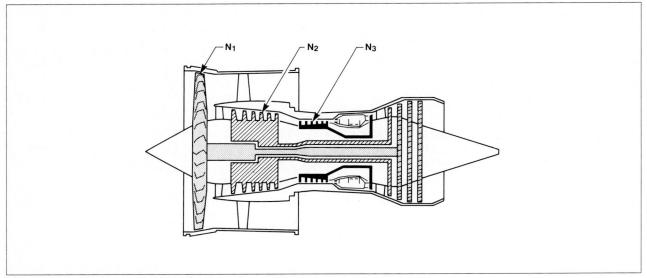

Figure 2-33. A triple spool compressor is used with this turbofan engine.

For any given power level setting, the high pressure compressor speed is held relatively constant by the fuel control governor. And, assuming that there is a fairly constant energy level available at the turbine, the low pressure compressors will speed up or slow down with changes in the aircraft inlet conditions resulting from the atmospheric changes or flight maneuvers. The N_1 compressor tries to supply the N_2 compressor with a fairly constant air pressure for each power setting by speeding up or slowing down to maintain a constant mass airflow at the inlet of N_2.

Low pressure compressors will speed up as altitude is gained, as the atmosphere is less dense and more speed is needed to force the required amount of air through the engine. Conversely, as the aircraft descends, the air becomes more dense and easier to compress so the N_1 compressor slows down.

2) Compressor Rotor Blades

The rotor blades used in an axial-flow compressor have an airfoil cross-section with a varying angle of incidence, or twist. This twisting compensates for the blade velocity variation caused by its radius. The further from the axis of rotation, the faster the blade section travels.

Axial flow compressors normally have from 10 to 18 stages of compression, with the fan considered to be the first stage. Some long fan blades have a mid-span shroud fitted to each blade to form a circular ring which helps support the blades against the bending forces from the

airstream. The shrouds, however, block some of the airflow, and the aerodynamic drag they produce reduces the efficiency of the fan. The roots of the compressor blades are often loosely fitted into the compressor disk for ease of assembly and for the vibration damping it provides. As the compressor rotates, centrifugal force

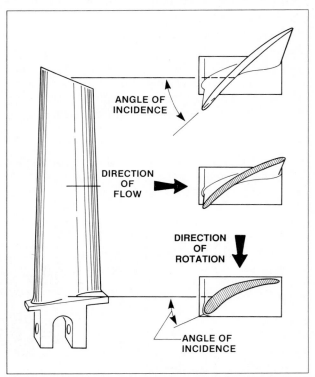

Figure 2-34. Typical compressor blade showing its twist.

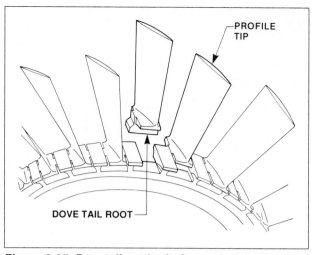

Figure 2-35. Dovetail method of securing compressor blades to the disk.

keeps the blade in its correct position, and the airstream over the airfoil provides a shock absorbing or cushioning effect. These blades are attached to the disk with a dovetail and are secured with a pin and a lock tab or locker.

Some blades are cut off square at the tip and these are referred to as flat machine tips. Other blades have a reduced thickness at the tips and are called profile tips. All rotating machinery has a tendency to vibrate, and profiling a compressor blade increases the natural frequency of the blade. By raising the natural frequency of the blade beyond the frequency of rotation, the vibration tendency is reduced.

The profile is also designed as a vortex tip. The thin trailing edge section causes a vortex which increases air velocity and insures minimum tip leakage and a smooth axial airflow.

On some newer engines the tips are designed with tight running clearances and rotate within a shroud strip of abradable material. This strip will wear away with no loss of blade length if contact loading takes place. The strip is later replaced at overhaul. This feature is the reason that profile blades may also be referred to as squealer tips. Sometimes, during coastdown, a high pitched noise can be heard if the blade tip and shroud strip are touching.

Another blade design aimed at compensating for the slow boundry layers of air formed at the inner and outer walls of the compressor is one which utilizes a localized increase in blade camber, both at the blade tip and blade root. In this design the blade extremities appear as if formed

by bending over each corner, hence the term "end bend". This design is shown in figure 2-36.

It becomes very difficult on small engines to design a practical method of attaching and fixing compressor blades to the disk. To overcome this problem the blades may be produced integral with the disk. This unit is sometimes referred to as a "blisk".

3) Compressor Stator Vanes

Stator vanes are also airfoil shaped, and may either be stationary or of variable angle. These vanes are normally produced from steel or nickel base alloys, chosen for their high fatigue strength. Titanium may be used for stator vanes in the low pressure section, but is unsuitable in the rear stages because of the pressures and temperatures involved.

The stator vanes are secured into the compressor casing or into stator vane retaining rings, which are then secured to the compressor. In the front sections of the compressor the vanes are often assembled in segments, and may be shrouded at their inner end to minimize the vibrational effect on the longer vanes. A shrouded vane segment is shown in figure 2-37.

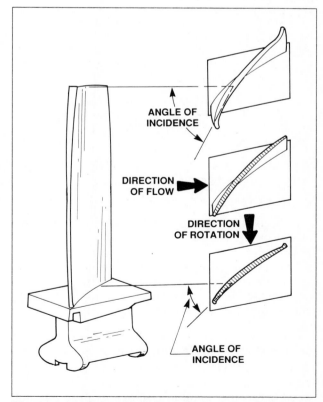

Figure 2-36. Rotor blade employing the "end bend" design.

2-21

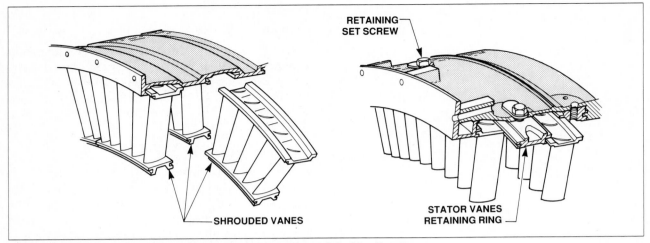

Figure 2-37. Shrouded vane segments may be used to minimize vibration.

The inlet guide vanes are the set of stator vanes immediately in front of the first stage rotor blades. These may be of stationary or variable design. The function of the inlet guide vanes is to direct the airflow into the compressor at the most desirable angle. When high pressure ratios are present on a single-spool engine it may become necessary to utilize variable inlet guide vanes for the first stage plus a number of stages of variable stator vanes.

Variable inlet guide vanes and stators will be automatically repositioned to maintain proper airflow through the engine under varying operating conditions. This is an important function in avoiding compressor stall.

Another special set of stator vanes is positioned at the discharge end of the compressor. These vanes are called straightening vanes, or the outlet vane assembly, and serve to eliminate any rotary motion (swirl) in the airflow and reduce turbulence.

4) Fan Pressure Ratio

Fan compression ratios for single low-by-pass fans are approximately 1.5:1 and for high-by-pass fans as high as 1.7:1. Most high-by-pass engines (those with fan by-pass ratios of 4:1 and above) are designed with high aspect ratio blades. That is, they are long and have a narrow chord (figure 2-38).

However, low aspect ratio (wide chord) blades are coming into wider use today because of their tolerance to foreign objects, and especially bird strike damage. Advances in blade construction have overcome some of the weight problems associated with low aspect ratio blades in the past. Hollow titanium blades with composite inner reinforcement materials have been developed. These blades have no mid-span support shrouds and thus produce more mass airflow as a result of the greater flow area.

5) Fan By-pass Ratio

The fan by-pass ratio is the ratio of the mass airflow which flows through the fan duct, divided by the mass airflow which flows through the core of the engine. Generally speaking, the higher the by-pass ratio, the higher the propulsive efficiency. Because of a number of aerodynamic and design limitations, by-pass ratios are currently limited to about 6:1 on aircraft designed to cruise at Mach 0.80 to Mach 0.85.

New, variable pitch airfoils in the ultra high by-pass (UHB) engines are presently being developed. These innovations will greatly change the by-pass figures that we are now looking at. Ducted propfans are predicted to be in the range of 10:1, and unducted propfans up to 100:1, with target cruising speeds remaining in the Mach 0.80 to Mach 0.90 range.

c. Combination Compressors

To take advantage of the good points of both the centrifugal and the axial flow compressor and eliminate some of their disadvantages, the combination axial-centrifugal flow compressor was developed. This is currently being used in some of the smaller flight engines installed on business jets and helicopters. One such engine is illustrated in figure 2-39.

d. Compressor Air Bleeds

A secondary function of the compressor is to supply high pressure, high temperature air for various purposes in the engine and aircraft. This air is referred to as bleed air, or customer bleed air.

The bleed air is taken from any of the various pressure stages of the compressor. The exact location of the bleed ports is, of course, dependent on the pressure or temperature required for a particular job. The ports are small openings in the compressor case adjacent to the particular stage from which the air is to be bled; thus, varying degrees of pressure or heat are available simply by tapping into the appropriate stage. Air is often bled from the final or highest pressure stage, since at this point, pressure and air temperature are at a maximum. At times it may be necessary to cool this high-pressure air. If it is used for cabin pressurization or other purposes where excess heat would be uncomfortable or detrimental, the air is sent through a refrigeration unit.

Bleed air is utilized in a wide variety of ways. Some of the current applications of bleed air are:

(1) Cabin pressurization, heating and cooling.

(2) Deicing and anti-icing equipment.

(3) Pneumatic starting of engines.

(4) Control-booster servo systems.

(5) Power for operating instruments.

(6) Compressor airflow control

e. Compressor Stall

The compressor blades are actually tiny airfoils and are subject to the same aerodynamic principles which apply to the wings of aircraft. Like a wing, the blade has an angle of attack,

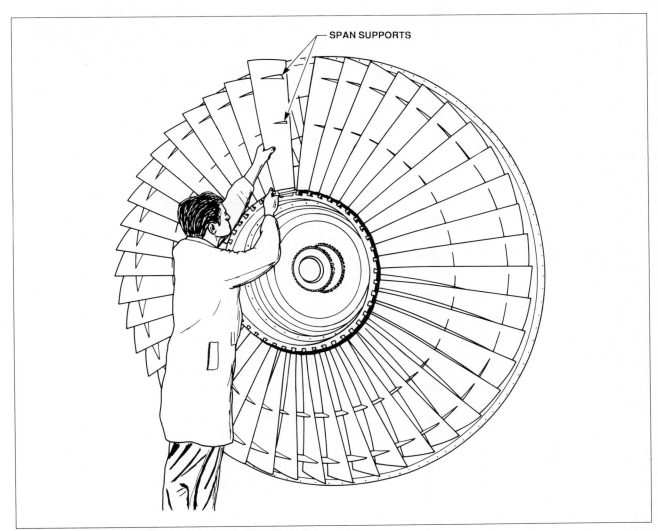

SPAN SUPPORTS

Figure 2-38. High-bypass fan with high aspect ratio blades.

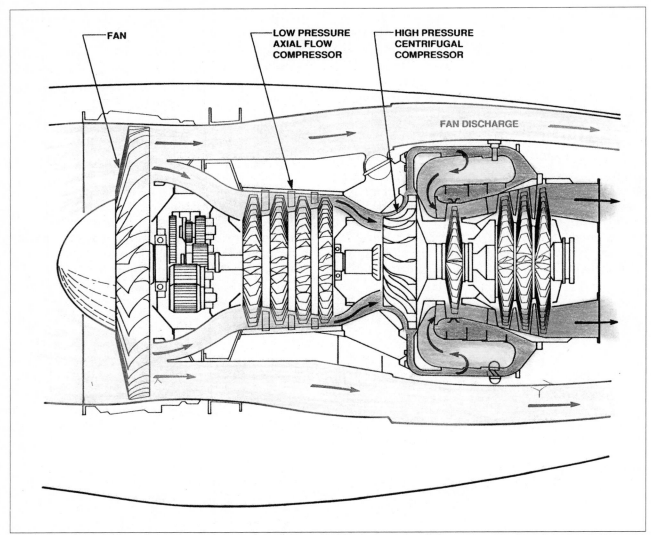

FAN

LOW PRESSURE
AXIAL FLOW
COMPRESSOR

HIGH PRESSURE
CENTRIFUGAL
COMPRESSOR

FAN DISCHARGE

Figure 2-39. The Garrett TFE731 engine uses an axial flow compressor for the low-pressure stage and a single-stage centrifugal compressor for the high-pressure compressor.

which is defined as the acute angle between the chord of the blade and the relative wind. The angle of attack of a compressor blade is the result of inlet air velocity and the compressor's rotational velocity (RPM). The two forces combine to form a vector, which is the actual angle of attack of air approaching the airfoil.

As with a wing if the angle of attack becomes too great, airflow across the airfoil section will be disturbed, and a stall will occur. A compressor stall, a condition all gas turbine engines experience from time to time, can be described as an imbalance between the two vector quantities, inlet velocity and compressor rotational speed. Compressor stalls cause air flowing in the compressor to slow down, to stagnate (stop), or to reverse direction, depending upon the intensity

of the stall. Stall conditions can usually be heard and range in audibility from an air pulsating, or fluttering sound in their mildest form, to a louder pulsating type sound, or to a violent explosion. Quite often the cockpit gauges do not show a mild stall condition, called a "transient stall". These stalls are usually not harmful to the engine and often correct themselves after one or two pulsations. Severe stalls, called "hung stalls", can significantly impair engine performance, cause loss of power, and can even damage the engine. The pilot can identify a stall condition by its audible noise, by fluctuations of the RPM, by an increase in the exhaust gas temperature, or by a combination of these clues.

Compressor stalls may be caused by:

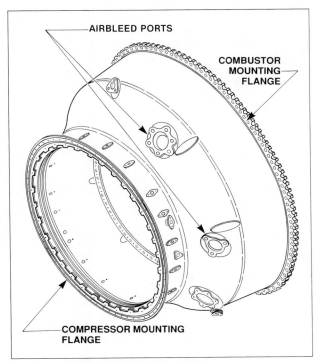

AIRBLEED PORTS

COMBUSTOR MOUNTING FLANGE

COMPRESSOR MOUNTING FLANGE

Figure 2-40. Typical diffuser section.

(1) Turbulent or disrupted airflow to the engine inlet, sometimes caused by parking crosswind, extremely steep climbs, or sudden abrupt flight maneuvers.

(2) Excessive fuel flow caused by abrupt engine acceleration.

(3) Contaminated or damaged compressor blades or stator vanes.

(4) Damaged turbine components which cause loss of shaft horsepower delivered to the compressor, and a decreased compressor speed.

(5) Excessively high or low RPM for a given airflow.

Design factors which contribute to the prevention of compressor stalls include:

(1) Variable inlet guide vanes and variable stator vanes in the first stages of the compressor.

(2) Bleed valves which can increase airflow in the compressor by venting some of the pressure overboard.

(3) Multiple-spool engines.

4. Compressor-Diffuser Section

The diffuser, located directly behind the compressor, provides the space for the air leaving the compressor to spread out. It is in the form of a divergent duct, and is usually a separate section bolted to the compressor case. The pressure in the diffuser is the highest in the engine. This provides, in effect, a wall of pressure which gives the combustion products something to push against.

5. Combustion Section

The combustion section houses the process, by which the energy contained in the air/fuel mixture is released.

The primary function of the combustion section is, of course, to burn the fuel/air mixture, thereby adding heat energy to the air. To do this efficiently the combustion chamber must:

(1) Provide the means for proper mixing of the fuel and air to assure good combustion.

(2) Burn this mixture efficiently.

(3) Cool the hot combustion products to a temperature which the turbine blades can withstand under operating conditions.

(4) Deliver the hot gases to the turbine section.

The location of the combustion section is directly between the compressor-diffuser and the turbine sections. Combustion chambers are always arranged coaxially with the compressor and turbine regardless of type.

All combustion chambers contain the same basic elements:

(1) An outer casing.

(2) A perforated inner liner.

(3) A fuel injection system.

(4) Some means for initial ignition.

(5) A fuel drainage system to drain off unburned fuel after engine shutdown.

To function properly, the combustors must mix the air and fuel for efficient combustion. Then it must lower the temperature of the hot combustion products enough that they will not overheat the turbine components. To do this, the airflow through the combustor is divided into primary and secondary airpaths. Approximately 25 to 35 percent of the air is routed to the area around the fuel nozzle for combustion. The secondary air, or the remaining 65 to 75 percent, forms a cooling air blanket on either side of the liner and centers the flames so they do not contact the metal. The secondary air also dilutes and cools the hot primary air to a temperature that will not shorten the service life of the turbine components.

Efficient combustion has become very important as traffic levels have increased around major airports. The high level of activity has

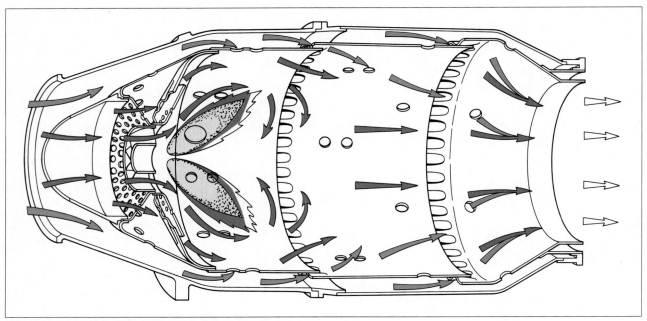

Figure 2-41. Flame stabilizing and general airflow patterns.

resulted in a new awareness of air pollution levels, especially visible smoke. Incomplete combustion in early designs left unburned fuel in the tailpipe where it entered the atmosphere as smoke. By shortening the flame pattern and using new materials that can withstand higher operating temperatures, manufacturers have been able to almost completely eliminate the smoke emissions from turbine engines.

The secondary air in the combustors may flow at a velocity of up to several hundred feet per second, but the primary airflow is slowed down by swirl vanes, which give the air a radial motion and retard its axial velocity to about five or six feet per second before it is mixed with the fuel and burned. The vortex created in the flame area provides the required turbulence to properly mix the fuel and the air. This reduction in the airflow is very important because of the slow flame propagation rate of kerosene-type fuels. If the primary airflow velocity is too high, it will literally blow the flame out of the engine. As it is, the combustion process is complete in the first third of the combustor length, and the burned and unburned gases then mix to provide an even distribution of heat to the turbine nozzle.

Although flameout is uncommon in modern engines, combustion instability still occurs and, occasionally, a complete flameout. Turbulent weather, high altitude, slow acceleration during maneuvers, and high-speed maneuvers are some

of the typical conditions which induce combustor instability which could lead to flameout.

There are usually two types of flameouts. A lean die-out usually occurs at low engine speed and low fuel pressure, at high altitude where the flame from a weak mixture can be blown out by the normal airflow. A rich flameout, occurs during rapid engine acceleration where an overly-rich mixture causes the combustion pressure to increase so much that the compressor airflow

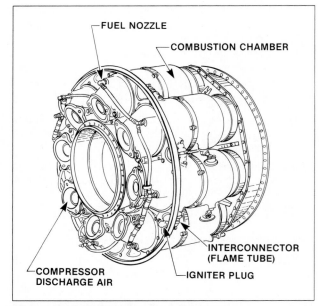

Figure 2-42. Multiple-can combustor.

stagnates and slows down, or even stops. The interruption of the airflow then causes the flame to go out. Turbulent inlet conditions and violent flight maneuvers can also cause compressor stalls which could result in airflow stagnation and flameout.

There are currently three basic types of combustion chambers, variations within these types being in detail only. These types are:

(1) The multiple can type.

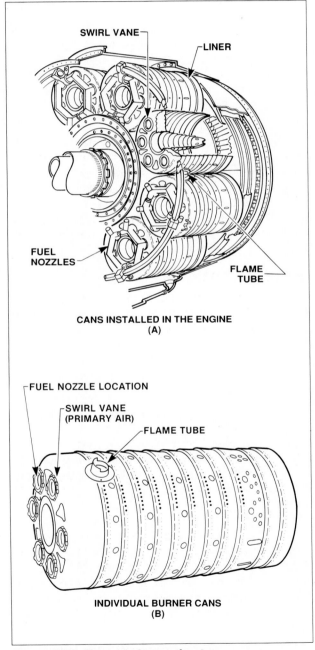

Figure 2-43. Can-annular combustor.

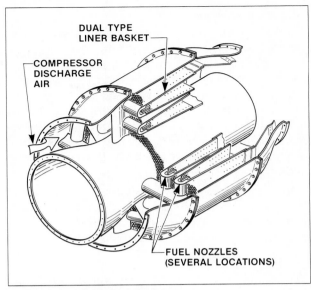

Figure 2-44. Annular combustor.

(2) The can-annular type.

(3) The annular or basket type.

a. Multiple-Can Type

This older type of combustion chamber is not in common use today. It consists of a series of outer housings, each with its own perforated inner liner. Each of the multiple combustor cans is actually a separate burner unit, with all of them discharging into the open area at the turbine nozzle inlet. The individual combustors are interconnected with small flame propagation tubes so that when combustion starts in the two cans equipped with igniter plugs, the flame will travel through the tubes and ignite the fuel/air mixture in the other cans. One advantage of this design was the ease with which any combustor could be removed for maintenance or replacement.

b. Can Annular Type

Can-annular combustion sections represent the evolutionary bridge between the older multiple-can combustor and the current annular-type combustor. The can-annular combustor is more common to commercial aircraft powered by Pratt & Whitney engines. This design consists of an outer casing containing multiple liners, located radially about the axis of the engine. Flame propagation tubes connect the individual liners, and two igniter plugs are used for starting. This design combines the ease of overhaul and testing of the multiple-can arrangement with the compactness of the annular combustor.

c. Annular Type

Annular combustors are in common use today in both small and large engines. They are the most efficient type from a standpoint of both thermal efficiency and weight, and they are also shorter than the other types. The small amount of surface requires less cooling air, and makes the best use of available space, especially for large engines where other types of combustors would be much heavier for the large mass airflow these engines require.

Unlike the can type combustors, the annular type must be removed as a single unit for repair or replacement. This usually involves complete separation of the engine at a major flange.

1) Through Flow

The through-flow annular combustor takes in air at the front and discharges it at the rear. The annular combustor consists of an outer housing with a perforated inner liner called a basket, with both parts encircling the engine. Multiple fuel spray nozzles stick out into the basket, and both primary and secondary air for combustion and cooling flow through it in the same way as in the other combustor designs.

2) Reverse Flow

The reverse-flow combustor serves the same function as the flow-through unit, but it differs

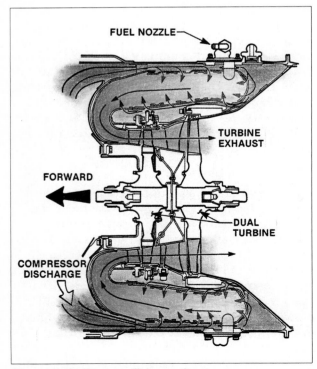

Figure 2-45. Reverse-flow combustor.

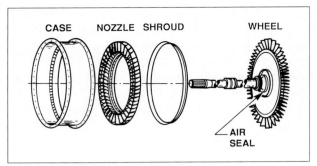

Figure 2-46. Turbine assembly.

by the air flowing around the chamber and entering from the rear. This results in the combustion gases flowing in the opposite direction of the normal airflow through the engine. This is not a new idea, and was employed by Whittle in his early designs.

Notice in figure 2-45 that the turbine wheels are inside the combustor area rather than in tandem, as they are with flow-through designs. This allows for a shorter and lighter engine, and it also uses the hot gases to preheat the compressor discharge air. These factors help make up for the loss of efficiency caused by the gases having to reverse their direction as they pass through the combustor.

6. Turbine Section

The turbine transforms a portion of the kinetic energy of the exhaust gases into mechanical energy to drive the compressor and accessories. In the turbojet engine, this is the sole purpose of the turbine and, this function absorbs approximately 60 to 80% of the total pressure energy from the exhaust gases.

The turbine section of a turbojet engine is located downstream of the combustion chamber section and consists of two basic elements, the stator and the rotor. These elements may be seen in figure 2-46 along with other components of the turbine section.

a. Turbine Nozzle

The stator element is known by a variety of names, of which turbine nozzle vanes, turbine guide vanes, and nozzle diaphragm are three of the most commonly used. The turbine nozzle vanes are located directly aft of the combustion chambers and immediately forward of the turbine wheel.

The function of the turbine nozzles is twofold. First, after the combustion chamber has introduced the heat energy into the mass airflow and delivered it evenly to the turbine nozzles, it becomes the job of the nozzles to prepare the mass air flow for driving the turbine rotor. The vanes of the turbine nozzle are contoured and set at such an angle that they form a number of small nozzles discharging the gas at extremely high speed; thus, the nozzle converts a varying portion of the heat and pressure energy to velocity energy which can then be converted to mechanical energy through the rotor blades.

The second purpose of the nozzle is to deflect the gases to a specific angle in the direction of turbine wheel rotation. Since the gas flow from the nozzle must enter the turbine blade passageway while it is still rotating, it is essential to aim the gas in the general direction of turbine rotation.

1) Shroud

The turbine nozzle assembly consists of an inner shroud and an outer shroud between which are fixed the nozzle vanes. The number of vanes employed vary with different types and sizes of engines. The vanes of the turbine nozzle may be assembled between the outer and inner shrouds or rings in a variety of ways. Although the actual elements may vary slightly in their configuration and construction features, there is one characteristic peculiar to all turbine nozzles; that is, the nozzle vane must be constructed to allow for thermal expansion. Otherwise, there would be severe distortion or warping of the metal components because of rapid temperature changes.

The thermal expansion of turbine nozzles is accomplished by one of several methods. One method necessitates the vanes being assembled loosely in the supporting inner and outer shrouds (see figure 2-47A).

Each vane fits into a contoured slot in the shrouds, which conforms with the airfoil shape of the vane. These slots are slightly larger than the vanes to give a loose fit. For further support the inner and outer shrouds are encased by an inner and outer support ring, which give increased strength and rigidity. These support rings also facilitate removal of the nozzle vanes as a unit; otherwise the vanes could fall out as the shrouds were removed.

Another method of thermal expansion construction is to fit the vanes into inner and outer shrouds; however, in this method the vanes are welded or riveted into position (see figure 2-47B).

Some means must be provided to allow for thermal expansion; therefore, either the inner or the outer shroud ring is cut into segments. These saw cuts dividing the segments will allow sufficient expansion to prevent stress and warping of the blades.

2) Case

The turbine casing encloses the turbine wheel and the nozzle vane assembly, and at the same time gives either direct or indirect support to the stator elements of the turbine section. It always has flanges provided front and rear for bolting the assembly to the combustion chamber housing and the exhaust cone assembly, respectively.

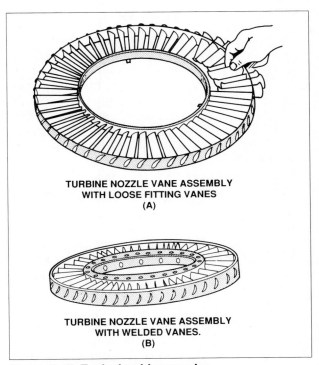

TURBINE NOZZLE VANE ASSEMBLY
WITH LOOSE FITTING VANES
(A)

TURBINE NOZZLE VANE ASSEMBLY
WITH WELDED VANES.
(B)

Figure 2-47. Typical turbine nozzles.

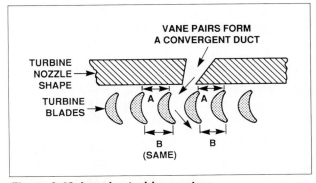

Figure 2-48. Impulse turbine system.

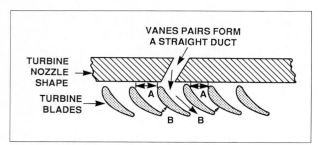

Figure 2-49. Reaction turbine system.

b. Turbine Wheel And Shaft

The rotating elements of the turbine section consists essentially of a shaft and a wheel. The turbine wheel is a dynamically balanced unit consisting of blades attached to a rotating disk. The disk, in turn, is attached to the main power transmitting shaft of the engine.

The jet gases leaving the turbine nozzle vanes act on the blades of the turbine wheel, causing the assembly to rotate at a very high rate of speed. The high rotational speed imposes severe centrifugal loads on the turbine wheel, and at the same time the elevated temperatures result in a lowering of the strength of the material. Consequently, the engine speed and temperature must be controlled to keep turbine operation within safe limits.

The turbine disk is referred to as such when in an unbladed form. When the turbine blades are installed, the unit becomes known as the turbine wheel. The disk acts an anchoring component for the turbine blades. Since the disk is bolted or welded to the shaft, the blades can transmit to the rotor shaft the energy they extract from the exhaust gases.

Turbine disks are subject to hot gases passing near their rim, and heat absorbed from the blades by conduction. Hence, disk rim temperatures normally are high, and well above the temperatures of the more remote inner portion of the disk. To limit the effect of these temperature variations cooling air may be passed over each side of the disk.

c. Turbine Blades

Turbine blades are airfoil shaped components designed to extract the maximum amount of energy from the flow of hot gases. Blades may be either forged or cast, depending on the composition of the alloys. Early blades were manufactured from steel forgings, but these are being replaced with cast nickel-base alloys. Most blades are now precision-cast and finish-ground

to the desired shape. A recent development that is showing promise is a non-metal blade manufactured from reinforced ceramic material. Their initial application is likely to be small, high speed turbines which operate at very high temperatures.

1) Blade Design

Turbines are classified as impulse, reaction, or a combination impulse-reaction type. In the impulse type turbine the total pressure drop across each stage occurs in the nozzle guide vanes. Because of their convergent shape, they will increase the velocity of the exhaust gases while decreasing their pressure. The gas is then directed onto the blades which experience an impulse force caused by the impact of the gas on the blades.

Reaction turbines produce their turning force by an aerodynamic action. The turbine nozzle vanes are shaped in such a way that they only aim the gas in the correct direction, they do not

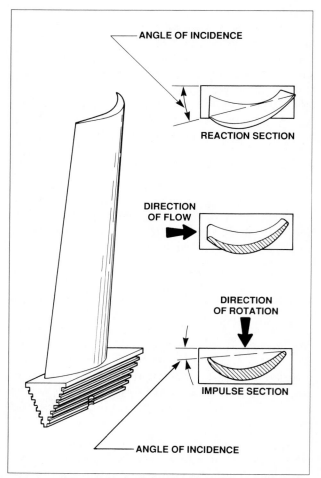

Figure 2-50. A typical impulse-reaction turbine blade.

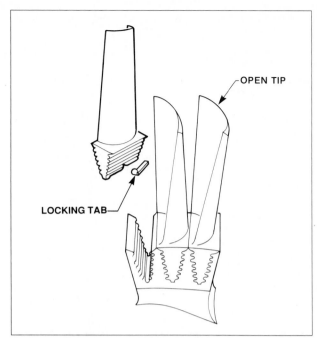

Figure 2-51. The fir-tree method of attaching turbine blades.

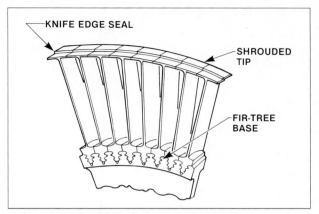

Figure 2-52. Shrouded turbine rotor blades.

increase its velocity. The gases pass between the blades of the turbine, which form converging passages that further increase the velocity of the gases. As the gases flow over the airfoil shaped blades, a force component in the direction of the plane of rotation causes the turbine to spin.

Normally, turbine engines do not use pure impulse or pure reaction type blades, but incorporate a design utilizing an impulse-reaction combination. With the combination blade the workload can be evenly distributed along the length of the blade, and axial velocity and pressure drop across the blade, from base to tip, is considered uniform. This type of blade is illustrated in figure 2-49.

2) Blade Attachment

The turbine blades fit into the disk with some form of fastening that allows them to be loose when the engine is cold, but to be firmly attached at operating temperature. The most commonly used method is the fir tree design we see in figure 2-51.

The blades are retained in their grooves by a variety of methods; some of the more common ones are peening, welding, locktabs, and riveting.

The turbine blades may be either open or shrouded at their ends, and both types of blades may be used in an engine. Open end blades are used in the high speed wheels, and shrouded blades are found in wheels having slower rotational speeds. Shrouded blades form a band around the perimeter of the wheel, which helps reduce blade vibration, and the weight of the shrouded tip is offset by the blades being thinner and more efficient.

A knife-edge seal around the outside of the shroud reduces air losses at the blade tip, keeps the airflow in an axial direction, and minimizes radial losses. The knife-edge seal fits with a close tolerance into a shrouded ring mounted in the outer turbine case.

d. Cooling

As we have seen in each section of the turbine engine, temperatures are very carefully considered in design. One of the basic operating limitations on a gas turbine engine is the turbine inlet temperature. Efforts to increase this value will ultimately increase the maximum power obtainable from an engine. Cooling of turbine nozzle vanes, and turbine blades is very important to the establishment of the maximum temperatures permitted in the turbine section. Cooling allows the components to operate in a thermal environment 600 to 800 degrees F. above the temperature limits of the alloys used for vane and blade construction.

The cooling methods generally employed are:

(1) Internal air flow cooling. Air flows through hollow blades and vanes and is carried away directly by cooling air.

(2) Surface film cooling. Air flows from small exit ports in leading and/or trailing edges of the vanes or blades to form a heat barrier on the surfaces.

(3) Combination convection and surface cooling.

e. Counter-Rotating Turbines

Some dual- and triple-spool engines have counter-rotating turbine wheels. It is not common in large engines, but it is sometimes seen in smaller ones, especially turboshaft engines. This is generally not a design for aerodynamic reasons, but rather for dampening gyroscopic effect and reducing engine vibration.

7. Exhaust Section

The exhaust section of the turbojet engine is made up of several components, each of which

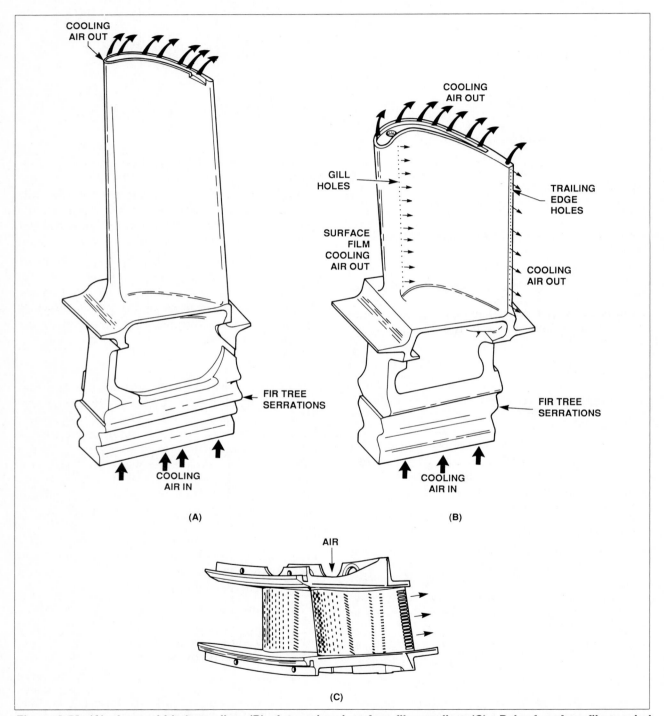

Figure 2-53. (A)—Internal blade cooling. (B)—Internal and surface film cooling. (C)—Pair of surface film cooled turbine vanes.

has its individual functions. Although the components have individual purposes, they also have one common function: They must direct the flow of gases rearward in such a manner as to prevent turbulence and at the same time impart a high final or exit velocity to the gases.

The exhaust section is located directly behind the turbine section and ends when the gases are ejected at the rear in the form of a high-velocity jet. The components of the exhaust section include the exhaust cone assembly, tailpipe (if required), and the exhaust or jet nozzle. Each component is discussed individually.

a. Exhaust Cone Assembly

The exhaust cone assembly consists of an outer shell or duct, an inner cone, three or four radial hollow struts or fins, and the necessary number of tie rods to aid the struts in supporting the inner cone from the outer duct. The outer shell or duct is usually made of stainless steel and is attached to the rear flange of the turbine case.

The exhaust cone collects the gases discharged from the turbine and gradually converts them into a single jet. In performing this, the velocity of the gases is decreased slightly and the pressure increased. This is due to the diverging passage between the outer duct and the inner cone; that is, the annular area between the two units decreases rearward. The collected gases are

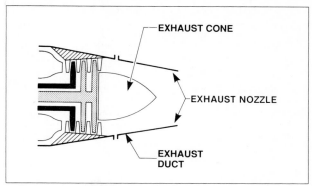

Figure 2-55. The convergent-type jet nozzle accelerates the gases as they leave the engine.

delivered either directly, or via the tailpipe to the jet nozzle, depending, of course, on whether or not a tailpipe is required.

The radial struts have a twofold function. They not only support the inner cone of the exhaust duct, but they also perform the important function of straightening the swirling exhaust gases that would otherwise leave the turbine at an angle of approximately 45 degrees.

The exhaust cone assembly is the terminating component of the basic engine. The remaining components (the tailpipe and jet nozzle) are usually considered to be airframe components.

b. Tailpipe

The tailpipe is used primarily to pipe the exhaust gases out of the airframe. The use of a tailpipe imposes a penalty on the operating efficiency of the engine in the form of heat and duct (friction) losses. These losses materially affect the final velocity of the exhaust gases and, hence, the thrust.

In some installations a tailpipe is not required. For instance, when the engine is installed in nacelles or pods, a short tailpipe is all that is required, in which case the exhaust duct and exhaust nozzle will suffice.

c. Jet Nozzle

The exhaust or jet nozzle imparts to the exhaust gases the all-important final boost in velocity. The jet nozzle, like the tailpipe, is not included as a part of the basic powerplant, but is supplied as a component of the airframe. The nozzle is attached to the rear of the tailpipe, if a tailpipe is required, or to the rear flange of the exhaust duct if a tailpipe is not necessary.

There are two types of jet nozzle designs. They are the converging design, for subsonic gas velocities, and the converging-diverging design

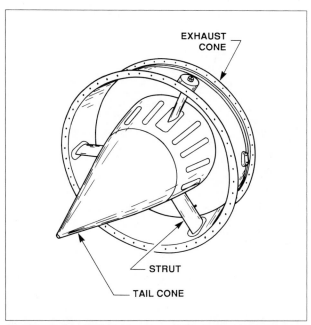

Figure 2-54. Exhaust cone, tail cone, and support struts.

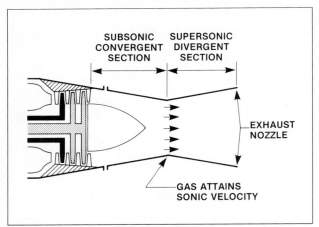

Figure 2-56. A convergent-divergent jet nozzle converts the pressure energy at its choked convergent nozzle into velocity energy.

for supersonic gas velocities. The jet nozzle opening may be either fixed-area or variable-area. The fixed-area is the simpler of the two jet nozzles. Since there are no moving parts, any adjustment in the nozzle are must be made mechanically. Adjustments in the nozzle area are sometimes necessary because the size of the exit orifice will directly affect the operating temperature of the engine.

1) Convergent Jet Nozzles

When gas initially flows down a convergent duct, the shape accelerates the gas; but, as more and more mass of air flows down the stream, the shape of the duct starts to constrict flow. At the point where the exhaust gas velocity reaches the speed of sound (Mach 1), the walls of the duct are constricting with a force equal to the air's

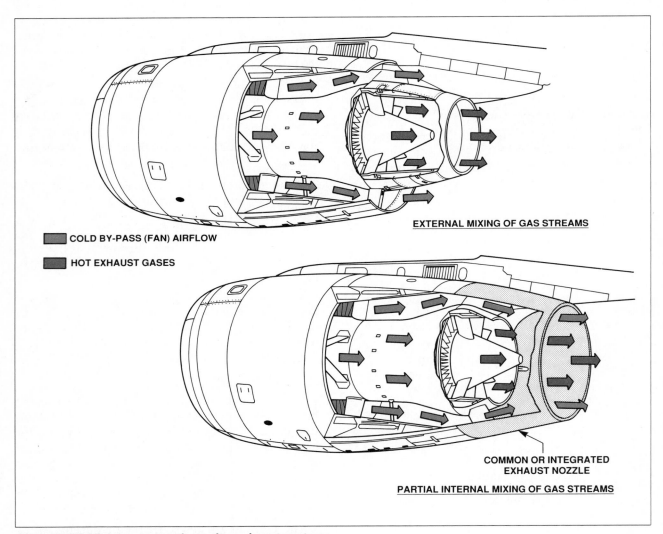

Figure 2-57. High by-pass ratio engine exhaust systems.

axial flow force and the nozzle is said to be "choked."

When the gas exits a chocked nozzle it accelerates radially (spreads out) faster than it accelerates axially, the axial velocity being fixed at Mach 1. If more fuel is added after Mach 1 gas velocity is reached, engine speed, compression, and mass airflow would increase and pressure in the tailpipe would increase.

The additional exhaust nozzle pressure will give a small increase in thrust; but, this condition would soon be uneconomical in terms of fuel consumption. Also, temperatures within the engine would elevate significantly. When supersonic exit velocities are needed for supersonic flight, a convergent-divergent nozzle is required rather than a simple convergent-type.

2) Convergent-Divergent Jet Nozzles

A convergent-divergent nozzle used on supersonic aircraft may also be found on certain engines with high pressure ratios. This design is used to recover some of the otherwise wasted energy, by obtaining a further increase in gas velocity and, consequently, an increase in thrust.

When the gas enters the converging section its velocity will increase with a corresponding decrease in pressure. As we have seen above, the velocity will reach Mach 1 at the throat of the nozzle. As the gases leaves the restriction of the throat and flow into the divergent section of nozzle, they will increase in velocity.

Gas traveling at supersonic speeds has the property of expanding outward faster than it accelerates rearward. This results in a pressure force acting on the inner wall of the nozzle. A component of this force acting parallel to the lon-

gitudinal axis of the nozzle produces a further increase in thrust.

d. By-Pass Type Engine Exhaust Systems

The fan or by-pass type engine has two gas streams to vent to the atmosphere, the high temperature gases being discharged by the turbine, and the cool gases that have been discharged from the fan section. These gases may be exhausted separately or together, depending upon engine design.

In a low by-pass engine, the flow of cool and hot air are combined in a mixer unit that ensures the mixing of the two streams prior to exiting the engine.

High by-pass type engines usually exhaust the two streams separately. The hot and cold nozzles are coaxial. A common or integrated nozzle may be used to partially mix the hot and cold gases prior to their ejection. Examples of both types may be seen in figure 2-57.

e. Afterburners

Afterburning provides the maximum exhaust velocity and maximum engine thrust for a given engine frontal area, but at the expense of fuel flow. The addition of an afterburner to a gas turbine engine is made possible by the fact that the gases in the tailpipe contain a large quantity of unburned oxygen. The 65-75% of the compressor discharge air used for combustor cooling mixes with the products of combustion at the turbine and then flows downstream to the tailpipe. A set of afterburner fuel nozzles, called "spray-bars" are fitted into the tailpipe entrance along with a suitable ignition system. When afterburner fuel and unburned oxygen mix and ignite, additional propulsive power is created as the gases are further accelerated.

Along with the fuel and ignition components, another device, called a flameholder, is required for good combustion (figure 2-58). It is a tubular grid or spoke-shaped obstruction placed downstream of the fuel nozzles. As the gases impinge on the flameholder, turbulence is created which enhances fuel-air mixing. This promotes complete and stable combustion in a very fast moving airstream.

Afterburning is used primarily for takeoff with heavy aircraft loading and for rapid climb-out speeds. Afterburning can result in as much as a 100% increase in thrust, with fuel flows increasing by three to five times.

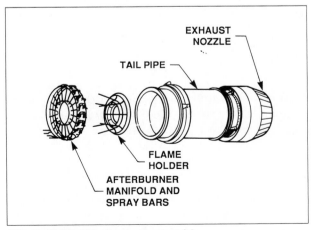

Figure 2-58. Afterburner assembly.

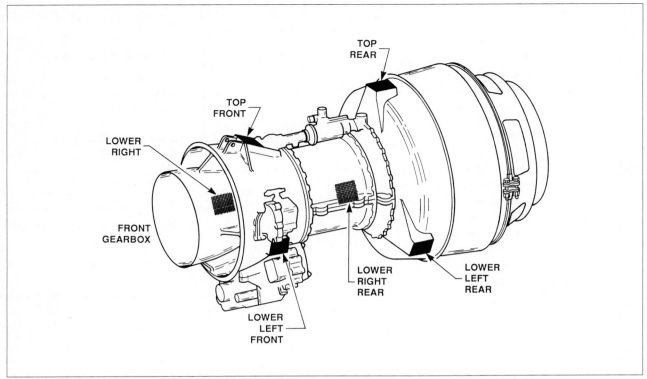

Figure 2-59. Engine mount arrangement of a turboshaft engine.

f. Thrust Reversers

Wheel brakes are not effective in providing all of the force needed to slow a heavy and fast jet airplane in a landing roll. The amount of kinetic energy that must be dissipated is so great that the wear on the brakes would be prohibitive. Propeller driven aircraft may be slowed down soon after touchdown by using reversing propellers, and turbojet and turbofan-powered aircraft may be slowed by reversing part of the exhaust gas flow to produce a reverse thrust. The design and operation of these units is discussed in detail in the chapter dealing with engine exhaust systems.

8. Engine Mounts

Engine mounts for gas turbine engines are of relatively simple construction, as seen in figure 2-59. Except for the turboprop, gas turbine engines produce little torque, and their mounts do not need to be of heavy construction. The mounts do, however, support the engine weight and also allow for transfer of stresses created by the engine to the aircraft structure. Because of induced propeller loads, the turboprop develops higher torque loads and mountings are proportionally heavier.

9. Noise Suppression

Much of the energy released by the burning fuel in a jet engine ultimately causes vibrations of the air which we hear as noise. As airplanes have become larger and flights from densely populated areas more frequent, control of noise is of real concern.

The majority of the noise produced by a turbine engine is created as the hot, high-velocity gases mix with the cold, low-velocity air surrounding the engine. This noise has a high intensity and it includes both low- and high-frequency vibrations, with low frequencies being predominant.

The increase in use of turbofan engines has probably done more to reduce noise levels both in the aircraft and on the ground than any other factor. Turbofan engines seldom require noise suppressors because the manner in which the hot and cold gas streams are exhausted, both their temperatures and their relative velocities contribute significantly to noise reduction.

Turbojet engines, especially older designs, may require additional noise suppression equipment. This is frequently in the form of some device to break up the airflow behind the tail cone and

2-36

reduce the noise. Additionally some new forms of sound insulating material and redesign of airframe components are being installed in the form of noise reduction kits to meet new Federal standards.

10. Bearings

The main bearings have the critical function of supporting the main engine rotor. The number of bearings necessary for proper engine support will, for the most part, be decided by the length and weight of the rotor. Naturally, split-spool axial compressors will require more support than a centrifugal compressor.

The gas turbine rotors are usually supported by either ball or roller bearings. This type of bearing is preferred because they:

(1) Offer little rotational resistance.

(2) Facilitate precision alignment of rotating elements.

(3) Are relatively inexpensive.

(4) Are easily replaced.

(5) Withstand high momentary overloads.

(6) Are simple to cool, lubricate, and maintain.

(7) Accommodate both radial and axial loads.

(8) Are relatively resistant to elevated temperatures.

Their main disadvantages are their vulnerability to foreign matter and tendency to fail without appreciable warning.

Usually the ball bearings are positioned on the compressor or rotor shaft so they can absorb any axial (thrust) loads or radial loads. Because the roller bearings present a larger working surface, they are better equipped to support radial loads than thrust loads. Therefore, they are used primarily for this purpose.

D. Turboprop Engine Design And Construction

The turboprop engine is a combination of a gas turbine engine and a propeller. Turboprops are similar to turbojet engines in that both have a

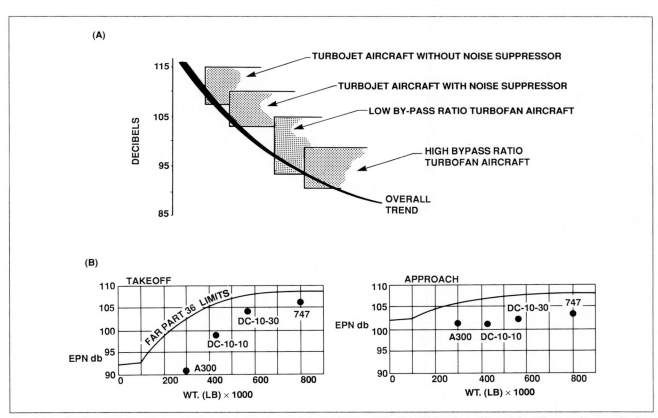

Figure 2-60. (A) Comparative noise levels of turbine engines. (B) Typical take-off and landing noise emission limits.

compressor, combustion chamber(s), turbine, and jet nozzle, all of which operate in the same manner on both engines. However, the difference is that the turbine in the turboprop engine usually has more stages than that in the turbojet engine.

In addition to operating the compressor and accessories, the turboprop turbine transmits increased power forward, through a shaft and a gear train, to drive the propeller. The increased power is generated by the exhaust gases passing through the additional stages of the turbine.

In some installations, the exhaust gases also contribute to engine power output through jet reaction, although the amount of energy available for jet thrust is considerably reduced.

Since the basic components of the turbojet and the turboprop engines differ only slightly in design features, it should be fairly simple to apply acquired knowledge of the turbojet to the turboprop.

The typical turboprop engine can be broken down into assemblies as follows:

(1) The power section assembly, which consists of the usual major components of gas turbine engines (compressor, combustion chamber, turbine, and exhaust sections).

(2) The reduction gear or gearbox assembly which contains those sections peculiar to turboprop installations.

(3) The torquemeter assembly, which transmits the torque from the engine to the gearbox of the reduction section.

(4) The accessory drive housing assembly.

E. Turboshaft Engine Design And Construction

A gas turbine engine that delivers power through a shaft to operate something other than a propeller is referred to as a turboshaft engine. Turboshaft engines are similar in design to turboprop engines, and in some instances, will use the same gas generator section design. The power takeoff may be coupled directly to the engine turbine, or the shaft may be driven by a turbine of its own (free turbine). This principle is used extensively in current production model engines. The turboshaft engine is very popular among helicopter manufacturers.

Chapter III
Engine Removal And Replacement

A. Reasons For Removal Of Reciprocating Engines

It would certainly keep down time to a minimum and reduce maintenance expense if all engine repairs could be made without removing the engine from the airframe. But, unfortunately, this is not always the case. There are certain maintenance items and inspections that require the technician to remove the engine. The following paragraphs outline the most common reasons for removing and replacing an aircraft engine. Information to aid in determining engine conditions that require removal is included; however, in every case, consult applicable manufacturer's instructions as the final authority in establishing the basis for engine removal.

1. Engine Life Span Exceeded

Engine life is dependent upon such factors as operational misuse, the quality of manufacture or overhaul, the type of aircraft in which the engine is installed, the kind of operation being carried out, and the degree to which preventive maintenance is accomplished. Thus, it is impossible to establish definite engine removal times. However, on a basis of service experience, it is possible to establish recommended time between overhauls.

a. Manufacturer's Recommended Time Between Overhaul (TBO)

When a new engine leaves the manufacturer, a permanent record of its operating time is begun. The *Total Time* (TT) record indicates hours of operation since new, and all maintenance entries may be referenced to this point. If, at some point, the engine is overhauled or rebuilt this total time record must be continued, although the engine may also be referenced to time *Since Major Overhaul* (SMOH). Engine maintenance requirements may be based on either time since new, or time since the most recent major overhaul.

Aircraft operated under FAR Part 91, generally, are not required to strictly comply with the manufacturer's recommended time between overhauls. Most other operators, including Air Taxi and airline type operations, must adhere to the maximum time in service established in their operating manuals.

b. Attrition Factors

Whether an engine has reached its recommended TBO or not, if it begins to show symptoms of deterioration, it may require removal and overhaul. As wear on certain components reach the limits of service certain symptoms may be manifested. Most commonly this will include increased oil consumption, higher engine operating temperatures, and deteriorating engine performance. Careful monitoring of these conditions may result in the decision to remove the engine for maintenance prior to the recommended time for overhaul.

2. Sudden Stoppage

Sudden stoppage is the very rapid and complete stoppage of the engine. This may be caused by engine seizure or by the propeller blades striking an object in such a way that RPM goes to zero in less than one complete revolution of the propeller. This may occur under such conditions as complete and rapid collapse of the landing gear, nosing over of the aircraft, or a crash landing. Damage to the engine may include cracked propeller gear teeth, gear train damage in the rear section, crankshaft bending, or damaged propeller bearings. The engine manufacturer's instructions for handling sudden stoppage must be complied with.

3. Sudden Reduction In Speed

Sudden reduction in speed can occur when one or more propeller blades strike an object at a low engine RPM. After impact, the foreign object is cleared and the engine recovers RPM and continues to run unless stopped to prevent further damage. This may also be referred to as a "prop strike" incident. When taxiing an aircraft, sudden reduction in speed can occur when the propeller strikes a foreign object, such as a raised section in the runway, a tool box, or a portion of another aircraft. Investigation of engines on which this type of accident has occurred has shown that, generally, no internal damage results when the RPM is low. This is because power output is low and the propeller absorbs most of the shock. However, when the accident occurs at high engine RPM, shocks are much more severe. When sudden reduction in engine speed occurs, the manufacturer's maintenance procedures for inspection should be followed. Below are listed the general criteria found in this type of inspection:

(1) Make a thorough external inspection of the engine mount, crankcase, and aircraft nose section to determine whether any parts have been damaged. If damage is found which cannot be corrected by line maintenance, remove the engine.

(2) Remove the engine oil screens, or filters. Inspect them for the presence of metal particles. Remove the engine sump plugs, drain the oil into a clean container, strain it through a clean cloth, and check both the cloth and the strained oil for metal particles. Heavy metal particles in the oil indicate a definite engine failure, and the engine must be removed. However, if the metal particles present are similar to fine filings, continue the inspection to determine serviceability.

(3) Remove the propeller and check the crankshaft, or propeller drive shaft on engines using propeller gear reduction, for misalignment. This is done by attaching a dial indicator to the nose section of the engine and letting the indicator arm ride on the crankshaft. Engines which use a flange-type propeller mounting must be checked at the outside edge of the flange. If a spline-type propeller installation is used, it should be checked at both the front and rear cone seats. Use a reversible-type indicator which has $1/1000$-inch graduations. Remove one spark plug from each cylinder, and slowly rotate the crankshaft while observing the indicator to see if the propeller shaft has been bent.

If the crankshaft or propeller drive shaft run out does not exceed the limits established by the manufacturer, install a serviceable propeller on the aircraft. Check the propeller tracking at the tip, using the method recommended by the manufacturer. The tracking must be within prescribed limits.

(4) Start the engine to see if operation is smooth and the power output adequate. If the engine operates properly during the

ground check, shut the engine down and repeat the inspection for metal particles in the oil system.

(5) If there are no heavy metal particles in the engine oil, give the engine a flight test. If the engine operates properly during the flight test, look again for metal in the oil system. If no metal is found, continue the engine in service, but recheck the oil screens for the presence of metal after 10 hours of operation, and again after 20 hours. If no indication of internal failure is found after 20 hours of operation, the engine probably requires no further special inspections.

4. Metal Particles In Oil

Metal particles on the engine oil screens or the magnetic sump plugs are generally an indication of an internal failure. However, due to the construction of aircraft oil systems, it is possible that metal particles have collected in the oil system sludge at the time of a previous engine failure. Furthermore, carbon tends to break loose from the interior of the engine in rock-like pieces which have the appearance of metal. It is necessary to consider these possibilities when foreign particles are found on the engine oil screens or sump plugs.

Before removing an engine for suspected internal failure as indicated by foreign material on the oil screens or oil sump plugs, determine if the

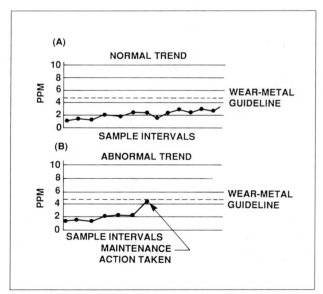

Figure 3-1. (A)—Spectrometric oil analysis, normal trend. (B)—Spectrometric oil analysis, abnormal trend.

foreign particles are metal by placing them on a flat metal object and striking them with a hammer. If the material is carbon, it will disintegrate, whereas metal will remain intact or change shape, depending upon its malleability. A magnet may also be used to detect ferrous metals.

If the particles are metal, determine the probable extent of internal damage. For example, if only small particles are found which are similar in nature to filings, drain the oil system, and refill it. Then ground run the engine and reinspect the oil screens and sump plugs. If no additional particles are found, the aircraft should be test flown, followed by an inspection of the oil screens and sump plugs. If no further evidence of foreign material is found, continue the engine in service.

The regular use of spectrometric oil analysis will give the operator a record of metals present in the oil. If a sudden increase is observed in any of the metals tested for, the laboratory will immediately contact the operator by telephone or telegraph. This information is reliable, and will give specifics on the type of metal found, along with suggested sources of that material. Do not wait until a failure is suspected to have an oil sample analyzed. It is only by regular testing and comparison of previous test results that accurate information can be obtained.

5. Unstable Engine Operation

Engines are usually removed when there is consistent unstable engine operation. Unstable engine operation generally includes one or more of the following conditions:

(1) Excessive engine vibration

(2) Back firing, either consistent or intermittent.

(3) Cutting out while in flight.

(4) Low power output.

Many turbine engines are now utilizing either manual or computerized monitoring of engine conditions, and using this information to provide a base line to which unstable engine operations can be compared. This information, and trend analysis techniques, may be used to accurately predict a failure before it occurs, or detect a problem suggesting the need for maintenance or overhaul.

B. Preparation Of Reciprocating Engines For Installation

After the decision has been made to remove an engine, the preparation of the replacement engine must be considered. The maintenance procedures and methods used vary widely. Commercial operators, whose maintenance operations require the most efficient and expeditious replacement of aircraft engines, usually rely on a system that utilizes the quick-engine-change assembly, or QECA, also sometimes referred to as the engine power package. The QECA is essentially a powerplant with the necessary accessories installed, and in some cases already installed in the engine mounting assembly.

The practice of using QECA's has a much wider application today than in the past. Because most maintenance shops are not equipped to overhaul engines, and small operators cannot afford to have an inventory of overhauled engines ready for installation, large Certified Repair Stations have grown up that will supply engines built up to QECA status, on an exchange basis. This allows the small shop to have the new engine on hand when the customer's aircraft arrives, and engine exchange times are reduced to a few days. These repair stations are generally able to supply the overhauled engine, all accessories, new ignition wiring, and new hoses as a package deal. When the exchange is complete, the run out engine is secured in the shipping container provided by the overhauler, and returned to the repair station.

1. QECA Buildup

QECA buildup may be accomplished by the operator or by the repair station, in the case of purchasing engines on an exchange basis. The units included will depend upon the specific aircraft/engine combination, and on the procedures established by the operator. Small engines used on training aircraft may include nothing more than ignition and carburetor components while some air carriers may build QECA's that include everything up to the cowling. These assemblies require only a few connections be made at the firewall, and the engine is operational.

2. De-preservation

Engines which are overhauled and are not to be installed immediately should be preserved to prevent corrosion and other forms of deterioration. The recommended procedures and time limits regarding storage are provided in the manufacturer's overhaul information.

a. De-preserving An Engine

Engines which have been preserved for storage must undergo de-preservation before they are put into service. The procedures for this should be included in the engine manufacturer's overhaul manual, and/or provided by the overhauler who preserved the engine. We will present here only a general overview of these procedures as they will vary with the type of engine, and the degree of preservation.

After the engine has been secured to a suitable stand, or installed in the aircraft mounts, all covers must be removed from the points where the engine was sealed or closed with ventilatory covers. This may include engine breathers, exhaust outlets, and accessory mounting pad cover plates. As each cover is removed, inspect the uncovered part of the engine for corrosion. Also, as the dehydrator plugs are removed from each cylinder, make a very careful check of the walls of any cylinder for which the dehydrator plug color indicates an unsafe condition. Care is emphasized in the inspection of the cylinders, even if it is necessary to remove a cylinder.

On radial engines, the inside of the lower cylinders and intake pipes should be carefully checked for the presence of excessive corrosion preventive compound that has drained throughout the interior of the engine and has settled at these low points. This excessive compound could cause the engine to become damaged from a hydraulic lock when an attempt to start the engine is made.

The oil screens should be removed from the engine and thoroughly washed in kerosene or an approved solvent to remove all accumulations that could restrict the oil circulation and cause engine failure. After the screens are cleaned, immerse them in clean oil and the reinstall them in the engine.

When the cover has been removed from the intake manifold, the silica gel desiccant bags must be removed before installing the carburetor. Take care not to accidently tear open one of the bags.

Remove the protective covering from the propeller shaft and wash all corrosion preventive compound from both the inside and outside surfaces of the shaft. Then coat the propeller shaft lightly with engine oil

As a final check, see that the exterior of the engine is clean. Usually a quantity of compound runs out of the engine when the dehydrator plugs and oil screens are removed. To clean the engine, spray it with a kerosene type safety solvent.

b. Inspection And De-preservation Of Accessories

An engine's performance is no better than that of its accessories. Though the engine has been completely overhauled and is in top condition, any oversight or error in installing the accessories can result in improper engine operation or even irreparable damage to it.

Before de-preserving any of the accessories enclosed with the engine, consult the storage data usually stenciled on the outside of the engine container, or with the records enclosed with the engine. It is necessary to determine how long the engine and accessories have been in storage. Certain accessories that may accompany an engine from overhaul are considered unsafe for use if their time in storage has exceeded the manufacturer's limits. This is largely due to components which have a finite shelf life.

Before installing any replacement accessory, check it visually for signs of corrosion and for freedom of operation. Always wipe the mounting pad, flange, and install the proper gasket between the mounting pad and the accessory. Lubricate the accessory drive shaft when indicated in the manufacturer's instructions.

3. Inspection And Replacement Of Powerplant External Units

Engine overhaul or exchange provides the ideal opportunity to thoroughly inspect and repair the entire engine installation, including nacelle, cowling, mountings, engine control mechanisms, electrical wiring, tubing, and flexible hoses.

Inspect the complete engine nacelle for condition of the framework and the sheet metal cowl-

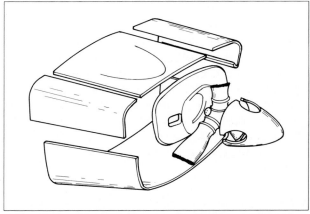

Figure 3-2. Cowling for a horizontally opposed engine.

ing and rivet plates that cover the nacelle. Any cracks in the cowling or ducts, if they do not exceed limits specified in the manufacturer's structural repair manual for the aircraft concerned, may be stop-drilled at the end of the crack and repaired by covering with a reinforcing patch.

The engine mounting frame assembly should be checked for any distortion of the steel tubing, such as bends, dents, flat spots, or cracks. The dye penetrant method of inspection may be used to reveal a crack, porous area, or other defects.

The engine mounting bolts are usually checked for condition by magnetic particle inspection or other approved process. While the bolts are removed, the bolt holes should be checked for elongation cause by movement of an improperly tightened bolt.

Check the outer surface of all exposed electrical wiring for breaks, chafing, or other damage. Also check the security of crimped or soldered cable ends. In addition, carefully inspect connector plugs for overall condition. Any item that is damaged must be repaired or replaced, depending upon the extent of damage.

Before installing an engine, inspect all tubing in the nacelle for dents, nicks, scratches, chafing, or corrosion. Check all tubing carefully for indications of fatigue or excessive flatness caused by improper or accidental bending. Thoroughly inspect all hoses used in various engine systems. This is the ideal time to replace all flexible lines, and many parts distributors are now providing hose kits containing all of the lines for a particular aircraft/engine combination.

Check bonding straps for fraying, loose attachments, and cleanness of terminal ends. The electrical resistance of the complete bond must not exceed the resistance values specified in the applicable manufacturer's instructions.

Inspect the exhaust stacks, collectors, muffler, and tailpipe assembly for security, cracks, and excessive corrosion. These and the related components require special consideration if the engine is turbocharged.

Check all air ducts for dents and the condition of the fabric or rubber anti-chafing strips at the points where sections of duct are joined. The dents may be pounded out; the anti-chafing strips should be replaced if they are pulled loose from the duct or are worn to the point where they no longer form a tight seal at the joint.

If the engine installation employs a dry sump oil system, the oil tank is generally removed to permit thorough cleaning. Also, the oil cooler and temperature regulator are removed and either sent to a repair facility for overhaul, or are included as an exchange unit and returned with the run out engine.

C. Preparing The Reciprocating Engine For Removal

Removal of the engine from an aircraft is a major task, and must be accomplished in an orderly fashion. There are dangers involved for the maintenance personnel, and the possibility of damage to the aircraft, if procedures are not properly followed.

1. Magneto, Fuel And Battery Disarming

Before starting to work on the aircraft or the engine, always be sure that the magneto switch is in the "OFF" position. Aircraft engines can be started accidently by turning the propeller if the magneto switch is on.

Check to see that all fuel selectors or solenoid-operated fuel shutoff valves are closed. The fuel selector valves are either manually or solenoid operated. If solenoid-operated fuel shutoff valves are installed, it may be necessary to turn the battery switch on before the valves can be closed. These valves close the fuel line at the firewall between the engine and the aircraft. After ensuring that all fuel to the engine is shut off, disconnect the battery to eliminate the possibility of a "hot" wire starting a fire. If it is anticipated that the aircraft will be out of service for more than a few days, the battery is normally removed and taken to the battery shop and placed on charge.

Also, a few other preparations should be made before starting to work on the engine removal. First, make sure that there are enough fire extinguishers near at hand to meet any possible emergency needs. During engine removal there may be some leakage of flammable fluids, resulting in a fire hazard. Check that the wheel chocks are in place, these will keep the aircraft from inching forward or back during some crucial operation. Also, if the aircraft has tricycle-type landing gear, be sure that the tail is supported so that the aircraft cannot tip back when the weight of the engine is removed from the forward end. It is not necessary to support the tail on some multi-engine aircraft if only one engine is being removed from the aircraft. The aircraft manufacturer's maintenance publications should include information of this type. In addition, the landing gear shock struts may need to be deflated to prevent them from extending as the engine weight is removed from the aircraft.

After taking these necessary precautions, begin removing the cowling from the engine. As it is removed, clean it and check for cracks so that the necessary repairs can be made while the engine change is in progress. Place all cowling that does not need repair on a rack where it can be readily found when the time comes to reinstall it around the new engine.

After removing the cowling, the propeller should be removed for inspection or repair. Many operators find that this is the ideal time for propeller overhaul, as it will eliminate the need for additional down time.

2. Draining The Engine

Place a large metal pan (drip pan) on the floor under the engine to catch any spills. Next, secure a clean container in which to drain the oil, and place it beneath the oil drain. Drain the oil by removing the drain plug or opening the drain valve. Other points at which oil may need to be drained will include the oil cooler, the oil return line, engine sumps, and oil filter. All valves and drains must remain open until the oil system has been completely drained.

After draining the oil, reinstall all drain plugs and close all drain valves. Then, wipe all excess oil from around the drain points.

3. Electrical Disconnects

Electrical disconnections are usually made at the engine firewall. This does not always apply when the basic engine is being removed, for then the electrical leads to such accessories as the starter and generator are disconnected at the units themselves. When disconnecting electrical leads, it is a good safety habit to disconnect the magneto "P" leads first, and immediately ground them at some point on the engine or the assembly being removed. This is not necessary if the magneto "P" lead connection includes the safety grounding device built into the breaker cover of the magneto. This spring steel strap will ground the magneto whenever the "P" lead is removed from the connector.

Most firewall disconnections of electrical conduit and cable are simplified by the use of AN and MS connectors. Each connector consists of two parts: (1) A plug assembly, and (2) a recep-

tacle assembly. To prevent accidental disconnection during operation of the aircraft, the outlet is threaded to permit a knurled sleeve nut to be screwed to the outlet and then fastened with safety wire, if necessary.

A typical plug fitting assembly is shown in figure 3-3. This figure also shows a typical junction box assembly, which is used as a disconnect on some aircraft engine installations. In the junction box, the electrical circuit is completed by fastening two leads to a common terminal. The lead which runs from the junction box to the engine is disconnected from the terminal, and the conduit is disconnected from the junction box when preparing to remove the engine.

After the safety wire is broken, remove all of the sleeve nuts which hold conduit to the junc-

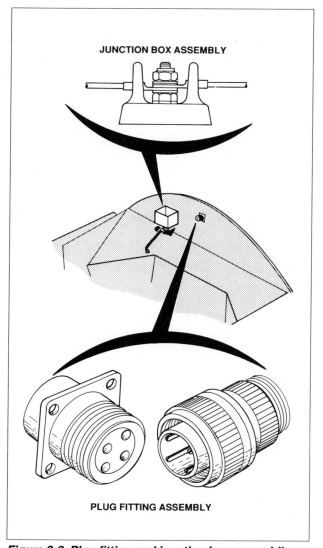

JUNCTION BOX ASSEMBLY

PLUG FITTING ASSEMBLY

Figure 3-3. Plug fitting and junction box assemblies.

tion boxes, as well as from the nuts on the connectors. Wrap moisture-proof tape over the exposed ends of the connectors to protect them from dirt and moisture. Also, do not leave long electrical cables or conduits hanging loose, since they may become entangled with some part of the aircraft while the engine is being hoisted. It is a good practice to coil all lengths of cable or flexible conduit neatly, and tie or tape them to some portion of the assembly being removed.

Small aircraft, with simple electrical systems, may utilize only knife-type or wrist-lock disconnects on some wiring. These may be protected by a plastic sleeve that is tied with cord at the ends. Carefully slide back the protective sleeve and disconnect the wire. If the installation does not have legible identification on the wires, the technician may want to use a write-on tape to provide identification, and eliminate confusion when reinstalling the engine.

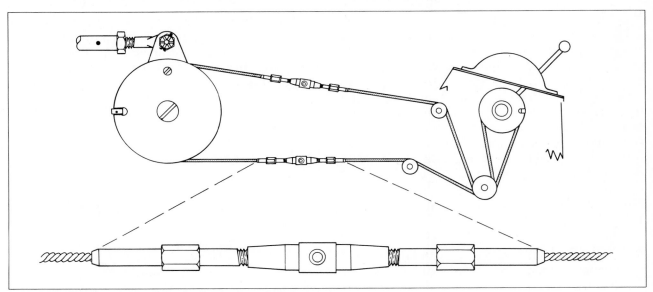

Figure 3-4. Engine control cable and turnbuckle assembly.

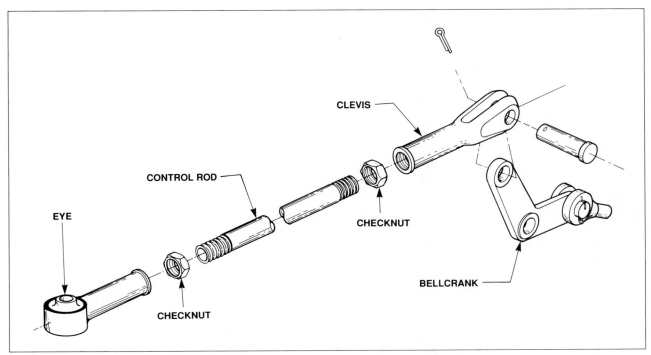

Figure 3-5. Engine control linkage assembly.

4. Disconnection Of Engine Controls

The engine control rods and cables connect such units as the carburetor or fuel control throttle valve and the mixture control valve with the manually actuated control in the cockpit. The controls are sometimes disconnected by removing the turnbuckle which joins the cable ends. A typical assembly is shown in figure 3-4.

Typical control linkage, consisting of a control rod attached to a bellcrank, is illustrated in figure 3-5.

The control rod in the linkage shown has two rod end assemblies, a clevis and an eye, screwed onto opposite ends. These rod end assemblies determine the length of the control rod by the distance they are screwed onto it, and are locked into position by check nuts. An anti-friction bearing is usually mounted in the eye end of a rod. This eye is slipped over a bolt in the bellcrank arm and is held in position by a castle nut safe-tied with a cotter pin. The clevis rod end is slipped over the end of a bellcrank arm, which also usually contains an anti-friction bearing. A bolt is passed through the clevis and the bellcrank eye, fastened with a castle nut, and safe-tied with a cotter pin.

Sometimes linkage assemblies do not include the anti-friction bearings and are held in position only by a washer and cotter pin in the end of a clevis pin which passes through the bellcrank and rod end. After the engine control linkages have been disconnected, the nuts and bolts should be replaced in the rod ends or bellcrank arms to prevent their being lost. All control rods should be removed completely or tied back to prevent them from being bent or broken if they are struck by the engine as it is being hoisted.

5. Disconnection Of Lines

The lines between units within the aircraft and the engine are either flexible rubber hoses or aluminum-alloy tubes joined by lengths of hose clamped to them. Lines which must withstand high pressure, such as hydraulic lines, are often fabricated from stainless steel tubing.

Figure 3-6 shows several basic types of line disconnects. Most lines leading from the engine are secured to a threaded fitting at the firewall by a sleeve nut around the tubing. Hoses are sometimes secured in this manner, but may also be secured by a threaded fitting on the unit to which they lead, or by a hose clamp. The firewall fittings for some lines have a quick-disconnect

fitting that contains a check valve to prevent the system from losing fluid, when the line is disconnected. Metal tubing on some installations may also be disconnected at a point where two lengths of it are joined together by a length of rubber hose. Such a disconnection is made by loosening the hose clamps and sliding the length of rubber hose over the length of tubing which remains on the aircraft. There may be some further variations in these types of disconnections, but basically they follow the same pattern.

Some type of container should be used to catch any fuel, oil, or other fluids that may drain from the disconnected lines. After the lines have drained, they should immediately be plugged or covered with moisture-proof tape to prevent foreign matter from entering them as well as to

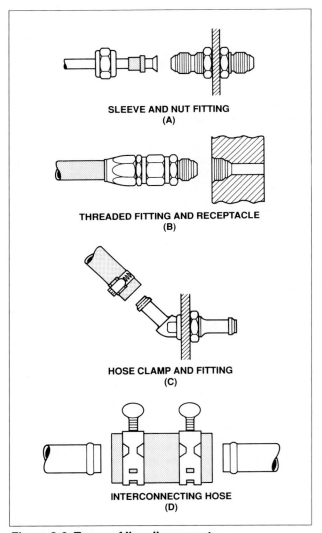

Figure 3-6. Types of line disconnects.

prevent any accumulated fluid from dripping out.

6. Other Disconnections

The points at which the various air ducts are disconnected depend upon the engine and the aircraft in which it is installed. Usually the air intake ducts and the exhaust system must be disconnected so the basic engine or the QECA can be removed. After the engine connections are free (except the engine mounts) and all the disconnections are entirely clear so they will not bind or become entangled, the engine can be prepared for hoisting.

D. Hoisting And Removing The Reciprocating Engine

If there has been thorough preparation of the engine for removal, the actual removal should be a relatively speedy operation.

If a QECA is being removed on some installations, the mount will accompany the engine; but if only the engine is being removed, the mount will remain on the aircraft. Before the engine can be freed from its attach points, a sling must be installed so that the engine's weight can be supported with a hoist when the mounting bolts are removed.

Aircraft engines have marked points for attaching a hoisting sling. The location of these points, and the type of sling arrangement will vary according to the size and weight of the engine. The engine manufacturer's maintenance publications generally indicate the location of lifting points and the type of apparatus required to safely hoist the engine. As a matter of safety, the sling should be carefully inspected for condition before installing it on the engine.

Before attaching the sling to the hoist, be sure that the hoist has sufficient capacity to lift the engine safely. Lifting capacity should be clearly marked on the hoist. Be certain to observe the change in capacity as the arm of the hoist is extended. At its fully extended point, the capacity will be greatly reduced. A manually operated hoist mounted in a portable frame is shown in figure 3-7. This hoist assembly is specifically manufactured for the purpose of removing engines and other large assemblies from aircraft. Some frames are fitted with power operated hoists. These should be used with care, since considerable damage can be done if an inexperienced operator allows a power operated hoist to overrun. The hoist and frame should also be checked for condition before being used to lift the engine.

Before the hoist is hooked onto the engine sling, recheck the aircraft tail supports and the wheel chocks. Hook the hoist onto the sling and raise the engine slightly—just enough to relieve the engine weight from the mount attachments. Remove the nuts from the mount attachments in the order recommended by the manufacturer's instructions for the aircraft. As the last nuts are being removed, be sure that the engine is steadied and secure. If bolts must be removed from the mount attachments, be sure that the engine is under control before doing so. If the bolts are to remain in the mount attachments, the hoist can be gently maneuvered upward or downward as necessary after all the nuts have been removed. Meanwhile, gently allow the engine to move free from the mount attachments. At the point where the hoist has removed all engine weight from the mount attachments, the engine should be eased gently forward or upward, as required, to move it away from the aircraft. If the engine binds at any point, maneuver it with the hoist until it slips free.

The procedure just discussed applies to the removal of most engines. Variations in details will be outlined in the manufacturer's instruc-

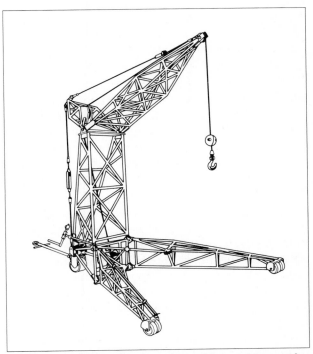

Figure 3-7. Hoist and frame assembly used for engine removal.

tions for the aircraft concerned. Before attempting any engine removal, always consult with these instructions.

When the engine has been removed, it can be carefully lowered onto a stand. The engine should be fastened to the stand and prepared for the required maintenance, overhaul, or shipping to a repair station.

E. Hoisting The Reciprocating Engine For Installation

When the new or overhauled engine is ready to be hoisted for installation, move the engine stand as close as possible to the aircraft on which it is to be installed. Then attach the sling to the engine and hook the hoist to the sling; take up the slack until the hoist is supporting most of the engine weight. Next, remove the engine attaching bolts from the stand and hoist the engine clear.

1. Mounting The Engine

The engine stand may be moved and the hoist frame positioned in a way that most easily permits the engine to be hoisted into place. To prevent injury to the crew or damage to the aircraft or engine, be sure that the engine is steadied when moving the hoist frame.

The engine must be guided into position and mated with its various connections, such as the mounting bolts and the exhaust tailpipe. This must be done despite such obstacles as the nacelle framework, ducts, or firewall connections and without leaving a trail of broken and bent parts, scratched paint, or crushed fingers.

When the engine has been aligned correctly, insert the mounting bolts into their holes and start all of the nuts on them. Always use the type of bolt and nut recommended by the manufacturer. Never make an unauthorized substitution of a different type or specification of nut and bolt.

The nuts on the engine mount bolts must be tightened to the torque recommended by the manufacturer. While the nuts are being tightened, the hoist should support the engine weight sufficiently to allow alignment of the mounting bolts. If the engine is permitted to exert upward or downward pressure on the bolts, it will be necessary for the nuts to pull the engine into proper alignment. This will result in nuts being tightened to the proper torque without actually holding the engine securely to the aircraft.

The applicable manufacturer's instructions outline the sequence for tightening the mounting bolts to ensure security of fastening. After the nuts are safetied and the engine sling and hoist removed, bonding straps should be connected across each engine mount to provide an electrical path from the mount to the airframe. Failure to provide adequate bonding could result in the starter seeking an electrical return path through engine controls, or metal fuel lines. This may result in fire, or extensive damage to engine connections.

Mounting the engine is, of course, only the beginning. All the ducts, electrical leads, controls, tubes, hoses, and conduits must be connected before the engine is ready for operation.

2. Connections And Adjustments

There are no hard and fast rules that direct the order in which units or systems should be connected to the engine. Each maintenance organization will normally supply a worksheet or checklist to be followed during this procedure. This list is based upon past experience with engine installation on that particular type of aircraft. If this is followed carefully, it will serve as a guide for an efficient installation. The following instructions, then, are not a sequence of procedures but are a discussion of correct methods for completing an engine installation.

The system of ducts for routing air to the engine varies with all types of aircraft. In connecting them, the goal is to fit the ducts closely at all points of disconnect so that the air they route will not escape from its intended path. The duct systems of some aircraft must be pressure checked for leaks. This is done by blocking the system at one end, supplying compressed air at a specified pressure at the other end, and then checking the rate of leakage.

The filters in the air induction system must be cleaned to assure an unrestricted flow of clean air to the engine and its units. Because methods for cleaning air filters differs with the materials used in the filtering element, clean or replace them in accordance with the instructions provided by the manufacturer.

The exhaust system should also be carefully connected to prevent the escape of hot gases into the nacelle. When assembling the exhaust system, check all clamps, nuts, and bolts and replace any in doubtful condition. During assembly, the nuts should be gradually and progressively tightened to the correct torque. The clamps should also be tapped with a rawhide mallet as they are being tightened to prevent binding at any point. On some systems, a ball joint connects the stationary portion of the exhaust system to the portion that is attached to the engine. This ball joint absorbs the normal engine movement caused by the unbalanced forces of the engine operation. Ball joints must be installed with the specified clearance to prevent binding when expanded by hot gases.

Hoses used with low pressure systems, such as vacuum and instrument air, are generally fastened into place with clamps. Before using a hose clamp, inspect it for security of welding or riveting and for smooth operation of the adjusting screw. A clamp that is badly distorted or materially defective should be rejected (material defects include extremely brittle or soft areas that may easily break or stretch when the clamp is tightened). After a hose is installed in a system, it should be supported with rubber lined supporting clamps at regular intervals.

Before installing metal tubing with threaded fittings, make sure that the threads are clean and in good condition. If required, apply sealing compound of the correct specification for the system to the threads of the fittings before installing them. While connecting metal tubing, follow the same careful procedure for connecting hose fittings to prevent cross threading and to assure correct torque. Remember, over torquing a fitting increases the likelihood of leaks and/or failures.

When connecting the leads to the starter, generator, or various other electrical units within the nacelle, make sure that all connections are clean and properly secured. On leads that are fastened to a threaded terminal with a nut, a lock washer is usually inserted under the nut to prevent the lead from working loose. When required, connector plugs can be safetied with steel wire to hold the knurled nut in the "full tight" position.

Electrical leads within the engine nacelle are usually passed through either a flexible or a rigid conduit. This conduit must be anchored as necessary to provide a secure installation, and bonded when required.

Engine cockpit controls may be panel mounted on single engine aircraft, or quadrant mounted on either single or multi-engine aircraft. Regardless of the type of mounting, aircraft of recent manufacturers employ a standard means of identification of controls. This system allows the

pilot to identify the engine control by any of three means: (1) position, relative to the other controls, (2) color or, (3) shape of the control handle. Figure 3-8 illustrates the controls and means of identification.

All engine controls must be accurately adjusted to assure instantaneous response to the control setting. The engine controls may be a combination of rods and cables, or the simple push-pull wire encased in a coiled wire sheath. Since these control systems are tailored to the model of aircraft in which they are installed, their adjustment must follow exactly the step-by-step procedure outlined in the manufacturer's instructions for each particular model of aircraft.

Figure 3-9 illustrates a simplified schematic drawing of a throttle system for a large reciprocating aircraft engine incorporating rod and cable controls. Using the drawing as a guide, follow a general procedure for adjusting throttle controls. First, loosen the serrated throttle control arm at the carburetor and back off the throttle stop until the throttle valve is in the "fully closed" position. After locking the cable drum into position with the locking pin, adjust the control rod to the specified length. Then, attach one end of the control rod to the locked cable drum and reinstall the throttle control arm on the carburetor in the serrations that will allow the other end of the control rod to be attached to it. This will correctly connect the control arm to the cable drum.

Now, loosen the cable turnbuckles until the throttle control can be locked at the quadrant with the locking pin. Then, with both locking pins in place, adjust the cables to the correct tension as measured with a tensionmeter. Remove the locking pins from the cable drum and quadrant.

Next, adjust the throttle control so that it will have a slight cushion action at two positions on the throttle quadrant: one when the carburetor

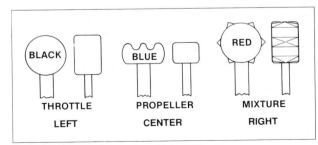

Figure 3-8. Engine control identification.

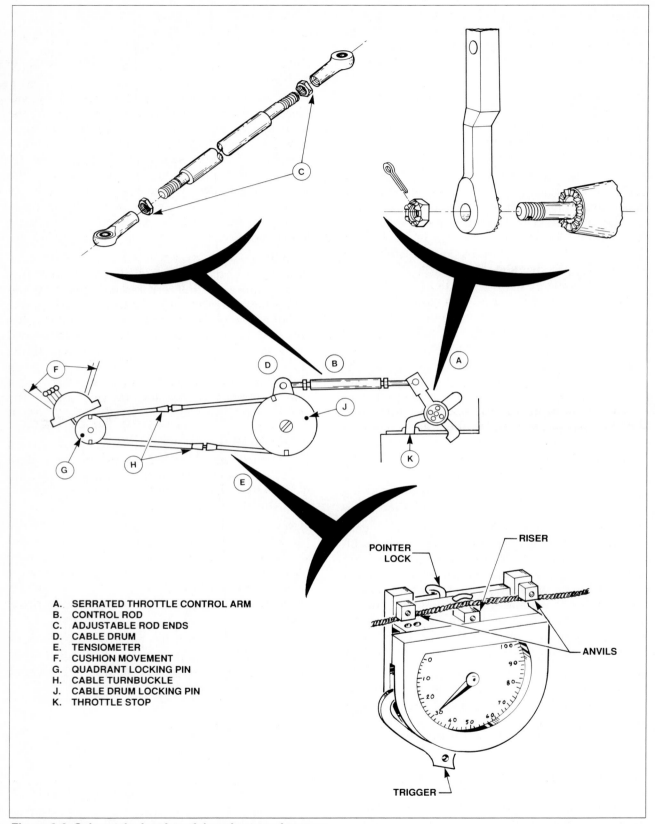

A. SERRATED THROTTLE CONTROL ARM
B. CONTROL ROD
C. ADJUSTABLE ROD ENDS
D. CABLE DRUM
E. TENSIOMETER
F. CUSHION MOVEMENT
G. QUADRANT LOCKING PIN
H. CABLE TURNBUCKLE
J. CABLE DRUM LOCKING PIN
K. THROTTLE STOP

POINTER LOCK

RISER

ANVILS

TRIGGER

Figure 3-9. Schematic drawing of throttle control system.

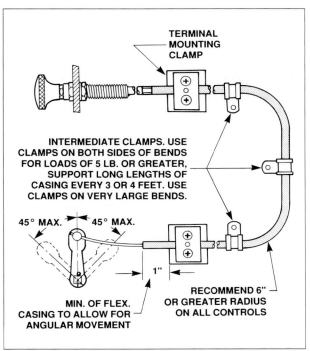

TERMINAL
MOUNTING
CLAMP

INTERMEDIATE CLAMPS. USE
CLAMPS ON BOTH SIDES OF BENDS
FOR LOADS OF 5 LB. OR GREATER,
SUPPORT LONG LENGTHS OF
CASING EVERY 3 OR 4 FEET. USE
CLAMPS ON VERY LARGE BENDS.

45° MAX. — 45° MAX.

1"

MIN. OF FLEX.
CASING TO ALLOW FOR
ANGULAR MOVEMENT

RECOMMEND 6"
OR GREATER RADIUS
ON ALL CONTROLS

Figure 3-10. Mounting of a push-pull type control (Arens Controls, Inc.).

throttle valve is in the "full-open" position, and the other when it is closed to the "idle" position.

Adjust the cushion by turning the cable turnbuckles equally in opposite directions until the throttle cushion is correct at the "full-open" position of the throttle valve. Then, when the throttle arm stop is adjusted to the correct "idle speed" setting, the amount of cushion should be within tolerance at the "idle speed" position of the throttle valve. The presence of this cushion assures that the travel of the throttle valve is not limited by the stops on the throttle control quadrant, but that they are opening fully and closing to the correct idle speed as determined by the throttle arm stop.

Adjustment of the engine controls is basically the same on all aircraft insofar as the linkage is adjusted to a predetermined length for a specific setting of the unit to be controlled. Finally, the full travel of the unit to be controlled is assured by establishing the correct cushion in the controls.

On multi-engine aircraft the amount of cushion of all throttle and mixture controls must be equal so that all will be aligned at any specific setting chosen. This eliminates the necessity of individually setting each control to synchronize engine operations.

After the engine has been installed, it is necessary to adjust the cowl flaps so that the passage of cooling air over the engine can be regulated accurately. When the cowl flap adjustments have been completed, operate the system and recheck for opening and closing to the specified limits. Also check the cowl flap position indicators, if installed, to assure that they indicate the true position of the flaps.

The final step will be to install the propeller on the aircraft. Before doing so, the propeller mounting flange or splined shaft must be prepared, as directed by the manufacturer. Have on hand the proper gaskets or O-rings necessary for the particular model of propeller. Large propellers may require the use of an appropriate sling and hoist arrangement. Do not attempt to lift a propeller into place if adequate personnel or equipment is not at hand. Following the manufacturer's recommended procedure, install the propeller and torque to the specified limits. Reconnect propeller anti-icing equipment, if installed.

F. Preparation Of Reciprocating Engines For Ground And Flight Testing

Before the newly installed engine is flight-tested, it must undergo a thorough ground check. Prior to this ground run, several operations are usually performed on the aircraft.

1. Pre-oiling

To prevent failure of the engine bearings during the initial start, pre-oiling is required. When an engine has been idle for an extended period of time, its internal bearing surfaces are likely to become dry at points where the corrosion preventive mixture or assembly oil has dried out or drained away. If the bearings are dry when the engine is started, the friction at high RPM may destroy the bearings before lubricating oil from the engine-driven oil pump can reach them. Hence, it is necessary to force oil throughout the entire engine oil system.

There are several methods of pre-oiling an engine. The method selected should provide an expeditious and adequate pre-oiling service. Before beginning any pre-oiling operation, remove one spark plug from each cylinder to allow the engine to be turned over more easily with the starter. Also, connect an external source of electrical power (APU) to the aircraft electrical system to prevent an excessive drain on the aircraft battery.

In using some types of pre-oilers, such as that shown in figure 3-11, the oil line from the inlet side of the engine-driven oil pump must be disconnected to permit the pre-oiler tank to be connected at this point. Then a line must be disconnected, or an opening made in the oil system at the nose of the engine to allow oil to flow out of the engine. Oil flowing out of the engine indicates the completion of the pre-oiling operation, since the oil has now passed through the entire system.

In order to force oil from the pre-oiler tank through the engine, apply air pressure to the oil in the tank while the engine is being turned through with the starter. When this action has forced oil through the disconnection in the nose of the engine, stop cranking the engine and disconnect the pre-oiler tank.

Pre-oiling of small reciprocating engines incorporating a wet sump may be accomplished by

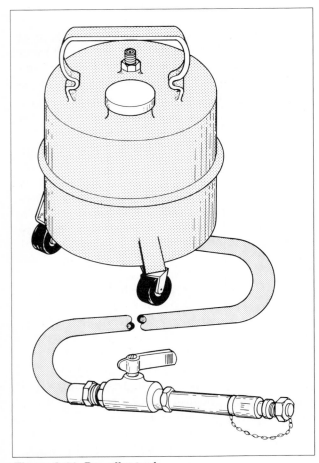

Figure 3-11. Pre-oiler tank.

connecting the pre-oiler at the oil temperature fitting located in the oil screen. With the oil introduced at this point, the engine is turned through with the starter. An indication of oil pressure on the cockpit mounted gauge will signal the successful operation.

When no external means of pre-oiling an engine are available, the engine oil pump may be used. Fill the engine oil tank to the proper level. Then, with the mixture in the "idle-cutoff" position, the fuel shutoff valve and ignition switches in the "off" position, and the throttles fully open, crank the engine with the starter until the oil pressure gauge mounted on the instrument panel indicates oil pressure.

After the engine has been pre-oiled, replace the spark plugs and connect the oil system. Generally the engine should be operated within 4 hours after it has been pre-oiled; otherwise, the pre-oiling procedure normally must be repeated.

2. Fuel System Bleeding

To purge the fuel system of air locks and to aid in flushing any traces of preservative oil from the lines or units, the system may be bled. Because this procedure varies with the type of carburetor or fuel injection unit installed, the technician must consult the manufacturer's maintenance instructions for specific direction. This operation will purge the system, and enable the technician to determine if all of the fuel valves and boost pumps are operating properly.

3. Propeller Checks

The propeller installed on the engine must be checked before, during, and after the engine has been ground operated.

a. Propeller Track

Blade tracking is the process of determining the positions of the tips of the propeller blades relative to each other. Tracking shows only the relative position of the blades, not their actual path. The blades should all track one another as closely as possible. The difference in track at like points must not exceed the tolerance specified by the manufacturer.

The design and manufacture of propellers is such that the tips of the blades will give a good indication of tracking. The following method for checking blade track is representative of the methods in use.

(1) Install a heavy wire or small rod on the leading edge of the aircraft wing or other

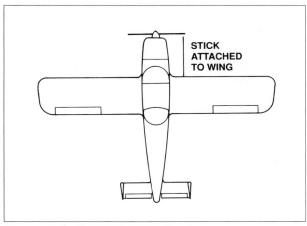

Figure 3-12. Checking blade track.

suitable area of the aircraft until it lightly touches the propeller blade face near the tip (figure 3-12).

(2) Rotate the propeller until the next blade is in the same position as the first, and measure the distance between the rod and the blade. Continue this process until all blades have been checked.

b. Operational

A propeller whose pitch changing mechanism is electrically actuated may be checked before the engine is operated. This is done by connecting an external source of electrical power to the aircraft, holding the selector switch in the "decrease RPM" position, and checking for an increase of the propeller blade angle. Continue the check by holding the switch in the "increase RPM" position and examining the propeller blades for a decrease in angle. Feathering type propellers may be checked for feathering operation by holding the selector switch in the "feather" position until the blade angle increases to the "full feather" position. Then return the propeller to a normal operating position by holding the switch in the "increase RPM" position.

Propellers whose pitch changing mechanisms are oil actuated must be checked during engine operation, after the normal operating oil temperature has been reached. In addition to checking the increase or decrease in RPM, the feathering cycle of the propeller should also be checked.

When an engine equipped with an oil operated propeller is stopped with the propeller in the "feather" position, never unfeather the propeller by starting the engine and actuating the feather-

ing mechanism. Remove the engine sump plugs to drain the oil returned from the feathering mechanism and turn the blades to their normal position using the feathering pump or a blade wrench. The blade wrench is a long handled device that slips over the blade to permit returning the blades to a normal pitch position manually.

4. Checks And Adjustments After Engine Run Up And Operation

After the engine has been ground operated, and again after flight test, operational factors must be adjusted as necessary, and the entire installation given a thorough visual inspection. These adjustments often include fuel pressure and oil pressure, as well as rechecks of such factors as ignition timing, valve clearances, and idle speed and mixture.

After both the initial ground run up and the test flight, remove the oil sump plugs and screens and inspect for metal particles. Clean the screens before reinstalling them.

Check all lines for leakage and security of attachment. Especially, check the oil system hose clamps for security as evidenced by oil leakage at the hose connections. Also, inspect the cylinder hold down nuts or cap screws for security and safe-tying. This check should also be performed after the flight immediately succeeding the test flight.

G. Turbojet Powerplant Removal And Installation

We will introduce the procedures common to the removal and installation of turbine engines in this section. The specific procedures described apply to only one particular installation, but are representative of those used for most installations. The engine and all engine-mounted accessories for a QECA.

Access to the engine is provided by doors that can be raised and locked open. Directional references, such as right and left, and clockwise and counterclockwise, apply to the engine as viewed from the aft or exhaust end.

1. Turbojet Powerplant QECA Removal

The engine may be removed from the aircraft by either of two methods. One method involves lowering the powerplant from the nacelle by using an engine dolly. The other method requires hoists and a special sling to lower the powerplant to a movable engine stand. The following preliminary steps are applicable to either method of removal:

(1) Adequately secure the aircraft either with wheel chocks or with tie-down provisions; attach ground wire or cable to aircraft.

(2) Open the nacelle doors and support them with the struts. Verify that no power is connected and that the electric power switch is off.

(3) Remove the mount access plates from both sides of the nacelle structure.

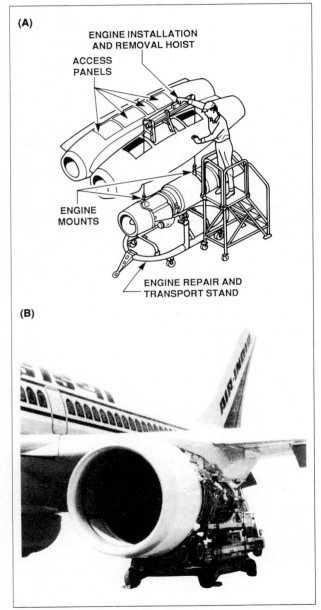

Figure 3-13. (A)—Engine installation with two-cable hoist. (B)—Engine installation with hydraulic lift stand (dolly).

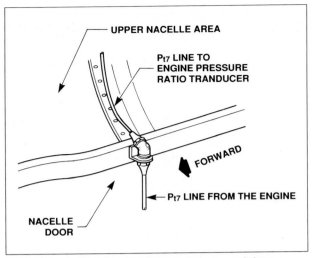

Figure 3-14. Turbine discharge pressure pickup.

(4) Remove the engine air-conditioning duct access plate, and disconnect the duct from the engine.

(5) Disconnect the turbine discharge pressure pickup line (figure 3-14).

(6) Disconnect the electrical wiring and the thermocouple leads from the connectors (figure 3-15).

(7) Disconnect the fuel line by removing the bolts from the hose flange (figure 3-16).

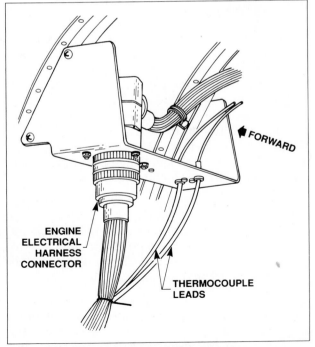

Figure 3-15. Electrical power disconnect.

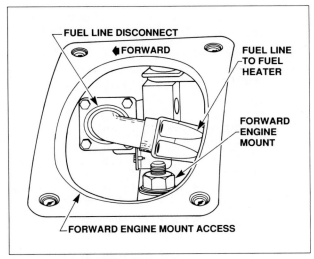

Figure 3-16. Fuel line disconnect.

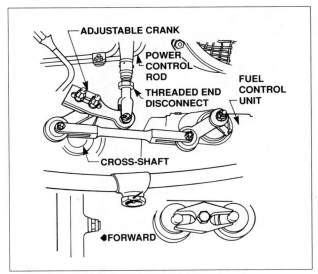

Figure 3-17. Power lever disconnect.

(8) Disconnect the power control rod (figure 3-17) from the power control lever cross shaft linkage at the threaded end disconnect. Secure the power control rod to the nacelle structure.

After the engine has been disconnected, except for the engine mounts, and a dolly is being used to remove the engine, position it under the engine. Attach it to the engine and raise the dolly until all the weight is relieved from the wing. If hoists are used connect the hoists to the engine mounts through the accesses on the pylon. When lowering the engine with hoists, operate them simultaneously to exert tension on the hoist cables at all times. Position a movable engine stand under the engine, before lowering it.

With either the hoists or dolly attached and the stand in place, the engine is now ready to be lowered.

Remove the rear engine mount bolt and bushing, and the front engine mount nuts and washers. Start lowering the engine, constantly observing the engine clearance with the nacelle to prevent damage to the engine or to the nacelle. Secure the engine to the dolly or stand. If hoists are used, detach them from the engine. Roll the engine clear of the aircraft. Care must be taken while moving the engine clear to prevent damage to the pylon or pod. Cap or plug all lines, hoses, and outlets. With the engine removed, inspect all power control rod brackets and crank assemblies for bearing looseness and the nacelle area for structural damage. Inspect for cracks or openings in the area where the pylon structure joins the nacelle structure.

2. Removal Of QECA Accessories

When an aircraft engine is to be replaced, the aircraft-furnished accessories and equipment may be removed for installation on the replacement engine or for overhaul, as required. Note carefully the location and attachments of all units before removal so as to aid in the assembly of the replacement powerplant. When accessories are to be sent to overhaul or storage, preserve them in accordance with the manufacturer's instructions and be sure to attach all pertinent data and the proper accessory record cards.

After removal of these accessories and equipment, cover all exposed drives and ports. Prepare the engine for shipment, storage, or disassembly as directed in applicable manufacturer's instructions.

3. Installation Of Turbojet Engines

As with the reciprocating engine, the installation process is basically the same as the removal, except in reverse order.

a. Installation With Dolly

The following procedures are typical of those used to install a turbine engine using a dolly. Specific ground handling instructions are normally placarded on the dolly.

(1) Operate the dolly and carefully raise the engine to the engine mount attach fittings.

(2) Align the rear engine mount with the mount attach fittings.

(3) Install the engine mount bolts and tighten to the specified torque.

93

b. Installation With Hoist

The following procedures are typical of those used to install a turbine engine using a hoist:

(1) Position the powerplant beneath the nacelle.

(2) Attach the engine sling to the engine.

(3) Carefully operate all the hoists simultaneously to raise the engine and guide the mounts into position.

c. Installation With Two-Cable Hoist

Figure 3-13A shows and engine being installed using a two-cable hoist. Hoists of this type are commonly used to install medium or small turbine engines.

4. Completing The Installation

The following procedures cover the typical final installation instructions:

(1) Install the bushing through the engine rear mount and the rear mount attaching fitting. Install the bolt through the bushing; install the nut and secure it with a cotter pin.

(2) Through the forward mount accesses, place the chamfered washer, flat washer, and nut on each engine forward mount bolt. Tighten the nut to the required torque. Then secure the nut with lock wire.

(3) Connect the air-conditioning duct from the pylon to the bleed air duct from the engine. Tighten the duct connection by applying the proper torque.

(4) Remove the dolly or slings and related equipment from the engine.

(5) Connect the fuel hose to the fuel line from the pylon. Use a new gasket between the flanges of the fuel hose and the line.

(6) Install the starter air inlet duct support brace.

(7) Sparingly apply anti-seize compound to the threads of the electrical harness receptacle and adjacent thermocouple receptacles. Connect the leads and secure the harness connector with lock wire.

(8) Connect the turbine discharge pressure pickup line from the engine to the line from the pressure ratio transducer.

(9) Connect the power control rod to the power control lever cross shaft linkage at the threaded end disconnect.

(10) Inspect the engine installation for completeness.

(11) Install the access covers.

(12) Adjust the power control linkage and trim the engine, if required. Close and secure the nacelle doors.

5. Rigging, Inspection And Adjustments

The following instructions cover some of the basic inspections and procedures for rigging and adjusting fuel controls, fuel selectors, and fuel shutoff valves.

(1) Inspect all bellcranks for looseness, cracks, or corrosion.

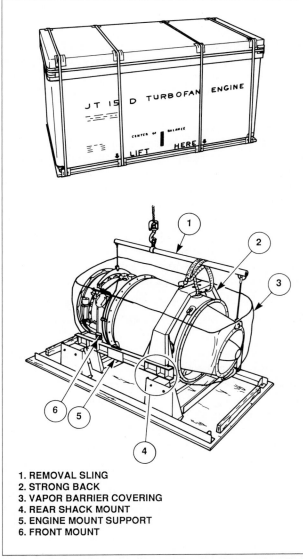

1. REMOVAL SLING
2. STRONG BACK
3. VAPOR BARRIER COVERING
4. REAR SHACK MOUNT
5. ENGINE MOUNT SUPPORT
6. FRONT MOUNT

Figure 3-18. Replacement engine from the manufacturer or overhauler.

(2) Inspect rod ends for damaged threads and the number of threads remaining after final adjustment.

(3) Inspect cable drums for wear and cable guards for proper position and tension.

While rigging the fuel selector, power control, and shutoff valve linkages, follow the manufacturer's step-by-step procedure for the particular aircraft model being rigged. The cables should be rigged for the proper tension with the rigging pins installed. The pins should be free to be removed without any binding. If they are hard to remove, the cables are not rigged properly and should be rechecked. The power lever should have the proper cushion at "idle" and "full power"

positions. The pointers or indicators on the fuel control should be within limits. The fuel selectors must be rigged so that they have the proper travel and will not restrict the fuel flow to the engines.

6. Rigging Power Controls

Modern turbine powered aircraft use various power lever control systems. One of the common types is the cable and rod system. This system uses bellcranks, push-pull rods, drums, fair leads, flexible cables, and pulleys. All of these components make up the control system and must be adjusted or rigged from time to time. As with reciprocating engines, multi-engine turbine powered aircraft must have the controls rigged

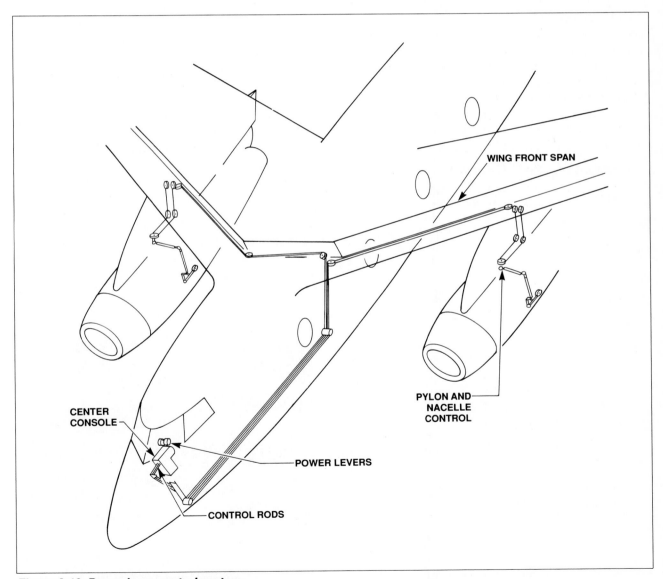

Figure 3-19. Power lever control system.

so that the power levers are aligned at all power settings.

The power lever control cables and push-pull rods in the airframe system to the pylon and nacelle are not usually disturbed at engine change time and will generally require no rigging. The control system from the pylon to the engine must be re-rigged after each engine or fuel control change. Figure 3-19 shows the control system for a large turbine powered aircraft. Note the control system from the bellcrank in the upper pylon to the fuel control—this is the portion of the system that will require rigging at engine change.

Before adjusting the power controls at the engine, be sure that the power lever is free from binding and the controls have full-throw at the console. If they do not have full-throw or are binding, the airframe system should be checked and discrepancies repaired.

After all adjustments have been made, move the power levers through their complete range, carefully inspecting for adequate clearance between the various push-pull rods and tubes. Secure all locknuts, cotter pins, and lock wire, as required.

7. Adjusting Fuel Control

The fuel control unit of a typical turbine engine is a hydro-mechanical device which schedules the quantity of fuel flowing to the engine so that the desired amount of thrust can be obtained. The amount of thrust is dictated by the position of the cockpit power lever.

To obtain the maximum thrust output of the engine, when desired, adjustments to the fuel control called "trimming" are made. Trimming is normally performed at engine change, anytime the fuel control is changed, or when the engine does not develop maximum thrust. This operation is accomplished using a screw type adjustment on the fuel control unit.

To obtain the most accurate results, the aircraft should always be headed into the wind while the engine is being trimmed. The most accurate trimming is obtained under conditions of no wind and clear, moisture-free, air.

After trimming the engine, the idle RPM can be adjusted. The idle RPM is changed by turning the INC. IDLE screw an eighth of a turn at a time, allowing sufficient time for the RPM to stabilize between adjustments.

H. Turboprop Powerplant Removal And Installation

The modular construction of modern turboprops make on-wing maintenance possible for many operations that would otherwise have required removal of the engine. Even with this advantage, there are still occasions when the entire engine must be removed for maintenance, overhaul, or replacement.

The following information provides a general picture of turboprop engine removal and installation.

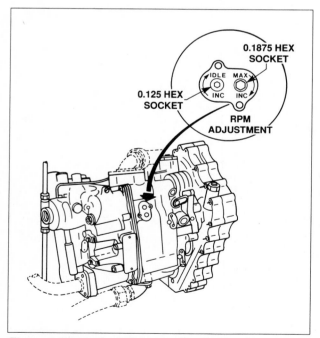

Figure 3-20. Typical fuel control adjustment.

Figure 3-21. Modular construction makes it possible to perform many maintenance tasks without removing the engine from the aircraft.

1. Turboprop QECA

Most turboprop powerplant removal and installation instructions are developed for QECA's. The procedures for turboprop engine removal and installation are similar to those presented in this section for other turbine engines, except for those systems related to the turboprop propeller.

2. Propeller Removal And Installation

Turboprop propeller systems on business-type aircraft are only slightly different than those used on piston powered multi-engine aircraft. They will usually be flange mounted propellers and will incorporate anti-icing provisions. Their removal and installation is essentially the same as the procedure discussed for reciprocating engine installations, one difference being that the turboprop propellers may be larger and heavier, requiring special handling to prevent damage to the propeller or injury to personnel.

Large turboprop installations may utilize a turbopropeller of a completely different design than those used on small turboprop engines. The removal and installation of these large propellers must be accomplished in accordance with the manufacturer's instructions, using any special tools called for.

I. Helicopter Engine Removal And Replacement

Because of the increased popularity of turbine powered helicopters, we will address our remarks here to that type of installation. The removal and replacement of the engine is compared to some of the reciprocating engine helicopters, because in most installations nothing has to be removed except the engine. On some of the larger turbine helicopters, a work crane that can be attached to the helicopter is provided as special ground support equipment. This is an advantage when engines must be changed in the field where hoists are not available.

1. Engine Change

In most situations the engine is preserved before removal. This may include spraying the inlet area with oil while motoring the engine, and preserving the fuel system. Only the type of

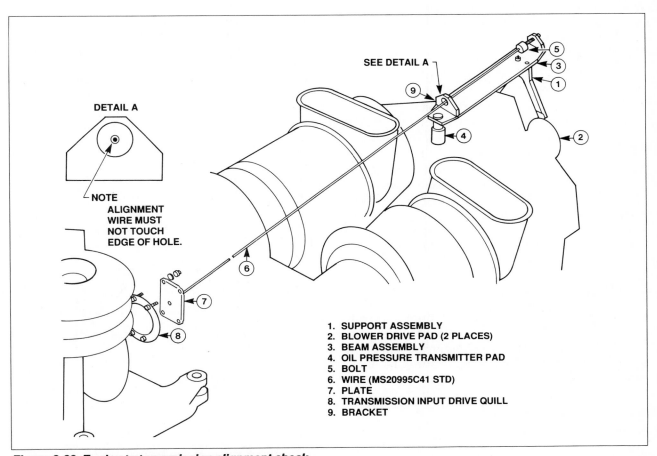

DETAIL A

NOTE
ALIGNMENT
WIRE MUST
NOT TOUCH
EDGE OF HOLE.

SEE DETAIL A

1. SUPPORT ASSEMBLY
2. BLOWER DRIVE PAD (2 PLACES)
3. BEAM ASSEMBLY
4. OIL PRESSURE TRANSMITTER PAD
5. BOLT
6. WIRE (MS20995C41 STD)
7. PLATE
8. TRANSMISSION INPUT DRIVE QUILL
9. BRACKET

Figure 3-22. Engine to transmission alignment check.

preservation and procedures recommended by the manufacturer should be used. The hoses and electrical connections often utilize quick disconnects for easy removal and installation.

Large operators will generally have QECA's built up for the specific installation, including plumbing, electrical system, and accessories. The changing of smaller items can be time consuming, often requiring several more hours of labor than the actual removal and replacement.

2. Engine Alignment

After a new or replacement engine is installed, it may be necessary to check the alignment of the engine to the transmission so that the main input shaft does not have undue stresses placed on the couplings. Misalignment will result in shaft failure in a very short time. The alignment is normally accomplished by shimming the legs of the mount between the fuselage and the engine mount. This procedure is not required at each engine change, unless the mount is also changed, the helicopter has been structurally damaged, or drive shaft wear is excessive. Some operators check the alignment with each installation of an engine.

Figure 3-22 shows the installation of special equipment to check alignment on one popular model helicopter. For this procedure, special tools are required. A support assembly is positioned on the engine's blower assembly. This is used to hold the beam assembly in which a knurled nut and safety wire are installed. The wire passes through a target on the beam and is attached to the transmission input shaft by means of a plate. When the wire is taut, it should pass through the hole of the target without touching the side of the hole. If it does touch, the mounts should be shimmed until the correct alignment is obtained.

3. Control Rigging

Probably the most difficult procedure in the installation of an engine is the rigging of the controls. The first step is preliminary rigging. In most instances, the final rigging cannot be made until the engine is in operation and flight tests can be conducted.

If the engine is a free turbine type, both N_1 and N_2 systems will be rigged. In a twin engine installation, both engines must be rigged and matched.

4. Engine Trimming

Following installation of a new or overhauled engine, trimming must be accomplished. These adjustments should be made only in accordance with the manufacturer's recommendations. Generally,, they include only idle and maximum speed of the engine. The trim changes are made with a screw-type adjustor while the engine is operating. The procedures are not significantly different than those for other turbine engine installations.

J. Engine Mounts

Engine mounting systems were discussed very briefly as the construction of each type of engine—reciprocating and turbine—were introduced. Here we will add to that knowledge, and examine the various methods of mounting the engines to the airframe and isolating engine vibration.

1. Engine Mounts For Reciprocating Engines

The engine mount structure may be a part of the airframe and constructed of riveted aluminum components. This type of mounting structure usually provides two mounting rails to which the engine mount legs will be bolted. Some sort of vibration isolating unit (shock mount) will be used at the point where the mount legs attach to the aluminum structure. This type of structure is generally associated with larger horizontally opposed engines, especially those used on multi-engine aircraft.

The steel tube mount structure is used on both large and small, radial and horizontally opposed engines. This structure bolts to the

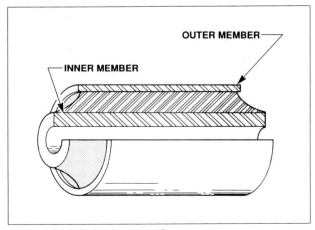

Figure 3-23. Tube form engine mount.

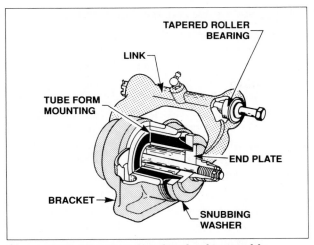

Figure 3-24. Link-type dynafocal subassembly.

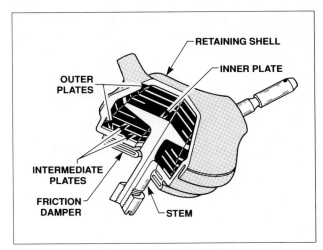

Figure 3-25. Pedestal-type dynafocal subassembly.

firewall, and the engine is attached to the mount using some type of shock mounts.

These engine mounting systems are designed so that the weight of the engine is supported on the rubber of the shock mounts. Supporting the engine in this manner prevents engine vibration from being transmitted to the engine mount, and then to the airframe. Engine mounting suspension may be divided into two main groups: (1) the tangential suspension type, and (2) the dynafocal type.

a. Tangential Mounting

The tangential suspension, also called tube form mounting, is used for all types of cylinder arrangements. A cutaway view of this type is shown in figure 3-23. This type of mounting is most flexible along its principal axis. Various means of attachment are used in different installations using tube form mountings.

b. Dynafocal Mounting

Dynafocal engine mounts, or vibration isolators, are units which give directional support to the engine. If you were to extend the stress axis of each of the dynafocal mounts used on a particular installation, you would find that they intersect at the center of gravity of the engine. This provides the most effective dampening of the engine vibrations.

The link-type dynafocal mount uses a tube form mounting for the flexible element. The outer member of this mounting is clamped into a forged bracket of aluminum alloy or steel and bolted rigidly to the engine mount pad or boss. The link is fitted with tapered roller bearings a the mounting ring attachment points. Rubber

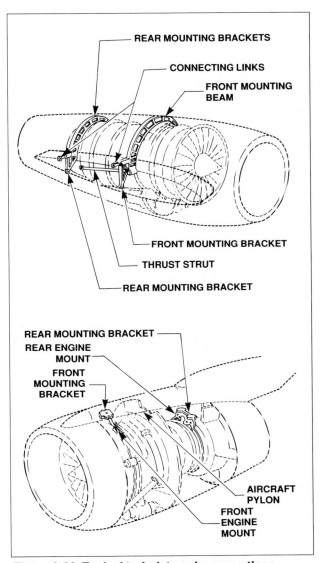

Figure 3-26. Typical turbojet engine mountings.

snubbing washers with backing end plates are provided on both extensions of the inner member. These snubbing washers limit the axial motions of the mounting without allowing metal-to-metal contact between subassembly parts.

The pedestal-type dynafocal has an outer shell composed of two steel forgings fastened securely together and bolted to the mounting ring structure. A predetermined amount of movement is allowed before the rubber is locked out of action by contact between the stem of the dynafocal and the retaining shell. Friction dampers are provided to limit excessive movement.

2. Turbojet Engine Mounts

The engine mounts on most turbojet engines are relatively simple when compared with the mounting structures installed on reciprocating engines. However, they perform the same basic function of supporting the engine and transmitting the loads imposed by the engine to the aircraft structure. Most turbine engine mounts are made of stainless steel, and are typically located as illustrated in figure 3-26. Some engine mounting systems use two mounts to support the rear end of the engine and a single mount at the front.

K. Preservation And Storage Of Engines

As we have discussed previously, engines awaiting overhaul or return to service must be given careful attention to prevent damage from corrosion.

1. Corrosion Prevention

An engine in regular service is, in a sense, "self-purging" of moisture, since the heat of combustion evaporates the moisture in and around the engine, and the lubricating oil circulated through the engine temporarily forms a protective coating on the metal it contacts. If the operation of an engine in service is limited or suspended for a period of time, the engine should be preserved to a varying extent, depending upon how long it is going to be inoperative.

Our discussion here will center primarily on engines that have been removed from the aircraft. However, the preservation materials discussed are used for all types of engine storage.

a. Corrosion Preventive Compounds

Corrosion preventive compounds are petroleum based products that form a wax-like film over the metal to which it is applied. Several types of these compounds are manufactured according to different specifications to fit the various aviation needs. The type mixed with engine oil to form a corrosion preventive mixture is a relatively light compound that blends with engine oil when then mixture is heated to the proper temperature.

The light mixture is intended for use when a preserved engine is to remain inactive for less than 30 days. It is also used to spray cylinders and other designated areas.

A heavy compound is used for the dip treatment of metal parts and surfaces. It must be heated to a high temperature to be sufficiently liquid to effectively coat the objects to be preserved. A commercial solvent or kerosene spray is used to remove the compound from the engine or parts when they are being prepared for return to service.

Although corrosion preventive compounds act as an insulator from moisture, in the presence of excessive moisture they will eventually break down and corrosion will begin. Also, the compounds will eventually become dried because their oil base gradually evaporates. This allows moisture to contact the metal and aids in corroding it. Therefore, when an engine is stored in a shipping case or container, some dehydrating (moisture removing) agent must be used to remove the moisture from the air around the engine.

b. Dehydrating Agents

There are a number of substances (referred to as desiccants) that can absorb moisture from the atmosphere in sufficient quantities to be useful as dehydrators. One of these is silica gel. This gel is an ideal dehydrating agent since it does not dissolve when saturated.

As a corrosion preventive, bags of silica gel are placed around and inside the various accessible parts of a stored engine. It is also used in clear plastic plugs, called dehydrator plugs, which can be screwed into engine openings such as the spark plug holes.

Cobalt chloride is added to the silica gel used in dehydrator plugs. This additive makes it possible for the plugs to indicate the moisture content or relative humidity of the air surrounding the engine. The treated silica gel remains a bright blue color with a low relative humidity; but as the humidity increases, the shade of blue becomes progressively lighter, becoming lavender at 30% relative humidity and fading through the various shades of pink, until at 60% relative humidity it is a natural or white color. When the relative humidity is less than 30%, corrosion does not normally take place. Therefore, if the dehydrator plugs are bright blue, the air in the engine has so little moisture that internal corrosion will be minimal.

This same cobalt chloride-treated silica gel is used in humidity indicator envelopes. These envelopes can be fastened to the stored engine so that they can be inspected through a small window in the engine container.

All desiccants are sealed in containers to prevent their becoming saturated with moisture before they are used. Care should be taken to never leave the container open or improperly closed.

2. Corrosion Preventive Treatment

Before an engine is removed it should be operated, if possible, with corrosion preventive mixture added in the oil system to retard corrosion by coating the engine's internal parts. If it is impossible to operate the engine before removal from the aircraft, it should be handled as much as possible in the same manner as an operable engine.

Any engine being prepared for storage must receive thorough treatment around the exhaust ports. Because the residue of exhaust gases is potentially very corrosive, a corrosion preventive mixture should be sprayed into each exhaust port, including the exhaust valve. After the exhaust ports have been thoroughly coated, a moisture-proof and oil-proof gasket backed by a metal or wooden plate, should be secured over the exhaust port. These covers form a seal to prevent moisture from entering the interior of the engine through the exhaust ports.

Spray each cylinder interior with corrosion preventive mixture to prevent moisture and oxygen from contacting the deposits left by combustion. Before spraying, each cylinder should be at the "bottom center" position. This will allow the entire inside of the cylinder to be coated. Spray the cylinder by inserting the nozzle of the spray gun into each spark plug hole and "playing" the gun to cover as much area as possible. After spraying each cylinder at "bottom center",

respray each cylinder while the crankshaft is stationary.

The crankshaft must not be moved after this final spraying, or the seal of the corrosion preventive mixture will be broken. Until it is safely stored in a shipping case, the engine should have a sign attached similar to the following: "DO NOT TURN CRANKSHAFT."

Dehydrator plugs may be screwed into the spark plug opening of each cylinder. If the engine is to be stored in a wooden shipping case, the ignition harness leads are attached to the dehydrator plugs as shown in figure 3-27.

Another point at which the engine must be sealed is the intake manifold. If the carburetor is to remain on the engine during storage, the throttle valve should be wired open and a seal installed over the air inlet. But, if the carburetor is removed, the seal is made at the carburetor mounting pad. The seal used in either case should be an oil-proof and moisture-proof gasket backed by a wooden or metal plate securely bolted into place. Silica gel should be placed in the intake manifold to absorb moisture. The silica gel bags are usually suspended from the cover plate. This eliminates the possibility of forgetting to remove the silica gel bags when the engine is eventually removed from storage.

If the engine has not been spray coated with corrosion preventive mixture, the propeller shaft must be coated with the compound. Then, a

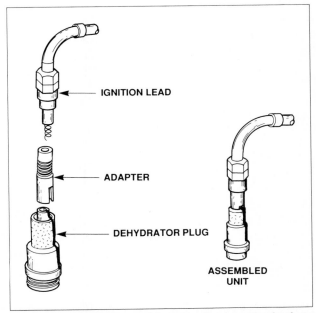

Figure 3-27. Ignition harness leads attached to dehydrator plugs.

plastic sleeve, or moisture-proof paper is secured around the shaft.

A final inspection should be performed to be certain that all openings are sealed, and that only the proper accessories have been included for storage or shipping.

3. Engine Shipping Containers

For protection, engines are sealed in plastic or foil envelopes and packed in a wooden shipping case. The engine is usually mounted in the shipping case in much the same manner as it mounts on the aircraft. The installation of the engine into the shipping case should be performed with the same care as the installation on the aircraft. Even a run-out engine being returned to the overhaul facility is still heavy, and expensive damage may occur if improperly handled.

When the engine has been lowered into the shipping case, it should be secured with the appropriate mounting bolts. Some cases provide a special mounting area for accessories that are not left attached to the engine. These units should be installed and secured to the container.

Before the protective envelope is sealed, silica gel should be placed around the engine to dehydrate the air sealed into the envelope. The amount of silica gel used is determined by the size of the engine. The protective envelope is then gathered around the engine and partially sealed, leaving an opening from which as much air is possible is exhausted. The envelope is then completely sealed.

While lowering the shipping case cover into position, be careful that it does not twist and tear the protective envelope. Secure the cover and mark the date of preservation on the case. Also, indicate whether the engine is repairable or serviceable.

4. Inspection Of Stored Engines

Most maintenance shops provide a scheduled inspection system for engines in storage. Normally the humidity indicators on engines stored in shipping cases are inspected every 30 days. When the protective envelope must be opened to inspect the humidity indicator, the inspection period may be extended to once every 90 days, if local conditions permit. The humidity indicator of a metal container is inspected every 180 days under normal conditions.

5. Preservation And De-preservation Of Turbine Engines

The procedures for preserving and de-preserving turbine engines vary depending upon the length of inactivity, the type of preservative used, and whether or not the engine may be rotated during the inactive period. Much of the basic information on corrosion control presented in the section on reciprocating engines is applicable to turbine engines. However, the requirements in the use and types of preservatives are normally different.

The lubrication system is usually drained, and may or may not be flushed with a preservative oil. Some engine manufacturers recommend spraying oil in the compressor while motoring the engine. Others caution against this practice.

Always follow the manufacturer's instructions for the particular model when performing any preservation or de-preservation of aircraft engines.

Chapter IV
Engine Maintenance And Operation

A. Reciprocating Engine Overhaul

Both maintenance and overhaul operations are performed on aircraft powerplants at specified intervals. This interval is usually governed by the number of hours the powerplant has been in operation. Tests and experience have shown that operation beyond this period of time will be inefficient and even dangerous because certain parts will be worn beyond their safe limits. For an overhauled engine to be as safe as a new one, worn parts as well as damaged ones must be detected and replaced during overhaul. The only way to detect all unairworthy parts is to perform a complete and thorough inspection while the engine is disassembled. Inspection is the most precise and the most important phase of the overhaul process. It cannot be slighted or performed in a careless or incomplete manner.

Each engine manufacturer provides very specific tolerances to which their engine parts must conform, and provides general instructions to aid in determining the airworthiness of the part. However, in many cases the final decision is left up to the technician. The technician must determine if the part is serviceable, repairable, or should be rejected. A knowledge of the operating principles, strengths, and stresses applied to a part is essential to making this determination. When the powerplant technician signs for the overhaul of an engine, it is certification that the work was accomplished using methods, techniques, and practices acceptable to the FAA Administrator.

1. Top Overhaul

Modern aircraft engines are constructed of such durable materials that top overhaul has largely been eliminated. Top overhaul means overhaul of those parts "on top" of the crankcase without completely dismantling the engine. The actual top overhaul consists of reconditioning the cylinder, piston, and valve operating mechanism, and replacing valve guides and piston rings, if needed. Usually at this time, the accessories require no attention other than that normally accomplished during ordinary maintenance functions.

Top overhaul is not recommended by all engine manufacturers. Many stress that if an engine requires this much disassembly it should be completely dismantled and receive a major overhaul.

2. Major Overhaul

Major overhaul consists of the complete reconditioning of the powerplant. The actual overhaul period for a specific engine will generally be determined by the manufacturer's recommendations or by the maximum hours of operation between overhaul, as approved by the FAA.

At regular intervals, an engine should be completely dismantled, thoroughly cleaned, and inspected. Each part should be overhauled in accordance with the tolerances and instructions provided by the manufacturer. At this time all accessories are removed, overhauled, and tested. Here again, instructions from the manufacturer of the accessory concerned should be followed.

When the manufacturer builds an engine, they establish a set of fits and limits between the moving parts that are considered allowable tolerances for new engine parts. Along with these limits for new parts, the manufacturer will also establish serviceable limits. These limits show the maximum amount of wear a part can have and still be considered serviceable. An engine overhaul may be accomplished using either set of limits, and it is in this area that the difference in overhauls exist.

There are three terms associated with engine overhaul that are often found confusing. Below are the "official" definitions, as provided by the FAR's, and the student should be familiar with how each one differs from the others.

Overhauled—No person may describe in any required maintenance entry or form an aircraft, airframe, aircraft engine, propeller, appliance, or component part as being overhauled unless—(1) Using methods, techniques, and practices acceptable to the Administrator, it has been disassembled, cleaned, inspected, repaired as necessary, and reassembled; and (2) It has been tested in accordance with approved standards and technical data, or in accordance with current standards and technical data acceptable to the Administrator, which have been developed and documented by the holder of the type certificate, supplemental type certificate, or material, part, process, or appliance approval under 21.305 of this chapter. (FAR 43.2 (a))

Rebuilt—No person may describe in any required maintenance entry or form an aircraft, airframe, aircraft engine, propeller, appliance, or component part as being rebuilt unless it has been disassembled, cleaned, inspected, repaired as necessary, reassembled, and tested to the *same tolerances and limits as a new item,* using either new parts or used parts that conform to new part tolerances and limits or to approved oversized or undersized dimensions. (FAR 43.2 (b))

Zero Time—The owner or operator may use a new maintenance record, without previous operating history, for an aircraft engine *rebuilt by the manufacturer* or by an agency approved by the manufacturer. (FAR 91.421)

What this means to you is that the term "overhaul" implies the work was accomplished using the service limits provided by the manufacturer, and a "rebuilt" engine tells you that the new parts limits were used. Only the original manufacturer may grant zero time to an engine as, at present, there are no other agencies approved for such work.

The term "remanufactured" occasionally surfaces in advertisements for engine overhauls or exchange programs. This word has no standard definition in the industry, and should be clearly defined by the vendor.

B. General Overhaul Procedures

Because of the continued changes and the many different types of engines in use, it is not possible to treat the specific overhaul of each in this manual. However, there are many overhaul practices and instructions of a nonspecific nature which will apply to all makes and models of engines. These general instructions will be described in this section.

We will follow a typical horizontally opposed engine as it progresses through the shop for a major overhaul. In this procedure we will assume that the engine is to be kept together as a unit, and is not part of a QECA package.

When the engine is brought into the shop for overhaul, the work order is started and a record is made of the serial numbers of all of the components that are to be kept with the engine.

When it arrives at the overhaul shop, the engine normally carries with it all of the intercylinder baffles, the carburetor or fuel injection system, the magnetos, ignition leads, as well as the induction system components between the carburetor and the cylinders.

The exhaust system, vacuum pump, hydraulic pump, propeller and its governor, and most other accessories are not considered to be part of the engine, as such, and are usually sent to specialty shops for overhaul. If these shops are a part of the same repair station, the accessories will probably be handled on separate work orders.

1. Disassembly

The engine is mounted on a stand and the magnetos and fuel metering system are removed and sent to the proper department for their overhaul. The engine is completely disassembled and laid out in an orderly fashion so that it can be given a preliminary inspection. Parts should not be cleaned before a preliminary visual inspection, since indications of a failure often may be detected from the residual deposits of metallic particles in some recesses in the engine. To guard against damage and to prevent loss, suitable containers should be available in which to place small parts, nuts, bolts, etc., during the disassembly operation.

Figure 4-1. Aircraft engine being disassembled for major overhaul.

Parts that are normally replaced may be discarded. Discarded parts normally include the crankshaft bearings, oil seals, gaskets, stressed bolts and nuts, exhaust valves, pistons and rings, and all of the ignition cables. For a complete listing of the 100% replacement items, consult the manufacturer's service information. This type of information is usually published as a service bulletin.

Other practices to observe during disassembly include:

(1) Drain the engine oil sumps and remove the oil filter. Drain the oil into a suitable container, straining it through a clean cloth. Check the oil and the cloth for abnormal levels of metal particles.

(2) Always use the proper tool for the job, and the one that fits. Use sockets and box end wrenches wherever possible. If special tools are required, use them rather than improvising.

(3) Dispose of all safety devices as they are removed. Never use safety wire, cotter pins, etc., a second time. Always replace with new safety devices.

(4) All loose studs and loose or damaged fittings should be carefully tagged to prevent their being overlooked during inspection.

2. Cleaning

After all of the parts have been disassembled, they must be degreased by soaking or spraying them with some form of mineral spirits or safety solvent. Water-mixed degreasing compounds usually contain some form of alkali. If allowed to remain in the pores of the metal it will, when the engine is returned to service, react with the hot lubricating oil to cause oil foaming. This may lead to a failure of the lubricating system.

Degreasing removes dirt, grease, and soft carbon, but many parts will have deposits of hard carbon on their interior surfaces. This hard carbon must be removed. An approved decarbonizing solution may be used, following the manufacturer's recommendations in detail. These solutions are usually quite active and care must be taken not to leave the parts in these solutions longer than necessary to loosen the carbon deposits. No magnesium parts should be put into the solution unless it is known that it will not react with the magnesium. Be especially careful with accessory housings, as many of these appear to be aluminum but have a high magnesium content.

After the parts have been removed from the decarbonizing vat, they must be thoroughly cleaned of any traces of the solution. This may be accomplished using a blast of wet steam, or by brushing them with mineral spirits.

Any hard carbon that was not removed by the decarbonizing solution may be removed by dry blasting with plastic pellets or with such organic materials as rice, baked wheat, or crushed walnut shells. Be sure that all machined surfaces are masked off and all passages are plugged or covered. Old hardware should be screwed into threaded holes to prevent the grit from getting into the screw threads, as it is very difficult to remove. Use as low pressure as practical and blast only enough to remove the carbon.

All bearing surfaces must be polished with crocus cloth moistened with mineral spirits, and afterward with dry crocus cloth. All passages in the crankcase must be thoroughly cleaned by flushing them with wet steam, and following this, with mineral spirits.

After all of the parts are thoroughly cleaned, the steel parts must be coated with a film of protective oil. Because the degreasing has removed all of the oil from these parts, they will quickly begin to rust if not protected.

Figure 4-2. Typical cleaning vat for washing engine parts during an overhaul.

3. Inspection

Before starting the inspection process, an inspection and overhaul form should have been started. This form, along with the manufacturer's overhaul manual, and all of the proper inspection equipment should be assembled. In addition to the manufacturer's overhaul manual, the technician should research all airworthiness directives, and manufacturer's service bulletins that might apply to the engine. Often there are special inspections, and/or modifications that must be accomplished at overhaul. Throughout the overhaul, the engine manufacturer's manuals, bulletins, and other service information must be available, as they are the final authority on the suitability of the parts for reuse.

The inspection of engine parts during overhaul is divided into three categories; (1) visual, (2) nondestructive and, (3) dimensional.

The first two methods are aimed at determining structural failures in the parts, while the last method deals with the size and shape of each part. Structural failures can be determined by several different methods. Nonaustenitic steel parts can easily be examined by the magnetic particle method. Methods such as X-ray, eddy-current, or ultrasonic inspection may be used on other parts.

a. Visual Inspection

Visual inspection should precede all other inspection procedures. Several terms are used to describe defects detected in engine parts during

Figure 4-3. An aircraft engine disassembled and laid out for the initial visual inspection.

inspection. Some of the more common terms and definitions are:

(1) Abrasion—An area of roughened scratches or marks usually caused by foreign matter between moving parts.

(2) Brinelling—One or more indentations on bearing races usually caused by high static loads or application of force during installation or removal. Indentations are rounded or spherical due to the impression left by the contacting balls or rollers of the bearing.

(3) Burning—Surface damaged due to excessive heat. It is usually caused by improper fit, defective lubrication, or over temperature operation.

(4) Burnishing—Polishing of one surface by sliding contact with a smooth, harder surface. Usually no displacement nor removal of metal is evident.

(5) Burr—A sharp or roughened projection of metal usually resulting from machine processing.

(6) Chafing—Describes a condition caused by a rubbing action between two parts under light pressure which results in wear.

(7) Chipping—The breaking away of pieces of material, which is usually caused by excessive stress concentration or careless handling.

(8) Corrosion—Loss of metal by a chemical or electrochemical action. The corrosion products generally are easily removed by mechanical means. Iron rust is an example of corrosion.

(9) Crack—A partial separation of material usually caused by vibration, overloading, internal stresses, defective assembly or fatigue. Depth may be a few thousandths to the full thickness of the piece.

(10) Cut—Loss of metal, usually to an appreciable depth over a relatively long and narrow area, by mechanical means, as would occur with the use of a saw blade, chisel or sharp-edged stone striking a glancing blow.

(11) Dent—A small, rounded depression in a surface usually caused by the part being struck with a rounded object.

(12) Erosion—Loss of metal from the surface by mechanical action of foreign objects, such as grit or fine sand. The eroded area will be rough and may be lined in the direction in which the foreign material moved relative to the surface.

(13) Flaking—The breaking loose of small pieces of metal or coated surfaces, which is usually caused by defective plating or excessive loading.

(14) Fretting—A condition of surface corrosion caused by minute movement between two parts, usually clamped together with considerable unit pressure. Found sometimes between crankcase halves.

(15) Galling—A severe condition of chafing or fretting in which a transfer of metal from one part to another occurs. It is usually caused by a slight movement of mated parts having limited relative motion and under high loads.

(16) Gouging—A furrowing condition in which a displacement of metal has occurred (a torn effect). It is usually caused by a piece of metal or foreign material between moving parts.

(17) Grooving—A recess or channel with rounded and smooth edges usually caused by faulty alignment of parts.

(18) Inclusion—Presence of foreign or extraneous material wholly within a portion of metal. Such material is introduced during the manufacture of rod, bar, or tubing by rolling or forging.

(19) Nick—A sharp sided gouge or depression with a "V" shaped bottom which is generally the result of careless handling of tools and parts.

(20) Peening—A series of blunt depressions in a surface.

(21) Pick Up or Scuffing—A buildup or rolling of metal from one are to another, which is usually caused by insufficient lubrication, clearances, or foreign matter.

(22) Pitting—Small hollows of irregular shape in the surface, usually caused by corrosion or minute mechanical chipping of surfaces.

(23) Scoring—A series of deep scratches caused by foreign particles between moving parts, or careless assembly or disassembly techniques.

(24) Scratches—Shallow, thin lines or marks, varying in degree of depth and width, caused by presence of fine foreign particles during operation or contact with other parts during handling.

(25) Stain—A change in color, locally, causing a noticeably different appearance from the surrounding area.

(26) Upsetting—A displacement of material beyond the normal contour or surface (a local bulge or bump). Usually indicates no metal loss.

Examine all gears for evidence of pitting or excessive wear. These conditions are of particular importance when they occur on the teeth; deep pit marks in this area are sufficient cause to reject the gear. Bearing surfaces of all gears should be free from deep scratches. However, minor abrasions usually can be dressed out with a fine abrasive cloth.

All bearing surfaces should be examined for scores, galling, and wear. Considerable scratching and light scoring of aluminum bearing surfaces in the engine do no harm and should not be considered a reason for rejecting the part, provided it falls within the clearances set forth in the Table of Limits in the engine manufacturer's overhaul manual. Even though the part comes within the specific clearance limits, it will not be satisfactory for reassembly in the engine unless inspection shows the part to be free from other serious defects.

Ball bearings should be inspected visually and by feel for roughness, flat spots on balls, flaking or pitting of races, or scoring on the outside of races. All journals should be checked for galling, scores, misalignment, or out-of-round condition. Shafts, pins, etc., should be checked for straightness. This may be done in most cases by using V-blocks and a dial indicator.

Pitted surfaces in highly stressed areas resulting from corrosion can cause ultimate failure of the part. The following areas should be examined carefully for evidence of such corrosion:

(1) Interior surfaces of piston pins.

(2) The fillets at the edges of crankshaft main and crankpin journal surfaces.

(3) Thrust bearing races.

If pitting exists on any of these surfaces to the extent that it cannot be removed by polishing with crocus cloth or other mild abrasive, the part usually must be rejected.

Parts, such as threaded fasteners or plugs, should be inspected to determine the condition of the threads. Badly worn or mutilated threads cannot be tolerated; the parts should be rejected. However, small defects such as slight nicks or burrs may be dressed out with a small file, fine abrasive cloth, or stone. If the part appears to be distorted, badly galled, or mutilated by over tightening, or from the use of improper tools, replace it with a new one.

b. Fluorescent Penetrant Inspection

All nonferrous parts that have been determined to be apparently serviceable are further inspected by the dye penetrant inspection

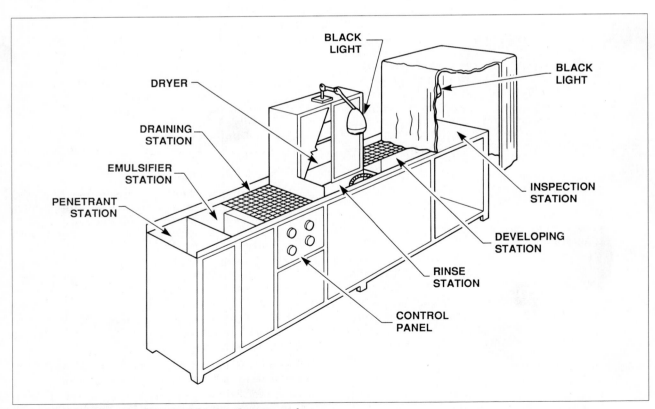

Figure 4-4. Florescent penetrant inspection procedure.

method. This procedure checks for cracks and discontinuities that cannot be detected by the naked eye.

While a variety of dye penetrant methods and materials are available, the post-emulsified technique, using a fluorescent penetrant, is the most sensitive and is commonly used in engine overhaul shops.

The most important requirement for a good fluorescent penetrant inspection is that the part being inspected be absolutely clean. After a thorough precleaning, the fluorescent penetrant is applied by brushing, spraying, or dipping. The penetrant must remain on the part for the specified dwell time. Dwell times will be dictated by the type of penetrant, the material from which the part is made, and the type of defect you are looking for. These times should be listed on the specification sheets for the inspection equipment being used.

At the conclusion of the dwell time, the emulsifier is applied, usually by dipping. The emulsifier also has a required dwell time which must be observed. Too short a time, and the penetrant will not be sufficiently removed from the surface, too long and the penetrant in any defects may become emulsified. At the conclusion of this dwell period, the part is washed thoroughly with water. An ultraviolet inspection lamp may be used to determine if the penetrant has been sufficiently removed from the surface.

After washing, if a dry developer is used, the part must be thoroughly dried. Care must be taken that the temperature of the air dryer not exceed specifications. The dry part is then ready for application of the dry developer.

Application of the developer may be accomplished with a brush, dusting bag, or a bulb-type applicator. The developer must remain on the surface for a short time before inspection begins. The final inspection is made using an ultraviolet (black light) lamp, in a darkened area. Defects will be seen as a bright green line.

The interpretation of the results of the fluorescent penetrant inspection is its most critical aspect. Knowing exactly where to look for cracks and being able to distinguish between a fatigue crack and a false indication can best be learned

**FLUORESCENT METHOD PREFFERED,
WET CONTINUOUS PROCEDURE REQUIRED**

PART	METHOD OF MAGNETIZATION	D.C. AMPERES	CRITICAL AREAS	POSSIBLE DEFECTS
CRANKSHAFT	CIRCULAR AND LONGITUDINAL	2500	JOURNALS, FILLETS, OIL HOLES, THRUST FLANGES, PROP FLANGE	FATIGUE CRACKS, HEAT CRACKS
CONNECTING ROD	CIRCULAR AND LONGITUDINAL	1800	ALL AREAS	FATIGUE CRACKS
CAMSHAFT	CIRCULAR AND LONGITUDINAL	1500	LOBES, JOURNALS	HEAT CRACKS
PISTON PIN	CIRCULAR AND LONGITUDINAL	1000	SHEAR PLANES, ENDS, CENTER	FATIGUE CRACKS
ROCKER ARMS	CIRCULAR AND LONGITUDINAL	800	PAD, SOCKET UNDER SIDE ARMS AND BOSS	FATIGUE CRACKS
GEARS TO 6 INCH DIAMETER	CIRCULAR OR ON CENTER CONDUCTOR	1000 TO 1500	TEETH, SPLINES, KEYWAYS	FATIGUE CRACKS
GEARS OVER 6 INCH DIAMETER	SHAFT CIRCULAR TEETH BETWEEN HEADS TWO TIMES 90°	1000 TO 1500	TEETH, SPLINES	FATIGUE CRACKS
SHAFTS	CIRCULAR AND LONGITUDINAL	1000 TO 1500	SPLINES, KEYWAYS, CHANGE OF SECTION	FATIGUE CRACKS, HEAT CRAKCS
THRU BOLTS ROD BOLTS	CIRCULAR AND LONGITUDINAL	500	THREADS UNDER HEAD	FATIGUE CRACKS

Figure 4-5. Typical magnetic particle inspection schedule for aircraft engine parts.

4-7

from working with an experienced NDI technician.

Following inspection, parts that are to be reused must be cleaned. All traces of the penetrant, emulsifier, and developer must be removed.

c. Magnetic Particle Inspection

Parts manufactured from ferrous metals, those containing iron, can be inspected for hidden cracks using magnetic particle inspection. With this method, the part is magnetized by passing an electrical current through it. Then, a fluid containing particles of iron oxide treated with a fluorescent dye is flowed over the parts. If there is a defect such as a fatigue crack in the part, the crack will interrupt the flow of magnetic flux and produce magnetic poles on the surface of the part. These poles will attract the iron oxide present in the suspension flowing over the part. When the area is inspected under black light, the crack will show as a bright green line.

Most engine manufacturers specify that the "wet continuous" procedure be used. In this procedure the magnetizing current is applied at the same time as the suspension containing the fluorescent particles. There are two directions in which magnetism may be induced in the part, and the overhaul manual will specify the method to be used. In figure 4-5 we have duplicated a page from an engine overhaul manual specifying the methods to be used and the type and value of magnetizing current. For example, the crankshaft must be magnetized both longitudinally and circularly to get an indication of all cracks which might appear.

Figure 4-6 illustrates the methods used to obtain each type of magnetization, and the way each type of magnetization will show up a crack. Study the illustrations carefully and you will discover an easy way to remember in which direction cracks will be indicated. The best indications will be in the same direction as the current is applied (and up to 45 degrees either way).

It is extremely important that after a piece has been magnetically inspected, every trace of the magnetism must be removed. This may be accomplished by placing the part in a coil through

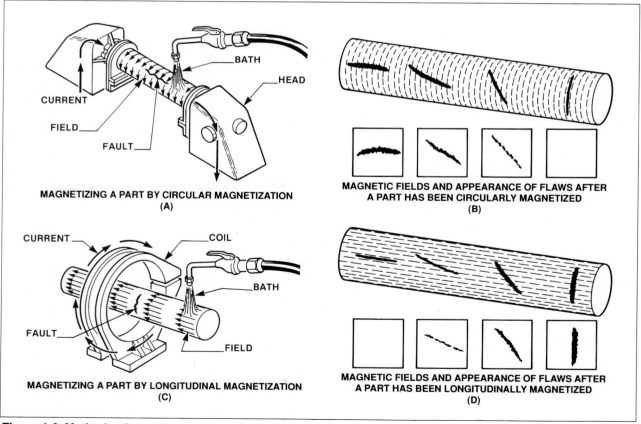

Figure 4-6. Methods of magnetic particle inspection.

DESCRIPTION	SERVICABLE LIMITS	NEW PARTS	
		MINIMUM	MAXIMUM
First piston ring in cylinder (P/N 635814) .... Gap:	0.059	0.033	0.049
First piston ring in cylinder (P/N 639273) .... Gap:	0.074	0.048	0.064
Second piston ring in cylinder (P/N 635814)............................ Gap:	0.050	0.024	0.040
Second piston ring in cylinder (P/N 639273)............................ Gap:	0.069	0.043	0.059
Third piston ring in cylinder .... Gap:	0.059	0.033	0.049
Fourth piston ring in cylinder... Gap:	0.050	0.024	0.040
Fifth piston ring in cylinder .... Gap:	0.059	0.033	0.049
Piston pin in piston (standard or 0.005" oversize) .... Diameter:	0.0013L	0.0001L	0.0007L
Piston pin in cylinder .... End Clearance:	0.090	0.031	0.048
Piston pin in connecting rod busing ....Diameter:	0.0040L	0.0022L	0.0026L
Bushing in connecting rod ....Diameter:		0.0025T	0.0050T
Connecting rod bearing on crankpin.............................Diameter:	0.006 L	0.0009L	0.0034L
Connecting rod on crankpin .... Side Clearance:	0.016	0.006	0.010
Bolt in connecting rod ....Diameter:		0.0000	0.0018L
Connecting bearing and busing twist or convergence per inch of length .... :	0.001	0.0000	0.0005
CRANKSHAFT			
Crankshaft in main bearing ....Diameter:	0.005 L	0.0012L	0.0032L
Propeller reduction gear shaft in bearing ....Diameter:		0.0012L	0.0032L
Propeller drive shaft in shaft ....Diameter:		0.0012L	0.0032L
Crankpins ....Out-of-Round:	0.0015	0.0000	0.0005
Main journals ....Out-of-Round:	0.0015	0.0000	0.0005
Propeller drive shaft...Out-of-Round:	0.002	0.0000	0.002
Propeller drive shaft in thrust bearing............................. End Clearance:	0.020	0.006	0.0152
Crankshaft run-out at center main journals (shaft supported at thrust rear journals) full indicator reading.. :	0.015	0.000	0.015
Propeller shaft run-out at propeller flange (when supported at front and rear journals) full indicator reading.. :	0.003	0.000	0.002
Damper pin bushing in crankcheek extension ....Diameter:		0.0015T	0.003 T
Damper pin busing in counterweigh ....Diameter:		0.0015T	0.003 T
Damper pin in counterweight .... End Clearance:	0.040	0.001	0.023
Alternator drive gear on reduction gear ....Diameter:		0.001 T	0.004 T
Crankshaft gear on crankshaft..Diameter:		0.000	0.002 T
CAMSHAFT			
Camshaft journals in crankcase ....Diameter:	0.005L	0.001 L	0.003 L
Camshaft in crankcase .... End Clearance:	0.014	0.005	0.009
Camshaft run-out at center (shaft supported at end journals) full indicator reading:.. :	0.003	0.000	0.001
Camshaft gear on camshaft flange ....Diameter:		0.0005 T	0.0015L
Governor drive gear on camshaft ....Diameter:	0.006 L	0.0005 L	0.002 L
CRANKCASE AND ATTACHED PARTS			
Thru bolts in crankcase ....Diameter:		0.0005 T	0.0013L
Hydraulic lifter in crankcase...Diameter:	0.0035L	0.001 L	0.0025L
Governor drive shaft in crankcase.................................Diameter:		0.0014 L	0.0034L

Figure 4-7. Table of limits for a reciprocating engine.

which a decreasing alternating current is passed. When demagnetizing is complete, check the part with a field strength meter to determine the effectiveness of the operation. If magnetic flux remains in the part, repeat the demagnetizing operation. When the part is demagnetized, apply a thin coat of oil to protect the part from rusting.

d. Dimensional Inspection

Use the proper measuring tools, such as micrometer calipers, telescoping gauges, and dial indicators to measure each part and determine that the fits are within the limits established by the manufacturer and published in the overhaul manual. You will notice in figure 4-7 that both new parts limits and serviceable limits are given. It is at this point that the decision must be made as to which set of limits the engine is going to conform.

It seems to be poor economy to overhaul an engine to the serviceable limits, as it is likely to run only a short while before it will wear outside of these dimensions. The increased clearances will accelerate wear and decrease the time between overhauls. When the engine is next overhauled, it will likely require more parts to be replaced. Engines built to new parts limits are most apt to give the best service, over the longest period of time.

Notice that the values given in the manufacturer's table of limits are clearance dimensions. Very few actual part sizes appear. The limits are specified as the fit of one part *in* another. For example, "Piston pin in piston" tells us to measure the diameter of the piston pin and measure the diameter of the hole in the piston where the piston pin fits. The limit given is the maximum difference in these two values.

Some measurements may require temporary assembly of some components. A typical situation like this is that of the crankshaft clearance. In this example, new main bearing inserts must be installed in the crankcase halves, and the case is reassembled and torqued to the values recommended in the table of torques. Telescoping gauges are adjusted to the inside diameter of the bearings and then are measured with micrometer calipers. The journals of the crankshaft are then carefully measured with the same micrometer, and the difference between the two values is calculated. This difference will represent the clearance between the journal and the crankshaft. For a new engine, this fit is allowed to be between 0.0012L and 0.0032L. The "L" fol-

lowing the dimension indicates that the fit is loose, meaning that the inside diameter of the bearing is larger than the outside diameter of the crankshaft journal.

Some fits, such as bushings in the small ends of the connecting rods, are called interference fits, and in our example are dimensioned as 0.0025T to 0.0050T. This means that the bushing must be from two and a half to five thousandths of an inch *larger* than the hole into which it fits. To press this bushing into place, you must use an arbor press and a special bushing installation drift. Other interference fits such as valve guides and valve seats in the cylinder heads are so tight that the cylinder heads must be heated in an oven and the guides chilled with dry ice and then assembled while they have a large dimensional difference because of the temperature extremes. When the assembly comes to room temperature, the proper fit will be established.

All of the dimensions specified in the table of limits must be measured, and if the part does not fall within the tolerances given, it must be replaced or repaired. The exception to this are those dimensions given for interference fits. If you did not have to replace the bushings in the connecting rods mentioned above, you would not remove them simply to measure their fit. As we examine the engine parts in the repair section of this chapter, specific information of dimensional inspection may accompany the repair methods.

4. Repair

If the inspection reveals that the parts need repair, they must be brought back to the standards established by the engine manufacturer before the engine is reassembled.

Damage such as burrs, nicks, scratches, scoring, or galling should be removed with a fine oil stone, crocus cloth, or any similar abrasive substance. Following any repairs of this type, the part should be thoroughly cleaned to be certain that all abrasive has been removed, and then checked with its mating part to assure that the clearances are not excessive. Flanged surfaces that are bent, warped, or nicked can be repaired by lapping on a surface plate. Again, the part should be cleaned to be certain that all abrasive has been removed. Defective threads can sometimes be repaired with a suitable die or tap. Small nicks can be removed satisfactorily with Swiss pattern files or small, edged stones. Pipe threads should not be tapped deeper to clean them, because this practice will result in an oversized tapped hole. If galling or scratches are removed from a bearing surface of a journal, it should be buffed to a high finish.

a. Crankcase

Crankcases are subject to such high stresses that cracks are likely to appear. Most of these are repairable. Crankcases are very expensive, and modern welding technology has made the welding of cracks an acceptable repair. It must be noted, however, that repairs of this nature must be done either by the engine manufacturer or by a Certified Repair Station approved for this specialized type of work.

Welding is done by one of the forms of inert gas arc welding, and after some of the metal has been deposited, the bead is peened to relieve stresses built up by the welding. After the complete weld is made, the repair is machined to match the rest of the surface. Not only are cracks repaired by welding, but bearing cavity damage may be repaired, and the crankcase line-bored to new tolerances.

Camshafts normally run in bearings cut in the crankcase without any bearing inserts. If the clearance between the case and the camshaft is greater than allowed, the bearings may be line-bored and an oversized camshaft installed.

All of the studs must be checked for any indication of their having loosened in operation. Any that are bent or loose must be removed and replaced, using oversize studs if necessary. Oversize studs may be identified by one of several methods which are shown in figure 4-9.

If the threads in the case are stripped out, they may be drilled clean with a special drill, the hole tapped with a special tap, and a stainless steel Heli-coil insert screwed into place. Heli-coils provide new threads for the hole and standard studs may then be installed. There is no decrease in strength when this type of repair is made.

b. Crankshaft

The crankshaft is the heaviest and most highly stressed part of an aircraft engine, and there are very few repairs that can be to it. Those repairs which are approved, must be made by either the

Figure 4-8. Crankcases may be repaired by welding and machining. When properly done, the repaired crankcase is as serviceable as a new one.

TYPICAL PART NO.	OVERSIZE ON PITCH DIA. OF COARSE THREAD (INCHES)	OPTIONAL IDENTIFICATION MARKS ON COARSE THREAD END		IDENTIFICATION COLOR CODE
		STAMPED	MACHINED	
XXXXXX	STANDARD	NONE		NONE
XXXXXXP003	.003			RED
XXXXXXP006	.006			BLUE
XXXXXXP009	.009			GREEN
XXXXXXP007	.007			BLUE
XXXXXXP012	.012			GREEN

Figure 4-9. Identification of oversize studs used in aircraft engines.

manufacturer or by a repair station that is specially approved for this type repair.

Carefully inspect all surfaces of the shaft for cracks using the magnetic particle inspection method. Check the bearing surfaces for evidence of galling, scoring, or other damage. When a shaft is equipped with oil transfer tubes, check them for tightness.

Some crankshafts are manufactured with hollow crankpins that serve as sludge removers. The sludge chambers may be formed by means of spool-shaped tubes pressed into the hollow crankpins or by plugs pressed into each end of the crankpin.

The sludge chambers or tubes must be removed for cleaning at overhaul. If these are not removed, accumulated sludge loosened during cleaning may clog the crankshaft oil passages and cause subsequent bearing failures. If the sludge chambers are formed by means of tubes pressed into hollow crankpins, make certain they are reinstalled correctly to avoid covering the ends of the oil passages.

Use extreme care in inspecting and checking the crankshaft for straightness. Place the crankshaft in vee-blocks at the location specified

in the overhaul manual. Using a surface plate and a dial indicator, measure the shaft run out. If the total indicator reading exceeds the dimensions given in the manufacturer's table of limits, the shaft must not be reused. A bent crankshaft should not be straightened. Any attempt to do so may rupture the nitrated surface of the bearing journals, a condition that will cause eventual failure of the crankshaft.

Measure the outside diameter of the crankshaft main and rod bearing journals. Compare the resulting measurements with those in the table of limits. If the journals are scored or out of round, the shaft can be ground to the proper undersize dimension. When it has been determined that there are no cracks in the crankshaft, and that the shaft is not bent, it is placed in a special lathe and all of the main and connecting rod journals are ground to the proper size. Special care must be taken with the radius between the bearing surface and the crank cheek because of the extremely high stresses encountered with aircraft crankshafts. After all of the journals have been ground, they are polished and the crankshaft is surface hardened by the nitrating process. The propeller flange is then cadmium plated. The crankshaft is given a final

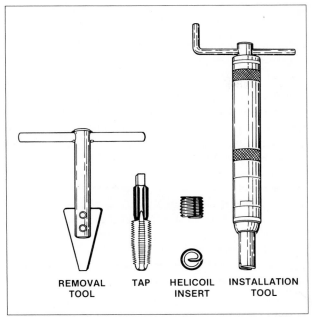

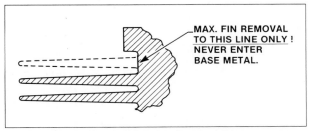

Figure 4-10. Heli-coil tools used for removing and installing Heli-coil inserts in an aircraft engine.

REMOVAL TOOL | TAP | HELICOIL INSERT | INSTALLATION TOOL

MAX. FIN REMOVAL TO THIS LINE ONLY ! NEVER ENTER BASE METAL.

Figure 4-11. When dressing a damaged fin on an aircraft cylinder head, do not remove more material than the manufacturer allows.

magnetic particle inspection and all of the sludge plugs, counterweights, and other removable components are reinstalled.

c. Cylinders

Inspect the cylinder head for internal and external cracks. Carbon deposits must be cleaned from the inside of the head, and paint must be removed from the outside for this inspection. Magnetic particle inspection may be used on the cylinder barrel, and the dye-penetrant inspection method used to find defects in the cylinder head.

Exterior cracks will show up on the head fins where they have been damaged by tools or contact with other parts because of careless handling. Cracks near the edge of the fins are not dangerous if the portion of the fin is removed and contoured properly. Cracks at the base of a fin are a reason for rejecting a cylinder. Note

carefully the percentage of the total fin area that is removed. This must not exceed the limits established by the manufacturer.

Inspect the head fins for damage besides cracks. Dents or bends in the fins should be left alone unless there is danger of cracking. Where pieces of the fin are missing, the sharp edges should be filed to a smooth contour. Fin breakage in a concentrated area will cause dangerous local hot spots. Breakage near the spark plug openings, or on the exhaust side of the cylinder, is obviously more dangerous than other areas.

Inspection of valve seat inserts before they are refaced is mostly a matter of determining if there is enough of the seat left to correct any pitting, burning, scoring, or out-of-trueness.

Inspect spark plug thread inserts for condition of the threads and looseness. Run a tap of the proper size through the insert. If there are threads missing or damaged, replace the thread insert.

Inspect the rocker shaft bosses for scoring, cracks, oversize, or out-of-roundness. Scoring is generally caused by the rocker shaft turning in the bosses, which means that either the shaft was too loose in the bosses or a rocker arm was too tight on the shaft. If a valve sticks, the rocker shaft tends to work up and down when the valve offers excessive resistance to opening. Inspect for

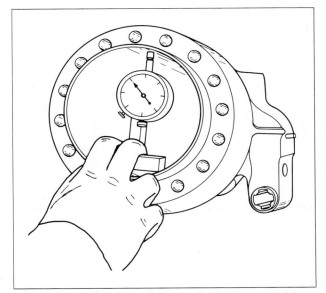

Figure 4-12. Checking cylinder bore with a dial bore indicator.

out-of-roundness and oversize using a telescoping gauge and a micrometer.

Inspect the cylinder barrel for wear, using a dial bore indicator, a telescoping gauge and micrometer, or an inside micrometer. Dimensional inspection of the barrel consists of the following measurements:

(1) Maximum taper of cylinder walls.

(2) Maximum out-of-roundness.

(3) Bore diameter.

(4) Step.

(5) Fit between piston skirt and cylinder.

All measurements involving cylinder barrel diameters must be taken at a minimum of two positions 90 degrees apart, in the particular plane being measured. The use of a dial bore indicator is shown in figure 4-12.

Taper of the cylinder walls is the difference between the diameter of the cylinder barrel at the bottom and the diameter at the top. The cylinder is usually worn larger at the top than at the bottom. This taper is caused by the natural wear pattern. At the top of the stroke, the piston is subjected to greater heat and pressure and more erosive environment than at the bottom of the stroke. Also, there is greater freedom of movement at the top of the stroke. Under these conditions, the piston will wear the cylinder wall.

Where cylinders are built with an intentional choke, measurement of taper becomes more complicated. It is necessary to know exactly how the size indicates wear or taper. Taper can be measured in any cylinder by a cylinder dial gauge as long as there is not a sharp step. This dial gauge tends to ride up on the step and causes inaccurate readings at the top of the cylinder.

The measurement of out-of-roundness is usually taken at the top of the cylinder. However, a reading should also be taken at the skirt of the cylinder to detect dents or bends caused by careless handling.

Inspect the cylinder walls for rust, pitting, or scores. Mild damage of this sort can be removed when the rings are lapped. With more extensive damage, the cylinder walls will have to be reground or honed. If the damage is too deep to remove by either of these methods, the cylinder usually will have to be rejected.

Check the cylinder flange for warpage by placing the cylinder on a suitable jig. Check to see that the flange contacts the jig all the way around. The amount of warp can be checked using a thickness gauge (figure 4-13). A cylinder whose flange is warped beyond allowable limits should be rejected.

Cylinder repair schemes include the replacement of rocker pin bushings, valve guides and seats, spark plug thread inserts, and several methods of dealing with barrel diameters. Cylinder barrels which are worn beyond limits, or have scoring or pitting, may be restored to use by one of three methods: (1) grinding oversize and installing oversize pistons and rings, (2) grinding oversize and applying porous chrome plating to restore the original diameter, and (3) installing a new cylinder barrel on the serviceable head. Each of these operations requires the services of a specialized repair station.

Welding is also being used for repair of cylinder heads. Many cracks are now being repaired by welding, as well as the restoration of damaged areas in the aluminum casting. Again,

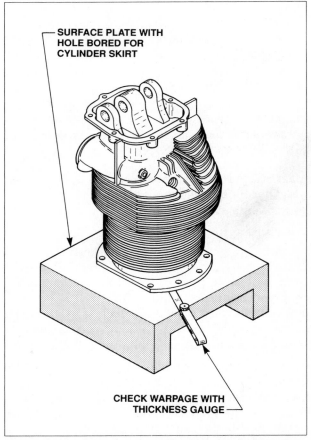

Figure 4-13. Check for cylinder flange warpage using a special surface plate.

SURFACE PLATE WITH HOLE BORED FOR CYLINDER SKIRT

CHECK WARPAGE WITH THICKNESS GAUGE

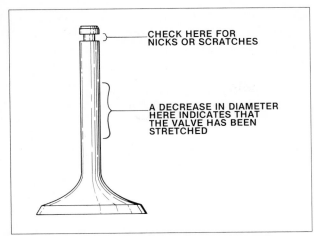

Figure 4-14. Method of checking a poppet valve stem for stretch.

this is very specialized work and must be accomplished by an appropriately certified repair station.

d. Valves And Valve Springs

Some valves may not be reused, and the manufacturer's service information will clearly indicate if that is the case. Where valves may be reused, they must be carefully examined for any indication of overheating that could render them unserviceable.

Any nicks or scratches in the valve stem near the spring retainer groove is cause for rejection of the valve. Valve stretch is also cause for rejection and is indicated by a valve whose stem diameter at the center measures less than the diameter at the spring end.

Chuck the valve in the valve grinding machine and, using a dial indicator, check to see that the face runs true with the stem. The allowable tolerance is usually very small.

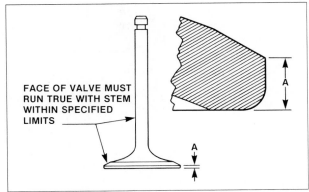

Figure 4-15. It is important that the valve margin (A) is within manufacturer's tolerances.

If the valve is in otherwise acceptable condition, the valve margin (dimension A in figure 4-15) should be examined to determine if refacing is possible. If there is sufficient margin, the valve may be refaced by grinding to the proper angle. Remove only enough material to clean up any wear marks or pits on the valve face, and be sure that the surfaced valve has at least the minimum edge thickness (margin) when the grinding is complete.

If the overhaul manual specifies an interference fit be ground between the valve face and the valve seat, the face is ground between one-half and one degree flatter than the seat. This is so that the valve will seat with a line contact at its outer edge.

Examine the valve springs for cracks, rust, broken ends, and compression. Cracks can be located by visual inspection or the magnetic particle method. Compression is tested with a valve spring tester. The spring is compressed until its total height is that specified by the manufacturer. The dial on the tester should indicate the pressure (in pounds) required to compress the spring to the specified height. This must be within the pressure limits established by the manufacturer.

e. Pistons And Rings

If it is permissible to reuse the pistons, they must be carefully inspected. The pistons must have been cleaned and all of the carbon removed from the ring grooves and the oil relief holes in the lower ring groove. Inspect the piston for cracks. The dye-penetrant method of inspection may be used here. Cracks are more likely to be formed at the highly stressed points; therefore, inspect carefully at the base of the pin bosses, inside the piston at the junction of the walls and the head, and at the base of the ring lands, especially the top and bottom lands.

When applicable, check for flatness of the piston head using a straightedge and a thickness

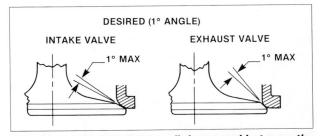

Figure 4-16. An interference fit is ground between the valve and its seat to provide a line contact seal.

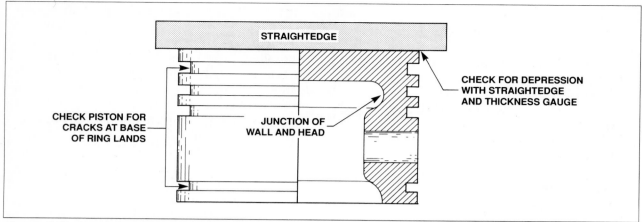

Figure 4-17. Checking a piston head for flatness.

gauge as shown in figure 4-17. If a depression is found, double check for cracks on the inside of the piston. A depression in the top of the piston usually means that detonation has occurred within the cylinder.

Inspect the exterior of the piston for scores and scratches. Scores on the top ring land are not cause for rejection unless they are excessively deep. Deep scores on the side of the piston are usually a reason for rejection.

Examine the piston for cracked skirts, broken ring lands, and scored piston-pin holes.

Measure the outside of the piston by means of a micrometer. Measurements must be taken in several directions and on the skirt as well as the lands. Check these sizes against the cylinder size.

A new set of piston rings may be installed after first measuring the end gap by placing the ring in the cylinder barrel, squaring it up with the piston, and using a thickness gauge to measure the gap between the two ends of the ring. If the gap is correct, the rings may be installed on the piston.

The new rings should be installed on the piston with the part number on the ring toward the top of the piston. Use a ring expander and be careful not to scratch the piston with the ends of the ring. When all of the rings are installed, check the clearance between the rings and the side of the ring groove. If tapered rings are installed, hold a straight edge against the side of the piston and measure the side clearance with a thickness gauge.

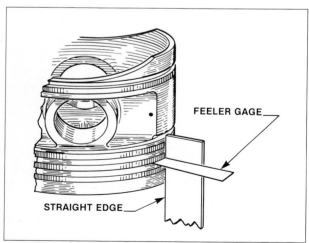

Figure 4-18. Method of checking side clearance of a tapered piston ring in the ring groove.

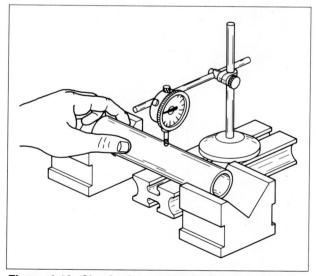

Figure 4-19. Check piston pins for bends using vee-blocks and a dial indicator.

4-16

118

It is extremely important that only piston rings approved for the engine be used, and that the ring is compatible with the cylinder walls. Only cast iron rings can be used with nitrated or chrome plated cylinders, but chrome plated rings may be used on plain steel cylinders.

Examine the piston pin for scoring, cracks, excessive wear, and pitting. Check the clearance between the piston pin and the bore of the piston pin bosses using a telescoping gauge and micrometer. Use the magnetic particle inspection to inspect the pin for cracks. Since pins are often case hardened, cracks will show up inside the pin more often than on the outside.

Check the pin for bends (figure 4-19), using vee-blocks and a dial indicator on a surface plate. Measure the fit of the plugs in the pin.

It is an important consideration for smooth operation of the engine that the piston weights be as close as possible to one another. The maximum allowable weight difference will be supplied by the manufacturer on the table of limits. New pistons may be purchased in matched sets whose weight differences are considerably below the manufacturer's maximum.

f. Connecting Rods

The inspection and repair of connecting rods include: (1) visual inspection, (2) check of alignment, (3) rebushing, and (4) replacement of bear-

Figure 4-20. Method of checking a connecting rod for bends.

Figure 4-21. Method of checking a connecting rod for twist.

ing inserts. Some manufacturers also specify a magnetic particle inspection of connecting rods.

Visual inspection should be done with the aid of a magnifying glass or bench microscope. A rod which is obviously twisted or bent should be rejected without further inspection.

Inspect all surfaces of the connecting rods for cracks, corrosion, pitting, galling, or other damage. Galling is caused by a slight amount of movement between the surfaces of the bearing insert and the connecting rod during periods of high loading, such as that produced during over speed or excessive manifold pressure. The visual evidence produced by galling appears as if particles from one contacting surface has welded to the other. Evidence of any galling is sufficient reason for rejecting the complete rod assembly. Galling is a distortion in the metal and is comparable to corrosion in the manner in which it weakens the metallic structure of the connecting rod.

Check bushings that have been replaced to determine if the bushing and rod bore are square and parallel to each other. The alignment of a connecting rod can be checked several ways.

To check for parallel (bend), a new bearing insert is installed in the large end and arbors are installed in both ends of the connecting rod. A measurement is made, using a parallelism gauge to check for a bent rod. This will be indicated if the two arbors are not exactly parallel. Figure 4-20 illustrates a connecting rod installed in this fixture.

With the arbors still installed, lay the rod across parallel blocks on a surface plate and check for squareness (twist). This is accomplished by trying to pass a thickness gauge between the arbor and the parallel block. The amount of twist will be determined by the thickness of the gauge leafs that can be inserted. If the rod is twisted or bent beyond limits specified, it must be replaced.

When installing a new rod, match it to the rod on the opposite side of the engine within one-half ounce to minimize vibration.

g. Camshaft

Since the camshaft is responsible for opening the valves at the proper time, all of the lobes must be examined to see that they are not excessively worn. If any of the hydraulic tappet bodies were spalled or pitted, the lobe that operated that valve should be inspected for surface irregularities or feathering of the edges. If any such conditions are found, the camshaft should be rejected.

If the overhaul manual specifies that the lobes be tapered, a dimensional check should be made to determine whether or not the amount of taper is within the limits specified.

If all of the lobes are in good condition, check the shaft for bends by supporting its end journals in vee-blocks and checking the center journal for run out. Then, check the journal diameters and compare them with the bearings in the crankcase for the proper fit.

h. Valve Operating Mechanism

The valve operating mechanism consists of the hydraulic lifter, push rod, rocker arm, and valve. Each of these items must be carefully inspected for damage and conformity with the table of limits.

1) Valve Lifters

Almost all modern horizontally opposed aircraft engines use hydraulic valve lifters to maintain zero clearance in the valve operating mechanism.

Remove the hydraulic plunger from the lifter bodies that ride on the cam lobes, and examine visually and dimensionally before using the magnetic particle method of inspection. The hydraulic plunger assembly must never be magnetized, as magnetization will prevent the steel check valve from seating.

The plunger and cylinder are matched units and parts from one should never be interchanged with parts from another. After the plunger is thoroughly cleaned and visually checked for any chipped shoulders or evidence of other damage, it is given a leakage test. This may be accomplished using equipment specially designed for this purpose, or by inserting the plunger in the cylinder and quickly depressing it. If it bounces back, it shows the check valve is seating properly and the assembly is satisfactory for reinstallation. If it does not bounce back, the valve is not seating and the unit must be replaced.

2) Push Rods

The push rods must be absolutely clean. Pay particular attention to the oil passage through the rod. The ball ends should be inspected to be sure they are tight in the rod. Straightness may be checked by rolling the rod across a surface plate.

3) Rocker Arms And Shafts

Inspect the valve rockers for cracks and worn, pitted, or scored tips. See that all oil passages are free from obstructions.

Inspect the shafts for correct size with a micrometer. Rocker shafts very often are found to be scored and burned because of excessive turning in the cylinder head. Also, there may be some pickup on the shaft (bronze from the rocker bushing transferred to the steel shaft). Generally this is caused by overheating and too little clearance between shaft and bushing.

Inspect the rocker arm bushing for correct size. Check for proper clearance between the bushing and the shaft. Very often bushings are scored because of mishandling during disassembly. Check to see that the oil holes line up. At least 50% of the hole in the bushing should align with the hole in the rocker arm.

4) Refacing Valve Seats

The valve seat inserts of aircraft engine cylinders usually are in need of refacing at every overhaul. They are refaced to provide a true, clean, and correct size seat for the valve. When valve guides or valve seats are replaced in a cylinder, the seats must be trued up to the guide.

Modern engines use either bronze or steel seats. Steel seats are commonly used as exhaust seats and are made of hard, heat resistant, and often austenitic steel alloy. Bronze seats are used for intake or for both seats; they are made of aluminum bronze or phosphor bronze alloys.

Steel valve seats are refaced by grinding equipment. Bronze seats are refaced preferably by the use of cutters or reamers, but may be ground when this equipment is not available. The only disadvantage of using a stone on bronze is that the soft metal loads the stone to such an extent that much time is consumed in redressing the stone to keep it clean.

The tooling used on steel seats can be either wet or dry valve seat grinding equipment. The wet grinder uses a mixture of soluble oil and water to wash away the chips and to keep the stone and seat cool; this produces a smoother, more accurate job than the dry grinder. The stones may be either silicon carbide or aluminum oxide.

Before refacing the seat, make sure that the valve guide is in good condition, it is clean, and will not have to be replaced.

Mount the cylinder firmly in the hold down fixture. An expanding pilot is inserted in the valve guide from the inside of the cylinder, and an expander screw is inserted in the pilot from the top of the guide as shown in figure 4-22. The pilot must be tight in the guide because any movement can cause a poor grind. The fluid hose is inserted through one of the spark plug inserts.

The three grades of stones available for use are classified as rough, finishing, and polishing stones. The rough stone is designed to true and clean the seat. The finishing stone must follow the rough to remove grinding marks and to produce a smooth finish. The polishing stone does just as the name implies, and is used only where a highly polished seat is desired.

The stones are installed on special stone holders. The face of the stone is trued by a diamond dresser. The stone should be refaced whenever it is grooved or loaded, and when the stone is first installed on the stone holder. The diamond dresser also may be used to cut down the diameter of the stone. Dressing of the stone should be kept to a minimum as a matter of conservation; therefore, it is desirable to have sufficient stone holders for all of the stones to be used on the job.

In the actual grinding job, considerable skill is required in handling the grinding gun. The gun must be centered accurately on the stone holder. If the gun is tilted off center, chattering of the stone will result and a rough grind will be produced. It is very important that the stone be

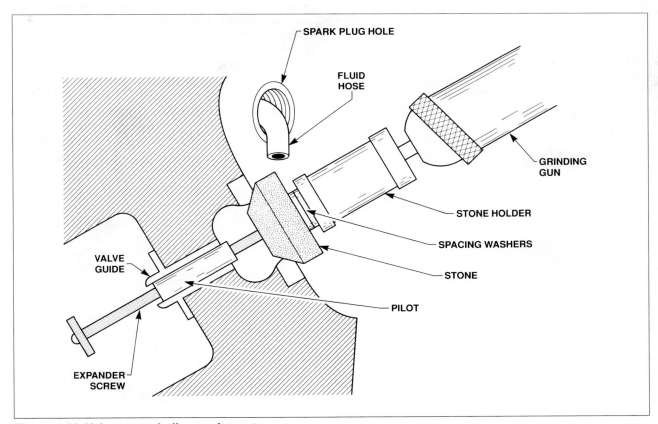

Figure 4-22. Valve seat grinding equipment.

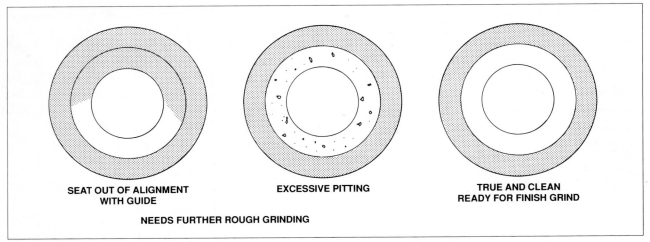

| SEAT OUT OF ALIGNMENT WITH GUIDE | EXCESSIVE PITTING | TRUE AND CLEAN READY FOR FINISH GRIND |

NEEDS FURTHER ROUGH GRINDING

Figure 4-23. Valve seat grinding.

rotated at a speed that will permit grinding instead of rubbing. This speed is approximately 8,000 to 10,000 RPM Excessive pressure on the stone can slow it down. It is not a good technique to let the stone grind at slow speed by putting pressure on the stone when starting or stopping the gun. The maximum pressure used on the stone at any time should be no more than that exerted by the weight of the gun.

Another practice which is conducive to good grinding is to ease off the stone every second or so to let the coolant wash away the chips on the seat; this rhythmic grinding action also helps keep the stone up to its correct speed. Since it is quite a job to replace a seat, remove as little material as possible during the grinding. Inspect the job frequently to prevent unnecessary grinding.

The rough stone is used until the seat is true to the valve guide and all pits, scores, or burned areas (figure 4-23) are removed. After refacing, the seat should be true and smooth.

The finishing stone is used only until the seat has a smooth, polished appearance. Extreme caution should be used when grinding with the finishing stone to prevent chattering.

The size and trueness of the seat can be checked by several methods. Run out of the seat is checked with a special dial indicator and should not exceed 0.002 in. The size of the seat may be determined using Prussian blue. To check the fit of the seat, spread a thin coat of Prussian blue evenly on the seat. Press the valve onto the seat. The blue transferred to the valve will indicate the contact surface. The contact surface should be one-third to two-thirds the width of the valve face, and in the middle of the face. If Prussian blue is not used, the same check may be made by lapping the valve lightly

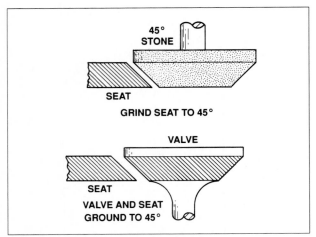

Figure 4-24. Fitting of valve and seat.

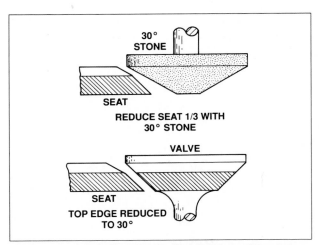

Figure 4-25. Grinding top surface of the valve seat.

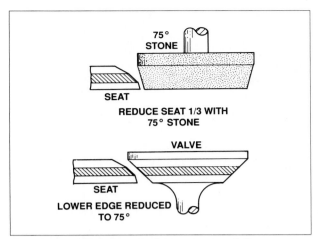

Figure 4-26. Grinding the inner corner of the valve seat.

to the seat. Examples of test results are shown in figure 4-24.

If the seat contacts the upper third of the valve face, grind off the top corner of the valve seat as shown in figure 4-25. Such grinding is called "narrowing the seat". This permits the seat to contact the center third of the valve face without touching the upper portion of the valve face.

If the seat contacts the bottom third of the valve face, grind off the inner corner of the valve seat as shown in figure 4-26.

The seat is narrowed by a stone other than the standard angle. It is common practice to use a 15° angle and 45° angle cutting stone on 30° valve seats, and a 30° angle and 75° angle cutting stone on a 45° valve seat (see figure 4-27).

If the valve seat has been cut or ground too much, the valve will contact the seat too far up into the cylinder head, and the valve clearance,

spring tension, and fit of the valve to the seat will be affected. To check the height of a valve, insert the valve into the guide and hold it against the seat. Check the height of the valve stem above the rocker box or some other fixed position.

Before refacing a valve seat, consult the overhaul manual for the particular model engine. Each manufacturer specifies the desired angle for grinding and narrowing the valve seat.

5) Valve Reconditioning

One of the most common jobs during engine overhaul is grinding the valves. The equipment used should preferably be a wet valve grinder. With this type of machine, a mixture of soluble oil and water is used to keep the valve cool and carry away the grinding chips.

Like many machine jobs, valve grinding is mostly a matter of setting up the machine. The following points should be checked or accomplished before starting a grind.

True the stone by means of a diamond dresser. The machine is turned on, and the diamond is drawn across the stone, cutting just deep enough to true and clean the stone.

Determine the face angle of the valve being ground, and set the movable head of the machine to correspond to this angle. Usually, valves are ground to the standard angles of 30° or 45°. However, in some instances, an interference fit of 0.5° or 1.5° less than the standard angle may be ground on the valve face.

The interference fit (figure 4-28) is used to obtain a more positive seal by means of a narrow contact surface. Theoretically, there is a fine line contact between the valve and seat. With this line contact, all the load that the valve exerts

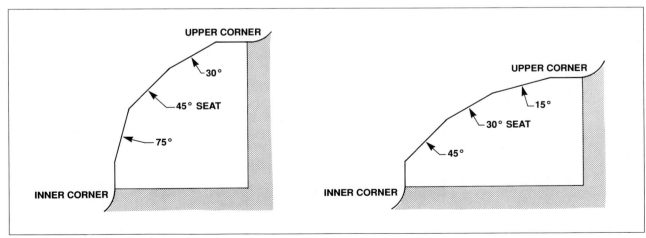

Figure 4-27. Valve seat angles.

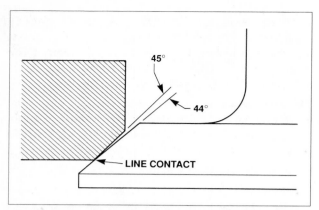

Figure 4-28. Interference fit of valve and valve seat.

against the seat is concentrated in a very small area, hereby increasing the unit load at any one spot. The interference fit is especially beneficial during the first few hours of operation after an overhaul. The positive seal reduces the possibility of a burned valve or seat that a leaking valve might produce. After the first few hours of running, these angles tend to pound down and become identical.

Notice that the interference angle is ground into the valve, not the seat. It is easier to change the angle of the valve grinder work head than to change the angle of a valve seat grinder stone. Do not use an interference fit unless the manufacturer approves it.

Install the valve into the chuck (figure 4-29) and adjust the chuck so that the valve face is approximately 2 in. from the chuck. If the valve is chucked any further out, there is danger of excessive wobble and also a possibility of grinding into the stem.

There are various types of valve grinding machines. In one type the stone is moved across the valve face; in another, the valve is moved across the stone. Whichever type is used, the following procedures are typical of those performed when refacing a valve.

Check the travel of the valve face across the stone. The valve should completely pass the stone on both sides and yet not travel far enough to grind the stem. There are stops on the machine which can be set to control this travel.

With the valve set correctly in place, turn on the machine and turn on the grinding fluid so that it splashes on the valve face. Back the grinding wheel off all the way. Place the valve directly in front of the stone. Slowly bring the wheel forward until a light cut is made on the valve. The intensity of the grind is measured more by sound than anything else. Slowly draw the valve back and forth across the stone without increasing the cut. Move the work head table back and forth using the full face of the stone but always keeping the valve face on the stone. When the sound of the grind diminishes,

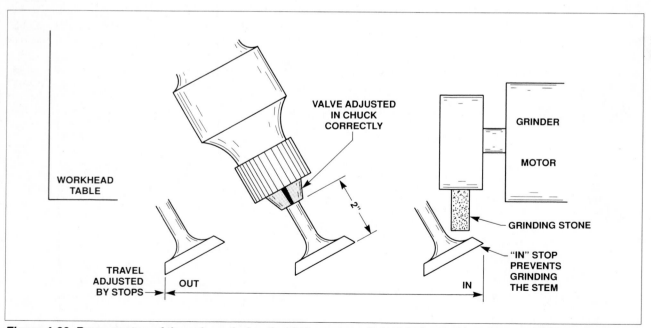

Figure 4-29. Proper setup of the valve grinder should be accomplished before attempting to resurface the valves.

indicating that some valve material has been removed, move the work head table to the extreme left to stop rotation of the valve. Inspect the valve to determine if further grinding is necessary. If another cut must be made, bring the valve in front of the stone, then advance the stone out to the valve. Do not increase the cut without having the valve directly in front of the stone.

An important precaution in valve grinding, as in any kind of grinding, is to make light cuts only. Heavy cuts cause chattering, which may make the valve surface so rough that much time is lost in obtaining the desired finish.

After grinding, check the valve margin to be sure that the valve edge has not been ground too thin. A thin edge is called a "feather edge" and can overheat and lead to preignition. The valve edge would burn away in a short period of time and the cylinder would have to be overhauled again. Figure 4-30 shows a valve with a normal margin and one with a feather edge.

The valve tip may be resurfaced on the valve grinder. The tip is ground to remove cupping or wear and also to adjust valve clearances on some engines.

The valve is held by a clamp (figure 4-31) on the side of the stone. With the machine and grinding fluid turned on, the valve is pushed lightly against the stone and swung back and forth. Do not swing the valve stem off either edge of the stone. Because of the tendency for the valve to overheat during this grinding, be sure plenty of grinding fluid covers the tip.

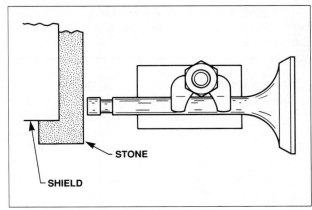
Figure 4-31. Grinding a valve tip.

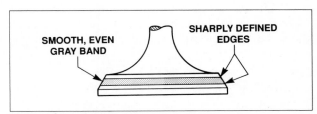
Figure 4-32. A correctly lapped valve.

Grinding of the valve tip may remove or partially remove the bevel on the edge of the valve. To restore this bevel, mount a vee-way approximately 45° to the grinding stone. Hold the valve onto the vee-way with one hand, then twist the valve tip onto the stone, and with a light touch grind all the way around the tip. This bevel prevents scratching the valve guide when the valve is installed.

6) Valve Lapping And Leak Testing

After the grinding procedure is finished, it is sometimes necessary that the valve be lapped to the seat. This is done by applying a small amount of lapping compound to the valve face, inserting the valve into the guide, and rotating the valve with a lapping tool until a smooth, gray finish appears at the contact area. The appearance of a correctly lapped valve is shown in figure 4-32.

After the lapping process is finished, be sure that all lapping compound is removed from the valve face, seat, and adjacent areas.

The final step is to check the mating surface for leaks to see if it is sealing properly. This is done by installing the valve in the cylinder, and pouring kerosene or solvent into the valve port. While holding finger pressure on the valve stem, check to see if the kerosene is leaking past the

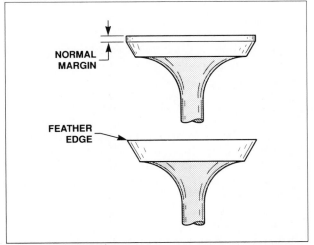
Figure 4-30. Engine valves showing normal margin and a feather edge.

valve into the combustion chamber. If it is not, the valve reseating operation is finished. If kerosene is leaking past the valve, continue the lapping operation until the leakage is stopped.

5. Reassembly

After all of the parts have been inspected and repaired as necessary, the engine is ready to be reassembled. The procedure here is typical, but the actual assembly is, naturally, done in strict accordance with the details in the manufacturer's overhaul manual.

a. Cylinders

Lubricate the valve stems with the recommended lubricant, and insert the valves in the valve guides. Place the cylinder over a post-type fixture to hold the valves in place while you slip the valve springs and retainers over each valve stem. Using the proper spring compressor, compress the valve springs, and install the valve stem keys (keepers) and valve rotators, if used.

Install any of the intercylinder baffles or fin stabilizers that are required, and slip the cylinder base seal around the skirt of the cylinder.

b. Pistons And Rings

Lubricate the piston, the rings, and the wrist pin with the appropriate lubricant. Stagger the piston ring gaps in the way specified in the overhaul manual. Slip the wrist pin into one side of the piston and, using the proper ring compressor, compress the piston rings and slip the piston into the cylinder up to the wrist pin.

c. Crankshaft

All of the sludge plugs and expansion plugs must be installed in the reconditioned crankshaft, all of the counterweights properly assembled, and any gears that are attached to the shaft properly secured and safetied. The crankshaft can now be mounted in a buildup fixture to hold it vertically, while the connecting rods are lubricated and assembled to the shaft, using new bolts and nuts. The rods are now torqued and safetied. Be very sure when assembling the rods to the crankshaft that the numbers stamped on the rods are on the side of the crankshaft specified in the overhaul manual.

d. Crankcase

Place the crankcase halves on a flat work surface and install the main bearing inserts. Be sure that the tangs or dowels are properly placed. Lubricate and install the hydraulic tappet bodies

in one of the crankcase halves and slip the camshaft in place after lubricating its bearing surfaces.

Now the main bearings may be lubricated, and the crankshaft installed. The front oil seal is installed around the propeller shaft and a thin layer of non-hardening gasket compound is applied to the outside mating surface of each half of the crankcase.

If the manufacturer recommends, a very fine silk thread may be embedded in the gasket compound on one of the crankcase halves. Follow the pattern recommended by the manufacturer for laying out the thread.

Very carefully, holding the tappet bodies in place (a rubber band often works here), lower the crankcase half over the one into which the camshaft and crankshaft have already been installed. Be very careful that the front oil seal is properly seated. Any special instructions regarding the seating of the main bearings must be observed. Install new nuts on all of the studs and through bolts. Using the recommended hold down plates over the cylinder pads, torque all of the fasteners to the specifications listed in the overhaul manual. Be very careful to use the exact torque and tighten in the sequence specified.

The crankcase may now be mounted in a vertical position in the buildup fixture, and the gears and accessory case installed. Careful attention should be given to the timing of the cam gear and the crankshaft gear.

The torque hold down plates may be removed and the cylinders slipped into place, installing the proper push rods and push rod housings with the appropriate seals.

The rocker arms and rocker shafts are lubricated and installed and the rocker shaft secured in the cylinder head.

e. Final Assembly

The oil sump is installed on the crankcase and the magnetos are installed and timed. The carburetor or fuel injection system and all of the induction system is installed, as well as all of the accessories such as the pumps, the alternator, and any baffles or other devices needed for the engine to operate properly.

6. Block Testing

After an engine has been overhauled, it must be block tested, or run in.

a. Block Testing Purpose

The block test serves a dual purpose: first, it accomplishes piston ring run in and bearing burnishing, and second, it provides valuable information that is used to evaluate engine performance and determine engine condition. To provide proper oil flow to the upper portion of the cylinder barrel walls with a minimum loss of oil, it is important that piston rings be properly seated in the cylinder in which they are installed. This process is called piston ring run in and is accomplished chiefly by controlled operation of the engine in the high speed range. Improper piston ring conditioning or run in may result in unsatisfactory engine operation. A process called "bearing burnishing" creates a highly polished surface on new bearings and bushings installed during overhaul. The burnishing is usually accomplished during the first periods of the engine run in at comparatively low engine speeds.

b. Block Testing Requirements

The operational test and test procedures vary with individual engines, but the basic requirements are discussed in the following paragraphs. The failure of any internal part during an engine run-in requires that the engine be returned for replacement of the necessary units, and then be completely retested. If any component part of the basic engine should fail, a new unit is installed; a minimum operating time is used to check the engine with the new unit installed.

Following successful completion of block test requirements, engines that are not going to be immediately installed on an aircraft for operation should be treated for corrosion prevention. These procedures were discussed in detail in the chap-

Figure 4-33. A vertical-type helicopter engine undergoing run in.

ter of this text dealing with engine removal and replacement.

c. Block Test Instruments

The test cell operator's control room houses the controls used to operate the engine and the instruments used to measure various temperatures and pressures, fuel flow, and other factors. These devices are necessary in providing an accurate check and an evaluation of the operating engine. The control room is separate from, but adjacent to, the test cell that houses the engine being tested. Modern test cells are incorporating an increasing number of computerized controls and monitoring equipment.

Engine instruments are operated in several different fashions, some mechanically, some electrically, and some by the pressure of a liquid. This chapter will not discuss how they operate, but rather the information they give, their common names, and the markings on them. Instrument markings and the interpretation of these markings will be discussed before considering the individual instruments.

Instrument markings indicate ranges of operation or minimum and maximum limits, or both. Generally, the instrument marking system consists of four colors (red, yellow, blue, and green) and intermediate blank spaces.

A red line, or mark indicates a point beyond which a dangerous operating condition exists. A red arc indicates a dangerous operating range. Of the two, the red mark is more commonly used, and is located radially on the cover glass or dial face.

The yellow arc covers a given range of operation and is an indication of caution. Generally, the yellow arc is located on the outer circumference of the instrument cover glass or face.

The blue arc, like the yellow arc, indicates a range of operation. The blue arc is used only with certain engine instruments, such as the tachometer, manifold pressure, cylinder head temperature, and torquemeter.

The green arc shows a normal range of operation.

When the markings appear on the cover glass, a white line is used as an index mark. The white radial mark indicates any movement between the cover glass and the case, a condition that would cause misalignment of other range and limit markings.

The instruments illustrated in figures 4-34 through 4-41 are range marked. The portion of the dial that is range marked on the instruments is also shown expanded for instructional purposes. The expanded portion is set off from the instrument to make it easier to identify the instrument markings.

1) Carburetor Air Temperature

Measured at the carburetor entrance, carburetor air temperature (CAT) is regarded by many as an indication of induction system ice formation. Although it serves this purpose, it also provides many other important pieces of information. The temperature of the induction air affects not only the fuel density but also the vaporization of the fuel.

In addition to the normal use of the CAT, it will be found useful for checking induction system condition. Backfiring will be indicated as a momentary rise on the gauge, provided it is of sufficient severity for the heat to be sensed at the carburetor entrance. A sustained induction system fire will show a continuous increase of carburetor air temperature.

The CAT should be noted before starting and just after shutdown. The temperature before starting is the best indication of the temperature of the fuel in the carburetor body and tells whether or not vaporization will be sufficient for the initial firing or whether the mixture ought to be augmented by priming. If an engine has been shut down for only a short time, the residual heat in the carburetor may make it possible to rely on the vaporizing heat in the fuel and powerplant, and priming would be unnecessary. After shutdown, a high CAT is a warning that fuel trapped in pressure-type carburetors will ex-

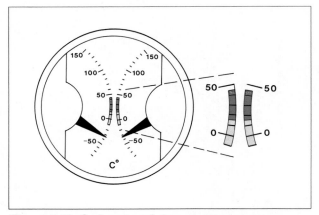

Figure 4-34. Carburetor air temperature gauge.

pand, producing high internal pressure. When a high temperature is present at this time, the fuel line and manifold valves should be open so that pressure can be relieved by allowing fuel passage back to the tank.

The temperature reading is sensed by a bulb. In the test cell, the bulb is located in the air intake to the engine, and in an aircraft it is located in the ram air intake duct. The carburetor air temperature gauge is calibrated using the Celsius scale. Figure 4-34 shows a typical CAT gauge. This gauge, like many other multi-engine aircraft instruments, is a dual gauge; that is, two gauges, each with a separate pointer and scale, are used in the same case. Notice the range markings used. The yellow arc indicates a range from -10°C to +40°C. The red line indicates the maximum operating temperature of 40°C; any operation at a temperature over this value places the engine in serious danger of detonation.

2) Fuel Pressure

The fuel pressure gauge is calibrated in pounds per square inch of pressure. It is used during the run in to measure the fuel pressure at the carburetor inlet, the fuel feed valve discharge nozzle, and the main fuel supply line. Fuel gauges are located in the operator's control room and are connected by flexible lines to the different points at which pressure readings are desired during the testing procedures.

In some aircraft installations, the fuel pressure is sensed at the carburetor inlet of each engine, and the pressure is indicated on individual gauges (figure 4-35) on the instrument panel. The dial is calibrated in 1-p.s.i. graduations, and every fifth graduation line is extended and numbered. The numbers range from 0 to 25. The red line on the dial at the 16-p.s.i. graduation shows the minimum fuel pressure allowed during flight. The green arc shows the desired range of operation, which is 16 to 18 p.s.i. The red line at the 18-p.s.i. graduation indicates the maximum allowable fuel pressure. Fuel pressures vary with the type of carburetor installation and the size of the engine. The pressure gauge illustrated in figure 4-35 has markings typical of engines using a pressure injection carburetor or some types of fuel injection systems.

When float-type carburetors are used, the fuel pressure range is of a much lower value. The minimum allowable pressure is 3 p.s.i., and the maximum is 5 p.s.i.

3) Fuel Flowmeter

The fuel flowmeter measures the amount of fuel delivered to the carburetor. During engine test procedures, the fuel flow to the engine is measured by a series of calibrated tubes located in the control room. The tubes are of various sizes to indicate different volumes of fluid flow. Each tube contains a float that can be seen by the operator. As the flow through the tube varies, the float is either raised or lowered, indicating the amount of fuel flow. From these indications, the operator can determine whether an engine is operating at the correct fuel/air mixture for a given power setting.

In an aircraft installation, the fuel flow indicating system consists of a transmitter and an indicator for each engine. The transmitter measures the fuel flow between the engine driven fuel pump and the carburetor. Gaining popularity are new computerized fuel flow systems that measure fuel flow and calculate fuel consumption, remaining fuel in the tanks, and when coupled with navigation equipment, fuel required to the destination.

Certain fuel injection systems incorporate a gauge that is calibrated like a fuel flowmeter, but actually is measuring fuel pressure at the injection nozzle.

4) Manifold Air Pressure

The preferred type of instrument for measuring the air pressure in the intake manifold is a gauge

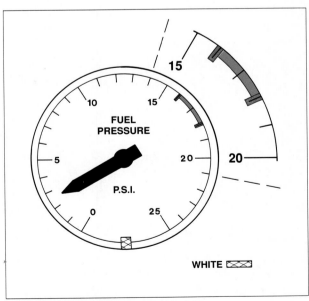

Figure 4-35. Fuel pressure gauge.

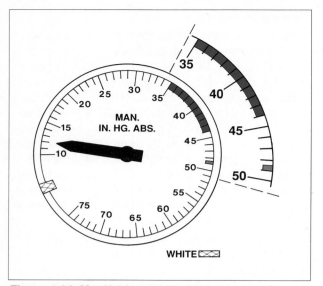

Figure 4-36. Manifold pressure gauge.

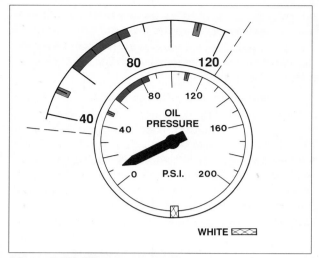

Figure 4-38. Oil pressure gauge.

that records the pressure as an absolute pressure reading. A mercury barometer, a tube calibrated in inches of mercury, is used during block test procedures. It is partially filled with mercury and connected to the manifold pressure adapter located on the engine. The manifold pressure gauges used on board the aircraft are marked in inches of mercury, but incorporate a sealed bellows (aneroid) to measure changes in air pressure.

On the manifold pressure gauge, the green arc indicates the normal operating range. The red arc indicates the maximum manifold pressure permissible during takeoff, and the red line shows the maximum manifold pressure allowable.

5) Oil Temperature

During engine run in, oil temperature readings are taken at the oil inlet and outlet. From these

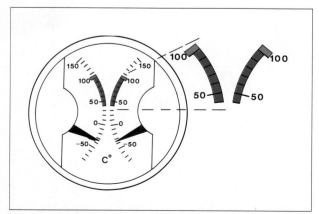

Figure 4-37. Oil temperature gauge.

readings, it can be determined if the engine heat transferred to the oil is low, normal, or excessive. This information is of extreme importance during the "breaking in" process of large reciprocating engines. The oil temperature gauge line in the aircraft is connected at the oil inlet to the engine.

Three range markings are used on the oil temperature gauge. The red mark in figure 4-37, at 40°C on the dial, shows the minimum operating oil temperature permissible for ground operational checks or during flight. The green arc between 60° and 75°C shows the desired oil temperature for continuous engine operation. The red mark at 100°C indicates the maximum permissible oil temperature.

6) Oil Pressure

The oil pressure on the block test engines may be checked at various points, depending upon the model of engine being tested. The main oil pressure reading is taken at the pressure side of the pump.

Generally, there is only one oil pressure gauge for each aircraft engine, and the connection is made at the pressure side (outlet) of the main oil pump.

The oil pressure gauge dial marked as shown in figure 4-38, does not show the pressure range or limits for all installations. The actual markings for specific aircraft may be found in the Aircraft Specifications or Type Certificate Data Sheet. The lower red line at 50 p.s.i. indicates the minimum oil pressure permissible in flight. The green arc between 60 and 85 p.s.i. shows the desired operating oil pressure range. The red line at 110 p.s.i. indicates the maximum permissible oil pressure.

The oil pressure gauge indicates the pressure that the oil of the lubricating system is being supplied to the moving parts of the engine. The engine should be shut down immediately if the gauge fails to register pressure when the engine is operating. Excessive oscillation of the gauge pointer indicates that there is air in the lines leading to the gauge, or that some unit of the oil system is functioning improperly. Low oil pressure or this type of fluctuating gauge indication is often a sign of low oil quantity.

7) Cylinder Head Temperature

During engine test procedures, a pyrometer indicates the cylinder head temperatures of various cylinders on the engine being tested. Thermocouples are connected to each of the cylinders, and by a selector switch any cylinder head temperature can be indicated on the pyrometer.

Cylinder head temperature measuring systems installed on aircraft may use a single gauge and switch to select the cylinder being monitored, or may use a single cylinder system where the temperature of the cylinder is expected to be the hottest is the only one measured. New computer controlled systems are being installed where all cylinders are connected to a single unit which will scan the readings and signal a warning if one cylinder exceeds the temperature of the others by a preselected amount.

Cylinder head temperatures are indicated by a gauge connected to a thermocouple attached to the cylinder. The thermocouple may be placed in a special well in the top or rear of the cylinder head, or it may replace the spark plug gasket.

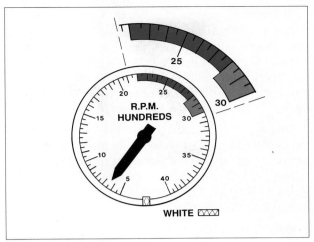

Figure 4-40. Tachometer.

The temperatures recorded at either of these points is merely a reference of control temperature; but as long as it is kept within the prescribed limits, the temperatures of the cylinder dome, exhaust valve, and piston will be within a satisfactory range.

8) Tachometer

The tachometer shows the engine crankshaft RPM. The system used for block testing the engine is the same as the system in the aircraft installation.

Figure 4-40 shows a tachometer with range markings on the cover glass. The tachometer is often referred to as the "*tach*," and is calibrated in hundreds with graduations at every 50-RPM interval. The dial shown here starts at 5 (500 RPM) and goes to 40 (4,000 RPM).

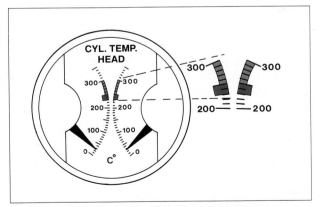

Figure 4-39. Cylinder head temperature gauge.

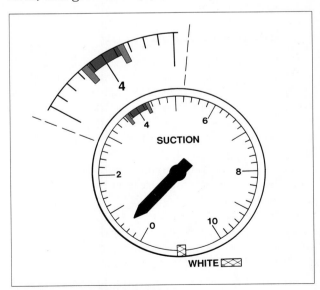

Figure 4-41. Suction gauge.

9) Suction

The suction gauge is not classed as an engine instrument, since it does not indicate any information in determining efficient engine operation. The technician will use this gauge to adjust the suction regulator and to check this value during engine operational checks.

The suction gauge (figure 4-41) is calibrated to indicate reduction of pressure below atmospheric pressure in inches of mercury; the space between the graduation lines represents 0.2 in. Hg. The red line at 3.75 in. Hg indicates the minimum desirable suction.

10) Oil Weighing System

The oil weighing system determines oil consumption during the engine run in at block test and measures the exact amount of oil consumed by the engine during various periods of operation. The system consists of a tank supplying oil to the engine, an oil inlet line to the engine, a return line from the engine oil scavenging and cooling system, and a weighing scale that registers weights up to and including the weight of the full oil tank. The oil consumed by the engine is determined merely by subtracting the scale readings at any given time from the full tank weight.

11) General Instrumentation

Many of the miscellaneous gauges and devices indicate only that a system is functioning or has failed to function. On some aircraft a warning light illuminates when the fuel pressure is low. A similar light may be used for oil pressure systems.

C. Reciprocating Engine Operation

With the exception of block testing an engine utilizing a test cell, most often the technician will be operating an engine that is installed on an aircraft. The operation of the powerplant is controlled from the cockpit. Some installations have numerous control handles and levers connected to the engine by rods, cables, bellcranks, pulleys, etc. The control handles, in most cases, are conveniently mounted on quadrants in the cockpit. Placards or other markings are placed on the quadrant to indicate the functions and positions of the levers. In some instances, friction clutches are installed to hold the controls in place.

Manifold pressure, RPM, engine temperature, oil temperature, carburetor air temperature, and the fuel/air ratio can usually be controlled by manipulating the cockpit controls. Coordinated movement of the controls with the instrument readings protects against exceeding the operating limits.

The procedures, pressures, temperatures and RPM's used throughout this section are solely for the purpose of illustration and do not have general application. The operating procedures and limits used on individual makes and models of aircraft engines vary considerably. For exact information regarding a specific engine model, consult the applicable manufacturer's instructions.

1. Ground Operations

Ground operations must be carried out in such a manner that both the safety of personnel and the possibility of damage to aircraft and equipment are taken into consideration. All ground operations should be conducted in an area designated for such. The aircraft should be positioned on a clean level surface and aimed so that the propeller blast will not cause damage. The wheels should be securely chocked, or the aircraft tied down so that there is no danger of movement during engine power checks. Do not rely solely on the aircraft brakes to prevent movement during high power operations.

Ground service equipment such as auxiliary power carts, hydraulic service units, etc. should be positioned well away from the propeller arc, and their wheels chocked or brakes set. Adequate fire protection should be provided, being certain that the fire extinguisher is clear of the propeller area.

2. Engine Starting

Correct starting technique is an important part of engine operation. Improper procedures often are used because some basic principles involved in engine operation are misunderstood. Starting procedures will vary with the type of fuel metering system installed, and sometimes between manufacturers of the same category (e.g. Continental and RSA fuel injection systems). The technician should always use a checklist prepared for the particular aircraft being operated.

3. Engine Warm-Up

Proper engine warm-up is important, particularly when the condition of the engine is unknown. Improperly adjusted idle mixture, intermittently firing spark plugs, and improperly adjusted engine valves all have an overlapping effect on engine stability. Therefore, the warm up should be made at the engine speed where maximum engine stability is obtained. This speed will be where the engine operation is the smoothest, since the smooth operation is an indication that all phases of engine operation are the most stable.

During warm-up, watch the instruments associated with engine operation. This will aid in making sure that all phases of operation are normal. For example, the engine oil pressure should be indicated within 30 seconds after the start. Furthermore, if the oil pressure is not up to or above normal within 1 minute after the engine starts, the engine should be shut down. Cylinder head temperatures should be observed continually to see that they do not exceed the maximum allowable limit.

A lean mixture should not be used to hasten the warm-up. Actually, at the warm-up RPM, there is very little difference in the mixture supplied to the engine, whether the mixture is in a "rich" or "lean" position, since metering in this range is governed by the throttle position.

Carburetor heat can be used as required under conditions conducive to icing. For engines equipped with a float-type carburetor, it may be desirable to raise the carburetor air temperature during warm-up to prevent ice formation and to ensure smooth operation. Remember, the warm air provided by the carburetor heat system is not filtered; this system should not be used on the ground if dust and dirt may be ingested.

The magneto safety check can be performed during warm-up. Its purpose is to ensure that all ignition connections are secure and that the ignition system will permit operation at the higher power settings used during later phases of the ground check. This test is accomplished at idle RPM with the propeller in the high RPM (low pitch) position. Move the ignition switch from the "both" position to "right" and return to "both"; from "both" to "left" and return to "both"; from "both" to "off" momentarily, and return to "both".

While switching from "both" to a single magneto position, a slight but noticeable drop in RPM should occur. This indicates that the opposite magneto has been properly grounded out. Complete cutting out of the engine when switching from "both" to "off" indicates that both magnetos are properly grounded. Failure to obtain any drop in RPM while in the single magneto

position, or failure of the engine to cut out while switching to "off" indicates that one or both ground connections are not secured.

4. Ground Check

The ground check is performed to evaluate the functioning of the engine by comparing power input, as measured by manifold pressure, with power output, as measured by RPM.

The engine may be capable of producing a prescribed power, even rated takeoff, and not be functioning properly. Only by comparing manifold pressure required during the check against a known standard will an unsuitable condition be disclosed. The magneto check can fail to show up shortcomings, since the allowable RPM drop is only a measure of an improperly functioning ignition system and is not necessarily affected by other factors.

The ground check is made after the engine is thoroughly warm. It consists of checking the operation of the powerplant and accessory equipment by ear, by visual inspection, and by proper interpretation of instrument readings, control movements, and switch reactions. Generally, the ground check items will be included in the preflight run-up checklist provided for the flight crew.

During the ground check, the aircraft should be headed into the wind, if possible, to take advantage of the cooling airflow. A ground check may be performed as follows:

Control position check:
Cowl flap ....open
Mixture ....rich
Propeller ....high RPM
Carburetor heat .....cold

Procedure:
(1) Check propeller operation according to propeller manufacturer's instructions.
(2) Open throttle to manifold pressure specified for ground checks.
(3) Move magneto switch from "both" to "right" and return to "both". Switch from "both" to "left" and return to "both". Observe the RPM drop while operating on the right and left positions. The drop while operating on either single magneto should be approximately the same, and the maximum drop should not exceed that specified by the engine manufacturer.
(4) Check the fuel pressure and oil pressure. They must be within the established tolerances for the subject engine.
(5) Note RPM.

(6) Retard throttle to idle position.

In addition to the operations outlined above, check the functioning of various items of aircraft equipment, such as generator systems, hydraulic systems, etc. The test procedures for these systems are generally detailed on the aircraft checklist for run-up.

Below we will examine the information obtained by the tests listed above.

a. Ignition Operation

By comparing RPM drop with a known standard, the following are determined:

(1) Proper timing of each magneto.

(2) General engine performance as evidenced by smooth operation.

(3) Additional check of the proper connection of the ignition leads.

Any unusual roughness on either magneto is an indication of faulty ignition caused by plug fouling or by malfunctioning of the ignition system. The operator should be very sensitive to engine roughness during this check. Lack of drop-off in RPM may be an indication of faulty grounding of one side of the ignition system. Complete cutting out when switched to one magneto is definite evidence that its side of the ignition system is not operating. Excessive difference in RPM between the left and right switch positions can indicate a difference in timing between the left and right magnetos.

Sufficient time should be given to check on each single switch position to permit complete stabilization of engine speed and manifold pressure. There is a tendency to perform this check too rapidly with resultant wrong indications. Single ignition operation for 1 minute is not excessive.

Another point that must be emphasized is the danger of a sticking tachometer. The tachometer should be tapped lightly with the finger to make sure that the indicator needle moves freely. In most cases tapping the instrument eliminates the sticking and results in an accurate reading.

Fast RPM drop is usually the result of either faulty spark plugs or faulty ignition harness. This is true because faulty plugs or bad leads take effect at once. The cylinder goes dead or starts firing intermittently the instant the switch is moved.

Slow RPM drop usually is caused by incorrect ignition timing or faulty valve adjustment. These conditions will result in a power loss, but it will not occur as rapidly as a dead spark plug. This explains the slow RPM drop as compared to the instantaneous drop with a dead plug or defective lead.

b. Propeller Pitch

The controllable, or constant speed propeller is checked to ensure proper operation of the pitch control mechanism. The operation of the propeller is checked by the indications of the tachometer and manifold pressure gauge when the propeller control is moved from one position to another. Because each type propeller requires a different procedure, the applicable manufacturer's instructions should be followed.

c. Power Check

Specific RPM and manifold pressure relationship should be tested during the ground check. This can be done at the time the engine is run-up to make the magneto check. The basic idea of this check is to measure the performance of the engine against an established standard. Calibration tests have determined that the engine is capable of delivering a given power at a given RPM and manifold pressure. With constant conditions of air density, the propeller, at any fixed pitch position, will always require the same RPM to absorb the same horsepower from the engine.

With the propeller in the low pitch (high RPM) position, advance the throttle to obtain the target RPM established by the manufacturer. Observe the manifold pressure. Under these conditions, the manifold pressure for any specific engine will indicate whether all the cylinders are operating properly.

With one or more dead or intermittently firing cylinders, the operating cylinders must provide more power for a given RPM. Consequently, the throttle must be opened further, resulting in higher manifold pressure. A higher than normal manifold pressure usually indicates a dead cylinder or late ignition timing. An excessively low manifold pressure indicates that the ignition timing is early. Early ignition can cause detonation and loss of power at takeoff power settings.

d. Idle Speed And Mixture

Plug fouling difficulty is the inevitable result of failure to provide a proper idle mixture setting. The tendency seems to be to adjust the idle mixture to the extremely rich side and to compensate by adjusting the throttle stop to a relatively high RPM for minimum idling. With a properly adjusted idle mixture setting, it is possible to run the engine at idle RPM for long periods. Such a setting will result in a minimum of plug fouling and exhaust smoking and it will pay dividends from the savings on the aircraft brakes during landing and taxiing.

If the wind is not too strong, the idle mixture setting can be checked easily during ground check as follows:

(1) Close throttle.

(2) Move the mixture control to the "idle cutoff" position and observe the change in RPM. Return the mixture control back to the "rich" position before engine cutoff.

As the mixture control lever is moved into the cutoff position, and before normal drop-off, one of two things may occur momentarily:

(1) The engine speed may increase. An increase in RPM, but less than that recommended by the manufacturer (usually 20 RPM), indicates proper mixture strength. A greater increase indicates that the mixture is too rich.

(2) The engine speed may not increase, or may drop immediately. This indicates that the idle mixture is too lean.

e. Acceleration And Deceleration

This check will, in many cases, show up borderline conditions that will not be revealed by any of the other checks. This is true because the high cylinder pressures developed in this check put added strain on both the ignition system and the fuel metering system. This added strain is sufficient to point out certain defects that otherwise would go unnoticed. Engines must be capable of rapid acceleration, since in an emergency, such as a go around during landing, the ability of an engine to accelerate rapidly is sometimes the difference between a successful go around and a crash landing.

Move the throttle from idle to takeoff, smoothly and rapidly. The engine RPM should increase without hesitation and with no evidence of engine backfire. The deceleration check is made while retarding the throttle from the acceleration test. The RPM should decrease smoothly and evenly. There should be little or no tendency for the engine to after-fire.

5. Engine Stopping

With each type of carburetor or fuel injection system installation, specific procedures are used in stopping the engine. Instructions provided by the manufacturer's checklist should be followed exactly. Generally engines are shutdown by placing the mixture control in the "idle cut off" posi-

tion. This procedure assures that there is little or no fuel in the system that could result in an accidental start, if the propeller were moved with the ignition activated. Generally aircraft are parked with the mixture control in the "idle cut off" position.

6. Basic Engine Operating Principles

A thorough understanding of the basic principles on which a reciprocating engine operates and the many factors which affect its operation is necessary to diagnose engine malfunctions. Some of these basic principles are reviewed not as a mere repetition of basic theory, but as a concrete, practical discussion of what makes for good or bad engine performance.

a. Combustion Process

Normal combustion occurs when the fuel/air mixture ignites in the cylinder and burns progressively at a fairly uniform rate across the combustion chamber. When ignition is properly timed, maximum pressure is built up just after the piston has passed top dead center at the end of the compression stroke.

The flame fronts start at each spark plug and burn in more or less a wavelike form (figure 4-42). The velocity of the flame travel is influenced by the type of fuel, the ratio of the fuel/air mixture, and the pressure and temperature of the fuel mixture. With normal combustion, the flame travel is about 1 ft/sec. The temperature and pressure within the cylinder rises at a normal rate as the fuel/air mixture burns.

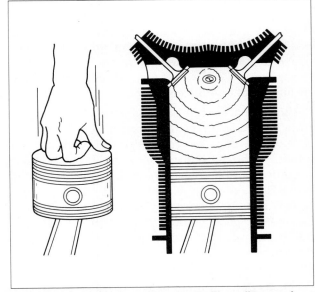

Figure 4-42. Normal combustion is like a firm push on the piston.

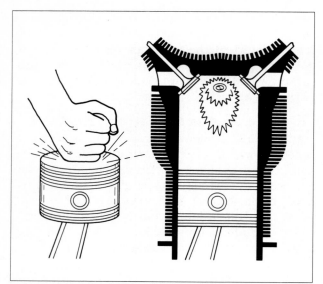

Figure 4-43. Detonation is a violent hammering on the piston head.

There is a limit, however, to the amount of compression and the degree of temperature rise that can be tolerated within an engine cylinder and still permit normal combustion. All fuels will have critical limits of temperature and compression. Beyond this limit, they will ignite spontaneously and burn with explosive violence. This instantaneous and explosive burning of the fuel/air mixture or, more accurately, of the latter portion of the charge, is called detonation.

Detonation (figure 4-43) is the spontaneous combustion of the unburned charge ahead of the flame fronts after the ignition of the charge. The explosive burning during detonation results in an extremely rapid pressure rise. This pressure rise and the high instantaneous temperature, combined with the high turbulence generated, cause a "scrubbing" action on the cylinder and the piston. This can burn a hole completely through a piston in seconds.

The critical point of detonation varies with the ratio of fuel to air in the mixture. Therefore, the detonation can be controlled by varying the fuel/air ratio. At high power output, combustion pressures and temperatures are higher than they are at low or medium power. Therefore, at high power the fuel/air ratio is made richer than needed for good combustion at low or medium power output. This is done because, in general, a rich mixture will not detonate as readily as a lean mixture.

Unless detonation is heavy, there is no cockpit evidence of its presence. Light to medium detonation does not cause noticeable engine roughness, temperature increase, or loss of power. As a result, it can be present during takeoff and climb without being known to the flight crew. In fact, detonation is often not discovered until after tear down of the engine. When the engine is overhauled, the presence of severe detonation during its operation may be indicated by dished piston heads, collapsed valve heads, broken ring lands, or eroded portions of valves, pistons, or cylinder heads.

The basic protection from detonation is provided in the design of the engine carburetor setting, which automatically supplies the rich mixtures required for detonation suppression at high power, the rating limitations, which include maximum operating temperatures, and selection of the correct grade of fuel. The design factors, cylinder cooling, magneto timing, mixture distribution, supercharging, and carburetor setting are taken care of in the design and development of the engine and its method of installation in the aircraft.

Preignition, as the name implies, means that the combustion takes place within the cylinder before the timed spark jumps across the spark plug terminals. This condition can often be traced to excessive carbon or other deposits which cause local hot spots. Detonation often leads to preignition. However, preignition may also be caused by high power operation on excessively lean mixtures. Preignition is usually indicated in the cockpit by engine roughness, backfiring, and by a sudden increase in cylinder head temperature.

Any area within the combustion chamber which becomes incandescent will serve as an igniter in advance of normal timed ignition. Preignition may be caused by an area roughened and heated by detonation erosion. A cracked valve or piston, or a broke spark plug insulator may furnish a hot point which serves as the "glow plug".

The most obvious method of correcting preignition is to reduce the cylinder temperature. The immediate step is to retard the throttle. This reduces the amount of fuel charge and the amount of heat generated. Following this, the mixture should be enriched, if possible, to lower combustion temperature.

If the engine is at high power when preignition occurs, retarding the throttle for a few seconds may provide enough cooling to chip off some of the lead, or other deposits within the combustion chamber. These particles may pass out through the exhaust.

b. Backfiring

When a fuel/air mixture does not contain enough fuel to consume all the oxygen, it is called a lean mixture. Conversely, a charge that contains more fuel than required is called a rich mixture. An extremely lean mixture will not burn at all or will burn so slowly that combustion is not complete at the end of the exhaust stroke. The flame lingers in the cylinder and then ignites the contents of the intake manifold or the induction system when the intake valve opens. This causes an explosion known as backfiring, which can damage the carburetor and other parts of the induction system.

A point worth stressing is that backfiring rarely involves the whole engine. Therefore, it is seldom the fault of the carburetor. In practically all cases, backfiring is limited to one or two cylinders. Usually it is the result of faulty valve clearance setting, defective fuel injector nozzles, or other conditions which cause these cylinders to operate leaner than the engine as a whole. There can be no permanent cure until these defects are discovered and corrected. Because these backfiring cylinders will fire intermittently and therefore will run cool, they can be detected by the cold cylinder check. The cold cylinder check is discussed later in this chapter.

In some instances, an engine backfires in the idle range, but operates satisfactorily at medium and high power settings. The most likely cause, in this case, is an extremely lean idle fuel/air mixture usually corrects this difficulty.

c. After-firing

After-firing, sometimes called afterburning, often results when the fuel/air mixture is too rich. Overly rich mixtures are also slow burning. Therefore, charges of unburned fuel are present in the exhausted gases. Air from outside the exhaust stacks mix with this unburned fuel which ignites. This causes an explosion in the exhaust system. After-firing is perhaps more common where long exhaust ducting retains greater amounts of unburned charges. As in the case of backfiring, the correction for after-firing is the proper adjustment of the fuel/air mixture.

After-firing can also be caused by cylinders which are not firing because of faulty spark plugs, defective fuel injection nozzles, or incorrect valve clearance. The unburned mixture from these dead cylinders passes into the exhaust system, where it ignites and burns. Unfortunately, the resultant torching or afterburning can easily be mistaken for evidence of a rich carburetor. Cylinders which are after-firing intermittently can cause a similar effect. Again, the malfunction can be remedied only by discovering the cause and correcting the defect. Either dead or intermittent cylinders can be located by the cold cylinder check.

7. Factors Affecting Engine Operation

a. Compression

To prevent loss of power, all openings to the cylinder must close and seal completely on the compression strokes. In this respect, there are three items that must be right for maximum efficiency. First, the piston rings must be in good condition so that there is no leakage between the piston and the walls of the combustion chamber. Second, the intake and exhaust valves must close tightly so that there will be no loss of compression at these points. Third, and very important, the timing of the valves must be such that highest efficiency is obtained when the engine is operating at its normal rated RPM.

b. Fuel Metering

The induction system is the distribution and fuel metering part of the engine. Obviously, any defects in the induction system seriously affects engine operation. For best operation, each cylinder must be provided with the proper fuel/air mixture.

The relationship between fuel/air ratio and power is illustrated in figure 4-44. Note that, as the fuel mixture is varied from lean to rich, the

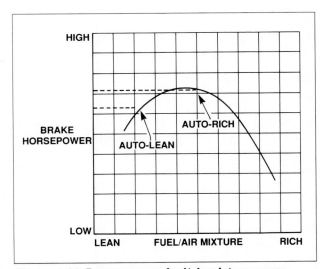

Figure 4-44. Power versus fuel/air mixture curve.

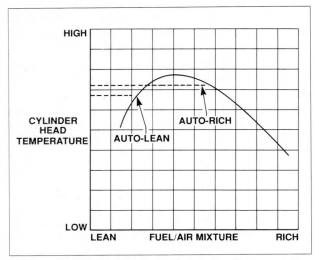

Figure 4-45. Variation in cylinder head temperature with fuel/air mixture (cruise power).

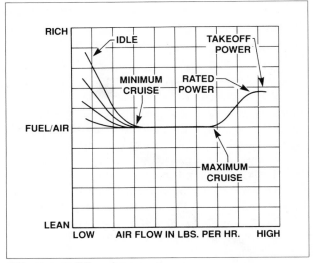

Figure 4-47. Idle mixture curve.

power output of the engine increases until it reaches a maximum. Beyond this point, the power output falls off as the mixture is further enriched. This is because the fuel mixture is now too rich to provide perfect combustion.

In establishing the detailed engine requirements regarding carburetor settings, the fact that the cylinder head temperature varies with the fuel/air ratio must be considered. This variation is illustrated in the curve shown in figure 4-45.

The final fuel/air mixture chart takes into account economy, power, engine cooling, idling characteristics, and all other factors which affect combustion.

Figure 4-46 shows a typical final curve for a float-type carburetor. Note that the fuel/air mix-

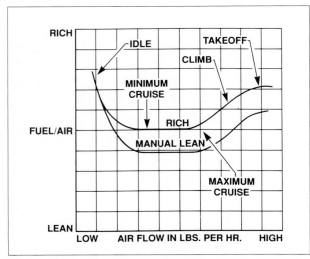

Figure 4-46. Typical fuel/air mixture curve for float-type carburetor.

ture at idle is the same in rich and manual lean. This mixture remains the same until low cruise is reached. At this point, the curves separate and then remain parallel through the cruise and power ranges.

c. Idle Mixture

The idle mixture curve (figure 4-47) shows how the mixture changes when the idle mixture adjustment is changed. Note that the greatest effect is at idling speeds. However, there is some effect on the mixture at airflows above idling. The airflow at which the idle adjustment effect cancels out varies from minimum cruise to maximum cruise. The exact point depends on the type of carburetor and the carburetor settings. In general, the idle adjustment affects the fuel/air mixture up to medium cruise on most engines having pressure injection carburetors and up to low cruise on engines equipped with float-type carburetors. This means that incorrect idle mixture adjustments can easily give faulty cruise performance as well as poor idling.

d. Induction Manifold

The induction manifold provides the means of distributing air, or the fuel/air mixture, to the cylinders. Whether the manifold handles a fuel/air mixture or air alone depends on the type of fuel metering system used.

The induction manifold is an important item because of the effect it can have on the fuel/air mixture that finally reaches the cylinder. When fuel is introduced into the airstream by the carburetor in a liquid form, the fuel must be vaporized by the air. This vaporization takes place in the induction manifold. Any fuel that does not vaporize will cling to the walls of the intake pipes. Obviously, this affects the effective fuel/air mixture which finally reaches the cylinder. This explains the reason for an apparently rich mixture required to start a cold engine. In a cold engine, some of the fuel in the airstream condenses out and clings to the walls of the manifold. This is in addition to that fuel which never vaporized in the first place. As the engine warms up, less fuel is required because less fuel is condensed out of the airstream and more of the fuel is vaporized, thus giving the cylinder the required fuel/air mixture for normal combustion.

Any leak in the induction system has an effect on the mixture reaching the cylinders. This is particularly true of a leak at the cylinder end of an intake pipe. At manifold pressures below atmospheric pressure, such a leak will lean out the mixture. This occurs because additional air is drawn in from the atmosphere at the leaky point. The affected cylinder may overheat, fire intermittently, or even cut out altogether.

e. Operational Effect Of Valve Clearance

While considering the operational effect of valve clearance, keep in mind that all reciprocating aircraft engines of current design use valve overlap. Engine, airplane, and equipment manufacturers provide a powerplant installation that will give satisfactory performance. Cams are designed to give best valve operation and correct overlap. But valve operation will be correct only if valve clearances are set and remain at the value recommended by the engine manufacturer.

When there is too much valve clearance, the valves will not open as wide or remain open as long as they should. This reduces the valve overlap period. At idling speed, it will affect the fuel/air mixture, since a less than normal amount of air or exhaust gases will be drawn back into the cylinder during the shortened overlap period. As a result, the idle mixture will tend to be too rich.

When valve clearance is less than it should be, the valve overlap period will be lengthened. This permits a greater than normal amount of air or exhaust gases to be drawn back into the cylinder at idling speeds. As a result, the idle mixture will be leaned out at the cylinder.

When valve clearances are wrong, it is unlikely that they will all be wrong in the same direction. Instead, there will be too much clearance on some cylinders and too little on others. Naturally, this gives a variation in valve overlap between cylinders. This, in turn, results in a variation in the fuel/air ratio at idling and lower power settings, since the carburetor delivers the same mixture to all cylinders. On such an engine, it would be impossible to set the idle adjustment to give correct mixtures on all cylinders, nor can all cylinders of such an engine be expected to produce the same power. Variations in valve clearance of as little as 0.005 in. have a definite effect on mixture distribution between cylinders.

Another aspect of valve clearance is its effect on volumetric efficiency. Considering the intake valve first, suppose valve clearance is greater than specified. As the cam lobe starts to pass under the lifter, the cam step or ramp takes up part of this clearance. However, it doesn't take up all the clearance as it should. Therefore, the cam roller is well up on the lobe before the valve starts to open. As a result, the valve opens later than it should. In a similar way, the valve closes before the roller has passed from the main lobe to the ramp at its end. With excessive clearance, then, the intake valve opens late and closes early. This produces a throttling effect on the cylinder. The valve is not open long enough to admit a full charge of fuel and air. This will cut down on power output, particularly at high power settings.

Insufficient intake valve clearance has the opposite effect. The clearance is taken up and the valve starts to open while the lifter is still on the cam step. The valve doesn't close until the rise at the end of the lobe has almost passed completely under the lifter. Therefore, the intake valve opens early, closes late, and stays open longer than it should. At low power, early opening of the intake valve can cause backfiring because of the hot exhaust gases backing out into the intake manifold and igniting the mixture there.

Excessive valve clearance causes the exhaust valve to open late and close early. This shortens the exhaust event and causes poor scavenging. The late opening may also lead to cylinder overheating because the hot exhaust gases are held in the cylinder beyond the time specified for their release.

When exhaust valve clearance is insufficient, the valve opens early and closes late. It remains open longer than it should. The early opening causes a power loss by shortening the power event. The pressure in the cylinder is released before all the useful expansion has worked on the piston. The late closing causes the exhaust valve to remain open during a larger portion of the intake stroke than it should. This may result in good mixture being lost through the exhaust port.

In all cases, variations in valve clearance from the value specified have the effect of changing the valve timing from that obtained with correct clearance. This is certain to give something less than perfect performance.

f. Ignition System

The next item to be considered regarding engine operation is the ignition system. Although basically simple, it is sometimes not understood clearly.

An ignition system consists of three main parts:

(1) The magneto (with built in distributor).

(2) The ignition harness.

(3) The spark plug.

The magneto is a high voltage generating device. It must be adjusted to give maximum voltage at the time the points open, and ignition occurs (internal timing). It must also be synchronized accurately to the firing position of the engine (magneto-to-engine timing). The magneto generates a series of peak voltages which are released by the opening of the breaker points. A distributor will route these voltages to the cylinders in proper order. The ignition harness constitutes the insulated and shielded high tension lines which carry the voltage from the distributor to the spark plugs.

The magneto-to-engine timing is established when the magneto is installed on the engine. The number 1 firing position on the distributor must be set to fire cylinder number 1 at the proper number of degrees before top center of the compression stroke. If the magneto is timed to any cylinder other than the one intended, severe backfiring and general malfunctioning of the engine will occur.

Although the ignition harness is simple, it is a critical part of the ignition system. A number of things can cause failure of the ignition harness. Insulation may break down on a wire inside the harness and allow the high voltage to leak through to the shielding (and to ground), instead of going to the spark plug. Open circuits may result from broken wires or poor connections. A bare wire may be in contact with shielding, or two wires may be shorted together.

Any serious defect in an individual lead prevents the high voltage impulse from reaching the spark plug to which it is connected. As a result, only one spark plug in the cylinder will fire. This causes the cylinder to operate on a single ignition. This may result in detonation at takeoff or high power operation. Two bad leads to the same cylinder will cause the cylinder to go completely dead.

Among the most common ignition harness defects, and the most difficult to detect, are high voltage leaks. However, a complete harness check will reveal these and other defects.

Although the spark plug is simple both in construction and in operation, it is, nevertheless, the direct or indirect cause of a great many malfunctions in aircraft engines. Proper precaution begins with plug selection. Be sure to install the plug specified for the particular engine. One of the reasons a particular plug is specified is its heat range. The heat range of the spark plug determines the temperature at which the nose of the plug operates. It also affects the ability of the spark plug to ignite mixtures which are borderline from the standpoint of high oil content or excessive richness or leanness.

A great many troubles attributed to spark plugs are the direct result of malfunctions somewhere in the engine. Some of these are excessively rich idle mixtures, improperly adjusted valves, and worn piston rings or valve guides.

g. Propeller Governor

The final item to be considered regarding engine operation is the effect of the propeller gover-

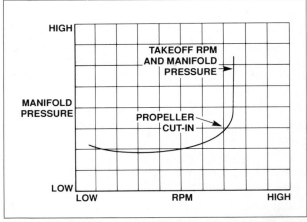

Figure 4-48. Effect of propeller governor on manifold pressure.

nor on engine operation. In the curve shown in figure 4-48, note that the manifold pressure change with RPM is gradual until the propeller governor cut-in speed is reached. Beyond this point, the manifold pressure increases, but no change occurs in engine RPM as the throttle is opened wider.

A true picture of the power output of the engine can be determined only at speeds below the propeller governor cut in speed. The propeller governor is set to maintain a given engine RPM Therefore, the relationship between engine speed and manifold pressure as an indication of power output is lost, unless it is known that all cylinders of the engine are functioning properly.

h. Overlapping Phase Of Engine Operation

Up to this point, the individual phases of engine operation have been discussed. The relationship of the phases and their combined effect on engine operation will now be considered. Combustion within the cylinder is the result of fuel metering, compression, and ignition. Since valve overlap affects fuel metering, proper combustion in all the cylinders involves correct valve adjustment in addition to all other phases. When all conditions are correct, there is a burnable mixture. When ignited, this mixture will give power impulses of the same intensity from all cylinders.

The system which ignites the combustible mixture requires that the following conditions occur simultaneously if the necessary spark impulse is to be delivered to the cylinder at the proper time.

    (1) The breaker points must be timed accurately to the magneto (internal timing).

    (2) The magneto must be timed accurately to the engine.

    (3) The ignition harness must be in good condition.

    (4) The spark plug must be clean, have no tendency to short out, and have the proper electrode gap.

If any one of these requirements are lacking, or if any phase of the ignition system is maladjusted or is not functioning properly, the entire ignition system can be disrupted to the point that improper engine operation results.

Only when all systems are in good condition, properly adjusted, and operating in harmony will the engine be able to produce maximum power and operate efficiently during all phases of the flight.

8. Engine Troubleshooting

The need for troubleshooting normally is dictated by poor operation of the complete powerplant. Efficient troubleshooting is based on a systematic analysis of what is happening so you will be able to determine the cause of a malfunction. There is no magic in successful troubleshooting, but it is rather the application of logic and a thorough knowledge of the basics of engine operation.

a. Trouble—Cause—Remedy

If you are faced with a problem of deteriorating engine performance, for example, the first thing to do is to get all of the facts. Take nothing for granted, but ask questions of the pilot to determine such things as: Did the trouble come about suddenly or was it a gradual decrease in performance? Under what conditions of altitude, humidity, temperature, or power setting does this performance loss show up? Does temporarily switching to one magneto cause any change in performance? What effect did leaning the mixture, or applying carburetor heat have on the problem? Did switching from one fuel tank to another, or turning on the fuel boost pump have any effect on the problem.

After getting all of the facts, the next step is to eliminate all of the areas that are not likely to cause the trouble. For example, if the magneto drop is normal, but there is a loss of power, the ignition system is more than likely not the problem.

Figure 4-49 lists general conditions or troubles which may be encountered with reciprocating engines, such as "engine fails to start." They are further divided into the probable causes contributing to such conditions. Corrective actions are indicated in the "remedy" column. The items are presented with consideration given to frequency of occurrence, ease of accessibility, and complexity of the corrective action indicated.

b. Cylinder Maintenance

Each cylinder is, in reality, an engine in itself. In most cases the cylinder receives its fuel and air from a common source such as the carburetor. Every phase of cylinder operation, such as compression, fuel mixture, and ignition must function properly, since even one type of malfunctioning will cause engine difficulty. Engine difficulties, therefore, can be corrected only after malfunctioning cylinders have been located and

TROUBLE	PROBABLE CAUSES	REMEDY
Engine fails to start.	Lack of fuel.	Check fuel system for leaks. Fill fuel tank. Clean dirty lines, strainers, or fuel valves.
	Underpriming.	Use correct priming procedure.
	Overpriming.	Open throttle and "unload" engine by rotating the propeller.
	Incorrect throttle setting.	Open throttle to one-tenth of its range.
	Defective spark plugs.	Clean and regap or replace spark plugs.
	Defective ignition wire.	Test and replace any defective wires.
	Defective or weak battery.	Replace with charged battery.
	Improper operation of magneto or breaker points.	Check internal timing of magnetos.
	Water in carburetor.	Drain carburetor and fuel lines.
	Internal failure.	Check oil sump strainer for metal particles.
	Dirty air filter.	Clean or replace.
Low power or engine running uneven.	Mixture too rich; indicated by sluggish engine operation, red exhaust flame, and black smoke.	Check primer. Readjust carburetor mixture.
	Mixture too lean; indicated by overheating or backfiring.	Check fuel lines for dirt or other restrictions. Check fuel supply.
	Leaks in induction system.	Tighten all connections. Replace defective parts.
	Defective spark plugs.	Clean or replace spark plugs.
	Improper grade of fuel.	Fill tank with recommended grade.
	Magneto breaker points not working properly.	Clean points. Check internal timing of magneto.
	Defective ignition wire.	Test and replace any defective wires.
	Defective spark plug terminal connectors.	Replace connectors on spark plug wire.
	Incorrect valve clearance.	Adjust valve clearance.
	Restriction in exhaust system.	Remove restriction.
	Improper ignition timing.	Check magnetos for timing and synchronization.
Engine fails to develop full power.	Throttle lever out of adjustment.	Adjust throttle lever.
	Leak in induction system.	Tighten all connections and replace defective parts.
	Restriction in carburetor airscoop.	Examine airscoop and remove restriction.
	Improper fuel.	Fill tank with recommended fuel.
	Propeller governor out of adjustment.	Adjust governor.
	Faulty ignition.	Tighten all connections. Check system. Check ignition timing.
Rough running engine.	Cracked engine mount (s).	Repair or replace engine mount(s).
	Unbalanced propeller.	Remove propeller and have it checked for balance.
	Defective mounting bushings.	Install new mounting bushings.
	Lead deposit on spark plugs.	Clean or replace plugs.
	Primer unlocked.	Lock primer.

Figure 4-49. Troubleshooting opposed engines.

defective phases of cylinder operation brought back up to normal.

1) Hydraulic Lock

Whenever a radial engine remains shut down for any length of time beyond a few minutes, oil or fuel may drain into combustion chambers of the lower cylinders, or accumulate in the lower intake pipes ready to be drawn into the cylinder when the engine starts (figure 4-50). As the piston approaches top center of the compression stroke, this liquid, being incompressible, stops piston movement. If the crankshaft continues to rotate, something must give.

Starting, or attempting to start an engine with a hydraulic lock may cause the affected cylinder to blow out or, more likely, may result in a bent or broken connecting rod.

Before attempting to start any radial engine that has been shut down for more than 30 minutes, check the ignition switches for "off" and then pull the propeller through in the direction of rotation a minimum of two complete turns to be sure that there is no hydraulic lock, or to detect a hydraulic lock if one is present. Any liquid present in a cylinder will be indicated by the abnormal effort required to rotate the propeller. However, never use force when a hydraulic lock is detected.

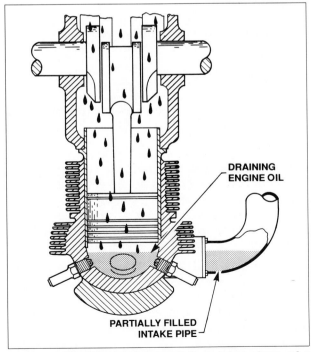

Figure 4-50. Oil seeping past the piston rings of a radial engine may cause hydraulic lock.

To eliminate a lock, remove either the front or rear spark plug of the cylinder and pull the propeller through in the direction of rotation. The piston will expel any liquid that may be present. Never attempt to clear the hydraulic lock by pulling the propeller through in the direction opposite to normal rotation, since this tends to inject the liquid from the cylinder into the intake pipe with the possibility of a complete or partial lock on the subsequent start.

2) Valve Blow-by

Valve blow-by is indicated by a hissing or whistle when pulling the propeller through prior to starting the engine, when turning the engine with the starter, or when running the engine at low speeds. It is caused by a valve sticking open, or warped to the extent that compression is not built up in the cylinder. Blow-by past exhaust valves can be heard at the exhaust stack, and blow-by past the intake valve is audible through the carburetor.

Correct valve blow-by immediately to prevent valve failure and possible engine failure by taking the following steps:

(1) Perform a differential compression test to locate the faulty cylinder.

(2) Check the valve clearance on the affected cylinder. If the valve clearance is incorrect, the valve may be sticking in the valve guide. To release the sticking valve, place a fiber drift on the rocker arm immediately over the valve stem and strike the drift several times with a mallet.

(3) If the valve is not sticking and the valve clearance is incorrect, adjust as necessary.

(4) Determine whether blow-by has been eliminated by pulling the engine through, or performing another compression test. If blow-by is still present, it may be necessary to replace the cylinder.

c. Compression Testing

The cylinder compression test determines if the valves, piston rings, and pistons are adequately sealing the combustion chamber. Although it is possible for the engine to lose compression for other reasons, low compression for the most part can be traced to leaky valves. Conditions which affect engine compression are:

(1) Incorrect valve clearances.

(2) Worn, scuffed, or damaged piston.

(3) Excessive wear of piston rings and cylinder walls.

(4) Burned or warped valves.

(5) Carbon particles between the face and the seat of the valve or valves.

(6) Early or late valve timing.

Perform a compression test as soon as possible after the engine is shut down so that piston rings, cylinder walls, and other parts are still freshly lubricated. However, it is not necessary to operate the engine prior to accomplishing compression checks during engine buildup or on individually replaced cylinders. In such cases, before making the test, spray a small quantity of lubricating oil into the cylinder or cylinders and turn the engine over several times to seal the piston and rings in the cylinder barrel.

The two basic types of compression testers are the direct compression tester and the differential compression tester. When performing a compression test, follow the manufacturer's instructions for the particular tester being used.

1) Direct

This type of compression test indicates the actual pressures within the cylinder. Although the particular defective component within the cylinder is difficult to determine with this method, the consistency of the readings is an indication of the condition of the engine as a whole. Because of its ability to indicate where the problem is, the differential compression tester is used almost universally today.

2) Differential Pressure

The differential pressure tester checks the compression of an aircraft engine by measuring the leakage through the cylinder. The design of this compression tester is such that minute leakages can be detected and their source quickly determined.

The operation of the tester is based on the principle that, for any given airflow through a fixed orifice, a constant pressure drop across the orifice will result. As the airflow varies, the pressure changes accordingly and in the same direction. If air is supplied under pressure to the cylinder with both intake and exhaust valves closed, the amount of air that leaks by the valves or piston rings indicates their condition; the perfect cylinder, of course, would have no leakage.

The differential pressure tester (figure 4-51) requires that the application of air pressure to the cylinder be tested with the piston at top dead center on the compression stroke.

Guidelines for performing a differential compression test are:

(1) Perform the test as soon a possible after engine shutdown to provide uniform lubrication of cylinder walls and rings.

(2) Remove the most accessible spark plug from the cylinder and install the compression tester adapter in the spark plug hole.

(3) Connect the compression tester to a 100 to 150-p.s.i. air supply. With the shutoff valve on the compression tester closed, adjust the regulator of the compression tester to obtain 80 p.s.i. on the regulated pressure gauge.

(4) By hand, rotate the engine over in the direction of normal operation until the piston in the cylinder comes up on the compression stroke. Continue turning the propeller slowly in the direction of rotation until the piston comes up to top dead center. If you past top center, back the propeller up at least one blade prior to turning the propeller again in the direction of rotation. This is necessary to eliminate the effect of backlash in the valve operating mechanism and to keep the piston rings seated on the lower ring lands.

(5) Recheck the regulated pressure gauge on the compression tester for 80 p.s.i. and connect the tester to the spark plug adapter. Open the shutoff valve on the compression tester, after making sure that the propeller path is clear of all objects and personnel. There will be sufficient air pressure in the combustion chamber to rotate the propeller if the piston is not on top dead center.

(6) With the regulated pressure at 80 p.s.i., if the cylinder pressure gauge pressure reading is below the minimum specified for the engine being tested, move the propeller in the direction of rotation to seat the piston rings in the grooves. If this is accomplished with the air pressure applied to the cylinder, make sure you have a tight enough grip on the propeller to prevent its rotation. Check all the cylinders and record the readings.

If low compression is obtained on any cylinder, turn the engine through with the starter, or restart and run the engine to takeoff power and recheck the cylinder or cylinders having low compression. When checking the compression, listen carefully to determine the source of the leakage.

Air can leak from the cylinder in three places: (1) past the intake valve, (2) past the exhaust valve and, (3) past the piston rings. Finding the source of the leak will determine the course of action necessary. Air leaking past the intake valve can be heard at the carburetor intake. Exhaust valve leaks will be evidenced by air heard

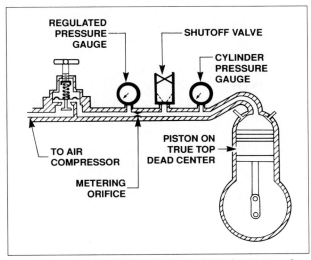

Figure 4-51. The differential compression tester is a simple but valuable diagnostic tool.

in the exhaust stacks. A hissing sound in the crankcase breather will indicate air leaking past the piston rings.

d. Cylinder Replacement

Reciprocating engine cylinders are designed to operate a specified time before normal wear will require their overhaul. If the engine is operated as recommended and proficient maintenance is performed, the cylinder will normally last until the engine reaches the recommended time between overhaul (TBO). It is known from experience that materials fail and engines are abused through incorrect operation; this has a serious effect on cylinder life. Another reason for premature cylinder change is poor maintenance. Therefore, exert special care to ensure that all the correct maintenance procedures are adhered to when working on the engine.

Some of the reasons for cylinder removal are:

(1) Low compression

(2) High oil consumption in one or more cylinders

(3) Excessive valve guide clearance

(4) Loose intake pipe flanges

(5) Loose or defective spark plug inserts

(6) External damage, such as cracks

When conditions like these are limited to one or a few cylinders, replacing the defective cylinders should return the engine to a serviceable condition.

Cylinder removal and installation procedures must be accomplished in strict accordance with the manufacturer's instructions. Because these operations will likely be carried out with the engine still installed on the aircraft, procedures will be slightly different than when the engine is installed on a build up stand.

Remove and mark each component so that it may be reinstalled in the same position. Where complete overhaul is not being accomplished, used parts should be returned to their original positions. Installation of the cylinder must include all new gaskets, seals and safety devices. Under no conditions are these considered reusable.

Replacement cylinders must be run in according to the manufacturer's specifications. Remember, the valves and piston rings in the replacement cylinder need to be seated, just as if the complete engine had been overhauled.

e. Valve And Valve Mechanisms

Valves open and close the ports in the cylinder head to control the entrance of the combustible mixture and the exit of the exhaust gases. It is important that they open and close properly and seal tightly against the ports to secure maximum power from the engine, and to prevent valve burning and warping.

Checking and adjusting valve clearance on engines equipped with solid lifters is perhaps the most important part of valve inspection, and certainly is the most difficult part. However, visual inspection should not be slighted.

f. Valve Adjustments

In order for a valve to seat, the valve must be in good condition, with no significant pressure being exerted against the end of the valve by the rocker arm. If the expansion of all parts of the engine were the same, the problem of ensuring valve seating would be very easy to solve. Practically no free space would be necessary in the valve system. However, since there is a great difference in the amount of expansion of various parts of the engine, there is no way of providing a constant operating clearance in the valve train on engines equipped with solid lifters.

The clearance in the valve actuating system is very small when the engine is cold but is much greater when the engine is operating at normal temperature. The difference is caused by differences in the expansion characteristics of the various metals and by the differences in temperatures of the various parts.

Valve clearances decrease with a drop in temperature; therefore insufficient clearance may cause the valve to hold open when extremely cold temperatures are encountered. This may make cold weather starting of the engine difficult, if not impossible, because of the inability of the cylinders to pull a charge into the combustion chamber.

Accurate valve adjustment also establishes the intended valve seating velocity. If valve clearances are excessive, the valve seating velocity is too high. The result is valve pounding and stem stretching, either of which is conducive to valve failure. Insufficient clearance may make starting difficult and cause valves to stick in the "open" position, causing blow-by and subsequent valve failure.

The engine manufacturer specifies the valve inspection period for each engine. In addition to the regular periods, inspect and adjust the valve mechanism any time there is rough engine operation, backfiring, loss of compression, or hard starting.

Because of variations in engine designs, various methods are required for setting valves to obtain correct and consistent clearance. In all cases, follow the exact procedure prescribed by the engine manufacturer, since obscure factors may be involved.

1) Radial Engines

Certain large radial engines may incorporate a "floating" cam ring which requires the use of established procedures to obtain satisfactory results when checking valve clearances. These procedures usually involve a chart indicating which two valves must be depressed to seat the cam ring so than an accurate measurement can be made on a third. This procedure will be repeated for each cylinder, two valves must be depressed so that a third can be checked.

2) Opposed-Type Engines

Horizontally opposed engines will use a cam shaft which is not subject to the type of movement mentioned above. This simplifies the procedure involved in checking valve clearances. As always consult the specific engine maintenance publications before attempting to make adjustments.

g. Valve Spring Replacement

A broken valve spring seldom affects engine operation and can, therefore, be detected only during careful inspection. Because multiple springs are used, one broken spring is hard to detect. When when a broken valve spring is dis-

covered, it can usually be replaced without removing the cylinder.

h. Cold Cylinder Check

The cold cylinder check determines the operating characteristics of each cylinder of an aircraft engine. The tendency of any cylinder or cylinders to be cold or only slightly warm indicates lack of combustion within the cylinder. This must be corrected if best operation and power conditions are to be obtained. The cold cylinder check is made with a cold cylinder indicator which is an accurate pyrometer with a probe that is touched to the cylinder. Engine difficulties which can be analyzed by use of the cold cylinder indicator are:

(1) Rough engine operation.
(2) Excessive RPM drop during the ignition system check.
(3) High manifold pressure for a given engine RPM during the ground check when the propeller is in the full low pitch position.
(4) Faulty mixture ratios cause by improper valve clearance.

In preparation for the cold cylinder check, head the aircraft into the wind to minimize irregular cooling of the individual cylinders and to ensure even propeller loading during engine operation.

Follow the starting checklist for the aircraft. After the engine is running, place the ignition switch in the position in which any excessive drop is obtained. Operate the engine at its roughest speed until a cylinder head temperature reading of 150° to 170°C is obtained, or until temperatures stabilize at a lower reading.

When the cylinder head temperatures have reached the above values, stop the engine by moving the mixture to idle cut off. When the engine ceases firing, turn off both ignition and master switches. Record the cylinder head temperature reading registered on the cockpit gauge.

As soon as the propeller has ceased rotating, check the temperature of each cylinder using the cold cylinder tester. Start with number one and proceed in numerical order around the engine as rapidly as possible. Recheck any low readings.

In interpreting the results of a cold cylinder check, remember that the temperatures are relative. A cylinder temperature taken alone means little, but when compared with the temperature of other cylinders on the same engine, it provides valuable diagnostic information.

D. Turbine Engine Maintenance

Turbine powerplant maintenance procedures vary widely according to the design and construction of the particular engine being serviced. The detailed procedures recommended by the engine manufacturer should be followed when performing inspections or maintenance. A good point to remember when working on turbine engines is that they are all lightweight, high speed machines which are manufactured to very close tolerances; therefore extreme care is required in their maintenance. This includes rigid adherence to established technical procedures, correct use of tools, and especially cleanliness of parts and shop environment.

For inspection purpose, the turbine engine is divided into two main sections, the cold section and the hot section.

1. Compressor Or Cold Section Inspection And Repair

Maintenance to the compressor, or cold section, is one of the concerns of the aviation technician. Damage to blades can cause engine failure and possible loss of the aircraft. Much of the damage to the blades arises from foreign matter being drawn into the turbine engine air intakes.

The atmosphere near the ground is filled with tiny particles of dirt, oil, soot, and other foreign matter. A large volume of air is drawn into the compressor, and centrifugal force throws the dirt particles outward so that they build up to form a coating on the casing, the vanes, and the compressor blades.

Accumulation of dirt on the compressor blades reduces the aerodynamic efficiency of the blades, with resultant deterioration in engine performance. The efficiency of the blades is impaired by dirt deposits in a manner similar to that of an aircraft wing under icing conditions. Unsatisfactory acceleration and high exhaust gas temperature can result from foreign particles on compressor components.

Gas path erosion occurs from ingestion of sand, dirt, dust, and other fine airborne contaminants. This ingestion affects both the compressor and the turbine sections. The abrasive effect of repeated ingestion can wear through the surface coating and even into the base metals of the fan, the compressor blades and vanes. It can even cause similar damage to the turbine before leaving the engine via the exhaust.

Designers of modern aircraft better understand this problem today and try to engineer the slip streams around the aircraft to carry contaminants around rather than into the inlets. However, many older aircraft have ingestion problems. Also, some have been reconfigured from narrow nacelles to wide, high by-pass fan engine nacelles and have very low ground clearance. These aircraft, especially, are experiencing performance loss and an increase in maintenance and fuel costs due to the effects of erosion on compressor and turbine parts.

a. Compressor Field Cleaning

Two common methods for removing dirt, salt, and corrosion deposits are a fluid wash and an abrasive grit blast.

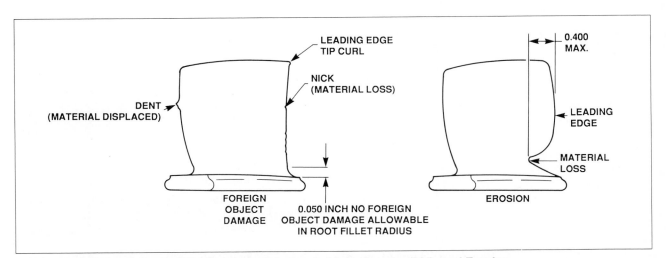

Figure 4-52. A comparison of damage to a compressor blade done by FOD, and Erosion.

1) Fluid Cleaning Procedure

The fluid cleaning procedure is easily accomplished by first spraying an emulsion type surface cleaner and then applying a rinse solution into the compressor. This is done while the engine is being motored over by the starter or during low speed operation. Figure 4-53 depicts a Pratt and Whitney PT-6 engine performance recovery wash apparatus. It cannot be overstressed that the wash procedure must be performed in strict accordance with the instructions set forth in the manufacturer's maintenance manual.

When the water wash is performed solely to remove salt deposits, the compressor wash is known as "desalination". If the solution wash is performed solely to remove baked on deposits to improve engine performance, the compressor wash is known as a "performance recovery wash".

Motoring wash is generally carried out at engine speeds of 14% to 25%, and with the cleaning mixture injected at a pressure of 30 to 50 pounds per square inch. A running wash may be performed at engine speeds of approximately 60%, with the cleaning mixture injected at 15 to 20 p.s.i. A typical wash schedule is seen in figure 4-54.

The timely use of fresh water rinsing, where prescribed, to remove salt deposits, and use of

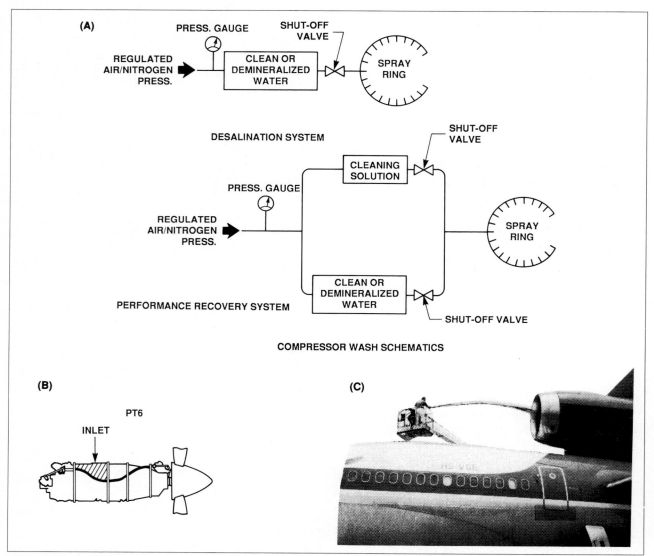

Figure 4-53. (A)—Compressor wash schematics of the PT-6 for desalination and power recovery washes. (B)—Water is introduced into engine inlet. (C)—Large engine compressor wash.

OPERATING ENVIRONMENT	NATURE OF WASH	RECOMMENDED FREQUENCY	RECOMMENDED METHOD	REMARKS
Continuously salt laden	Desalination	Daily	Motoring	Strongly recommended after last flight of day.
Occassionally salt laden	Desalination	Weekly	Motoring	Strongly recommended. Adjust washing frequency to suit condition.
All	Performance Recovery	100 to 200 hours	Motoring or Running	Strongly recommended. Performance recovery required less frequently. Adjust washing frequency to suit engine operating conditions as indicated by engine condition monitoring system. Motoring wash for light soil and multiple motoring or running wash for heavy soil is recommended.

Figure 4-54. Typical wash schedule.

inlet and exhaust plugs will greatly reduce the need for heavy cleaning procedures.

2) Abrasive Grit Process

A second more vigorous method of compressor cleaning is to inject an abrasive grit into the engine at selected power settings. The grit used may be ground walnut shells or apricot pits. The type and amount of material, and the operational procedure is prescribed by the manufacturer for each particular engine. The greater capability of this procedure over the solvent and water methods allows the time interval between cleaning to be longer, but because the cleaning grit is mostly burned up in combustion, the agent does not clean turbine blades and vanes as effectively as the fluid wash.

b. Causes Of Blade Damage

Loose objects often enter an engine either accidently or through carelessness. Items, such as pencils, handkerchiefs, and cigarette lighters, are often drawn into the engine. Do not carry any objects in shirt pockets when working around turbine engines.

A compressor rotor can be damaged beyond repair by tools that are left in the air intake, where they are drawn into the engine on subsequent starts. A simple solution to the problem of tools being drawn into an engine is to check the tools against a tool checklist. Prior to starting a turbine engine, make a minute inspection of engine inlet ducts to assure that items such as nuts, bolts, lock wire, or tools were not left there after work had been performed.

Figure 4-56 shows some examples of blade damage to an axial flow engine. The descriptions and possible causes of blade damage are given on the chart in figure 4-57.

c. Blending And Blade Replacement

Minor damage to engine compressor and fan blades may be repaired, if the damage can be removed without exceeding the allowable limits established by the manufacturer. Typical fan blade repair limits are shown in figure 4-58. Well rounded damage to leading and trailing edges that is evident on the opposite side of the blade is usually acceptable without rework, provided that the damage is in the outer half of the blade only, and the indentation does not exceed the values specified in the engine manufacturer's service and overhaul manual. All repairs must be well blended so that surfaces are smooth (figure 4-59). No cracks of any extent are tolerated in any area.

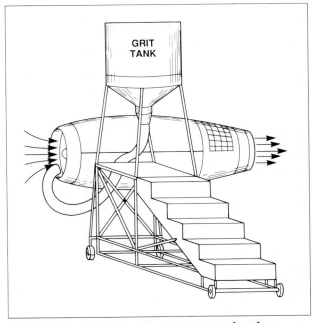

Figure 4-55. Abrasive grit compressor cleaning.

Because of the thin sheet construction of hollow vanes, blending on the concave and convex surfaces, including the leading edge, is limited.

Small, shallow dents are acceptable, if the damage is of a rounded or gradual contour type and not a sharp or V-type, and if no cracking or

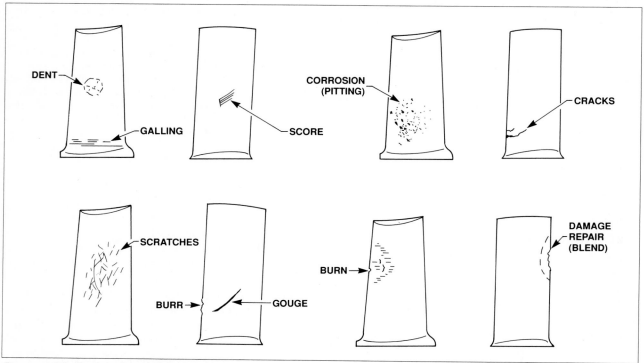

Figure 4-56. Compressor blade damage.

Term	Appearance	Usual Causes
Blend	Smooth repair of ragged edge or surface into the contour of surrounding area.	
Bow	Bent blade.	Foreign objects.
Burning	Damage to surfaces evidenced by discoloration or, in severe cases, by flow of material.	Excessive heat.
Burr	A ragged or turned out edge.	Grinding or cutting operation.
Corrosion (pits)	Breakdown of the surface; pitted appearance.	Corrosive agents - moisture, etc.
Cracks	A partial fracture (separation).	Excessive stress due to shock, overloading, or faulty processing; defective materials; overheating.
Dent	Small, smoothly rounded hollow.	Striking of a part with a dull object.
Gall	A transfer of metal from one surface to another.	Severe rubbing.
Gouging	Displacement of material from a surface; a cutting or tearing effect.	Presence of a comparatively large foreign body between moving parts.
Growth	Elongation of blade.	Continued and/or excessive heat and centrifugal force.
Pit	See Corrosion.	
Profile	Contour of a blade or surface.	
Score	Deep scratches.	Presence of chips between surfaces.
Scratch	Narrow shallow marks.	Sand or fine foreign particles; careless handling.

Figure 4-57. Blade maintenance terms.

tearing of vane material is evident in the damaged area.

Trailing edge damage (figure 4-60) may be blended, if one-third of the weld seam remains after repair. Concave surfaces of rubber filled vanes may have allowable cracks extending inward from the outer airfoil, provided there is no suggestion of pieces breaking away. Using a light and mirror, inspect each guide vane trailing edge and vane body for cracks or damage caused by foreign objects.

2. Hot Section Inspection And Repair

The hot section includes all components in the combustion and turbine sections of the engine. Hot section maintenance and inspection seems to naturally divide between those inspection items that may be performed with little or no disassembly and those which require removal and repair or replacement of engine components. Routine maintenance checks may involve visual inspection of hot section components, and limited dimensional checks of fits and clearances. The

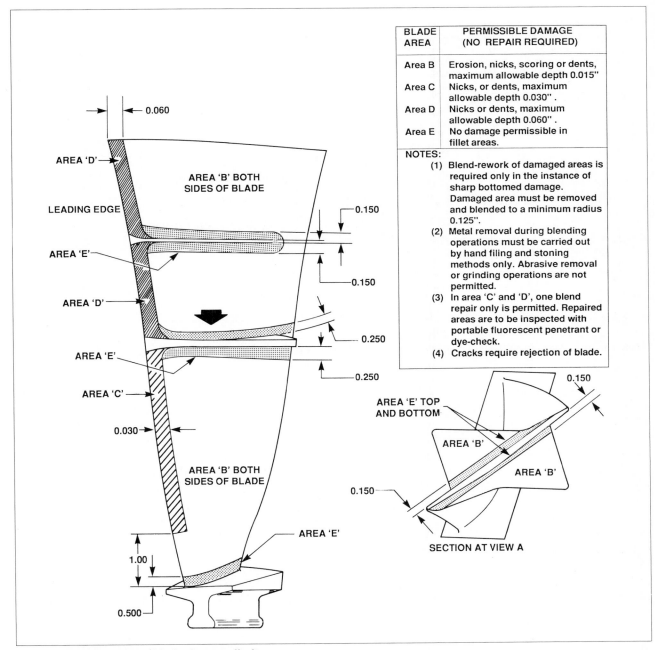

BLADE AREA	PERMISSIBLE DAMAGE (NO REPAIR REQUIRED)
Area B	Erosion, nicks, scoring or dents, maximum allowable depth 0.015"
Area C	Nicks, or dents, maximum allowable depth 0.030".
Area D	Nicks or dents, maximum allowable depth 0.060".
Area E	No damage permissible in fillet areas.

NOTES:
(1) Blend-rework of damaged areas is required only in the instance of sharp bottomed damage. Damaged area must be removed and blended to a minimum radius 0.125".
(2) Metal removal during blending operations must be carried out by hand filing and stoning methods only. Abrasive removal or grinding operations are not permitted.
(3) In area 'C' and 'D', one blend repair only is permitted. Repaired areas are to be inspected with portable fluorescent penetrant or dye-check.
(4) Cracks require rejection of blade.

Figure 4-58. Typical fan blade damage limits.

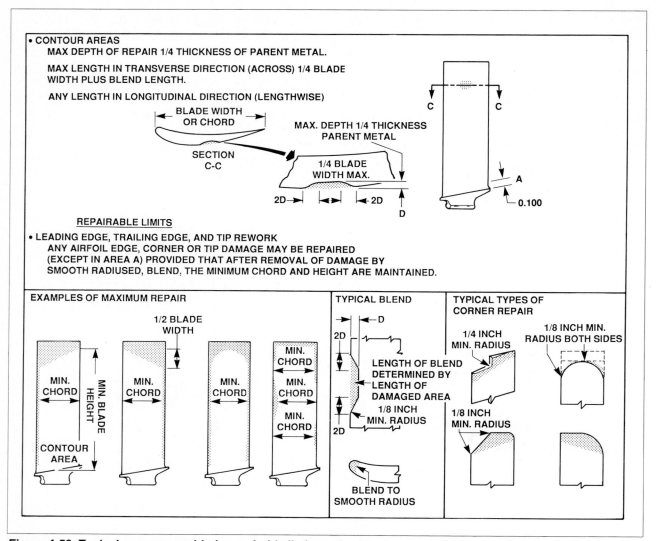

CONTOUR AREAS
MAX DEPTH OF REPAIR 1/4 THICKNESS OF PARENT METAL.

MAX LENGTH IN TRANSVERSE DIRECTION (ACROSS) 1/4 BLADE WIDTH PLUS BLEND LENGTH.

ANY LENGTH IN LONGITUDINAL DIRECTION (LENGTHWISE)

BLADE WIDTH OR CHORD

SECTION C-C

MAX. DEPTH 1/4 THICKNESS PARENT METAL

1/4 BLADE WIDTH MAX.

2D   2D

D

C   C

A
0.100

REPAIRABLE LIMITS
LEADING EDGE, TRAILING EDGE, AND TIP REWORK
ANY AIRFOIL EDGE, CORNER OR TIP DAMAGE MAY BE REPAIRED (EXCEPT IN AREA A) PROVIDED THAT AFTER REMOVAL OF DAMAGE BY SMOOTH RADIUSED, BLEND, THE MINIMUM CHORD AND HEIGHT ARE MAINTAINED.

EXAMPLES OF MAXIMUM REPAIR

1/2 BLADE WIDTH

MIN. CHORD
MIN. CHORD
MIN. CHORD
MIN. CHORD
MIN. CHORD
MIN. CHORD
MIN. BLADE HEIGHT
CONTOUR AREA

TYPICAL BLEND
D
2D
LENGTH OF BLEND DETERMINED BY LENGTH OF DAMAGED AREA
1/8 INCH MIN. RADIUS
2D
BLEND TO SMOOTH RADIUS

TYPICAL TYPES OF CORNER REPAIR
1/4 INCH MIN. RADIUS
1/8 INCH MIN. RADIUS BOTH SIDES
1/8 INCH MIN. RADIUS

Figure 4-59. Typical compressor blade repairable limits and examples of maximum repair by blending.

term "hot section inspection" usually is interpreted to indicate a time related overhaul of hot section components. Hot section inspections may also be required following certain operational events, such as a hot start.

Because of the modular construction of many turbine engines this inspection may be accomplished by removing only the affected modules, and does not require removal of the engine from the aircraft. To reduce downtime, some operators maintain an inventory of "hot section kits" for popular models of engines. These are complete hot section modules that are ready for installation. When the new module is installed, the one which has been removed is sent to the shop for the required maintenance.

Certain materials may be used for temporary marking during assembly and disassembly of hot section components. Layout die (lightly applied) or chalk may be used to mark parts that are directly exposed to the engine's gas path, such as turbine blades and disks, turbine vanes, and combustion chamber liners. A wax marking pencil may be used for parts that are not directly exposed to the gas path. Do not use a wax marking pencil on a liner surface or a turbine rotor. A commercial felt tip marker or certain special marking pencils may be used.

A note of caution to observe when marking any hot section part is to refrain from using a substance which leaves a carbon, copper, zinc, or lead deposit. When the metal is heated, these deposits are drawn into the metal and can cause intergranular stress. Marking with a common graphite lead pencil is strictly prohibited. Specific marking procedures always take precedence over general "rules of thumb".

The following caution note was excerpted from a current gas turbine engine maintenance manual.

CAUTION: Deposits left on stainless and high temperature alloy parts where marked with car- *bonaceous materials, such as graphite, wax, or grease pencils, may lead to failure of the parts in service. Even dychem (layout die) is potentially dangerous if not completely removed. This type of failure occurs when parts are heat treated, welded, or exposed in any manner to elevated temperatures of 700°F or more. The exposure causes localized carbon enrichment and intergranular embrittlement, which can in turn lead to crack initiation and propagation.*

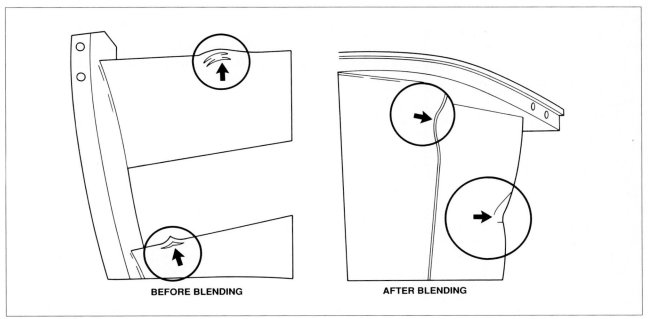

BEFORE BLENDING AFTER BLENDING

Figure 4-60. Guide vane trailing edge damage.

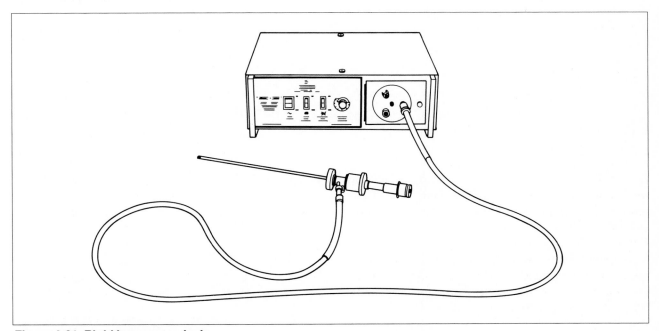

Figure 4-61. Rigid borescope device.

a. Combustion Section

Cracking is one of the most frequent discrepancies that will be detected while inspecting the combustion section of a turbine engine. The combustion liner is constructed of thin stainless steel material that is subjected to high concentrations of heat.

The most common method of checking for misalignment, cracks, and other distress in the hot section of a turbine engine is by using an internal viewing device known as a borescope. There are both rigid and flexible types available with different methods and intensities of illumination, and varying levels of magnification. A typical borescope is seen in figure 4-61.

With the borescope, the maintenance technician can easily view internal engine components and determine airworthiness of engine parts. During a borescope inspection, the operator looks for distress which is out of the manufacturer's limits, such as obvious cracking, warpage, burning, erosion, and sometimes obscure, but telltale hot spots. These hot spots are possible indicators of a serious condition, such as malfunctioning fuel nozzles or other fuel system malfunctions, and require careful interpretation.

Another important aspect of borescoping is to check for misalignment of combustion liners. It has been determined that "burner can shift", as it is called, can seriously affect combustor efficiency and engine performance.

There are now available repair schemes for the restoration of certain combustion section components. They involve replacement of unairworthy sections and the restoration of ceramic or other coatings used. This type of repair requires very specialized equipment and is accomplished only by facilities certified for that work.

b. Turbine Section

On-wing inspection of the inner turbine section is also done with a borescope, visually through the tailpipe with a strong light, mirror, and magnifying glass or by disassembly of the engine. On the flight line, nondestructive inspection methods such as the dye penetrant inspection are also useful.

As in other hot section inspections, the technician is most likely to see small cracks caused by compression and tension loading during heating and cooling. Other than on turbine blades, much of this type of distress is acceptable and

requires no maintenance action. This is because, after the initial cracks relieve the stress, no elongation of cracks occur.

Erosion is another common finding during turbine inspection. This is the result of the wearing away of metal, either from the gas flow across the surface, or the impingement of impurities in the gases on internal components.

3. Inspection And Repair Of Turbine Disk

a. Turbine Disk Inspection

The inspection for cracks is of the utmost importance. Crack detection during on-wing inspections is practically all visual. The material of which the turbine disk and blades are made do not generally lend themselves to field-type dye penetrant inspection. Cracks, on the disk, however minute, necessitate the rejection of the disk and replacement. Slight pitting cause by the impingement of foreign matter may, generally, be blended by stoning and polishing.

b. Turbine Blade Inspection

Figure 4-63 shows turbine blade blend repair limits which are typical of either shop or flight line maintenance. According to this manufacturer, cracks are never acceptable (which is the case with most manufacturers).

Of particular concern during visual inspections are stress rupture cracks on turbine blade leading edges or trailing edges. Stress rupture cracks are perceptible as minute hairline cracks at right angles to the blade length. This condition, and rippling of the trailing edge, is an indication of a serious over temperature, and a special in-shop inspection will probably be required.

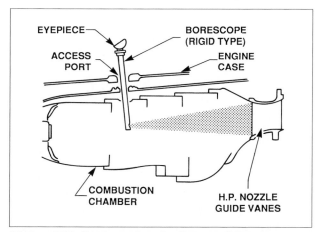

Figure 4-62. Borescoping the liner and first stage turbine stator.

INSPECTION	MAXIMUM SERVICEABLE	MAXIMUM REPAIRABLE	CORRECTION ACTION
BLADE SHIFT	Protrusion of any blade root must be equal within 0.015" either side of disk.	Not repairable	Return bladed disk assembly to an overhaul facility.
AREA A Nicks (3 maximum.)	0.015" long by 0.005" deep	.015 long by 0.010" deep	Blend out damage area/ Replace blade
Dents and pits (3 maximum.)	0.010" deep	.015 long by 0.010" deep	Blend out damaged area/ Replace blade
Cracks	Not acceptable	Not repairable	Replace blade
AREA B Nicks, dents, and pits (No cracks allowed)	One 0.020" deep	Not repairable	Replace blade
LEADING AND TRAILING EDGES Nicks, dents, and pits	One 0.020" deep	Two 1/8" deep	Blend out damaged area/ Replace blade
Cracks	Not acceptable	Not repairable	Replace blade

(A)

1/4″

FILLET AREA

B

1/8″

TRAILING EDGE

LEADING EDGE

1/8″

A

1/8″

1/4″

1/8″

B

FILLET AREAS CRITICAL NO DAMAGE PERMITTED

NOTE:
RIPPLING OF TRAILING EDGE IS NOT ACCEPTABLE

(B)

REPAIRED BLADE

(C)

"W" WIDTH = (APPROX) 8 "D" DEPTH

W

D

A

A

VIEW A

ROUNDED EDGE

SECTION A-A

B

B

VIEW B

BLENDED

NICK, DENT, PIT, ETC.

D

W

SECTION B-B

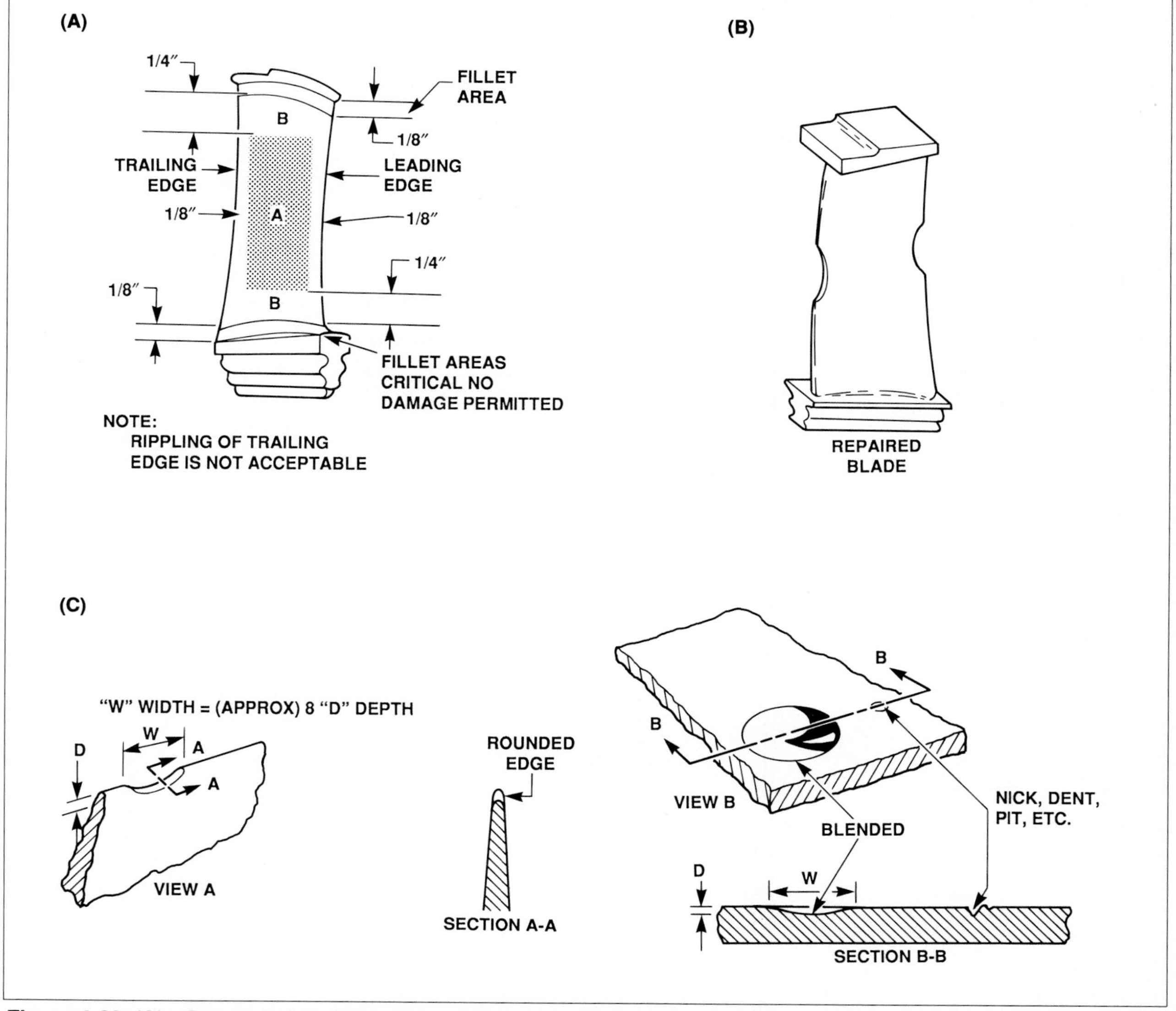

Figure 4-63. (A)—Power turbine blade repair limits. (B)—Repaired blade. (C)—Typical blending guides for turbine blade defects other than cracks.

155

4-53

Creep is a term used to describe the permanent elongation which occurs in rotating parts. Creep is most pronounced in turbine blades because of the heat loads and centrifugal loads imposed during operation. Each time a turbine blade is heated, rotated, and then stopped (referred to as an engine cycle), it remains slightly longer than it was before. The additional length may be only millionths of an inch, but over time the effect will be noticeable.

Untwist occurs in both turbine blades and turbine vanes, from gas loads upon their surfaces. Loss of correct pitch affects efficiency of the turbine system, and engine performance deterioration results. The check for untwist is generally possible only after engine tear down when parts can be measured in special shop fixtures.

c. Turbine Blade Replacement Procedure

To maintain turbine wheel balance, a single turbine blade replacement is generally accomplished by installing a new blade of equal moment weight. If the blades moment weight cannot be matched, the damaged blade and one 180° out are replaced with blades of equal moment weight; or, the damaged blade and the blades 120° from it are replaced with three blades of equal moment weight. Code letters indicating moment weight in inch-ounces or inch-grams, are marked on the fir tree section of the blade as shown in figure 4-64.

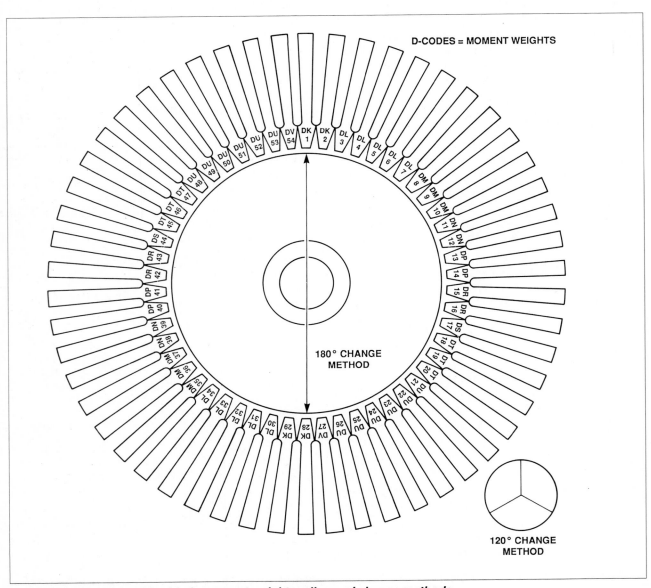

Figure 4-64. Typical turbine blade moment weight coding and change methods.

d. Turbine Nozzle Vane Inspection

Inspect turbine nozzle vanes for bowing, measuring the amount of bowing on the trailing edge of each vane. Bowed nozzle vanes may be an indication of a malfunctioning fuel nozzle. Reject vanes which are bowed more than the allowable amount. Bowing is always greater on the trailing edge; thus if this edge is within limits, the leading edge is also acceptable.

Figure 4-65 shows a vane that is ready for a bowing check on a flat plate. This check is accomplished by inserting a thickness gauge under the leading and trailing edge. If the piece is out of limits, it can usually be repaired by straightening if the material will permit such a process. If it cannot be straightened, a section can often be removed and a new section welded in. This usually involves an electron beam welding process and is accomplished only in specialized repair facilities.

e. Turbine Clearances

Checking the clearances is one of the procedures in the maintenance of the turbine section. The manufacturer's service manual will give the procedures and tolerances for checking the turbine. Figure 4-66 shows the measurement of tip clearances. To obtain accurate readings, special tools provided by each manufacturer must be used as described in their service instruction for the specific model of engine.

f. Exhaust Section

The exhaust section of a turbine engine is susceptible to heat cracking. Inspect the exhaust cone and tailpipe for cracks, warping, buckling, or hot spots. Hot spots on the tail cone are a good indication of a malfunctioning fuel nozzle or combustion chamber.

The inspection and repair procedures for the hot section of any one gas turbine engine are similar to those of other gas turbine engines. One usual difference is the nomenclature applied to the various parts of the hot section by the different manufacturers. Other differences include the manner of disassembly, the tooling necessary, and the repair methods and limits.

4. Commercial Ratings

An understanding of gas turbine engine ratings is necessary to use intelligently the engine operating curves contained in the aircraft and engine maintenance manuals. The ratings for commercial engines are defined by the SAE (Society of Automotive Engineers).

a. Takeoff (Wet Or Dry)

This is the maximum allowable thrust for takeoff. The wet rating is obtained by actuating the water injection system and setting the computed "wet" thrust with the throttle. The rating is restricted to takeoff, is time-limited, and will have an altitude limitation. Engines without water injection do not have this rating.

The dry rating is obtained by adjusting the throttle to the takeoff (dry) thrust for the existing ambient conditions, in terms of a predetermined engine pressure ratio (EPR) or fan speed. The rating is time limited and is to be used for takeoff only.

b. Maximum Continuous

This rating is the maximum thrust which may be used continuously and is intended for emergency use at the discretion of the pilot. The rating is obtained by adjusting the throttle to a predetermined engine pressure ratio or fan speed.

c. Normal Rated

Normal rated thrust is the maximum thrust approved for normal climb. The rating is obtained in the same manner as maximum continuous. Maximum continuous thrust and normal rated thrust are the same on some engines.

d. Maximum Cruise

This is the maximum thrust approved for cruising. It is obtained in the same manner as maximum continuous.

e. Idle

This is not an engine rating, but rather a throttle position suitable for minimum thrust operations on the ground or in flight. It is obtained by placing the throttle in the idle detent on the throttle quadrant.

5. Engine Instrumentation

Although engine installations may differ, depending upon the type of both the aircraft and the engine, gas turbine engine operation is usually controlled by observing the instruments discussed in the following paragraphs.

Engine thrust is indicated by either an engine pressure ratio indicator or fan speed indicator, depending upon the installation. Both types of pressure instruments are discussed here because either indicator may be used. The engine pressure ratio system is the most widely used today. By its design the EPR readout is automatically

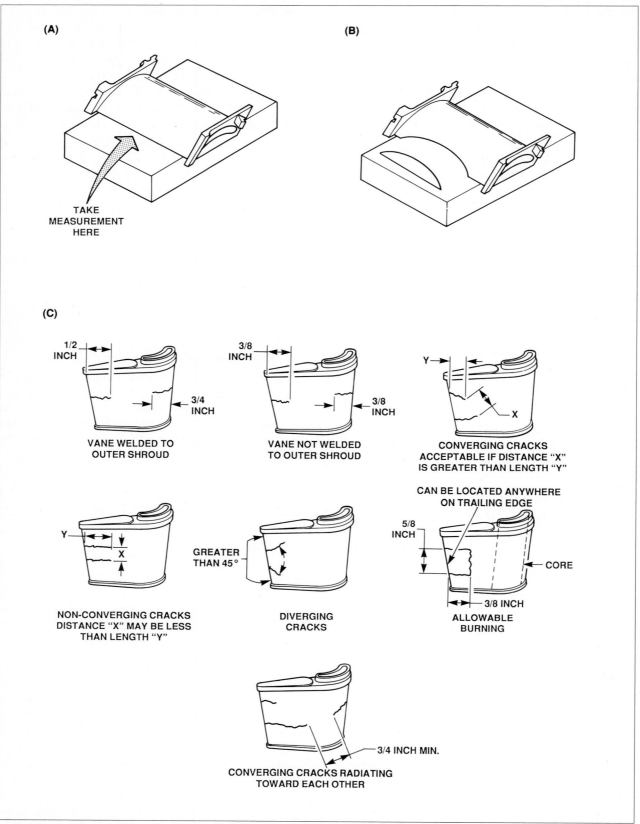

Figure 4-65. (A)—Turbine nozzle vane bowing check. (B)—Vane repair by welding in a new segment. (C)—Vanes acceptable if they do not exceed these limits (dimensions typical of small engines).

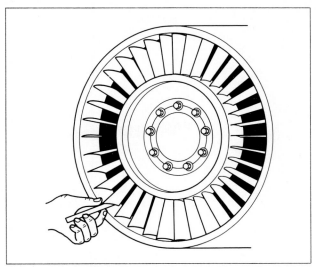

Figure 4-66. Measuring the turbine blade to shroud (tip) clearance.

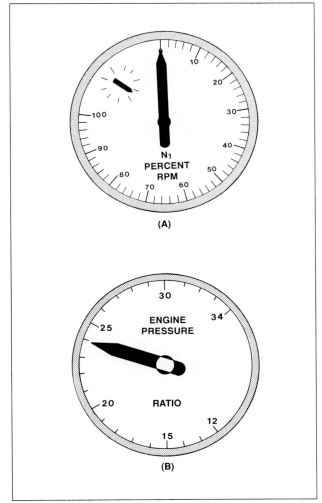

Figure 4-67. (A) Fan speed, and (B) Engine pressure ratio indicators.

compensated for the effects of airspeed and altitude by incorporating an input of compressor inlet pressure. Fan speed in percent is coming more into general use with the advent of electronic computer produced tachometer readouts.

a. Fan Speed N₁

This instrument indicates the percent RPM or the fan (N_1 compressor) on a turbofan engine. The cockpit tachometer indicator provides the operator with a continuous fan speed indication which has a linear relationship with ongoing engine thrust.

b. EPR Indicator

EPR (engine pressure ratio) is an indication of the thrust being developed by the engine. It is measured by total pressure pickups in the engine inlet and in the turbine exhaust. The reading is displayed in the cockpit by the EPR gauge, which is used in making engine power settings. Figure 4-67 illustrates a fan speed indicator (A) and EPR gauge (B).

c. Torquemeter (Turboprop Engines)

Because only a small part of the propulsive force is derived from the jet thrust, neither turbine discharge pressure nor engine pressure ratio is used as an indicator of the power produced by a turboprop engine. Turboprops are usually fitted with a torquemeter. The torquemeter (figure 4-68) can be operated by a torquemeter ring gear in the engine nose section, or by pickups on a torque shaft. The torque being developed by the engine is proportional to the horsepower, and is used to indicate shaft horsepower.

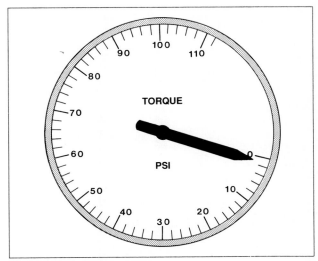

Figure 4-68. Torquemeter.

d. Tachometer

Gas turbine engine speed is measured by the compressor RPM, which will also be the turbine RPM Tachometers (figure 4-69) are usually calibrated in percent RPM so that various types of engines can be operated on the same basis of comparison.

e. EGT Indicator

EGT (exhaust gas temperature), TIT (turbine inlet temperature), tailpipe temperature, and turbine discharge temperature are one and the same. Temperature is an engine operating limit and is used to monitor the mechanical integrity of the turbines, as well as to check engine operating conditions. Actually, the turbine inlet temperature is the most important consideration, since it is the most critical of the engine variables. However, it is impractical to measure turbine inlet temperature in most engines, especially large models. Consequently, temperature thermocouples are inserted at the turbine discharge, where the temperature provides a relative indication of that at the inlet. Although the temperature at this point is much lower than at the inlet, it provides surveillance over the engine's internal operating conditions. Several thermocouples are usually used, which are spaced at intervals around the perimeter of the engine exhaust duct near the turbine exit. The EGT indicator (figure 4-70) in the cockpit shows the average temperature measured by the individual thermocouples.

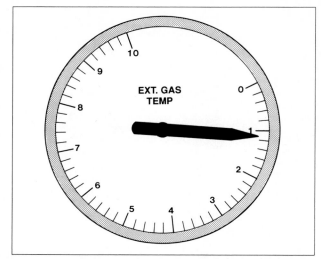

Figure 4-70. Exhaust gas temperature (EGT) indicator.

f. Fuel Flow Indicator

Fuel flow instruments indicate fuel flow in lbs./hr. from the engine fuel control. Fuel flow is of interest in monitoring fuel consumption and checking engine performance. A typical fuel flow indicator is illustrated in figure 4-71.

g. Engine Oil Pressure

To guard against engine failure resulting from inadequate lubrication and cooling of the various engine parts, the oil supply to critical areas must be monitored. The oil pressure indicator (figure 4-72) usually shows the engine oil pump discharge pressure.

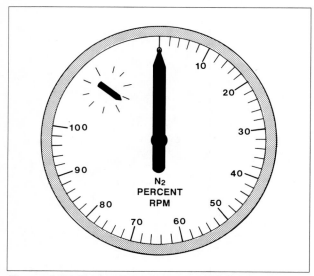

Figure 4-69. Tachometer for a gas turbine engine.

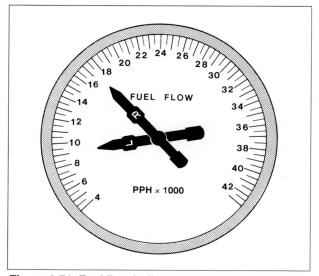

Figure 4-71. Fuel flow indicator for a turbine engine.

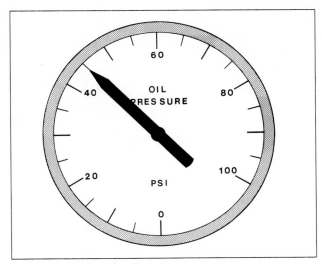

Figure 4-72. Engine oil pressure gauge.

h. Engine Oil Temperature

The ability of the engine oil to lubricate and cool depends upon the temperature of the oil, as well as the amount of oil supplied to critical areas. An oil inlet temperature indicator frequently is provided to show the temperature of the oil as it enters the oil pressure pump. Oil inlet temperature is also an indication of proper operation of the engine oil cooler.

6. Turbine Engine Operation

There are many instances when ground personnel other than pilots may be required to operate a gas turbine engine. Some of these situations are as follows:

(1) To duplicate a flight crew reported discrepancy for troubleshooting.

(2) To perform a basic engine or engine system check following maintenance.

(3) To taxi an aircraft from one maintenance area to another, or to perform a taxi related maintenance check.

The engine operating procedures presented here apply generally to all turbine engines. The procedures, pressures, temperatures, and RPM's which follow are intended to serve only a guide. The manufacturer's operating instructions should be consulted before attempting to start and operate any aircraft engine. The aircraft checklist should be used for all ground operations.

a. Ground Operations

Prior to the start, particular attention should be paid to the engine air inlet, the visual condition and free movement of the compressor and turbine assembly, and the parking ramp area fore and aft of the aircraft.

Turbojet and turbofan engines will usually only have a single cockpit control lever, known as the power lever (figure 4-73). Adjusting the power lever sets up a thrust condition for which the fuel control meters fuel to the engine. To start the engine, the following procedure is used:

(a) Master switch—*ON*

(b) Select battery or external power--*ON*

(c) Fuel valves—*ON*

(d) Fuel boost pumps—*ON*

(e) Starter—*ON* (starter, ignition, and fuel are often time sequenced)

(f) Ignition—*ON* (usually between 5 and 10% RPM);

(g) Power lever—to *IDLE* position (start should be indicated by rise in EGT within 10 20 seconds)

(h) Ignition and starter—*OFF*

1) Engine Fires

If an engine fire occurs or if the fire warning light is illuminated during the start cycle, move the fuel shutoff lever to the "off" position. Continue cranking or "motoring" the engine until the fire has been expelled from the engine. If the fire persists, CO_2 can be discharged into the inlet duct while the engine is being cranked. Do not discharge CO_2 directly into the engine because it may cause damage. If the fire cannot be extinguished, secure all switches and leave the aircraft.

If the fire is on the ground because of fuel dripping, discharge the CO_2 on the ground rather than the engine.

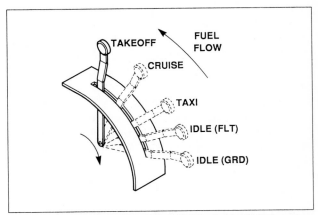

Figure 4-73. Power lever (throttle) of a turbojet or turbofan engine.

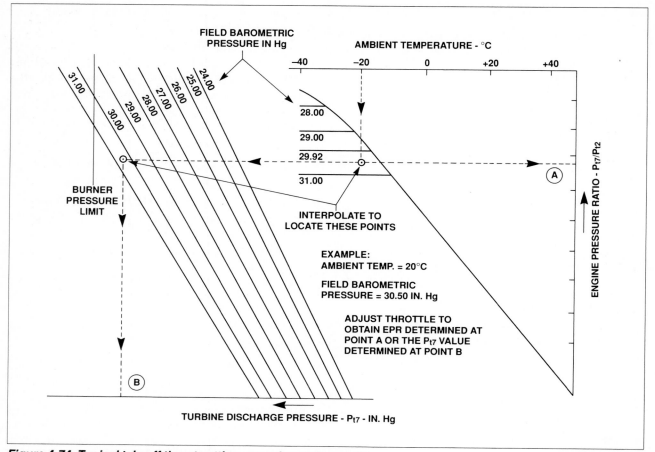

Figure 4-74. Typical takeoff thrust setting curve for static conditions.

2) Engine Checks

Checking turbojet and turbofan engines for proper operation consists primarily of simply reading the engine instruments and then comparing the observed values with those known to be correct for any given engine operating condition.

a) Idle Check

After the engine has started, idle RPM has been attained, and the instrument readings have stabilized, the engine should be checked for satisfactory operations at idling speed. The oil pressure indicator, the tachometer, and the exhaust gas temperature readings should be compared with the allowable ranges. Fuel flow is not considered a completely reliable indication of engine condition at idling RPM because of the inaccuracies frequently encountered in fuel flowmeters and indicators in the low range on the meters.

b) Checking Takeoff Thrust

Takeoff thrust is checked by adjusting the throttle to obtain a single, predicted reading on

the EPR indicator in the aircraft. The value for engine pressure ratio which represents takeoff thrust for the prevailing atmospheric conditions is calculated from a takeoff thrust setting curve similar to that shown in figure 4-74.

This curve has been computed for static conditions. Therefore, for all precise thrust checking, the aircraft should be stationary, and stable engine operation should be established. Appropriate manuals should be consulted for these charts for a specific make and model of engine.

The EPR computed from the thrust setting curve represents either wet or dry takeoff thrust. The aircraft throttle is advanced to obtain this predicted reading on the engine pressure ratio indicator in the aircraft. If an engine develops the predicted thrust and if all the other engine instruments are reading within their proper ranges, engine operation is considered satisfactory.

3) Ambient Conditions

The sensitivity of gas turbine engines to compressor inlet air temperature and pressure necessitates that considerable care be taken to

INDICATED MALFUNCTION	POSSIBLE CAUSE	SUGGESTED ACTION
Engine has low RPM, exhaust gas temperature, and fuel flow when set to expected engine pressure ratio.	Engine pressure ratio indication has high reading error.	Check inlet pressure line from probe to transmitter for leaks. Check engine pressure ratio transmitter and indicator for accuracy.
Engine has high RPM, exhaust gas temperature, and fuel flow when set to expected engine pressure ratio.	Engine pressure ratio indication has low reading error due to: Misaligned or cracked turbine discharge probe. Leak in turbine discharge pressure line from probe to transmitter. Inaccurate engine pressure ratio transmitter or indicator.	Check probe condition. Pressure test turbine discharge pressure line for leaks. Check engine pressure ratio transmitter and indicator for accuracy.
NOTE: Engines with damage in turbine section may have tendency to hang up during starting.	If only exhaust gas temperature is high, other parameters normal, the problem may be thermocouple leads or instrument.	Recalibrate exhaust gas tempeature instrumentation.
Engine vibrates throughout RPM range, but indicated amplitude reduces as RPM reduced.	Turbine damage.	Check turbine as outlined in preceeding item.
Engine vibrates at high RPM and fuel flow when compared to constant engine pressure ratio.	Damage in compressor section.	Check compressor section for damage.
Engine vibrates throughout RPM range, but is more pronounced in cruise or idle RPM range.	Engine-mounted accessory such as constant-speed drive, generator, hydraulic pump, etc.	Check each component in turn.
No change in power setting parameters, but oil temperature high.	Engine main bearings.	Check scavenge oil filters and magnetic plugs.
Engine has higher than normal exhaust gas temperature during take-off, climb, and cruise. RPM and fuel flow higher than normal.	Engine bleed air valve malfuntion. Turbine discharge pressure probe or line to transmitter leaking.	Check operation of bleed valve. Check condition of probe and pressure line to transmitter.
Engine has high exhaust gas temperature at target engine pressure ratio for takeoff.	Engine out of trim.	Check engine with jetcal. Retrim as desired.
Engine rumbles during starting and at low power cruise conditions.	Pressurizing and drain valve malfunction. Cracked air duct. Fuel control malfunction.	Replace pressurizing and drain valves. Repair or replace duct. Replace fuel control.
Engine RPM hangs up during starting.	Subzero ambient temperatures. Compressor section damage. Turbine section damage.	If hang up is due to low ambient temperature, engine usually can be started by turning on fuel booster pump or by positioning start lever to run earlier in the starting cycle. Check compressor for damage. Inspect turbine for damage.
High oil temperature.	Scavenge pump failure. Fuel heater malfunction.	Check lubricating system and scavenge pumps. Replace fuel heater.
High oil consumption.	Scavenge pump failure. High sump pressure. Gearbox seal leakage.	Check scavenge pumps. Check sump pressure as outlined in manufacturer's maintenance manual. Check gearbox seal by pressurizing overboard vent.
Overboard oil loss.	Can be caused by high airflow through the tank, foaming oil, or unusual amounts of oil returned to the tank through the vent system.	Check oil for foaming; vacuum-check sumps; check scavenge pumps.

Figure 4-75. Troubleshooting turbojet engines.

TROUBLE	PROBABLE CAUSE	REMEDY
Engine unit fails to turn over during attempted start.	No air to starter.	Check starter air valve solenoid and air supply.
	Propeller brake locked.	Unlock brake by turning propeller by hand in direction of normal rotation.
Engine unit fails to start.	Starter speed low because of inadequate air supply to starter.	Check starter air valve solenoid and air supply.
	If fuel is not observed leaving the exhaust pipe during start, fuel selector valve may be inoperative because of low power supply or may be locked in "off."	Check power supply or electrically operatived valves. Replace valves if defective.
	Fuel pump inoperative.	Check pump for sheared drives or internal damage; check for air leaks at outlet.
	Aircraft fuel filter dirty.	Clean filter and replace filtering elements if necessary.
	Fuel control cutoff valve closed.	Check electrical circuit to ensure that actuator is being energized. Replace actuator or control.
Engine fires, but will not accelerate to correct speed.	Insufficient fuel supply to control unit.	Check fuel system to ensure all valves are open and pumps are operative.
	Fuel control main metering valve sticking.	Flush system. Replace control.
	Fuel control by-pass valve sticking open.	Flush system. Replace control.
	Drain valve stuck open. Starting fuel enrichment pressure switch setting too high.	Replace drain valve. Replace pressure switch.
Acceleration temperature too high during starting.	Fuel control by-pass valve sticking closed.	Flush system. Replace control.
	Fuel control acceleration cam incorrectly adjusted.	Replace control.
	Defective fuel nozzle.	Replace nozzle with a known satisfactory unit.
	Fuel control thermostat failure.	Replace control.
Acceleration temperature during starting too low.	Acceleration cam of fuel control incorrectly adjusted.	Replace control.
Engine speed cycles after start.	Unstable fuel control governor operation.	Continue engine operation to allow control to condition itself.
Engine unit oil pressure drops off severely.	Oil supply low. Oil pressure transmitter or indicator giving false indication.	Check oil supply and refill as necessary. Check transmitter or indicator and repair or replace if necessary.

Figure 4-76. Troubleshooting turboprop engines.

obtain correct values for the prevailing ambient air conditions when computing takeoff thrust. Some things to remember are:

(a) The engine senses the air temperature and pressure at the compressor inlet. This will be the actual temperature of the air just above the runway surface. When the aircraft is stationary, the pressure at the compressor inlet will be the static field or true barometric pressure and not the barometric pressure corrected to seal level that is normally reported by airport control towers as the altimeter setting.

(b) Some airports provide the runway temperature,which should be used when available. The aircraft free air temperature indicator may or may not suffice for obtaining the temperature to be used, depending on the location of the sensing bulb. For an accurate thrust computation, it is best to measure the actual temperature at the compressor inlet just before the engine is started, by means of a hand held thermometer of known accuracy.

(c) If only the altimeter setting or the barometric pressure corrected to sea level is available, this pressure must be recorrected to field elevation. A method of obtaining the true pressure is to set the aircraft altimeter to zero altitude and read the field barometric pressure directly in the altimeter setting window on the face of the instrument.

(d) Relative humidity, which affects reciprocating engine power appreciably, has a negligible effect on turbojet engine thrust, and is usually not considered.

b. Engine Shutdown

When shutting down the engine, ensure the power lever is in the manufacturer's recommended shutdown position, wait until the RPM has stabilized, then move the fuel shutoff to the closed position. Failure to observe this procedure will result in uneven cooling of the engine hot section, and can cause turbine seal rub. In addition, a rapid shutdown can lead to incorrect oil consumption figures due to variable oil tank levels that result from poor scavenging.

c. Troubleshooting Turbine Engines

Included in this section are typical guidelines for locating engine malfunctions on most turbine engines. Since it would be impractical to list all the malfunctions that could occur, only the most common ones are covered. A thorough knowledge of the engine systems, applied with logical reasoning will solve any problems that may occur.

d. Turboprop Troubleshooting Procedures

All test run-ups, inspections, and troubleshooting should be performed in accordance with the applicable engine manufacturer's instructions. In figure 4-76, the troubleshooting procedures for the turboprop reduction gear, torquemeter, and power sections are combined because of their interrelationships. The figure includes the principal troubles, together with their probable causes and remedies.

e. Jet Calibration Test Unit

Two of the most important factors affecting turbine engine life are EGT and engine speed. Excess EGT of a few degrees will reduce turbine blade life by as much as 50%. Low exhaust gas temperature materially reduces turbine engine efficiency and thrust. Excessive engine speed can cause premature engine failures.

Indications of fuel system troubles, tailpipe temperature, and RPM can be checked more accurately from the jet calibration unit than from the cockpit gauges. One type of calibration test unit used is the Jetcal Analyzer. Jetcal is the trade name for an EGT and RPM system test unit. This is a portable instrument with a wide variety of applications.

1) Jetcal Analyzer Uses

The Jetcal analyzer may be used to:

(a) Functionally check the aircraft EGT system for error without running the engine or disconnecting the wiring.

(b) Check individual thermocouples before placement in a parallel harness.

(c) Check each engine thermocouple in a parallel harness for continuity.

(d) Check the thermocouples and parallel harness for accuracy.

(e) Check the resistance of the EGT circuit.

(f) Check the insulation of the EGT circuit for shorts to ground, or for shorts between leads.

(g) Check EGT indicators (either in or out of the aircraft) for error.

(h) Determine engine RPM with a accuracy of ± 0.1% during engine run-up. Added to this is the checking and troubleshooting of the aircraft tachometer system.

(i) Establish the proper relationship between the EGT and engine RPM on engine run-up.

(j) Check aircraft fire detector, overheat detector, and wing anti-icing systems by using tempcal probes.

2) Operating Instructions For The Jetcal Tester

The complete step-by-step procedure on the instruction plate of the Jetcal analyzer can be followed during actual operation of the unit. The operation plate is visible at all times when operating the analyzer.

It would be useless to list the detailed procedure in this section, so we will address the operational aspects of the Jetcal analyzer in a general sense.

3) Safety Precautions

Observe the following safety precautions while operating the Jetcal analyzer:

(a) Never use a volt-ohmmeter to check the potentiometer for continuity. If a VOM is used, damage to the galvanometer and standard battery cells will result.

(b) Check the thermocouple harness before engine run-up. This must be done because the circuit must be correct before the thermocouples can be used for true EGT pickup.

(c) For safety, ground the Jetcal when using an AC power supply.

(d) Use heater probes designed for use on the engine thermocouples to be tested. Temperature gradients are very critical in the design of heater probes. Never attempt to modify heater probes to test other types of thermocouples.

(e) Do not leave heater probe assemblies in the tailpipe during engine run-up.

(f) Never allow the heater probes to go over 900°C. Exceeding these temperatures will result in damage to the Jetcal analyzer and heater probe assemblies.

4) Continuity Check Of Aircraft EGT Circuits

To eliminate any error caused by one or more inoperative aircraft thermocouples, a continuity check is performed. The check is made by heating one heater probe to between 500 and 700°C and placing the hot probe over each of the aircraft thermocouples, one at a time. The EGT indicator must show a temperature rise as each thermocouple is checked. When large numbers of thermocouples are used in the harness (eight or more), it is difficult to see a rise on the aircraft instrument because of the electrical characteristics of the parallel circuit. Therefore, the temperature indication of the aircraft thermocouples is read on the potentiometer of the Jetcal unit by using the check cable and necessary adapter.

5) Functional Test Of Aircraft EGT Circuit

The time required to test the EGT system of any one aircraft will depend on several factors: (1) The number of engines; (2) the number of thermocouples in the harness, and their position in the engine; (3) the errors, if any are found; and (4) the time required to correct the errors. The normal functional test of a single engine can be performed in 10 to 20 minutes; special conditions may require more time.

During the EGT system functional test and the thermocouple harness checks, the Jetcal analyzer has a guaranteed accuracy of ± 4°C at the test temperature, which is usually the maximum operating temperature of the engine. Each engine has its own maximum operating temperature, which can be found in the applicable technical instructions.

The test is made by heating the engine thermocouples in the tail cone to the engine test temperature. The heat is supplied by the heater probes through the necessary cables. When the engine thermocouple is hot, their temperature is registered on the aircraft EGT indicator. At the same time, the thermocouples embedded in the heater probes, which are compelled isolated from the aircraft system, are picking up and registering the same temperature on the Jetcal.

The temperature registered on the aircraft EGT indicator (figure 4-78) should be within the specified tolerance of the aircraft system and the temperature reading on the Jetcal potentiometer. The thermocouples imbedded in the heater probes are of U.S. Bureau of Standards accuracy; therefore, Jetcal readings are accepted as the standard and are used as the basis of

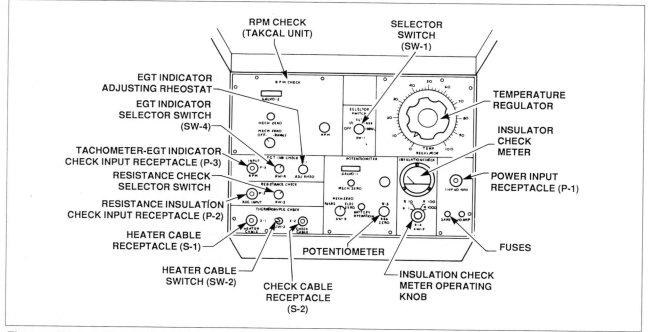

Figure 4-77. Jetcal analyzer instrument compartment.

comparison for checking the accuracy of aircraft EGT systems.

When the temperature difference exceeds the allowable tolerance, troubleshoot the aircraft system to determine which parts are in error. Troubleshooting is discussed at the end of this section.

6) Functional Test Of Thermal Switches

The tempcal probe functionally tests the operation of the fire detection, overheat, and wing anti-icing systems that incorporate a thermal switch as the detection device. Test the thermal switch in position on the aircraft by placing the probe over the thermal switch. The tempcal probe incorporates the principles of the heater probe for its temperature pickup. The temperature is controlled by the temperature regulator and is read on the Jetcal potentiometer.

With the tempcal probe over the thermal switch, the temperature of the probe is raised and lowered to take the switch through its operating temperatures. The indicator on the aircraft instrument panel, generally a red light, is then checked for indication to make sure that the switch is actuating at the proper tempera-

ture. If the system is not indicating properly, the circuit must be corrected.

7) EGT Indicator Test

The EGT indicator is tested after being removed from the aircraft instrument panel and disconnected from the aircraft EGT circuit leads. Attach the instrument cable and EGT indicator adapter leads to the indicator terminals and place the indicator in its normal operating position. Adjust the Jetcal analyzer switches to the proper settings. The indicator reading should correspond to the potentiometer readings on the Jetcal, within the allowable limits of the EGT indicator.

Correction for ambient temperature is not required for this test, as both the EGT indicator and Jetcal analyzer are temperature compensated.

8) Resistance And Insulation Check

The thermocouple harness continuity is checked while the EGT system is being checked functionally. The resistance of the thermocouple harness is held to very close tolerances, since a change in resistance changes the amount of cur-

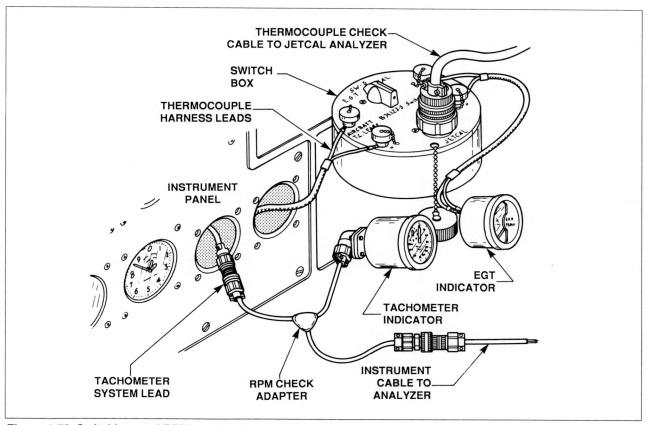

Figure 4-78. Switchbox and RPM check adapter connections.

rent flow in the circuit. A change of resistance will give erroneous temperature readings.

The resistance and insulation check circuits make it possible to analyze and isolate any error in the aircraft system. How the resistance and insulation circuits are used will be discussed with the troubleshooting procedures.

9) Tachometer Check

To read engine speed with an accuracy of ± 0.1% during engine run, the frequency of the tachometer-generator is measured by the RPM check (takcal) circuit in the Jetcal analyzer. The scale of the RPM check circuit is calibrated in percent RPM to correspond with the aircraft tachometer indicator. The calibration intervals are 0.2%. The aircraft tachometer and the RPM check circuit are connected in parallel, and both are indicating during engine run-up.

10) Troubleshooting The EGT System

The Jetcal analyzer is used to test and troubleshoot the aircraft thermocouple system at the first indication of trouble or during periodic maintenance checks.

The test circuits of the Jetcal make it possible to isolate all the troubles listed below. Following the heading is a discussion of each trouble mentioned.

a) One Or More Inoperative Thermocouples In Engine Parallel Harness.

This error is found in the regular testing of aircraft thermocouples with a hot heater probe and will be a broken lead wire in the parallel harness or a short to ground in the harness. In the latter case the current from the grounded thermocouple can leak off and never be shown on the indicator.

However, this grounded condition can be found by using the insulation resistance check.

b) Engine Thermocouples Out Of Calibration

When thermocouples are subjected for a period of time to oxidizing atmospheres, such as encountered in turbine engines, they will drift appreciably from their original calibration. On engine parallel harnesses, when individual thermocouples can be removed, these thermocouples can be bench checked, using one heater probe. The temperature reading obtained from the thermocouples should be within manufacturer's tolerances.

c) EGT Circuit Error

This error is found by using the switch box and comparing the reading of the aircraft EGT indicator with the Jetcal temperature reading. With the switch (SW-5) in the Jetcal position, the indication of the thermocouple harness is carried back to the Jetcal analyzer. With the switch in the EGT position, the temperature reading of the thermocouple harness is indicated on the aircraft EGT indicator. The Jetcal and aircraft temperature readings are then compared.

f. Spectrometric Oil Analysis Program

Spectrometric analysis for metal content is possible because metallic ions emit characteristic light spectra when vaporized in an electric arc or spark. The spectrum produced by each metal is unique for that metal. The position, or wavelength, of a spectral line will identify the particular metal and the intensity of the line can be used to measure the quantity of the metal in a sample.

1) How It Works

Periodic samples of used oil are taken from the engine. This is usually accomplished after shutdown, and prior to servicing. The sample is taken from a sediment free location in the main oil tank, and is sent to the oil analysis laboratory. Here is a brief description of how the spectrometer measures the wear metals present in the sample.

(a) A film of the used oil sample is picked up on the rim of a rotating, high purity, graphite disc electrode (see figure 4-79).

(b) Precisely controlled, high voltage, ac spark discharge is initiated between the vertical electrode and the rotating disc electrode, burning the small film of oil.

(c) Light from the burning oil passes through a slit which is positioned precisely to the wave length for the particular metal being monitored.

(d) As the light passes through the slit, photomultiplier tubes transform the light waves electronically into energy which automatically prints the analytical results on the laboratory record sheets.

(e) These records are interpreted and, when a sharp trend or abnormal concentration of metal is present, the participant is notified by telephone or message depending upon the urgency.

2) Application

Under certain conditions, and within certain limitations, the internal condition of any mechanical system can be evaluated by the spectrometric analysis of lubricating oil samples. The concept and application are based on the following facts:

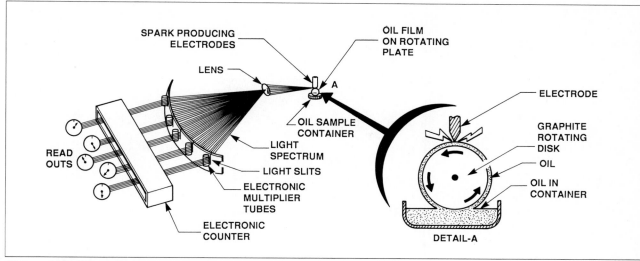

Figure 4-79. Oil spectrometer.

(a) The components of aircraft mechanical systems contain aluminum, iron, chromium, silver, copper, tin, magnesium, lead, and nickel as the predominant alloying elements.

(b) The moving contact between the metallic components of any mechanical system is always accompanied by friction. Even though this friction is reduced by a film of oil, some microscopic particles of metal do wear away and are carried in suspension in the oil. Thus, a potential source of information exists that directly relates to the condition of the system. The chemical identity of the worn surfaces and the particles worn from those surfaces will always be the same. If the rate of each kind of metal particle can be measured and established as being normal or abnormal, the rate of wear of the contacting surfaces will also be established as normal or abnormal.

3) Measurement Of The Metals

The important wear metals produced in a mechanical system can be separately measured in extremely low concentrations by the spectrometric analysis of oil samples taken from the system.

Silver is accurately measured in concentrations down to one-half part, by weight, of silver in 1,000,000 parts of oil. Most other metals are measured accurately in concentrations down to two or three parts per million. The maximum amount of normal wear has been determined for each metal of the particular system in the program. This amount is called its threshold limit of contamination and is measured by weight in parts per million (PPM).

It must be understood that the wear metals present are of such microscopic size that they cannot be seen by the naked eye, cannot be felt with the fingers, and flow freely through the system filters. The spectrometer therefore measures the particles that move in suspension in the oil and are too small to appear on either the oil screen or chip detector.

4) Advantages

The Oil Analysis Program is not a cure-all, as normal maintenance practices must be followed. There are several side benefits of the program worth mentioning, however.

Analysis of oil samples after a maintenance action has been accomplished can be used as a quality control tool by maintenance. An analysis which continues to show abnormal concentrations of wear metal present in the system would be positive proof that maintenance had not corrected the discrepancy and further troubleshooting techniques must be employed.

Analysis of samples from engines on test stands has reduced the possibility of installing a newly overhauled engine in the aircraft that contains discrepancies not detected by test stand instruments.

Spectrometric oil analysis has been used mainly in analyzing conditions of both reciprocating and gas turbine engines, and helicopter transmissions. The technique is also applicable to constant speed drives, cabin superchargers, gear boxes, hydraulic systems, and other oil wetted mechanical systems.

Chapter V
Induction And Exhaust Systems

A. Reciprocating Engine Induction Systems

It is the responsibility of the induction system to provide the reciprocating engine with air in sufficient quantity to support normal operation. Since many engines installed in light aircraft do not use any type of compressor or supercharging device induction systems for reciprocating engines can be broadly classified as naturally aspirated (non-supercharged) or supercharged.

1. System Components

The induction system consists of four major components or sections: (1) the air scoop, (2) the air filter, (3) the carburetor or other air metering device, and (4) the intake manifold which delivers the air, or fuel/air mixture, to the cylinders.

These four units are usually supplemented by a temperature indicating system and a temperature controlling unit or alternate air valve. Additionally, a system for compressing the fuel/air mixture may be included.

a. Air Intakes

Air intakes are generally placed to take as much advantage of ram air pressure as possible. The intake opening is usually located in the propeller slipstream. The effect of this additional air velocity adds to the ram pressure. A well designed intake scoop can have a substantial effect on the power output of the engine.

b. Induction System Filtering

It is very important that the air supplied to the engine be free of foreign material. Some means must be provided to prevent sand, dust, ice, or other contaminants from entering the induction system.

1) Dust Removal

While dust is a mere annoyance to most individuals, it is a serious source of trouble to an aircraft engine. Dust consists of small particles of hard, abrasive material that can be carried into the engine cylinders by the very air the engine breathes. It can also collect on the fuel metering elements of the carburetor, upsetting

the proper relation between airflow and fuel flow at all powers. It acts on the cylinder walls by grinding down these surfaces and the piston rings. It then contaminates the oil and is carried through the engine, causing further wear on the bearings and gears. In extreme cases an accumulation may clog an oil passage and cause oil starvation.

The efficiency of any filter system depends upon proper maintenance and servicing. Periodic removal and cleaning or replacement of the element is essential to satisfactory engine performance.

Many of the early air filters were made of screen wire that was filled with a fiber material called flock. These filters could be cleaned and serviced by washing them in safety solvent and, after they were clean, soaking them in a mixture of engine oil and preservative oil, and allowing the excess oil to drain. Later, paper filters similar to those used in automobiles were adapted and approved for use in aircraft. Air passes through the porous paper filter element, but any dust and sand particles are trapped on its surface. Paper filters may be cleaned by blowing all of the dust out of them in a direction opposite the normal airflow, and then washing them in a mild soap and water solution and allowing them to dry. When servicing this type of filter by washing, be sure to follow any recommendations or restrictions imposed by the aircraft manufacturer.

The most effective filter today is a polyurethane foam filter impregnated with a glycol solution. The glycol gives these filters an affinity for dust, and at the time recommended for filter change, the foam element is removed and discarded and a new one is installed. It is not recommended that these filters be cleaned.

2) Ice Removal

An engine equipped with a float-type carburetor has the problem of vaporization icing, commonly referred to as carburetor ice. The fuel is released into the airstream at the main discharge nozzle in the form of atomized liquid gasoline, and as it turns into a vapor, it absorbs heat from the surrounding air. This loss of heat drops the temperature of the air in the induction system enough to condense moisture in the air and form liquid water. The water may then freeze and restrict airflow to the engine.

To prevent the formation of carburetor ice the FAA requires each reciprocating engine air induction system to have the means to prevent and eliminate icing. The air used in this carburetor heat system is normally taken from a source inside the engine cowling and is routed through a thin sheet metal shroud which surrounds the exhaust pipe. This air-to-air heat exchanger warms the intake air which is then delivered to the carburetor air box.

In the "cold" position, the engine is using the filtered ram air from the main air scoop. When icing conditions are encountered and the "hot" position is selected by the pilot, unfiltered warm air from the carburetor heat source is routed to the carburetor. Because this warm air is unfiltered, the carburetor heat valve should always be in the "cold" position when the aircraft is on the ground, especially in sandy or dusty locations.

Improper or careless use of the carburetor heat can be just as dangerous as the most advanced state of induction system ice. Increasing the temperature of the air causes it to expand and decrease in density. This action reduces the weight of the charge delivered to the cylinder, and causes a noticeable loss in power because of decreased volumetric efficiency. In addition, the high intake air temperature may cause detonation, especially during takeoff and high power operations. Therefore, during all phases of engine operation, the carburetor temperature must afford the greatest protection against icing, and detonation. Because of the 30°F or more drop in air temperature due to vaporization of the fuel, severe icing conditions may occur with the outside air temperature between 50 and 60°F and the humidity above 60 percent.

Where there is no danger of icing, the heat control is normally kept in the "cold" position. It is best to leave the control in this position if there are particles of dry snow or ice in the air. The use of heat may melt the ice or snow, and the resulting moisture may collect and freeze on the walls of the induction system. To prevent damage to the heater valves in the case of backfire, carburetor heaters should not be used while starting the engine.

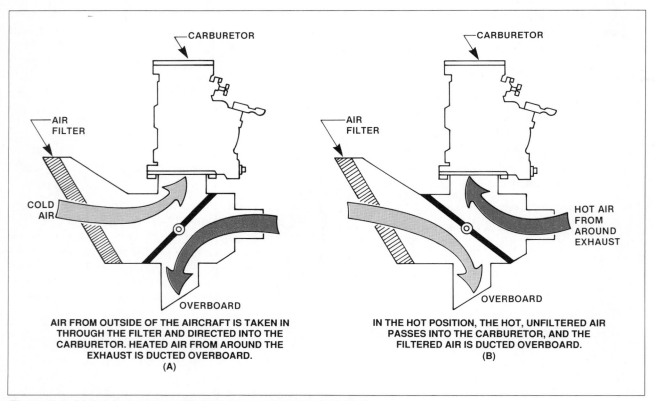

Figure 5-1. Air intake system with float-type carburetor installed.

Many modern reciprocating engines utilize a system that enhances fuel vaporization and lessens the risk from vaporization icing. The carburetor on these engines is mounted on the oil sump and the induction pipes pass through the warm oil. This serves the double function of cooling the oil and at the same time warming the induction air without heating it to the point that detonation could occur. The carburetor, when mounted in this position, is quite centrally located, and it can provide as even a fuel/air mixture to all cylinders as is possible with a horizontally opposed engine.

2. Non-Supercharged Induction Systems

The non-supercharged, or naturally aspirated engine is commonly used in light aircraft. The induction system of these engines may be equipped with either a carburetor or a fuel injection system. On the current fleet, if a carburetor is used, it is most likely a float-type and when fuel injection is used, it will be a continuous flow system.

Figure 5-1 is a diagram of an induction system used in a non-supercharged engine equipped with a carburetor. Normally, inlet air is taken from the front end of the cowling where it can take advantage of the ram effect during normal flight to provide a slight increase in the amount of air the engine can take in. In this system, carburetor cold air is admitted at the leading edge of the nose cowling below the propeller spinner, and is passed through the air filter into a carburetor air box attached to the carburetor. A carburetor heat valve is provided for selecting an alternate warm air source to prevent carburetor icing.

Engines equipped with fuel injection systems deliver the fuel directly to the intake port of the cylinder, and are not susceptible to vaporization icing. They may, however, be in danger from impact icing when operating in snow and sleet. Provisions must be made to assure adequate airflow in the event that the normal intake scoop and/or air filter become clogged. An alternate air system serves that purpose.

In figure 5-2, we have a typical alternate air system. When the alternate air valve is in the "cold" or "closed" position a butterfly valve allows air to flow through an opening in the nose cowling and through the air filter into the air metering unit. Moving the alternate air control in the cockpit to the "alternate air" position closes the

butterfly valve which shuts off the flow of air through the filter. The low pressure created by the pistons moving inward pulls open the spring-loaded alternate air door, and air that has passed through the cylinder cooling fins is taken into the fuel injection system.

This spring-loaded alternate air door also opens if the aircraft flies into freezing rain or snow and the air filter ices over enough to shut off the flow of air into the engine. Rather than starving the engine of air, the door will automatically open and allow the warm air from inside of the cowling to be drawn into the fuel injection unit.

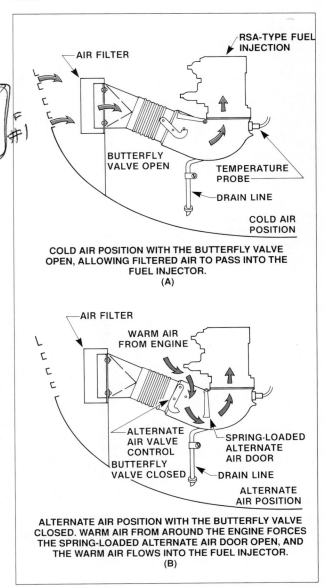

Figure 5-2. Alternate air system for an engine equipped with an RSA type fuel injected system.

3. Supercharged Induction Systems

Supercharging systems used in reciprocating engine induction systems are normally classified as either internally driven or externally driven (turbo-supercharged).

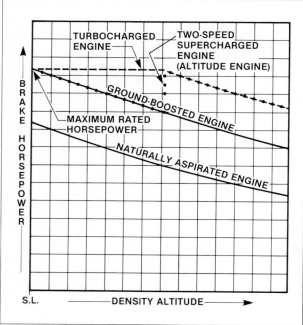

Figure 5-3. Relationship between power and density altitude for engines with various types of induction systems.

a. Internally Driven Superchargers

Internally driven superchargers compress the fuel/air mixture after it leaves the carburetor, while externally driven superchargers compress the air before it is mixed with the metered fuel from the carburetor. Each increase in the pressure of the fuel/air mixture in an induction system is called a stage. Superchargers can be classified as single stage, two stage, or multi stage, depending on the number of times compression occurs. Superchargers may also operate at different speeds. Thus, they can be referred to as single speed, two speed, or variable speed superchargers.

1) Single Stage, One Speed Supercharger

One early development in single stage, one speed superchargers was known as a sea level supercharger, or ground boost blower. Technically, these units may not have qualified as superchargers. To be considered a supercharger the unit must raise the manifold air pressure above 30 in. Hg. At any rate, these gear driven impellers increased the power produced by the engine at sea level as well as the power produced at all altitudes. The power, however, decreased as altitude increased, in the same way it does with a naturally aspirated engine. Figure 5-3 illustrates the power curve for a ground boosted engine.

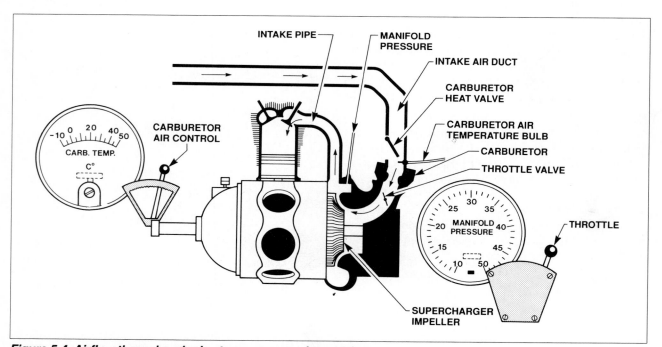

Figure 5-4. Airflow through a single stage, one speed supercharger.

The simple induction system shown in figure 5-4 is used to explain the location of units and the path of the airflow through a system employing a single stage, one speed supercharger.

Air enters the system through the ram air intake. The intake opening is located so that the air is forced into the induction system, giving a ram effect.

The air passes through ducts to the carburetor. The carburetor meters the fuel in proportion to the air to satisfy the demands established by throttle position. The carburetor is controlled from the cockpit to regulate the flow of air. In this way, the power output of the engine can be controlled.

The manifold pressure gauge measures the pressure of the fuel/air mixture before it enters the cylinders. It is an indication of the performance that can be expected of the engine.

The carburetor air temperature indicator measures either the temperature of the inlet air,

or of the fuel/air mixture. This reading serves as a guide so that the temperature of the incoming charge may be kept within safe limits.

The fuel, as atomized into the airstream which flows in the induction system is in globular form. The problem, then, becomes one of uniformly breaking up and distributing the fuel remaining in globular form to the cylinders.

One method of improving fuel distribution is known as a distribution impeller. The impeller is attached directly to the end of the rear shank of the crankshaft by bolts or studs. Since the impeller is attached to the end of the crankshaft and operates at the same speed, it does not materially boost or increase pressure on the mixture flowing to the cylinders.

When greater pressure is desired on the fuel/air mixture to charge the cylinders and increase power output, a high speed impeller is used. Unlike the distribution impeller, which is connected directly to the crankshaft, the super-

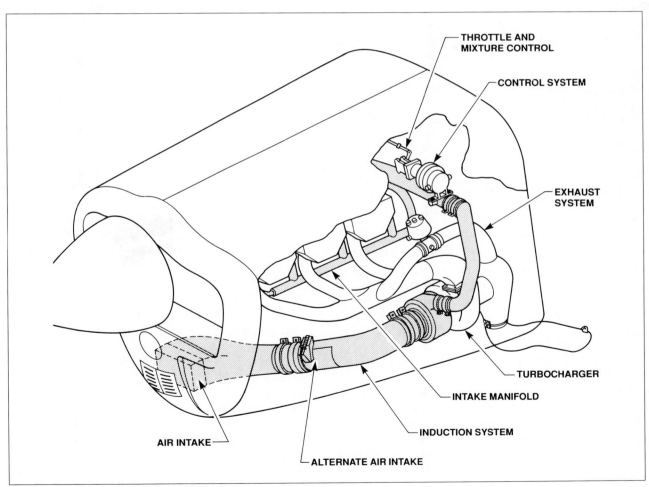

Figure 5-5. Typical turbocharger installation.

charger, or blower impeller, is driven through a gear train from the crankshaft.

The impeller is located centrally within the diffuser chamber. Air is drawn into the center of the impeller and then accelerated outward in the same manner as a centrifugal compressor used on a turbine engine. In the diffuser the velocity is traded for pressure energy and the air is then directed to the cylinders.

The gear ratio of the impeller gear train varies from approximately 6:1 to 12:1. Impeller speed on an engine equipped with a 10:1 impeller gear ratio operating at 2,600 RPM would be 26,000 RPM. This requires that the impeller unit be a high grade forging, usually of aluminum alloy.

2) Single Stage, Two Speed Supercharger

Some of the large radial engines used up through World War II had two speed superchargers that used an oil operated clutch to drive the supercharger impeller through either a low gear ratio of about 8:1 or a high gear ratio of 11:1.

Takeoff was made with the supercharger in the low blower position. In this mode the engine acted in the same way as a ground boosted engine, the power would drop off with altitude. When the aircraft reached a specified altitude, the throttle was reduced somewhat, and the blower control moved to the high position. The throttle was then reset to the desired manifold pressure. An engine equipped with this type of supercharger is called an altitude engine, and its power curve is shown by the dotted line on figure 5-3.

b. Turbocharger Systems

Gear driven superchargers use a great deal of energy for the amount of power increase they produce. Turbo-superchargers, or turbochargers as they are usually called, are powered by the energy of exhaust gases that would otherwise be vented overboard.

1) Induction Air System

The induction air system for a light aircraft using a turbocharger is seen in figure 5-5. It consists of a filtered ram air intake located on the nose of the aircraft, below the propeller. An alternate air door is provided within the cowling to provide an air source in case of filter clogging. The air is then drawn through the compressor section of the turbocharger and sent to the air metering section of the fuel injection system. The metered air is routed through the intake manifold to the cylinder intake ports where it is mixed with a metered amount of fuel.

Figure 5-6 illustrates the components of the turbocharger unit. Between the compressor housing and the turbine housing, there is the center housing that contains two aluminum bearings that are free to rotate within their respective housings, and the shaft rotates in these bearings. Oil flows between the housing and the bearings, and also through the holes drilled in the bearings. This assures a continuous flow of oil is provided between the wheel shaft and the inside of the bearings. Lubricating oil from the engine oil systems flows into the top of the center housing, and a scavenger pump inside the engine receives the oil from the turbocharger scavenger sump, through the large opening in the bottom of the housing.

About four to five gallons of oil per minute are pumped through the turbocharger center housing, not only to lubricate the bearings, but to take away heat from the housing. The turbine inlet temperature may get as high as 1,600 °F, and the large flow of oil is needed through the bearings to keep them well below this temperature.

2) Turbocharger Control Systems

If a turbocharger system were built where all of the exhaust gases were made to pass through the turbine section of the turbocharger, the turbine speed, and thus the speed of the compressor and the amount of air it compresses would become a function of the throttle position. In this system it would be very easy to get an excess of manifold pressure, which could cause detonation. This excess of manifold pressure is called over-boosting the engine. The system could be designed so that, under standard conditions, the turbine could not turn fast enough to over-boost the engine. Standard conditions do not, however, exist throughout a flight, and this system would prove impractical.

This limitation is overcome by using a valve to control the amount of exhaust gases routed to the turbocharger. This valve is known as a waste gate, and is seen in figure 5-7. When the waste gate is fully open, all of the exhaust goes out the tail pipe without passing through the turbocharger. When the waste gate is fully closed, all of the exhaust must pass through the turbine to get to the tail pipe.

The difference in the various turbocharger systems installed in general aviation aircraft have to do with the way the waste gate is controlled.

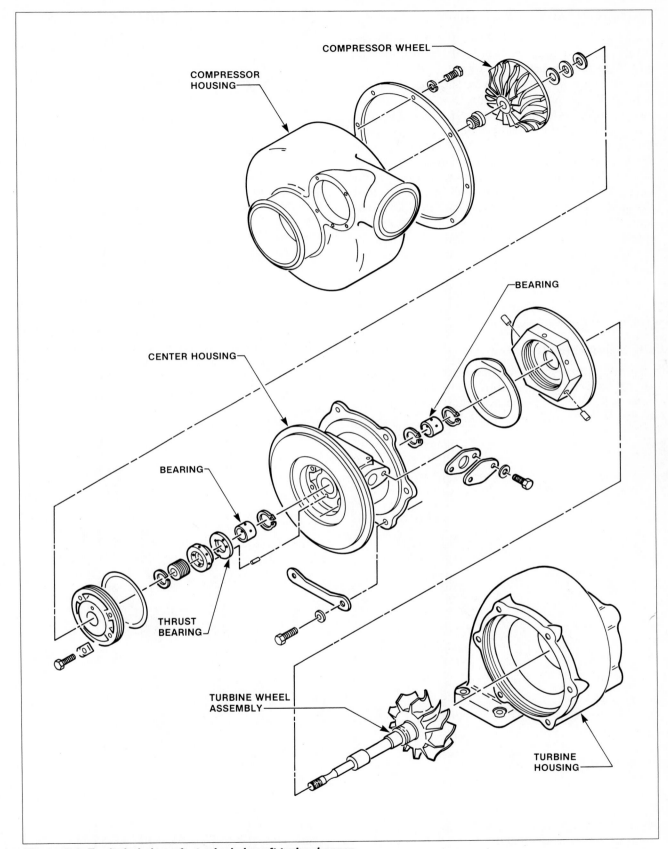

COMPRESSOR WHEEL

COMPRESSOR HOUSING

BEARING

CENTER HOUSING

BEARING

THRUST BEARING

TURBINE WHEEL ASSEMBLY

TURBINE HOUSING

Figure 5-6. Exploded view of a typical aircraft turbocharger.

177

a) Manual Control System

One of the simplest systems for turbocharger control uses a manual linkage between the engine throttle valve and the waste gate valve. For takeoff at low density altitude, the throttle is advanced to the takeoff position, and the engine develops full takeoff power with the waste gate fully open. As the airplane goes up in altitude, the engine power drops until full throttle will not produce the rated power. Then the throttle is advanced beyond its takeoff position, and the additional movement of the throttle begins to close the waste gate valve causing the manifold pressure to go up and the engine to produce the rated horsepower. When the throttle is retarded, the waste gate opens, and the fuel to the engine is decreased.

Some manual installations may have two controls: one for the engine throttle, and a separate control for the waste gate valve.

b) Adjustable Waste Gate

Another very simple turbocharger system uses an adjustable, rather than controllable, waste gate valve and a pressure relief valve. We see such a system in figure 5-8.

This system is used on some of the newer generation aircraft that are designed for simplicity of operation. An adjustable waste gate valve has a threaded bolt sticking out of the portion of the exhaust system that bypasses the turbocharger. Screwing this bolt in or out determines the amount of exhaust gas that is forced to flow through the turbocharger. This, in turn, determines the amount of air that is forced into the induction system.

The waste gate is adjusted so the engine will produce its rated horsepower under sea level, standard day conditions when the throttle is wide open. As the aircraft goes up in altitude and the air density decreases, the maximum manifold pressure will also decrease.

On takeoff when the outside air temperature is lower than standard, the pilot must monitor the manifold pressure gauge to prevent over-boosting the engine. To protect the engine from inadvertent over-boost, the induction system is equipped with a pressure relief valve. This valve begins to off-seat about one inch of manifold pressure below the maximum allowed, and by the time the maximum manifold pressure is reached, the valve is off its seat enough to bleed off all of the pressure in excess of maximum.

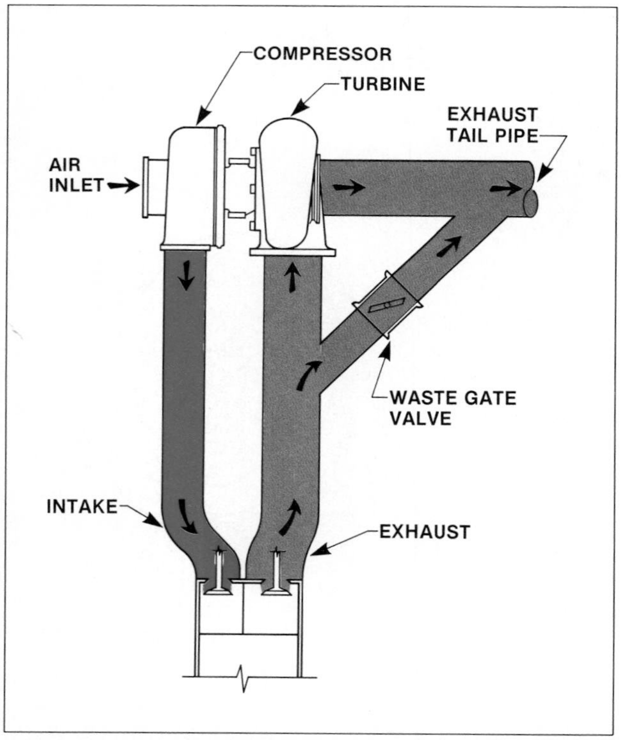

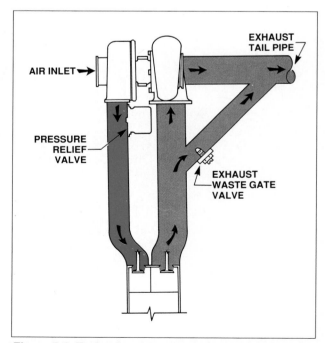

Figure 5-7. A waste gate is used to direct the exhaust gases to the turbocharger.

Figure 5-8. Turbocharger control system, using an adjustable waste gate valve and a pressure relief valve.

c) Absolute Pressure Controller

More efficient control of the turbocharger pressure is maintained with an absolute pressure controller, often spoken of simply as an APC. Figure 5-9 illustrates a turbocharger installation using an APC.

A waste gate valve that is opened by a spring and closed by engine oil pressure acting on a piston, controls the flow of exhaust gas. When the valve is fully open, all of the exhaust gas flows out the tailpipe without passing through the turbine. When the waste gate valve is closed, the exhaust gas must pass through the turbocharger turbine.

Oil flows from the engine lubricating system into the cylinder of the waste gate actuator through a capillary tube restrictor and out of the actuator through the APC and then into the engine oil sump. The APC is a variable restrictor in the oil return line from the waste gate actuator, and the size of the orifice is determined by the engine upper deck pressure, which is the turbocharger discharge pressure.

When the engine is started and is idling, the throttle is closed and the manifold pressure is low. The upper deck pressure is near atmospheric. The chamber in the APC in which the bellows is mounted is connected to the induction

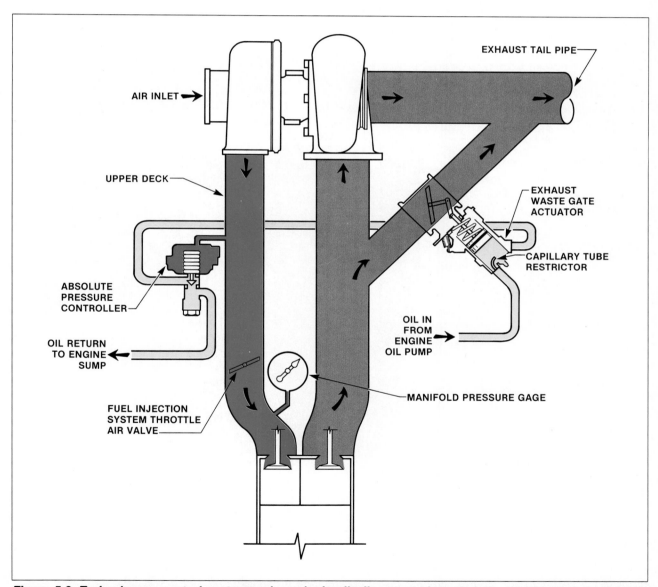

Figure 5-9. Turbocharger control system, using a hydraulically actuated waste gate actuator and an absolute pressure controller.

system, and it senses the upper deck pressure. When this pressure is very low, the valve is closed.

The spring inside the waste gate actuator holds the waste gate open, but as engine oil flows into the actuator cylinder and out the APC, which is closed, the pressure builds up and forces the piston over against the spring. This closes the waste gate so that all of the exhaust gases must flow through the turbine which spins the compressor.

At takeoff the throttle is opened, and the increased flow of exhaust gases increases the speed of the turbine, and both the upper deck pressure and the manifold pressure increase. Let's assume that the controller is required to maintain the manifold pressure at a constant 32 inches of mercury. In order to do this, the upper deck pressure will have to be approximately 33 inches of mercury, because of the pressure drop across the fully open throttle valve. As the upper deck pressure builds up to the 33 in. Hg., the APC begins to open and drain the oil back into the engine sump. The oil can flow out of the waste gate actuator easier than it can flow in, because of the restriction in the oil inlet line. As the oil begins to drain out of the actuator, the spring begins to open the waste gate so that some of the

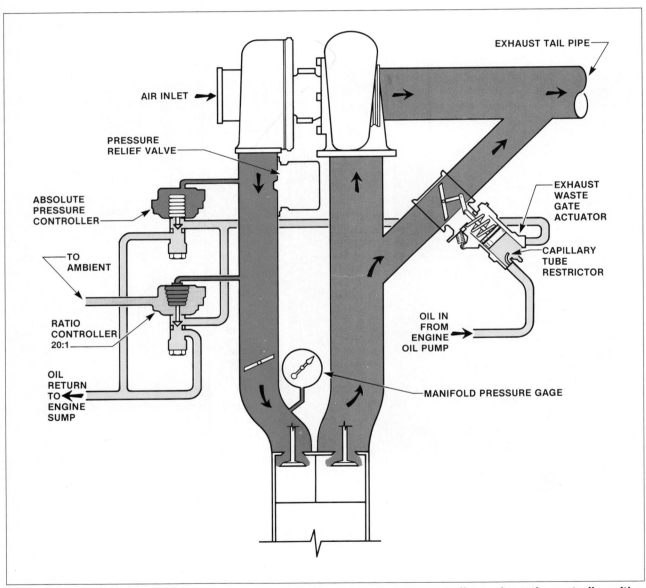

Figure 5-10. Turbocharger control system, using an absolute pressure controller and a ratio controller with a pressure relief valve as an emergency backup.

exhaust gases can flow out the tail pipe. The turbine will slow down a bit to hold the manifold pressure at a constant 32 in. Hg.

As the airplane goes up in altitude and the air becomes less dense, the upper deck pressure will decrease. This decrease is sensed by the APC, which closes a bit to restrict the oil flow from the waste gate actuator. The oil pressure will build up and move the waste gate valve toward its closed position to raise the upper deck pressure and maintain a constant 32 inches of manifold pressure.

If the aircraft continues to ascend, the upper deck pressure will decrease. The waste gate valve will continue to close until an altitude is reached when even with the throttle fully open and the waste gate fully closed, the turbocharger cannot maintain 33 inches of mercury upper deck pressure. This is the critical altitude of the engine and the manifold pressure will decrease above this altitude.

The engine may be restricted to a maximum altitude at which it is allowed to maintain its maximum rated manifold pressure. If this is the case, a stop may be installed on the waste gate to limit the amount it can close. This will prevent the engine from reaching its maximum rated manifold pressure above its critical altitude.

d) Ratio Controller Used With APC

To allow the engine to maintain a specific critical altitude and at the same time have enough capacity to compensate for some leakage, a more powerful turbine may be used and a ratio controller installed in parallel with the APC.

In figure 5-10, we have a system that incorporates an absolute pressure controller, a ratio controller, and a pressure relief valve. The APC works in the same way we have just described, and for our explanation, we will assume that it will limit the maximum manifold pressure to 32 inches of mercury at 16,000 feet.

The ratio controller valve will remain seated as long as the upper deck pressure is no more than 2.0 times the ambient air pressure. At standard sea level pressure, the ratio controller will remain seated until an upper deck pressure of 59.84 inches of mercury (29.92 × 2.0 = 59.84) is reached. At 16,000 feet, the ambient pressure is approximately 16.2 in. Hg. and the ratio controller will prevent the manifold pressure from exceeding 32.4 in. Hg. Ascending above 16,000 feet will cause the ratio controller to reduce the upper deck pressure and the manifold pressure

by bleeding some of the oil from the waste gate actuator to keep the manifold pressure no more than 2.0 times the ambient pressure.

The system illustrated also has a pressure relief valve that is normally adjusted to off-seat at about 1.5 inches of mercury above the maximum allowable upper deck pressure.

e) Variable Automatic Pressure Controller

A final type of controller used with some turbocharged engines is the variable absolute pressure controller, which is often called a VAPC. This controller uses a cam, actuated by the engine throttle to maintain a constant upper deck pressure for each position of the throttle valve, rather than just for full throttle operation. The VAPC works in a manner similar to the APC with the bellows controlling the position of the valve, but in this controller, the engine throttle controls the position of the valve seat.

Figure 5-11 shows a typical turbocharger system for a general aviation aircraft. The upper deck pressure is used not only to supply air for the cylinders, but some of this pressure is take-off to serve as a reference pressure for all of the fuel discharge nozzles, as well as for the fuel pump and the fuel flow gauge. The air for pressurizing the cabin is also taken from the turbocharger discharge, and it first passes through a sonic venturi which acts as a flow limiter. Air passing through the venturi reaches sonic speed and produces a shock wave. This shock wave will slow down the air passing through it and limit the amount of air that can flow into the cabin.

c. Sea Level Boosted Turbocharger Systems

Some turbocharger systems are designed to operate from sea level up to their critical altitude. These engines, sometimes referred to as sea level boosted engines, can develop more power at sea level than an engine without turbocharging.

Figure 5-12 is a schematic of a sea level boosted turbocharger system. This system is automatically regulated by three components shown in the schematic: (1) the exhaust by-pass valve assembly, (2) the density controller, and (3) the differential pressure controller.

The position of the waste gate valve, which determines power output, is controlled by oil pressure. Engine oil pressure acts on a piston in the waste gate assembly which is connected by linkage to the waste gate valve. When oil pressure is increased on the piston, the waste gate valve moves toward the "closed" position, and engine power increases. Conversely, when the oil pressure is decreased, the waste gate valve moves toward the "open" position, and output power is decreased.

The position of the piston attached to the waste gate valve is dependent on bleed oil which controls the engine oil pressure applied to the top of the piston. Oil is returned to the engine crankcase through two control devices, the density controller and the differential pressure controller. These two controllers, acting independently, determine how much oil is bled back into the crankcase, and thus establishes the oil pressure on the piston.

The density controller is designed to limit the manifold pressure below the turbocharger's critical altitude, and regulates bleed oil only at the "full throttle" position. The pressure and temperature sensing bellows of the density controller react to pressure and temperature changes between the fuel injector inlet and the turbocharger compressor. The bellows, filled with

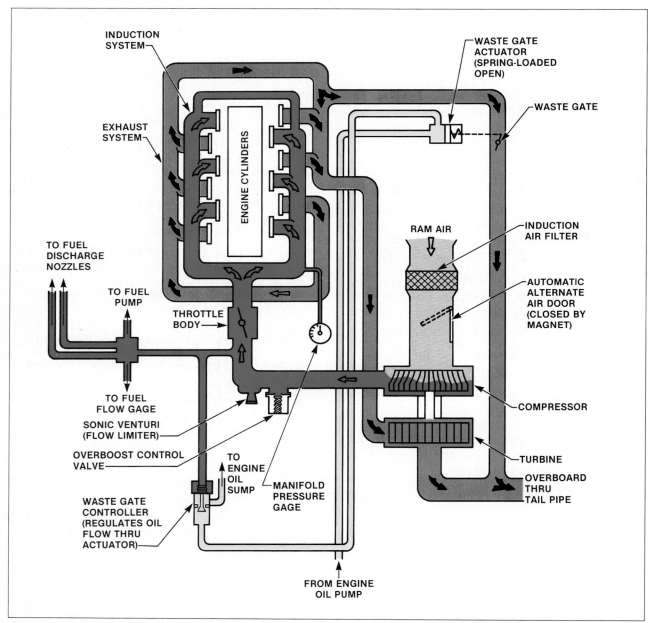

Figure 5-11. Typical turbocharger system for a general aviation aircraft. The turbocharger not only supplies the compressed air for the engine induction system, but it also provides air for cabin pressurization.

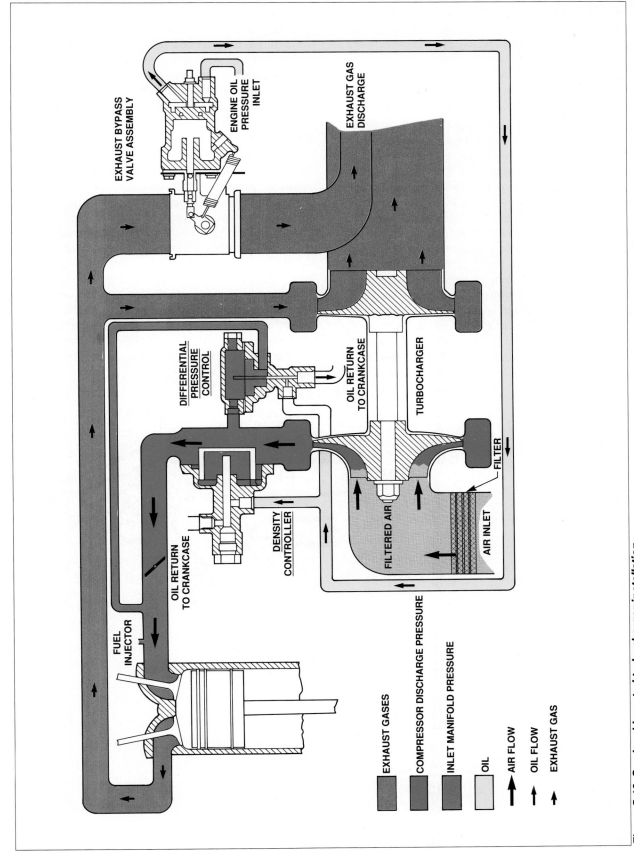

EXHAUST BYPASS VALVE ASSEMBLY

ENGINE OIL PRESSURE INLET

EXHAUST GAS DISCHARGE

DIFFERENTIAL PRESSURE CONTROL

OIL RETURN TO CRANKCASE

TURBOCHARGER

FILTER

FILTERED AIR

AIR INLET

DENSITY CONTROLLER

OIL RETURN TO CRANKCASE

FUEL INJECTOR

EXHAUST GASES

COMPRESSOR DISCHARGE PRESSURE

INLET MANIFOLD PRESSURE

OIL

AIR FLOW

OIL FLOW

EXHAUST GAS

Figure 5-12. Sea level boosted turbocharger installation.

183

5-135-13

dry nitrogen, maintains a constant density by allowing the pressure to increase as the temperature increases. Movement of the bellows repositions the bleed valve, causing a change in the quantity of bleed oil, which changes the oil pressure on top of the waste gate piston (see figure 5-12).

The differential pressure controller functions during all positions of the waste gate valve other than the "fully open" position, which is controlled by the density controller. One side of the diaphragm in the differential pressure controller senses air pressure upstream from the throttle; the other side samples air pressure on the cylinder side of the throttle valve (figure 5-12). At the "wide open" throttle position when the density controller controls the waste gate, the pressure across the differential pressure controller diaphragm is at a minimum and the controller spring holds the bleed valve closed. At "part throttle" position, the air differential is increased, opening the bleed valve to bleed oil to the engine crankcase and reposition the waste gate piston.

Thus the two controllers operate independently to control the turbocharger operation at all positions of the throttle. Without the overriding function of the differential pressure controller during part throttle operation, the density controller would position the waste gate valve for maximum power. The differential pressure controller reduces injector entrance pressure and continually repositions the valve over the whole operating range of the engine.

The differential pressure controller reduces the unstable condition known as "bootstrapping" during part throttle operation. Bootstrapping is an indication of unregulated power change that results in the continual drift of manifold pressure. This condition can be illustrated when considering the operation of a system when the waste gate is fully closed. During this time, the differential pressure controller is not modulating the waste gate valve position. Any slight change in power caused by a change in temperature or RPM fluctuation will be magnified and will result in manifold pressure change, since the slight

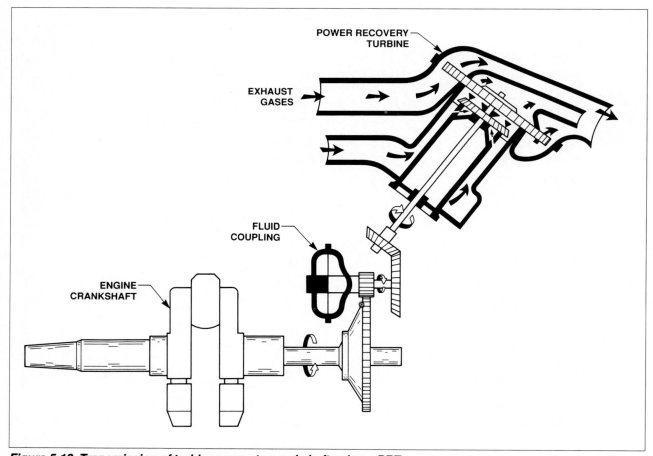

Figure 5-13. Transmission of turbine power to crankshaft using a PRT.

change will cause a change in the amount of exhaust gas flowing to the turbine. Any change in the exhaust gas flow to the turbine will be reflected in manifold pressure indications. Bootstrapping, then, is an undesirable cycle of turbocharging events causing the manifold pressure to drift in an attempt to reach a state of equilibrium.

Bootstrapping is sometimes confused with the condition known as "over-boost," but bootstrapping is not a condition which is detrimental to engine life. An over-boost condition is one in which manifold pressure exceeds the limits prescribed for a particular engine and can cause serious damage.

Thus, the differential pressure controller is essential to smooth functioning of the automatically controlled turbocharger, since it reduces bootstrapping by reducing the time required to bring a system into equilibrium. There is still a great deal more throttle sensitivity with a turbocharged engine than with a naturally aspirated engine. Rapid movement of the throttle can cause a certain amount of manifold pressure drift in a turbocharged engine. This condition, less severe than bootstrapping, is called "overshoot." While overshoot is not a dangerous condition, it can be a source of concern to the pilot or operator, who selects a particular manifold pressure setting only to find it has changed in a few seconds and must be reset. Since the automatic controls cannot respond rapidly enough to abrupt changes in throttle settings to eliminate the inertia of turbocharger speed changes, overshoot must be controlled by the operator. This can best be accomplished by slowing making changes in throttle setting, accompanied by a few seconds' wait for the system to reach a new equilibrium. Such a procedure is effective with turbocharged engines, regardless of the degree of throttle sensitivity.

d. Turbocompound Systems

The turbocompound engine consists of a conventional, reciprocating engine in which exhaust driven turbines are coupled to the engine crankshaft. This system of obtaining additional power is sometimes called a PRT (power recovery turbine) system. It is not a supercharging system, and it is not connected in any manner to the air induction system of the aircraft.

The PRT system enables the engine to recover power from the exhaust gases that would otherwise be directed overboard. Depending on the type of engine, the amount of horsepower recovered varies with the amount of input horsepower. An average of 130 horsepower from each of the three turbines in a system is typical for large reciprocating engines.

A power recovery turbine's geared connections to the engine crankshaft is shown in figure 5-13.

Typically there are three power recovery turbines on each engine, located 120° apart. The exhaust collector nozzle for each segment of the cylinders directs the exhaust gases onto the turbine wheel. The turbine wheel shaft transmits the power to the engine crankshaft through gears and a fluid coupling. The fluid coupling prevents torsional vibration from being transmitted to the crankshaft.

Power recovery turbine systems, because of weight and cost considerations, were used exclusively on very large radial engines, of the type used to power certain military, and airline transport aircraft.

B. Reciprocating Engine Exhaust Systems

The reciprocating engine exhaust system is fundamentally a scavenging system that collects and disposes of the high temperature, noxious gases as they are discharged by the engine. Its basic requirement is to dispose of the gases with complete safety to the airframe and the occupants of the aircraft. The exhaust system can be adapted to take advantage of the thermal and kinetic energy contained in the gases, but its first duty is to provide against the potentially destructive action of the exhaust gases. Modern exhaust systems, though comparatively light, adequately resist high temperatures, corrosion, and vibration to provide long, trouble-free operation with a minimum of maintenance.

1. Types Of Exhaust Systems

There are two general types of exhaust systems in use on reciprocating aircraft engines: the short stack (open) system and the collector system. The short stack system is generally used on non-supercharged engines and low powered engines where noise level is not a factor. The collector system is used on most large non-supercharged engines and on all turbosupercharged engines. It may also be found on installations where it would improve nacelle streamlining or provide easier maintenance in the nacelle area.

a. Short Stacks

Early in-line and V-engines often used straight stacks which were simply short sections of steel tubing welded to a flange and bolted to the cylinder exhaust port. These short stacks were effective at getting the exhaust out of the engine compartment, but they had no silencing capability, and when the aircraft was side-slipped, cold air could flow into these stacks and warp the exhaust valves.

The short (or straight) stack system is relatively simple, and its removal and installation consists essentially of removing and installing the hold-down nuts and clamps.

b. Radial Engine Exhaust Collector Rings

Radial engines use an exhaust manifold made up of a number of pieces of tubing that are fitted together with loose slip fits. When the engine is running, the components expand and fit together tightly, so there is no leakage. This collector system may be seen in figure 5-14.

As you can see in this figure, the sections of the collector ring are graduated in size. The small sections are on the inboard side, and the largest sections are on the outboard side at the

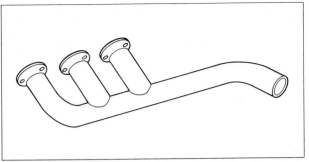

Figure 5-15. Short stacks and collector used on horizontally opposed engines.

point where the tailpipe connects to the collector. Each section of the collector is bolted to a bracket on the blower section of the engine, and is partly supported by a sleeve connection between the collector ring ports and the short stack on the engine exhaust ports. The exhaust tailpipe is joined to the collector ring by a telescoping expansion joint, which allows enough slack for the removal of segments of the collector ring without removing the tailpipe.

c. Opposed Type Engine Exhaust Manifold

The typical exhaust collector for one side of an six-cylinder horizontally opposed engine is shown in figure 5-15. The exhaust system consists of a down stack from each cylinder, and an exhaust collector on each side of the engine. The down stacks are attached to each cylinder with high temperature nuts, and often secured to the collector tube by ring clamps.

A cabin or carburetor heater exhaust shroud may be installed around the collector tube to serve as an air-to-air heat exchanger. These units will be discussed later in this chapter.

The exhaust collector tube may be routed to a turbocharger, a muffler, an exhaust augmentor, or simply overboard, depending upon the installation.

In figure 5-16 we have the exhaust system of a turbocharged six-cylinder horizontally opposed engine. A crossover tube connects the exhaust stacks on the left side of the engine with the stacks on the right side. At each location where expansion and contraction must be provided for, there are bellows that allow for the change in physical dimensions without any leakage. The waste gate valve is hydraulically opened to allow exhaust gases to pass directly out the tail pipe, or closed to force these gases out through the turbocharger turbine section.

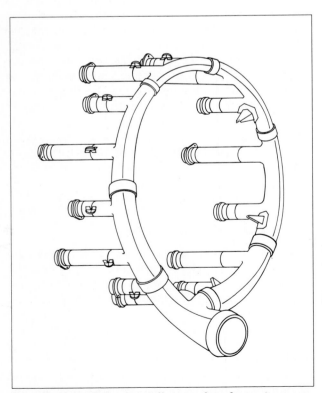

Figure 5-14. Exhaust collector ring for a two row, radial engine.

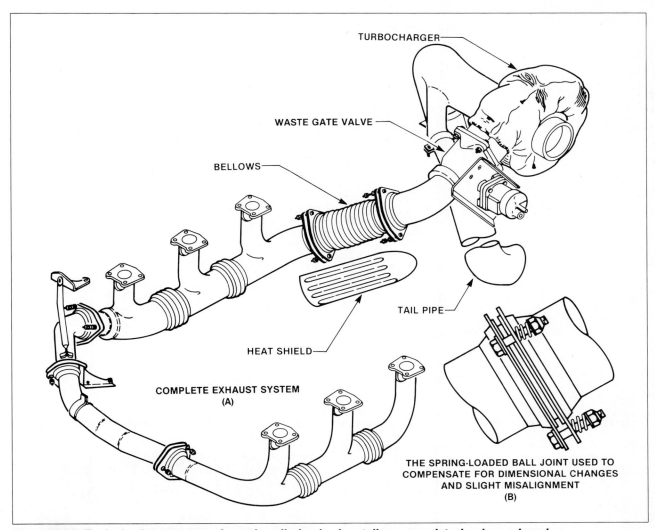

TURBOCHARGER

WASTE GATE VALVE

BELLOWS

TAIL PIPE

HEAT SHIELD

COMPLETE EXHAUST SYSTEM
(A)

THE SPRING-LOADED BALL JOINT USED TO
COMPENSATE FOR DIMENSIONAL CHANGES
AND SLIGHT MISALIGNMENT
(B)

Figure 5-16. Typical exhaust system for a six cylinder, horizontally opposed, turbocharged engine.

The sections of the exhaust system are joined with spring-loaded ball joints that allow movement without leakage and allow for slight misalignment of the parts.

2. Exhaust Augmentors

Engine exhaust augmentors are designed to use the velocity of the exiting exhaust gases to produce a venturi effect to draw an increased airflow over the engine to augment engine cooling. This system is illustrated in figure 5-17.

The exhaust from the cylinders on each side, flow through a collector and discharge into the inlet of a stainless steel augmentor tube. This flow of high velocity gas creates a low pressure and draws air from above the engine through the cylinder fins.

3. Mufflers And Heat Exchangers

Noise is a problem in aviation engines, and studies have been made to find practical ways of increasing the frequency and reducing the intensity of the noise. Propellers produce a large portion of the total noise, but the energy in the exhaust also accounts for an appreciable amount.

Exhaust collectors carried the gases safely away from the engine, but did little to nothing about reducing noise levels. It was discovered that if the ends of the collectors were cut at a taper and the exhaust discharged through a relatively narrow slot rather than through the straight open pipe, the noise was reduced. The air flowing over this bayonet, as it was called, created a slightly low pressure that helped

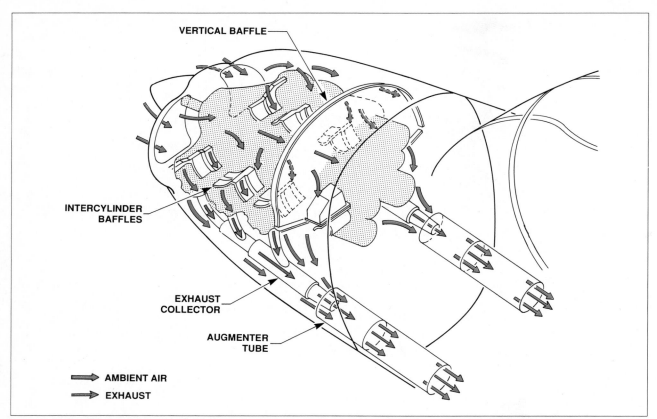

VERTICAL BAFFLE

INTERCYLINDER
BAFFLES

EXHAUST
COLLECTOR

AUGMENTER
TUBE

⟹ AMBIENT AIR
⟹ EXHAUST

Figure 5-17. Augmentor tube installation for a six cylinder horizontally opposed aircraft engine.

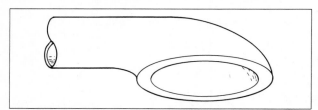

Figure 5-18. A bayonet-type discharge of an exhaust stack.

reduce exhaust back pressure. A bayonet type discharge is illustrated in Figure 5-18.

In the last forty years, mufflers similar to those used on automobiles have been used to reduce engine noise to a tolerable level. The muffler in figure 5-19 receives the exhaust from two cylinders of a four cylinder engine and passes it through a series of baffles to break up the sound energy, and then this exhaust is passed out through a single tailpipe. The flanges around the end of the muffler support a sheet metal shroud that holds cabin air or carburetor air in contact with the outside of the muffler skin so it can absorb heat from the muffler.

Figure 5-19. Muffler for reciprocating engine, with heat muff removed.

4. Reciprocating Engine Exhaust System Maintenance Practices

The corrosion resistant steel of which exhaust systems are made is thin, and the systems operate at high temperatures. These difficult conditions, coupled with the fact that exhaust system failure almost always causes a fire hazard as well as allowing toxic fumes to enter the aircraft cabin, make inspection of the exhaust system extremely important.

Before discussing inspection and maintenance procedures for exhaust system components, a precaution to be observed must be mentioned. Galvanized or zinc plated tools should never be used on the exhaust system, and exhaust system parts should never be marked with a lead pencil. The lead, zinc, or galvanized mark is absorbed by the metal of the exhaust system when heated, creating a distinct change in its molecular structure. This change softens the metal in the area of the mark, causing cracks and eventual failure.

a. Exhaust System Inspection

Cracks are the more common problem with an exhaust system, and on all inspections the entire system should be carefully inspected for any indication of cracks. A crack will usually allow exhaust gas to escape, and this often shows up as a flat gray or a sooty black streak on the outside of the stack or muffler. Weld areas are especially subject to cracks, as the expansion and contraction of the thin material of which the system is made produces enough stresses to cause cracks to form.

One effective method of checking an exhaust system for cracks is to remove the heater shrouds and connect the output to the discharge side of a vacuum cleaner to the exhaust tail pipe. Then, paint a soap and water solution over all of the joints and welds. Cracks will allow enough air to pass through that soap bubbles will form.

Figure 5-20 illustrates the areas of primary interest during inspection of exhaust system components.

b. Muffler And Heat Exchanger Failures

Approximately half of all muffler and heat exchanger failures can be traced to cracks or ruptures in the heat exchanger surfaces used for cabin and carburetor heat sources. Failures in the heat exchanger surface (usually in the outer wall) allow exhaust gases to escape directly into the cabin heat system. These failures, in most cases, are caused by thermal and vibration fatigue cracking in areas of stress concentration.

c. Exhaust Manifold And Stack Failures

Exhaust manifold and stack failures are usually fatigue failures at welded and clamped points. Although these failures are primarily fire hazards, they also present carbon monoxide problems. Exhaust gases can enter the cabin via defective or inadequate seals at firewall openings, wing strut fittings, doors, and wing root openings.

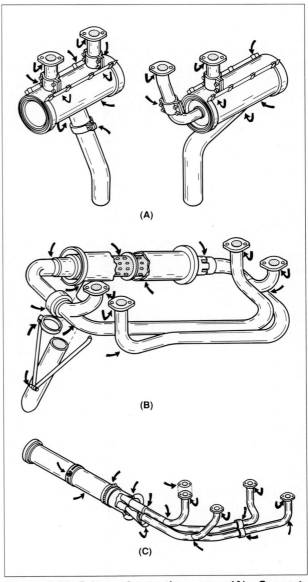

Figure 5-20. Primary inspection areas. (A)—Separate system. (B)—Crossover-type system. (C)—Exhaust augmentor system.

189

d. Internal Muffler Failures

Internal failures (baffles, diffusers, etc.) can cause partial or complete engine power loss by restricting the flow of the exhaust gases. As opposed to other failures, erosion and carburization caused by extreme thermal conditions are the primary causes of internal failures. Engine backfiring and combustion of unburned fuel within the exhaust system are probable contributing factors. In addition, local hot spot areas caused by uneven exhaust gas flow can result in burning, bulging, or rupture of the outer muffler wall.

e. Exhaust Systems With Turbocharger

When a turbocharger is included, the engine exhaust system operates under greatly increased pressure and temperature conditions. Extra precautions should be taken in exhaust system care and maintenance. During high altitude operation, the exhaust system pressure is maintained at or near sea level values. Due to the pressure differential, any leaks in the system will allow the exhaust gases to escape with torch-like intensity that can severely damage adjacent structures.

A common cause of malfunction is coke deposits (carbon buildup) in the waste gate unit causing erratic system operation. Excessive deposit buildup may cause the waste gate to stick in the "closed" position, causing an overboost condition. Coke deposit buildup in the turbo itself will cause a gradual loss of power in flight and a low manifold pressure reading prior to takeoff. Clean, repair, overhaul, and adjust the system components and controls in accordance with the applicable manufacturer's instructions.

f. Augmentor Exhaust System

On exhaust systems equipped with augmentor tubes, the augmentor tubes should be inspected at regular intervals for proper alignment, security of attachment, and general overall condition. Even where augmentor tubes do not contain heat exchanger surfaces, they should be inspected for cracks along with the remainder of the exhaust system.

g. Exhaust System Repairs

It is generally recommended that exhaust stacks, mufflers, tailpipes, etc. be replaced with new or reconditioned components rather than repaired. Welded repairs to exhaust systems are complicated by the difficulty of accurately iden-

tifying the base metal so that the proper repair materials can be selected.

Steel or low temperature, self-locking nuts should not be substituted for brass or high temperature locknuts used by the manufacturer. Old gaskets should never be reused. When disassembly is necessary, gaskets should be replaced with new ones of the same type provided by the manufacturer.

C. Turbojet Engine Inlet Duct Systems

Although no direct parallel can be drawn, the turbine engine air inlet duct is somewhat analogous to the air induction system of reciprocating engines.

The engine air inlet and the inlet ducting of a turbine engine furnish a relatively distortion free, high energy supply of air, in the required quantity, to the face of the compressor. A uniform and steady airflow is necessary to avoid compressor stall and excessive internal engine temperature at the turbine. The high energy air enables the engine to produce an optimum amount of thrust. Normally, the air inlet is considered an airframe part, and not a part of the engine. However, the duct is so important to engine performance that it must be considered in any discussion of the complete engine.

1. Turbojet Inlet Systems

A gas turbine engine consumes six to 10 times as much air per hour as a reciprocating engine of the equivalent size. The air entrance passage is correspondingly larger. Furthermore, it is more

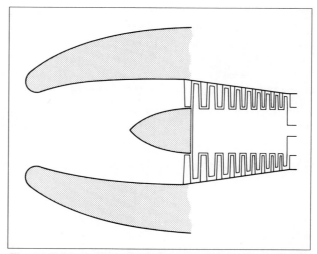

Figure 5-21. A divergent inlet duct used on subsonic aircraft.

critical than a reciprocating engine in determining engine and aircraft performance, especially at high airspeeds. Inefficiencies of the duct result in successively magnified losses through other components of the engine.

The inlet duct has two engine functions and one aircraft function. First, it must be able to recover as much of the total pressure of the free airstream as possible and deliver this pressure to the front of the compressor with a minimum loss of pressure or differential. This is known as "ram recovery" or, sometimes as, total pressure recovery. Secondly, the duct must uniformly deliver air to the compressor inlet with as little turbulence and pressure variation as possible. As far as the aircraft is concerned, the duct must hold to a minimum the drag effect, which it creates.

Pressure drop or differential is caused by the friction of the air along both sides of the duct and by the bends in the duct system. Smooth flow depends upon keeping the amount of turbulence to a minimum as the air enters the duct. The duct must have a sufficiently straight section to ensure smooth, even airflow within. The choice of configuration of the entrance to the duct is dictated by the location of the engine within the aircraft and the airspeed, altitude, and attitude at which the aircraft is designed to operate.

With entrance ducts of any type, careful construction is very essential. Good workmanship is also needed when an inlet duct is repaired. Surprisingly small amounts of airflow distortion can result in appreciable loss in engine efficiency or can be responsible for otherwise unex-

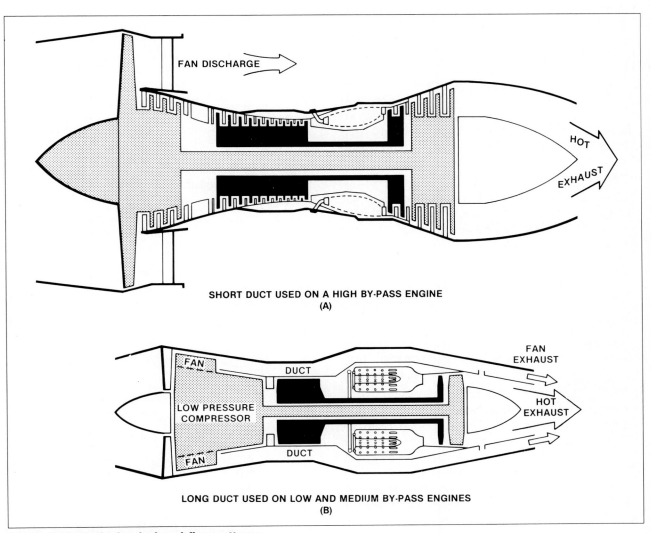

SHORT DUCT USED ON A HIGH BY-PASS ENGINE
(A)

LONG DUCT USED ON LOW AND MEDIUM BY-PASS ENGINES
(B)

Figure 5-22. Typical turbofan airflow patterns.

plainable compressor stalls. Protruding rivet heads or poor sheet metal work can play havoc with an otherwise acceptable duct installation.

a. Subsonic Inlet Duct

The turbojet and turbofan aircraft in today's fleet generally have their engines mounted on wing or fuselage pylons. This allows for the shortest possible inlet duct, and a minimum of problems associated with intakes. The exception to this is the tail-mounted engine on several popular designs. These incorporate quite a long inlet duct to route air from the base of the vertical stabilizer to the engine mounted deep inside the tail cone of the aircraft.

Inlet ducts used on multi-engine subsonic aircraft, such as we find in the business and commercial fleet, are fixed geometry ducts whose diameter progressively increases from the front to back, as we see in figure 5-21. A diverging duct is sometimes called an inlet diffuser because of the effect it has on the pressure of the air entering the engine. As air enters the inlet at ambient pressure, it begins to spread out, or diffuse, and by the time it arrives at the inlet to the compressor, its pressure is slightly higher than ambient. Usually the design is such that the air diffuses in the front portion of the duct, and then it progresses along at a fairly constant pressure. This allows the engine to receive the air with less turbulence and at a more uniform pressure.

This added pressure adds significantly to the mass airflow when the aircraft reaches its design cruising speed. It is at this design cruising speed that the inlet, the compressor, the combustor, the turbine, and the tail pipe are designed to match each other as a unit. If any section mismatches any other because of damage, contamination, or ambient conditions, the engine performance will be affected.

The inlet for a turbofan is similar in design to that for a turbojet except that is discharges only a portion of its air into the engine; the remainder passes only through the fan.

Figure 5-22 shows two common turbofan flow patterns: one is the short duct design used for high by-pass turbofans, and the other is the full duct used on low or medium by-pass engines. The long duct configuration reduces surface drag of the fan discharge air and enhances the thrust. A high by-pass engine cannot take advantage of this drag reduction concept, however, because the weight penalty caused by such a large diameter duct would cancel any gain.

b. Supersonic Inlet Duct

Supersonic inlet ducts must be designed to operate efficiently in three speed modes: (1) subsonic, (2) transonic, and (3) supersonic. This is accomplished using a variable geometry inlet duct.

In order to vary the geometry, or the shape of the inlet duct, a movable restrictor is sometimes used to give this duct a convergent-divergent, or C-D shape. A C-D shaped duct is necessary to reduce the supersonic airflow to a subsonic speed. This speed reduction is important because at subsonic flow rates, air acts as though it were an incompressible fluid; but at supersonic flow rates, air can be compressed, and when it is it creates shock waves.

Figure 5-24 shows a fixed C-D duct in which the supersonic airflow is slowed by the formation

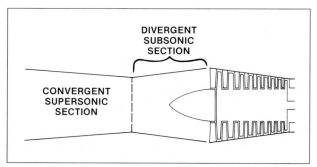

Figure 5-23. Convergent-divergent inlet duct used on supersonic aircraft.

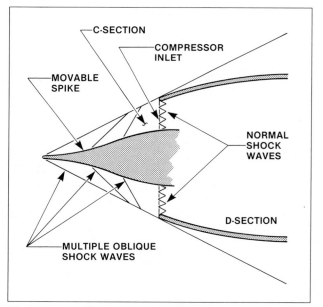

Figure 5-24. Supersonic inlet duct equipped with a movable spike.

Figure 5-25. Bellmouth inlet ducts are used in engine test cells for calibrating gas turbine engines.

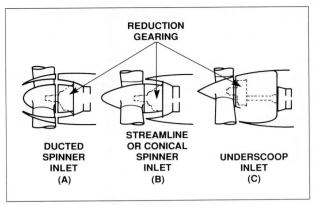

Figure 5-26. Turboprop inlet designs.

of both oblique and normal shock waves. Once the speed of the inlet air is reduced to Mach 1.0, it enters the subsonic diffuser section where velocity is further reduced and its pressure is increased before it enters the compressor.

c. Bellmouth Compressor Inlet Duct

When turbine engines are calibrated in test stands they use a bellmouth inlet fitted with an anti-ingestion screen. Duct loss is so slight with this design that it is considered to be zero. Engine performance data is collected when the engine is fitted with a bellmouth compressor inlet.

2. Turboprop Compressor Inlets And Inlet Screens

The air inlet on a turboprop is more of a problem than that on a turbojet because the propeller drive shaft, hub, and the spinner must be considered in addition to the usual other inlet design factors. The ducted spinner arrangement (figure 5-26, view A) is generally considered to be the best inlet design for the turboprop engine, as far as airflow and aerodynamic characteristics are concerned. However, the ducted spinner is heavier, and is more difficult to maintain and to anti-ice than the conventional streamline spinner arrangement which is frequently used. A conical spinner (view B), which is a modified ver-

sion of the streamline spinner, is sometimes employed. When the nose section of the turboprop engine is offset from the main axis of the engine, an arrangement similar to that seen in view C of the figure may be employed.

Reverse flow turboprop engines whose air entrance may be midway or further back along the length of the engine may employ an air scoop at the front of the nacelle, below the propeller and utilize ducting similar to that seen on reciprocating engines.

3. Turboshaft Filter/Separator Units

One of the most critical criteria when designing the air inlet system for a turboshaft engine is that the air be clear of foreign objects. This can be difficult in helicopter operations where landings are often conducted in unimproved areas, with dust and sand being blown into the air by the down-wash of the main rotors. This often requires the use of a particle separator on the inlet of the engine. While most separators are available as an option, some helicopters have them as standard equipment.

There are several particle separator systems in use today, and they operate on one of two principles. For this reason, only two systems will be discussed. The first will be that used on the Bell 206 helicopter. On this aircraft a total of 283 individual elements are used for the inlet filter. Each of these filter elements acts as a swirl chamber (figure 5-27). As the air passes through each element, it is swirled and dirt particles are thrown to the outside of the tube by centrifugal force, causing the particles to drop into the bottom of the unit. Compressor bleed air is routed into the bottom of the unit to sweep the particles overboard through three holes on each side of the filter unit.

The system used on Bell 212 helicopters is illustrated in figure 5-28. It consists of a separate duct system for each of the two engines. This duct provides for inlet air particle separation, and cools and carries off exhaust gases. Each system is composed of an air inlet, a forward duct, engine induction baffles, particle separator valve, transition duct, power section exhaust duct, and ejector.

Each particle separator valve is controlled by a 28 volt actuator. The particle separator valve is open under normal conditions to provide inertia separation. The door, however, will close under two conditions. One of these occurs anytime N_1 drops below 52% RPM and the other, when the fire extinguisher handle is pulled. Whenever the valve is closed, the particle separator caution light will illuminate.

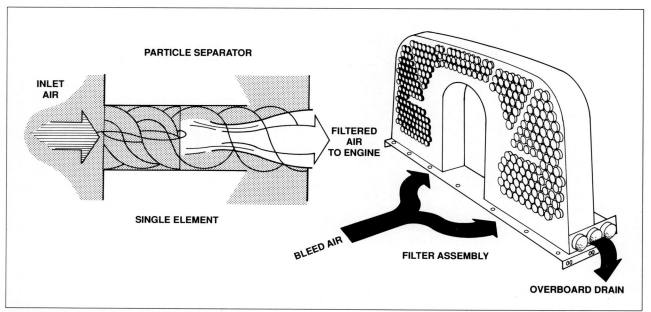

Figure 5-27. Particle separator used on the Bell 206.

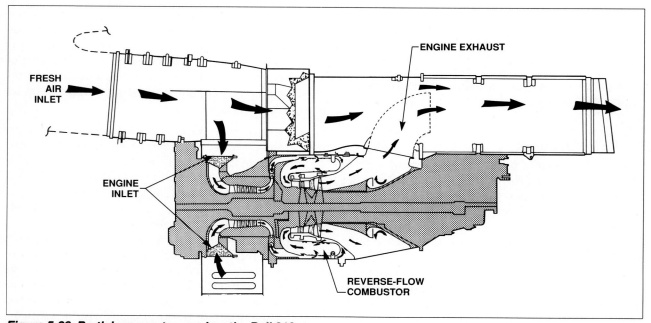

Figure 5-28. Particle separator used on the Bell 212.

Using figure 5-28, the airflow pattern may be traced. Air enters the forward duct through the air inlet section and has two paths of airflow: into the engine inlet and into the ejector. A portion of the air and the heavy particles move aft through the particle separator valve into the ejector, separating particles because of their inertia. Inlet air enters the compressor through a wire mesh screen.

D. Turbine Engine Exhaust Systems

The term "exhaust duct" is applied to the engine exhaust pipe, or tail pipe, which connects the turbine outlet to the jet nozzle of a non-afterburning engine.

If the engine exhaust gases could be discharged directly into the outside air in an exact axial direction at the turbine exit, an exhaust duct might not be necessary. This however, is not practical. A larger thrust can be obtained from the engine if the gases are discharged from the aircraft at a higher velocity than is permissible at the turbine outlet. An exhaust duct is therefore added, both to collect and straighten the gas flow as it comes from the turbine, and to increase the velocity of the gases before they are discharged from the exhaust nozzle. Increasing the velocity of the gases increases their momentum, and increases the thrust produced.

1. Turbojet Exhaust

Because all of the airflow of a turbojet engine passes through the engine core, only a single exhaust flow need be dealt with.

The turbine engine exhaust system must be capable of withstanding very high temperatures and is usually manufactured from nickel or titanium. This heat must not be allowed to transfer to nearby airframe components or structures. This may be accomplished by routing ventilating air around the exhaust pipe, and by lagging the exhaust pipe with an insulating blanket. These insulating blankets use an inner layer of insulating material and an outer skin of stainless steel, which is dimpled to increase its strength.

a. Convergent Exhaust Nozzle

The convergent tail pipe is used on most subsonic aircraft. The shape is generally of fixed geometry and cannot be altered. In this design the gases never travel faster than the speed of sound.

b. Convergent-Divergent Exhaust Nozzle

Supersonic aircraft utilize the C-D type of tail pipe. The advantage of this shape is the greatest at high Mach numbers.

2. Turbofan Exhaust

The by-pass engine has two gas streams to eject to the atmosphere, the cool fan air, and the hot gases being discharged from the turbine. In a low by-pass engine these two flows may be combined in a mixer unit, and discharged through the same nozzle. In a high by-pass engine the fan air is usually discharged separately from the hot gases.

3. Turboprop Exhaust

In a typical turboprop exhaust system, the exhaust gases are directed from the turbine section of the engine to the atmosphere through a tail pipe assembly. The exhaust arrangement will depend upon the type of engine. Turboprop engines utilizing a through flow burner will probably exhaust the gases straight out the back of the engine, and out of the nacelle. This will allow for the maximum thrust component from the velocity of the hot gases. Engines using a reverse flow combustor may exhaust the hot gases near the front of the engine. This design will probably collect the exhaust gases and vent them overboard through two exhaust stacks. There is very little additional thrust provided by this type of exhaust.

4. Thrust Reversers

Airliners powered by turbojets and turbofans, most commuter aircraft, and an increasing number of business jets, are equipped with thrust reversers to:

(1) Aid in braking and directional control during normal landing, and reduce brake maintenance.

(2) Provide braking and directional control during emergency landings and balked take-offs.

(3) Be deployed in flight as speed brakes to increase the rate of descent.

(4) Back an aircraft out of a parking spot in what is called a "power back" operation.

Thrust reversers are controlled by a cockpit lever, at the command of the pilot. After reverse thrust is selected, the pilot can move the reverse throttle lever from "idle-select" up to "takeoff" position, as required by the landing conditions. Thrust reversers provide approximately 20% of the braking force under normal conditions. Reversers are capable of producing between 40 and 50% of rated thrust in the reverse direction.

Operating in reverse at low ground speeds can cause re-ingestion of hot gases and compressor stalls. It can also cause ingestion of fine sand and other runway debris.

The most successful thrust reversers can be divided into two categories, the mechanical-blockage type and the aerodynamic-blockage type.

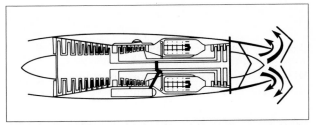

Figure 5-29. Operation of mechanical blockage-thrust reverser.

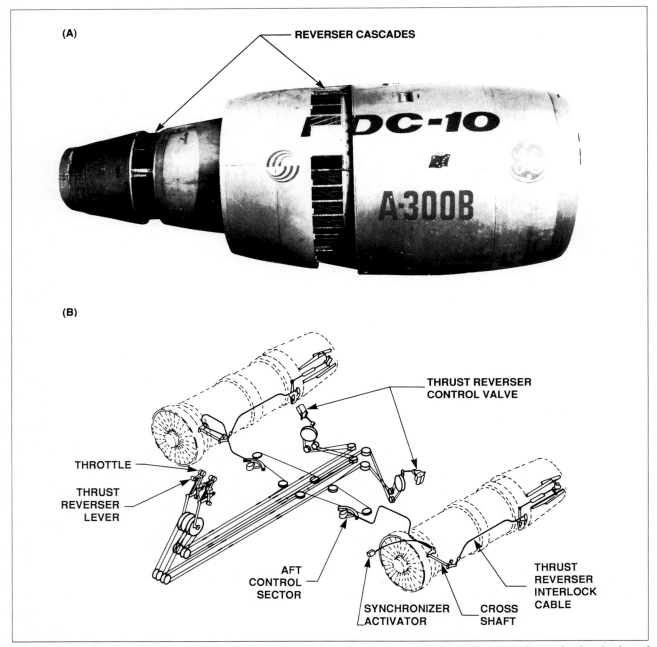

Figure 5-30. (A)—DC-10 during landing. Aerodynamic blockage fan and turbine reverser shown in the deployed position. (B)—Throttle and thrust reverse system.

a. Mechanical-Blockage Type

Mechanical blockage is accomplished by placing a removable obstruction in the exhaust gas stream, and it may be in either a pre-exit or post-exit position. The engine exhaust gases are mechanically blocked and diverted at a suitable angle in the reverse direction by an inverted cone, half-sphere, or other means of obstruction, which is placed in position to reverse the flow of exhaust gases. This type is also known as the "clamshell" thrust reverser because of its shape.

b. Aerodynamic-Blockage Type

The aerodynamic-blockage type of thrust reverser uses thin airfoils or obstructions placed in the gas stream, either along the length of the exhaust duct or immediately aft of the exhaust nozzle. These vanes turn the escaping gases to a forward direction, which in turn causes a rearward thrust. Some aircraft may use a combination of the aerodynamic-blockage and the mechanical-blockage type reversers.

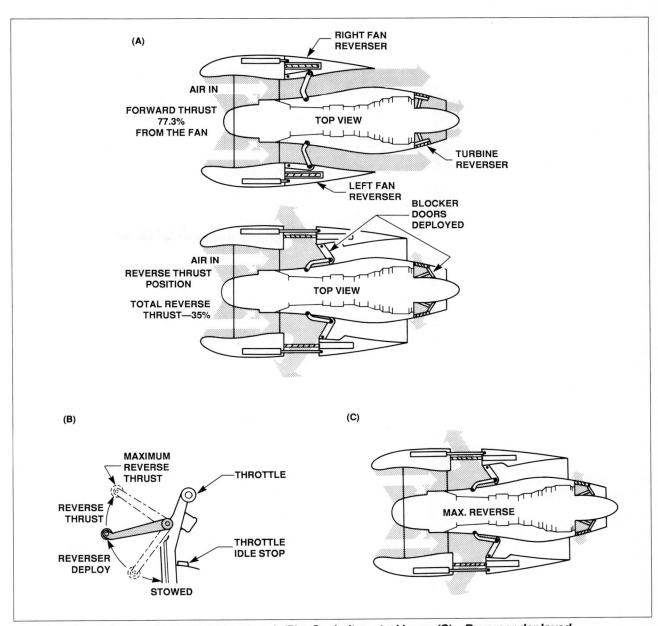

Figure 5-31. (A)—Aerodynamic reverser stored. (B)—Cockpit control lever. (C)—Reverser deployed.

c. Turbofan Reverser Installations

Mixed exhaust turbofans are configured with one reverser; unmixed exhaust turbofans often have both cold stream and hot stream reversers. Some high by-pass turbofans will have only cold stream reversing because most of the thrust is present in the fan discharge and a hot stream reverser would be of minimum value and become a weight penalty.

5. Noise Suppressors

Noise is best defined as "unwanted sound" and can be both irritating and harmful. With the current "hub and spoke" system utilized by the airlines, the highest concentration of jet aircraft traffic coincide with the highest densities of population. The aircraft industry has reacted to the sensitivity of the public by continually improving noise reduction techniques on every new generation of engine and aircraft. A continual effort is being made to reduce noise levels both on the ground, and in the air.

Noise suppressors used on the ground include portable devices which may be positioned near the rear of an engine whenever prolonged ground

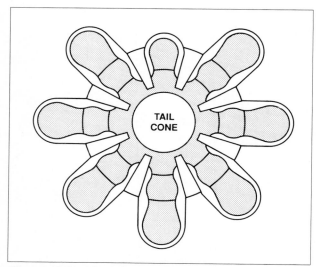

Figure 5-32. Rear view of old style corrugated-perimeter noise suppressor.

operation is anticipated. Additionally, blast fences, and designated run-up areas are provided on most large airports.

Noise suppression units as such, are not generally required on business jets or airliners today, but FAR Part 36 requires their use on many older commercial jet aircraft. Newer aircraft have inlets and tail pipes lined with noise attenuating materials to keep sound emission within the established effective perceived noise decibel (Epndb) limits. However, one can still find that which looks like the old style noise suppressor being retrofitted to some engines to meet the new noise standards.

The noise generated by a turbofan engine is much less than that generated by a turbojet. This is due in part by the fact that turbofan engines employ more turbine wheels to drive the compressor and the fan. This, in turn, causes the hot exhaust velocity, and hence the noise level, to be reduced. Some new generation fully ducted turbofan engines blend the fan discharge air with the hot exhaust gases more effectively and lessen the sound emission. On these engines, the sound from the inlet is likely to be louder than from the tail pipe. This is also the case with many high by-pass engines, where the fan will emit the greater noise.

Because of the characteristic of low frequency noise to linger at a relative high volume, noise reduction is often accomplished by increasing the frequency of the sound. Frequency change is accomplished by increasing the perimeter of the exhaust stream. This will provide more cold and hot air mixing space. This reduces the tendency of hot and cold air molecules to shear against each other and also to break up the large turbulence in the jet wake.

As previously mentioned, certain older aircraft will require modification to meet the current noise standards. This may be accomplished by the installation of "hush kits" as seen in figure 5-33.

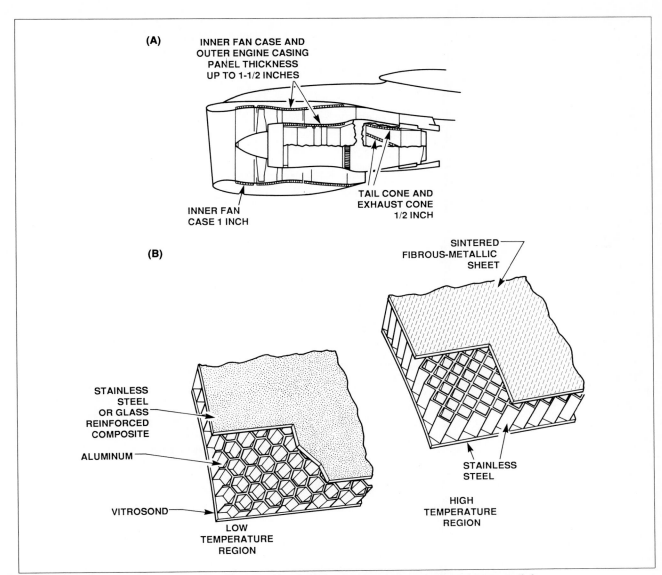

(A)

INNER FAN CASE AND
OUTER ENGINE CASING
PANEL THICKNESS
UP TO 1-1/2 INCHES

TAIL CONE AND
EXHAUST CONE
1/2 INCH

INNER FAN
CASE 1 INCH

(B)

SINTERED
FIBROUS-METALLIC
SHEET

STAINLESS
STEEL
OR GLASS
REINFORCED
COMPOSITE

ALUMINUM

VITROSOND

LOW
TEMPERATURE
REGION

STAINLESS
STEEL

HIGH
TEMPERATURE
REGION

Figure 5-33. (A)—Location of noise suppression materials. (B)—Noise suppression materials.

200

Chapter VI
Engine Fuel And Fuel Metering

A. Fuel System Requirements

Improvements in aircraft and engines have increased the demands on the fuel system. To meet these requirements, more sophisticated equipment has been developed and is in use today. These new systems require more expertise on the part of the technicians installing, adjusting, and performing maintenance on them. The fuel system must supply fuel to the carburetor or other metering device under all conditions of ground and air operation. It must function properly at constantly changing altitudes and in any climate. The system should be free of tendency to vapor lock, which can result from changes in ground and in-flight climatic conditions.

Normally the fuel remains in a liquid state until it is discharged into the air stream and then instantly changes into a vapor. Under certain conditions, however, the fuel may vaporize in the lines, pumps, or other units. The vapor pockets formed by this premature vaporization restrict the fuel flow through units which are designed to handle liquids rather than gases. The resulting partial or complete interruption of the fuel flow is called vapor lock. The three general causes of vapor lock are the lowering of pressure on the fuel, high fuel temperatures, and excessive fuel turbulence.

To reduce the possibility of vapor lock, fuel lines are kept away from sources of heat; also, sharp bends and steep rises are avoided. In addition, the volatility of the fuel is controlled in manufacture so it does not vaporize too readily. The major improvement in reducing vapor lock, however, is the incorporation of booster pumps in the fuel system. These pumps keep the fuel in the lines to the engine-driven pump under pressure. The slight pressure on the fuel reduces vapor formation and aids in moving a vapor pocket along. The booster pump also releases vapor from the fuel as it passes through the pump.

On small aircraft, a simple gravity feed fuel system consisting of a single tank to supply fuel to the engine is often installed. On multi-engine aircraft, complex systems are necessary so that fuel can be pumped from any combination of tanks to any combination of engines. Provisions for transferring fuel from one tank to another may also be included on large aircraft.

B. Fuel Metering Devices For Reciprocating Engines

This section explains the systems which deliver the correct mixture of fuel and air to the engine combustion chambers. In the discussion of each system, the general purpose and operating principles are stressed, with particular emphasis on the basic principles of operation. No attempt is made to give detailed operating and maintenance instructions for specific types and makes of equipment. For the specific information needed to inspect or maintain a particular installation or unit, consult the manufacturer's service information.

The basic requirement of a fuel metering system is the same, regardless of the type of system used or the model of engine on which the equipment is installed. It must meter fuel proportionally to air to establish the proper fuel/air mixture ratio for the engine at all speeds and altitudes for which the engine was designed to operate.

A second requirement of the fuel metering system is to atomize and distribute the fuel from the carburetor into the mass airflow in such a manner that the air charges going to all cylinders will hold similar amounts of fuel, so that the fuel/air mixture reaching each cylinder is the same ratio.

Carburetors tend to run richer at altitude than at ground level, because of the decreased density of the airflow through the carburetor throat for a given volume of air. Thus, it is necessary that a mixture control be provided to lean the mixture and compensate for this natural enrichment.

1. Fuel/Air Mixtures

Gasoline and other liquid fuels will not burn at all unless they are mixed with air. If the mixture is to burn properly within the engine cylinder, the ratio of air to fuel must be kept within a certain range.

It would be more accurate to state that the fuel is burned with the oxygen in the air. Seventy-eight percent of air by volume is nitrogen, which is inert and does not participate in the combustion process. The remaining 21 percent is oxygen. Heat is generated by burning the mixture of gasoline and oxygen. Nitrogen and gaseous by-products of combustion absorb this heat energy and turn it into power by their expansion. The ratio of fuel to air by weight is of extreme importance to engine performance. The characteristics of a given mixture can be measured in terms of flame speed and combustion temperature.

The composition of the fuel/air mixture is described by the mixture ratio. For example, a mixture with a ratio of 12 to 1 (12:1) is made up of 12 pounds of air and 1 pound of fuel. The ratio is expressed in weight because the volume of air varies greatly with temperature and pressure. The mixture ratio can also be expressed as a decimal. Thus a fuel/air ratio of 12:1 and a fuel/air ratio of 0.083 describe the same mixture. Air and gasoline mixtures as rich as 8:1 and as lean as 16:1 will burn in an engine cylinder. The engine develops maximum power with a mixture of approximately 12 parts of air and 1 part of gasoline.

From the chemist's point of view the perfect mixture for combustion of fuel and air would be 0.067 pound of fuel for 1 pound of air (mixture ratio of 15:1). The scientist calls this chemically correct combination a stoichiometric mixture (pronounced stoy-key-o-metric). With this mixture (given sufficient time and turbulence), all the fuel and all the oxygen in the air will be completely used in the combustion process. The stoichiometric mixture produces the highest combustion temperatures because the proportion of heat released to a mass of charge (fuel and air) is the greatest. However, the mixture is seldom used because it does not result in either the greatest economy or the greatest power for the airflow or manifold pressure.

There are specific instructions concerning mixture ratios for each type of engine under various operating conditions. Failure to follow these instructions will result in poor performance and often in damage to the engine. Excessively rich mixtures result in loss of power and waste of fuel. With the engine operating near its maximum output, very lean mixtures will cause a loss of power and under certain conditions, serious overheating. When the engine is operated on a lean mixture, the cylinder head temperature gauge should be watched closely. If the mixture is excessively lean, the engine may backfire through the induction system or stop completely. Backfire results from slow burning of the lean mixture. If the charge is still burning when the intake valve opens, it ignites the fresh mixture and the flame travels back through the combustible mixture in the induction system.

2. Carburetion Principles

The float carburetor used on aircraft engines has changed little in design over the years. Float carburetors are dependable, but have certain limitations primarily caused by their non-uniform distribution of the fuel/air mixture and their susceptibility to carburetor icing.

a. Venturi Principles

The carburetor must measure the airflow through the induction system and use this measurement to regulate the amount of fuel discharged into the airstream. The air measuring unit is the venturi, which makes use of a basic law of physics: as the velocity of a gas or liquid increases, the pressure decreases. As shown in the diagram of the simple venturi (figure 6-1), it is a passageway or tube in which there is a narrow portion called the throat. As the air speeds up to get through the narrow portion, its pressure drops. Note that the pressure in the throat is lower than that in any other part of the venturi. The main discharge nozzle of the carburetor will be located in the throat of the venturi to take advantage of the low pressure occurring at this point. This pressure drop is proportional to the

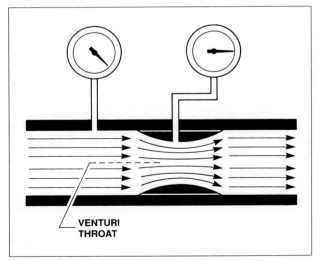

Figure 6-1. Simple venturi.

velocity and is, therefore, a measure of the airflow. The basic operating principle of most carburetors depends on the differential pressure between the inlet and the venturi throat.

b. Application Of Venturi Principles To Carburetor

The carburetor is mounted on the engine so that air to the cylinders passes through the carburetor barrel (the part of the carburetor which contains the venturi). The size and shape of the venturi depends on the requirements of the engine for which the carburetor is designed. A carburetor for a high powered engine may have one large venturi or several small ones. The air may flow either up or down the venturi, depending upon the design of the engine and the carburetor. Those in which the air passes downward are known as downdraft carburetors, and those in which the air passes upward are called updraft carburetors.

Air can be drawn through a soda straw by placing one end in the mouth and exerting a sucking action. Actually, the pressure inside the straw is lowered and atmospheric pressure pushes air into the open end. Air flows through the induction system in the same manner. When a piston moves toward the crankshaft on the intake stroke, the pressure in the cylinder is lowered. Air rushes through the carburetor and intake manifold to the cylinder due to the higher pressure at the carburetor intake. Even in a supercharged engine operating at high manifold pressure, there is still a low pressure at the engine side of the carburetor. Atmospheric pressure at the air intake pushes air through the carburetor to the supercharger inlet.

The throttle valve is located between the venturi and the engine, and is sometimes referred to as a butterfly valve. Mechanical linkage connects this valve with the throttle lever in the cockpit. By means of the throttle, airflow to the cylinders is regulated and controls the power output of the engine. It is the throttle valve in your automobile carburetor which opens when you "step on the gas". Actually, more air is admitted to the engine, and the carburetor automatically supplies enough additional gasoline to maintain the correct fuel/air ratio. The throttle valve obstructs the passage of air very little when it is parallel with the flow. This is the wide open position. Throttle action is illustrated in figure 6-2. Note how it restricts the airflow more and more as it rotates toward the closed position.

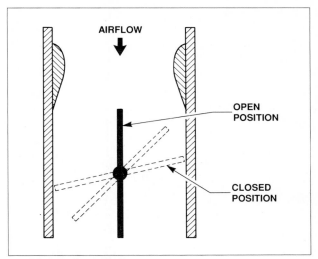

Figure 6-2. Throttle action.

c. Metering And Discharge Of Fuel

Fuel from the aircraft tank is delivered to the carburetor by the aircraft fuel system, and in some cases an engine driven fuel pump. Inside the carburetor the fuel first passes through a fine mesh wire screen, and then into the float chamber as we see in figure 6-3.

A float actuated needle valve maintains the fuel in the float bowl at a specific level which is just below the outlet of the discharge nozzle. As the fuel is used from the bowl, the float drops down and opens the needle valve, allowing more fuel to flow in and restore the level.

The fuel is metered by a balance of forces. One force is that required to lift the fuel in the discharge nozzle from its static level up to the outlet. This is called the fuel metering head. The other force is caused by the pressure differential between the atmospheric pressure inside the float bowl P_1, and the lowered pressure at the discharge nozzle P_2.

The fuel metering head remains relatively constant throughout the entire range of engine operation, but the air pressure differential varies with the volume of air taken in to the engine. The more air, the greater the differential. The maximum amount of fuel that can flow from the float bowl is determined by the size of the main metering jet.

3. Carburetor Systems

To provide for engine operation under various loads and at different engine speeds, a carburetor may require the following systems:

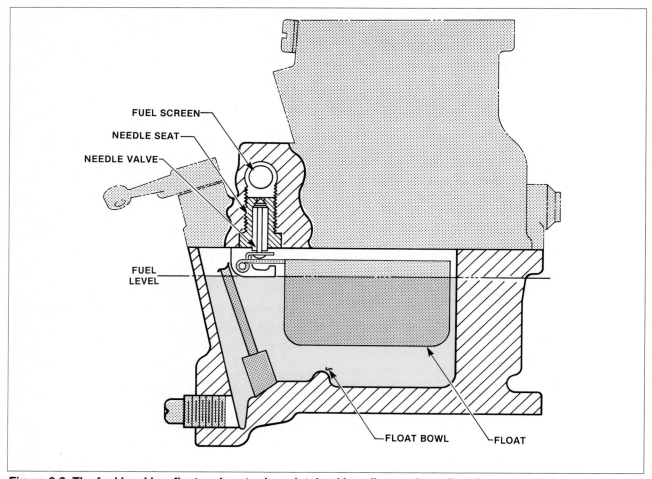

Figure 6-3. The fuel level in a float carburetor is maintained by a float and needle valve.

(1) Main metering.

(2) Idling.

(3) Accelerating.

(4) Mixture control.

(5) Idle cutoff

(6) Power enrichment or economizer.

Each of these systems has a definite function, and may act alone or with one of the others.

The main metering system supplies fuel to the engine at all speeds above idling. The fuel discharged by this system is determined by the drop in pressure at the venturi throat.

A separate system is necessary for idling because the main metering system is unreliable at very low engine speeds. At low speeds the throttle is nearly closed. As a result, the velocity of the air through the venturi is low and there is little drop in pressure. Consequently, the differential pressure is not sufficient to operate the main

metering system, and no fuel is discharged from this system. Therefore, most carburetors have an idling system to supply fuel to the engine at low speeds.

The accelerating system supplies extra fuel during increases in engine power. When the throttle is opened to obtain more power from the engine, the airflow through the carburetor increases. The main metering system then increases the fuel discharge. During sudden acceleration, however, the increase in airflow is so rapid that there is a slight time lag before the increase in fuel discharge is sufficient to provide the correct mixture ratio with the new airflow. By supplying extra fuel during this period, the accelerating system prevents a temporary leaning out of the mixture and gives smooth acceleration.

The mixture control system determines the ratio of fuel to air in the mixture. By means of a cockpit control the technician, pilot, or flight engineer, can select the mixture ratio to suit operating conditions. This is necessary because as the airplane climbs and the atmospheric pressure decreases, there is a corresponding decrease in the weight of the air passing through the induction system. The volume, however, remains constant, and, since it is the volume of the airflow which determines the pressure drop at the throat of the venturi, the carburetor tends to meter the same amount of fuel to this thin air as to the dense air at sea level. Thus, the natural tendency is for the mixture to become richer as the airplane gains altitude. The mixture control can be used to compensate for the decrease in air density.

The carburetor has an idle cutoff system so that the fuel can be shut off to stop the engine. This system stops the fuel discharge from the carburetor completely when the mixture control lever is set to the "idle cutoff" position. In any discussion of the idle cutoff system, this question usually comes up: Why is an aircraft engine stopped by shutting off the fuel rather than by turning off the ignition? To answer this question, it is necessary to examine the results of both methods.

If the ignition is turned off with the carburetor still supplying fuel, fresh fuel/air mixture continues to pass through the induction system to the cylinders while the engine is coasting to a stop. If the engine is excessively hot, this combustible mixture may be ignited by local hot spots within the combustion chambers, and the engine may keep on running or kick backward. Again, the mixture may pass out of the cylinders unburned but be ignited in the hot exhaust manifold. More often, however, the engine will come to an apparently normal stop but have a combustible mixture in the induction passages, the cylinders, and the exhaust system. This is an unsafe condition since the engine may kick over after it has been stopped and seriously injure anyone near the propeller.

On the other hand, when the engine is shut down by means of the idle cutoff system, the spark plugs continue to ignite the fuel/air mixture until the fuel discharge from the carburetor ceases. This alone should prevent the engine from coming to a stop with a combustible mixture in the cylinders. After the engine has come to a complete stop, the ignition switch is turned to the "off" position.

The power enrichment system automatically increases the richness of the mixture during high power operation. In this way, it makes possible the variation in the fuel/air ratio necessary to fit different operations. At cruising speeds a lean mixture is desirable for economy reasons, while at high power output the mixture must be rich to obtain maximum power and to aid in cooling the engine. The power enrichment system automatically brings about the necessary change in the fuel/air ratio. Essentially, it is a valve which is closed at cruising speeds and opens to supply extra fuel to the mixture during high power operations. Although it increases the fuel flow at high power, the power enrichment system is actually a fuel saving device. Without this system, it would be necessary to operate the engine on a rich mixture over the complete power range. The mixture would then be richer than necessary at cruising speed to ensure safe operation at maximum power. The power enrichment system is sometimes called an "economizer" or a "power compensator."

Although the various systems have been discussed separately, the carburetor functions as a unit. The fact that one system is in operation does not necessarily prevent another from functioning. At the same time that the main metering system is discharging fuel in proportion to the airflow, the mixture control system determines whether the resultant mixture will be rich or lean. If the throttle is suddenly opened wide, the accelerating and power enrichment systems act to add fuel to that already being discharged by the main metering system.

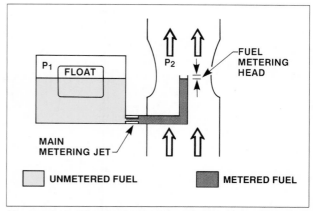

Figure 6-4. The fuel metering force in a float carburetor is determined by the pressure difference between the air in the float chamber and that at the main discharge nozzle, and by the distance that the fuel must be lifted from its normal level to the lip of the discharge nozzle.

a. Float-Type Carburetors

A float-type carburetor consists essentially of a main air passage through which the engine draws its supply of air, a mechanism to control the quantity of fuel discharged in relation to the flow of air, and a means of regulating the quantity of fuel/air mixture delivered to the engine cylinders.

1) Float Mechanism

A float chamber is provided between the fuel supply and the metering system of the carburetor. The float chamber provides a nearly constant level of fuel to the main discharge nozzle. This level is usually about ⅛ inch below the opening in the main discharge nozzle. The fuel must be maintained slightly below the discharge nozzle outlet to provide the correct amount of fuel flow and to prevent leakage from the nozzle when the engine is not operating.

The level of fuel in the float chamber is kept nearly constant by means of a float operated needle valve and seat (see figure 6-3). The needle seat is usually made of bronze. The needle valve is constructed of hardened steel, or it may have a synthetic rubber section which fits to the seat. With no fuel in the float chamber, the float drops toward the bottom of the chamber and allows the needle valve to open wide. As fuel is admitted from the supply line, the float rises and closed the valve when the fuel reaches a predetermined level. When the engine is running and fuel is being drawn out of the float chamber, the valve

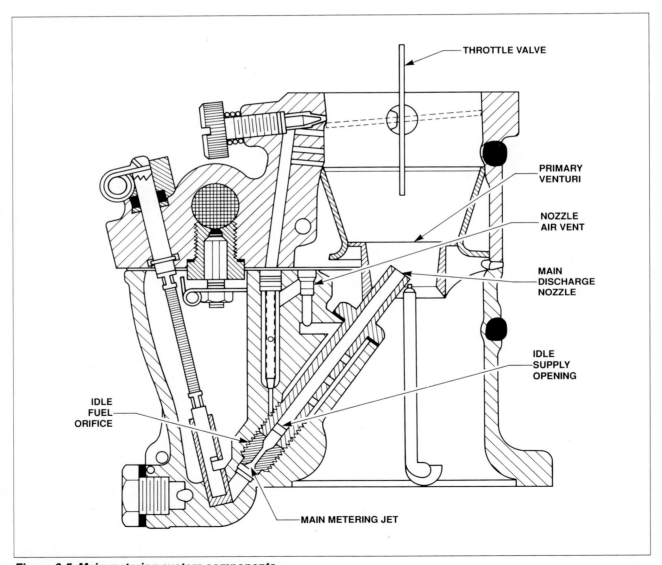

Figure 6-5. Main metering system components.

assumes an intermediate position so that the valve opening is just sufficient to supply the required amount of fuel and keep the level constant.

With the fuel at the correct level, the discharge rate is controlled accurately by the air velocity through the carburetor and atmospheric pressure on top of the fuel in the float chamber. A vent or small opening in the top of the float chamber allows air to enter or leave the chamber as the level of fuel rises or falls. This vent passage is open into the engine air intake; thus the air pressure in the chamber is always the same as that existing in the air intake.

2) Main Metering System

The main metering system supplies fuel to the engine at all speeds above idling and consists of: (1) A venturi, (2) a main metering jet, (3) a main discharge nozzle, (4) a passage leading to the idle system, and (5) the throttle valve. The components of the main metering system may be seen in figure 6-5.

The venturi performs three functions: (1) Proportions the fuel/air mixture, (2) decreases the pressure at the discharge nozzle, and (3) limits the airflow at full throttle.

When the engine crankshaft is revolved with the throttle open, the low pressure created in the intake manifold acts on the air passing through the carburetor barrel. Due to the difference in pressure between the atmosphere and the intake manifold, air will flow from the air intake through the carburetor barrel into the intake manifold. The volume of airflow depends upon the degree of throttle opening.

As the air flows through the venturi, its velocity increases. This velocity increase creates a low pressure area in the venturi throat. The fuel discharge nozzle is exposed to this low pressure. Since the float chamber is vented to atmospheric pressure, a pressure drop across the discharge nozzle is created. It is this pressure difference, or metering force, that causes fuel to flow from the discharge nozzle. The fuel comes out of the nozzle in a fine spray, and the tiny particles of fuel in the spray quickly vaporize in the air.

The metering force in most carburetors increases as the throttle opening is increased. A pressure drop of at least 0.5 inch Hg is required to raise the fuel in the discharge nozzle to a level where it will discharge into the airstream. At low engine speeds where the metering force is considerably reduced, the fuel delivery from the discharge nozzle would decrease if an air bleed were not incorporated in the carburetor.

The decrease in fuel flow in relation to airflow is due to two factors: (1) The fuel tends to adhere to the walls of the discharge nozzle and break off

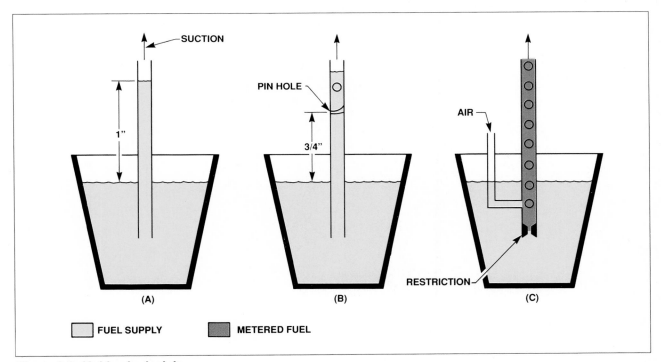

Figure 6-6. Air bleed principle.

intermittently in large drops instead of forming a fine spray, and (2) a part of the metering force is

required to raise the fuel level from the float chamber level to the discharge outlet.

The basic principle of the air bleed can be explained by simple diagrams as shown in figure 6-6. In each case, the same degree of suction is applied to the vertical tube placed in the container of liquid. As shown in A, the suction applied on the upper end of the tube is sufficient to lift the liquid a distance of about 1 in. above the surface. If a small hole is made in the side of the tube above the surface of the liquid, as in B, and suction is applied, bubbles of air will be drawn up in a continuous series of small slugs or drops. Thus, air "bleeds" into the tube and partially reduces the forces tending to retard the flow of liquid through the tube. However, the large opening in the bottom of the tube effectively prevents any great amount of suction from being exerted on the air bleed hole or vent. Similarly, an air bleed hole which is too large in proportion to the size of the tube would reduce the suction available to lift the liquid. If the system is

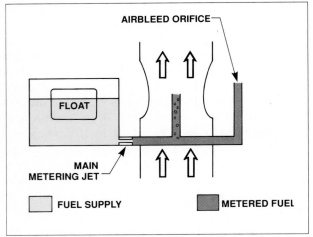

Figure 6-7. By the proper choice of airbleed orifice and main metering jet sizes, the fuel/air mixture ratio may be maintained relatively constant as the air volume through the carburetor changes.

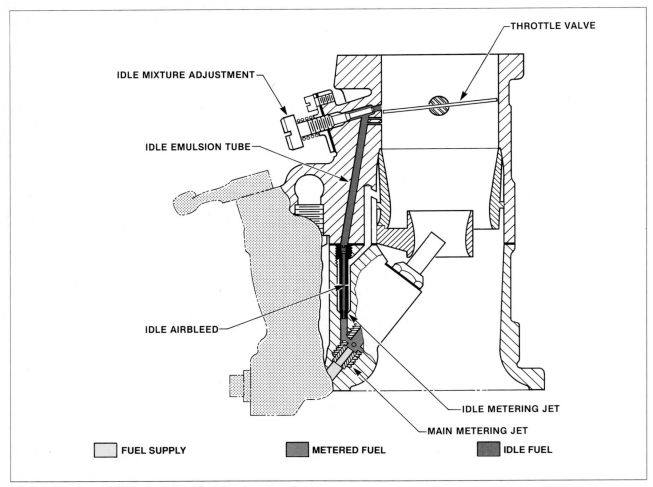

Figure 6-8. Typical idling system in a float carburetor.

modified by placing a metering orifice in the bottom of the tube and air is taken in below the fuel level by means of an air bleed tube, a finely divided emulsion of air and liquid is formed in the tube, as shown in C.

In a carburetor, a small air bleed is led into the fuel nozzle slightly below the fuel level. The open end of the air bleed is in the space behind the venturi wall, where the air is relatively motionless and approximately at atmospheric pressure. The low pressure at the tip of the nozzle not only draws fuel from the float chamber but also draws air from behind the venturi. Air bled into the main metering system decreases the fuel density and destroys surface tension. This results in better vaporization and control of fuel discharge, especially at lower engine speeds.

3) Idling System

When the throttle valve is closed at idling speeds, air velocity through the venturi is so low that it cannot draw enough fuel from the main discharge nozzle; in fact, the spray of fuel may stop altogether. However, low pressure exists on the engine side of the throttle valve. In order to allow the engine to idle, a fuel passageway is incorporated to discharge fuel from an opening in the low pressure area near the edge of the throttle valve. This opening is called the idling jet.

With the throttle open enough so that the main discharge nozzle is operating, fuel does not flow out the idling jet. As soon as the throttle is closed far enough to stop the spray from the main discharge nozzle, fuel flows out the idling jet. A separate air bleed, known as the idle air bleed, is included as part of the idling system. It functions the same as the main air bleed. An idle mixture adjusting device is also incorporated. A typical idling system is illustrated in figure 6-8.

In the wall of the throttle body where the butterfly valve almost touches, there are two or three small holes, or idle discharge ports. These ports are connected by an idle emulsion tube to a supply of fuel between the float bowl and the discharge nozzle. This emulsion tube contains the idle metering jet and the idle airbleed. The upper discharge port is fitted with a tapered needle valve to control the amount of fuel/air emulsion allowed to flow from the discharge ports when the throttle valve is closed.

As the throttle valve is opened, the edge of the butterfly valve moves down over the lower idle discharge holes and provides a smooth transition between idle RPM and the speed that provides enough airflow to pull fuel from the main discharge nozzle.

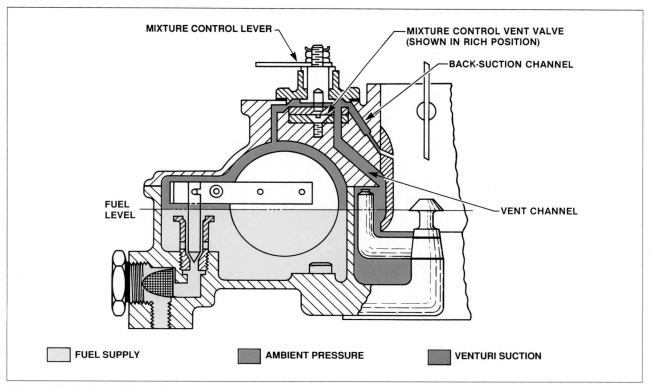

Figure 6-9. Back suction mixture control.

4) Mixture Control System

The amount of fuel that is metered into the air in a float carburetor may be controlled by varying the pressure drop across a fixed size orifice, or by varying the size of the orifice while maintaining a constant pressure differential across it. Both methods have been used in mixture control systems on aircraft carburetors.

a) Back Suction Mixture Control

The back suction mixture control we see in figure 6-9 varies the pressure in the float chamber between atmospheric pressure and a pressure slightly below atmospheric. This pressure variation is accomplished by using a control valve located in the float chamber vent line.

The float chamber is vented to the low pressure area near the venturi through a back suction channel. This lowers the pressure in the float bowl. When the mixture control is in the "rich" position, the vent valve is open and the pressure in the float bowl is raised to essentially atmospheric, and a pressure differential exists across the main metering jet. This causes fuel to flow out of the discharge nozzle. When the mix-

ture control is moved to the "lean" position, it closes the vent valve, and pressure in the float chamber is decreased to a pressure that is essentially the same as that of the discharge nozzle. This decrease pressure differential decreases the flow of fuel.

b) Variable Orifice Mixture Control

A more widely used method of varying the fuel/air mixture is by controlling the size of the opening in the fuel passage between the float bowl and the discharge nozzle. The float chamber has an unrestricted vent to maintain atmospheric pressure on the fuel in the float bowl, and either a needle valve or a step cut rotary valve, such as the one we seen in figure 6-10, is in series with the main metering jet. When the valve is completely closed, no fuel can flow and the engine can not run. This is the idle cutoff position.

When the valve is open, fuel flows to the discharge nozzle and is metered by the mixture control valve as long as the area of the opening of the valve is smaller than the area of the main metering jet. When the mixture control is fully open (the full rich position), the area of the open-

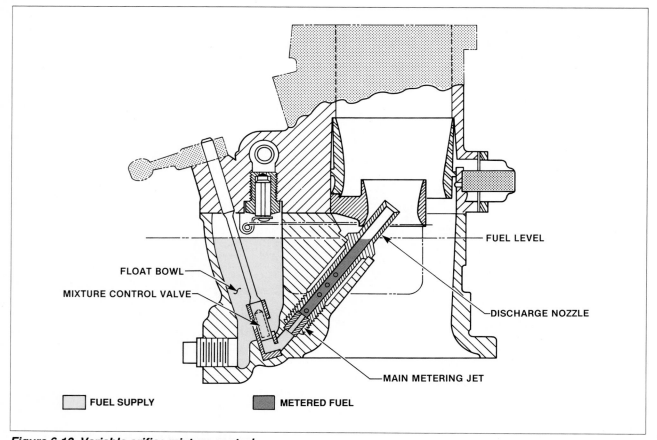

Figure 6-10. Variable orifice mixture control.

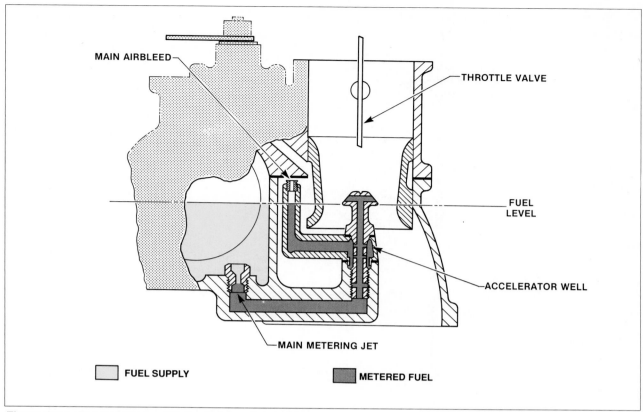

MAIN AIRBLEED

THROTTLE VALVE

FUEL LEVEL

ACCELERATOR WELL

MAIN METERING JET

FUEL SUPPLY   METERED FUEL

Figure 6-11. Acceleration well-type acceleration system.

ing of the mixture control is larger than the area of the main metering jet, and the jet limits the amount of fuel which can flow to the discharge nozzle.

5) Accelerating System

When the throttle valve is opened quickly, a large volume of air rushes through the air passage of the carburetor. However, the amount of fuel that is mixed with the air is less than normal. This is because of the slow response of the main metering system. As a result, after a quick opening of the throttle, the fuel/air mixture leans out momentarily. To overcome this tendency, the carburetor is equipped with an acceleration system.

a) Acceleration Well

The acceleration system may be as simple as the acceleration well we see in figure 6-11. In this simple system, an enlarged annular chamber around the main discharge nozzle at the main airbleed junction stores a supply of fuel. This fuel is readily available between the airbleed and the discharge nozzle to produce a rich mixture when the throttle is suddenly opened.

b) Accelerator Pump

In figure 6-12 we see a typical accelerator pump which uses a leather packing held against the walls of the pump chamber by a coiled spring. The pump is actuated by a linkage from the throttle. When the throttle is closed, the piston moves upward, filling the pump chamber with fuel from the float bowl through the pump inlet check valve. When the throttle is opened, the piston moves downward, closing the inlet check valve and forcing fuel out past the pump discharge check valve into the airstream through the accelerator pump discharge nozzle.

The piston is mounted on a spring loaded telescoping shaft. Then the throttle is opened, fuel is unable to discharge immediately because of the restriction of the nozzle, so the shaft telescopes and compresses the spring. The spring pressure sustains the discharge, providing a rich mixture during all the transition period.

6) Economizer System

Aircraft engines are designed to produce a maximum amount of power consistent with their weight. But since they are not designed to dissipate all of the heat the fuel is capable of releasing, provisions must be made to remove some of this heat. This is done by enriching the mixture at full throttle. The additional fuel absorbs this

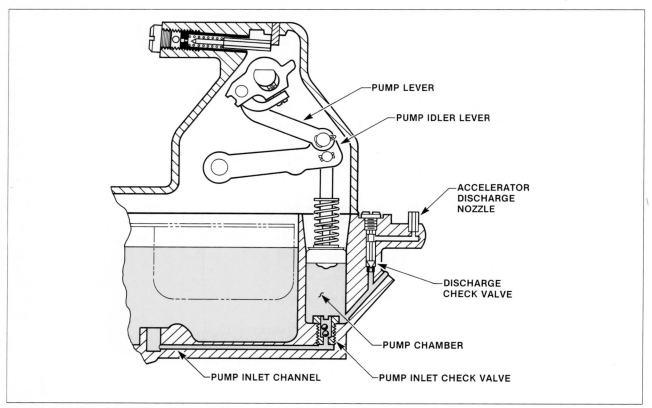

Figure 6-12. Movable piston-type accelerator pump used on a float carburetor.

PUMP LEVER

PUMP IDLER LEVER

ACCELERATOR DISCHARGE NOZZLE

DISCHARGE CHECK VALVE

PUMP CHAMBER

PUMP INLET CHANNEL

PUMP INLET CHECK VALVE

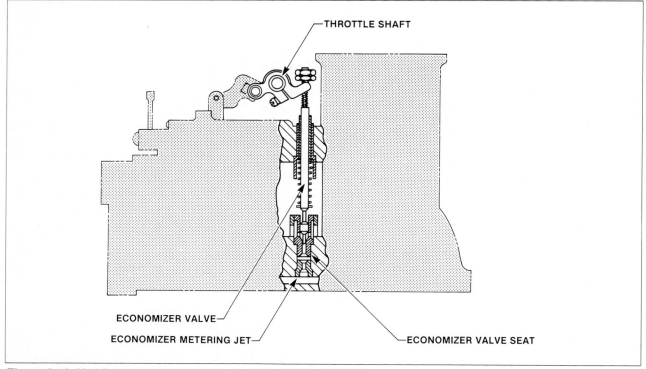

Figure 6-13. Needle-type enrichment system for a float carburetor.

THROTTLE SHAFT

ECONOMIZER VALVE

ECONOMIZER METERING JET

ECONOMIZER VALVE SEAT

heat as it changes to a vapor. Economizer, or power enrichment systems allow the engine to operate with a relatively lean and economical mixture for all conditions other than full power.

a) Needle-Type Economizer System

One of the simplest type of economizer systems uses an enrichment metering jet in parallel with the main metering jet. In series with this jet is a needle valve that is operated by the throttle. When the engine is operating at all conditions other than full throttle, the spring holds the needle on its seat and no fuel flows to the economizer jet. But when the throttle is wide open, the economizer needle is pulled out of the valve and additional fuel flows to the discharge valve. This system is illustrated in figure 6-13.

b) Airbleed Economizer System

When we increase the air velocity through the main venturi, we get an increased pressure drop that enriches the mixture. To prevent this en-richment, an airbleed of a very precise size is used between the float chamber and the discharge nozzle. If we increase the size of this airbleed, we lean the mixture, and if we decrease it, more fuel is pulled from the discharge nozzle and the mixture becomes richer.

The air for the airbleed comes from the float chamber and passes through the airbleed metering valve. The needle for this valve is held off of its seat by a spring, and is closed by an operating lever attached to the throttle shaft. When the throttle is wide open, the lever closes the airbleed valve and enriches the fuel/air mixture. An airbleed type economizer is seen in figure 6-14.

In the discussion of the basic carburetor principles, the fuel was shown stored in a float chamber and discharged from a nozzle located in the venturi throat. With a few added features to make it workable, this becomes the main metering system of the float-type carburetor. This type of carburetor, complete with idling, accelerating, mixture control, idle cutoff, and power enrich-

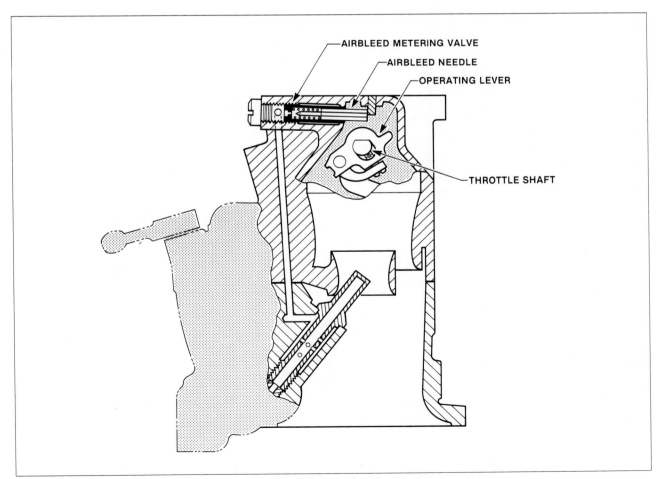

Figure 6-14. Airbleed-type economizer system for a float carburetor.

ment systems, is probably the most common of all carburetor types.

However, the float-type carburetor has several distinct disadvantages. In the first place, imagine the effect that abrupt maneuvers have on the float action. In the second place, the fact that its fuel must be discharged at low pressures leads to incomplete vaporization and difficulty in discharging fuel into some types of supercharged systems. The chief disadvantage of the float carburetor, however, is its icing tendency. Since the float carburetor must discharge fuel at a point of low pressure, the discharge nozzle must be located at the venturi throat, and the throttle valve must be on the engine side of the discharge nozzle. This means that the drop in temperature due to vaporization takes place within the venturi. As a result, ice readily forms in the venturi and on the throttle valve.

b. Pressure Injection Carburetors

A pressure-type carburetor discharges fuel into the airstream at a pressure well above at-

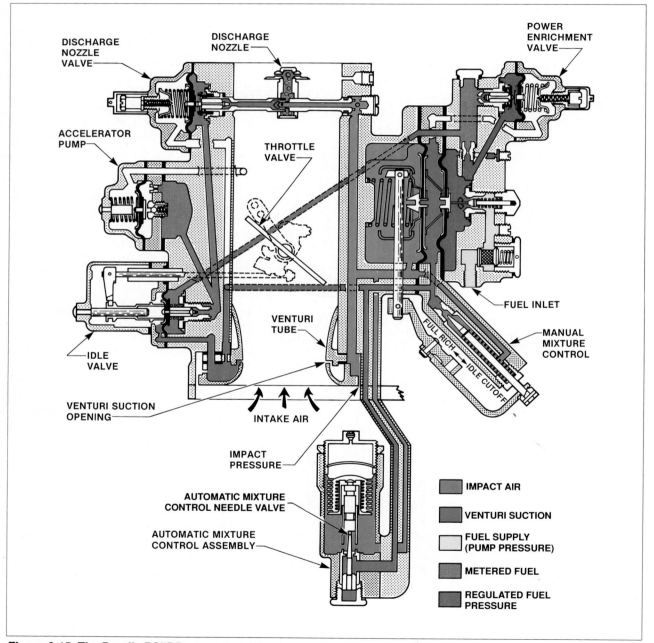

Figure 6-15. The Bendix PS7BD pressure carburetor.

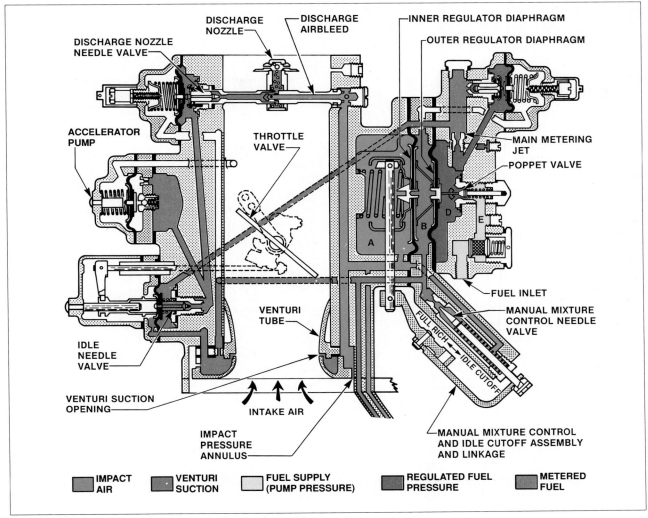

Figure 6-16. Regulator section of a pressure carburetor.

The following labels appear in the figure:

DISCHARGE NOZZLE NEEDLE VALVE

DISCHARGE NOZZLE

DISCHARGE AIRBLEED

INNER REGULATOR DIAPHRAGM

OUTER REGULATOR DIAPHRAGM

ACCELERATOR PUMP

THROTTLE VALVE

MAIN METERING JET

POPPET VALVE

FUEL INLET

MANUAL MIXTURE CONTROL NEEDLE VALVE

IDLE NEEDLE VALVE

VENTURI TUBE

VENTURI SUCTION OPENING

INTAKE AIR

IMPACT PRESSURE ANNULUS

MANUAL MIXTURE CONTROL AND IDLE CUTOFF ASSEMBLY AND LINKAGE

FULL RICH   IDLE CUTOFF

IMPACT AIR

VENTURI SUCTION

FUEL SUPPLY (PUMP PRESSURE)

REGULATED FUEL PRESSURE

METERED FUEL

mospheric. This results in better vaporization and permits the discharge of fuel into the airstream on the engine side of the throttle valve. With the discharge nozzle located at this point, the drop in temperature takes place after the air has passed the throttle valve and at a point where engine heat tends to offset it. Thus, the danger of fuel vaporization icing is practically eliminated. The effects of rapid maneuvers and rough air on the pressure-type carburetors are negligible since its fuel chambers remain filled under all operating conditions.

The pressure carburetor uses a closed fuel system; that is, one that is not open to the atmosphere at any point from the tank to the discharge nozzle. Fuel leaves the tank under pressure from the boost pump and goes through the filter and engine-driven fuel pump to the car-

buretor. Here the fuel is metered and is directed to the discharge nozzle.

Pressure of the fuel delivered to the metering jet is controlled by the volume and the density of the air flowing into the engine. In this way, the fuel flow becomes a function of the mass airflow.

The Bendix PS7BD carburetor shown in figure 6-15 is typical of pressure carburetors used on light reciprocating engine aircraft, and is the unit we will discuss in this text.

1) Air Metering Force

Air flows into the engine, passing first through the air inlet filter and then into the carburetor throttle body. It then flows through the venturi, past the throttle valve and discharge nozzle, and into the intake manifold. As the air enters the carburetor body, some of it flows into the channel around the venturi where its pressure increases due to its decrease in velocity. This impact pressure is directed into chamber A of the regulator unit, and any change in the pressure of the air entering the carburetor is reflected in a change of the pressure in chamber A.

The air flowing through the venturi produces a low pressure that is proportional to the velocity of the air entering the induction system. This low pressure is directed into chamber B of the regulator, where it operates on the opposite side of the diaphragm from the impact air pressure. These two forces work together to move the inner regulator diaphragm proportional to the volume of the air entering the engine.

2) Fuel Metering Force

Fuel enters the carburetor from the engine driven fuel pump under a pressure of approximately nine to 14 pounds per square inch, and passes through a fine mesh wire screen into chamber E, on its way to the poppet valve.

The amount the poppet valve opens is determined by the balance between the air metering force and the regulated fuel pressure. The air metering force moves the diaphragm to the right, and opens the poppet valve. When the poppet valve opens, the fuel flows from chamber E into chamber D and exerts a force on the outer regulator diaphragm, moving it back enough to allow the spring to close the poppet valve. The fuel pressure in chamber D is, in this way, regulated so that it is proportional to the mass of the air flowing into the engine.

When the engine is idling without enough airflow to produce a steady air metering force, the large coil spring in chamber A forces the diaphragm over and opens the poppet valve to provide the fuel pressure required for idling.

Fuel from chamber D, regulated but unmetered, flows through the main metering jet and through the idle needle valve. For all conditions other than idle, this valve is off its seat enough that its opening is larger than that of the main metering jet, so that no metering is done by the idle valve. Fuel flows from the idle valve to the discharge valve and the discharge nozzle where air from the impact annulus is mixed with the fuel in the nozzle to produce a spray for better vaporization.

The spring loaded diaphragm type discharge valve provides a fast and efficient cutoff when the mixture control valve is placed in the "idle cutoff" position. When the fuel pressure drops low enough, a spring forces the needle valve onto its seat, stopping all flow of fuel from the nozzle. This valve also provides a constant pressure downstream of the metering jet; so the variable pressure from the regulator will force a flow through the jet proportional to the mass airflow.

3) Mixture Control System

As altitude increases, the air density becomes less, and unless a correction is made for this, the mixture will become richer and the engine will lose power. To maintain an essentially constant fuel/air mixture, the pilot must decrease the weight of the fuel flowing to the discharge nozzle. This is done by decreasing the pressure differential across the air metering diaphragm (the inner regulator diaphragm) by opening the bleed between the two chambers.

When the pilot wishes to stop the engine, the mixture control is moved to the idle cutoff position. The mixture control needle valve is pulled back so that the pressures in chambers A and B are essentially equalized. When the control is in this position, the idle spring is depressed by the release contact lever, and its force is removed from the diaphragm, closing the poppet valve, and shutting off all of the flow to the metering sections.

An automatic mixture control (seen on figure 6-15) relieves the pilot of the necessity of regulating the mixture as altitude changes. A brass bellows, filled with helium and attached to a reverse tapered needle, varies the flow of air between chambers A and B as the air density changes. An inert oil in the bellows damps out vibrations.

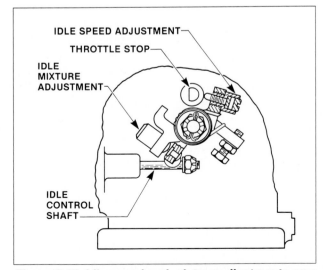

Figure 6-17. Idle speed and mixture adjustments on a pressure carburetor.

This automatic mixture control (AMC), by varying the amount of air bleed between the two chambers, maintains a pressure differential across the air diaphragm appropriate for any air density.

4) Idle System

The idle system of the PS series carburetors controls both the idle air and the idle fuel. All of the air which flows into the engine during idle must flow around the almost closed throttle valve. The amount this valve is held away from closing is controlled by the idle speed adjustment, which is an adjustable stop on the throttle shaft extension. The amount of fuel allowed to flow during idling is regulated by the amount the idle fuel valve is held off its seat by the control rod, as it contacts a yoke on the throttle shaft extension. We see this in figure 6-17.

5) Acceleration System

A single diaphragm pump is used on most carburetors of this type to provide a momentarily rich mixture at the main discharge nozzle when the throttle is opened suddenly.

The accelerator pump is located between the idle valve and the discharge nozzle. One side of the diaphragm is vented to the manifold pressure downstream of the throttle, and the other side is in the fuel line between the main metering jet and the discharge nozzle. The coil spring in the air side compresses when the manifold pressure is low, and fuel fills the pump. When the throttle is opened, the manifold pressure increases and the spring pushes the diaphragm over. This forces the fuel out of the discharge nozzle, momentarily enriching the mixture.

Some pumps, such as the one in figure 6-18, have a divider in the fuel chamber with a combination check valve and relief valve and a bleed. The valve allows a rapid discharge of fuel when the throttle is first opened, but it soon seats, and a lesser but sustained flow of fuel discharges through the pump bleed. When the throttle is suddenly closed, the decrease in manifold pressure causes a rapid movement of the pump diaphragm and the check valve closes to prevent the pump from starving the discharge nozzle.

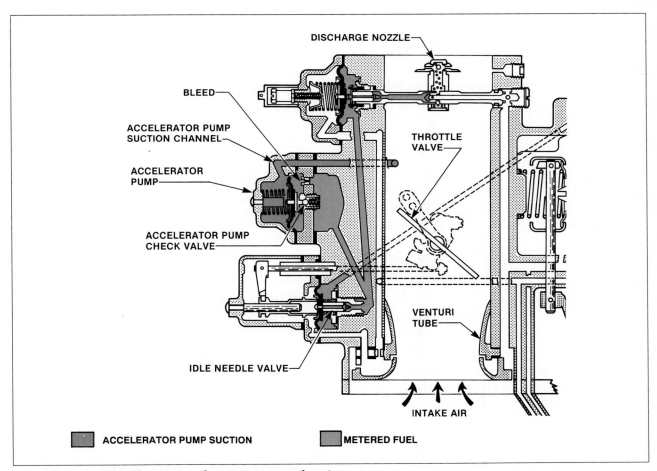

Figure 6-18. Acceleration system for a pressure carburetor.

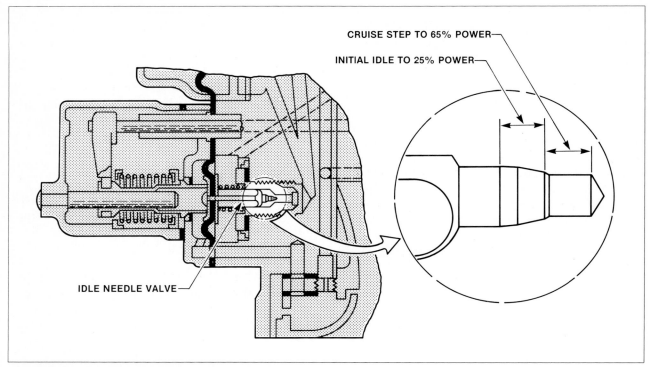

CRUISE STEP TO 65% POWER

INITIAL IDLE TO 25% POWER

IDLE NEEDLE VALVE

Figure 6-19. Manually controlled power enrichment valve.

This would cause the mixture to go momentarily lean.

6) Power Enrichment System

The power enrichment system will provide extra fuel for operations above high cruise. This may be accomplished using a double step idle valve or a separate fuel passage parallel to the main metering jet.

a) Manually Controlled Power Enrichment Valve

A double step idle valve is used on some pressure carburetors. For operation up to approximately 65% power, the needle in the orifice limits the flow of fuel, but at powers above 65%, the pressure differential across the diaphragm is great enough to pull the needle completely out of the orifice, and the fuel flow is limited by the main metering jet. This valve is illustrated in figure 6-19.

b) Airflow Power Enrichment Valve

A spring loaded valve is located in the fuel passage parallel with the main metering jet, as seen in figure 6-20. When this valve is closed, the main metering jet limits the flow, providing a lean mixture for cruise. At the higher power settings, the venturi air pressure and unmetered fuel pressure are great enough to overcome the

spring force and open the valve, enriching the mixture.

4. Carburetor Maintenance

Float carburetor servicing logically divides itself into three levels, and the level attempted by any technician should be governed by their experience and by the availability of proper replacement parts and the required service equipment.

The first level of service may be considered as all that can be done with the carburetor on the aircraft. It consists of checking control linkages for proper travel, freedom of movement, and proper contact with the stops. The fuel lines and air hoses are checked for kinks or distortion or indication of leakage. The main fuel filter and carburetor strainer are checked on this level of service to assure the proper amount of fuel is being delivered to the carburetor. The air filter may be checked for proper installation, and to be sure that there is no air leaking around the filter. The carburetor heat valve should be checked for proper travel and for any leakage of warm air into the carburetor when the control is in the COLD position. The idle RPM and mixture can be adjusted to provide the smoothest running engine at the closed throttle speed recommended by the aircraft manufacturer.

While this level of service requires a knowledge of engine and carburetor operation and the same professional integrity as any other aircraft maintenance, it can be performed with a very minimum of stock and equipment. Replacement air filters and fuel filter gaskets are the only parts required, and no special tools are needed for this level of servicing.

Maintenance facilities which perform work beyond that normally considered as line maintenance do what might be considered as second level servicing. This level requires that the carburetor be removed from the aircraft and opened for closer inspection, and parts replaced if necessary. This level of maintenance should never be attempted without the proper replacement parts available.

The third level of carburetor service is major overhaul. This level of maintenance requires some specialized tools, all required parts, and access to the latest service information provided by the manufacturer.

A pressure carburetor is a precision piece of equipment that requires the use of a flow bench for any major maintenance or calibration. The manufacturer has established a network of authorized service facilities equipped to handle any maintenance with a minimum of down time for the aircraft. The maintenance technician in the field will be limited to installation, removal, and normal field adjustments on this type of carburetor.

a. Field Adjustment

Field adjustments to carburetors are generally limited to rigging the controls, and adjusting idle speed and mixture.

1) Rigging Carburetor Controls

Connect and adjust carburetor controls so that full movement of the throttle is obtained with corresponding full movement of the control in the cockpit. In addition, check and adjust the throttle control linkages so that spring-back on the throttle quadrant in the aircraft is equal in both the "full open" and "full closed" positions.

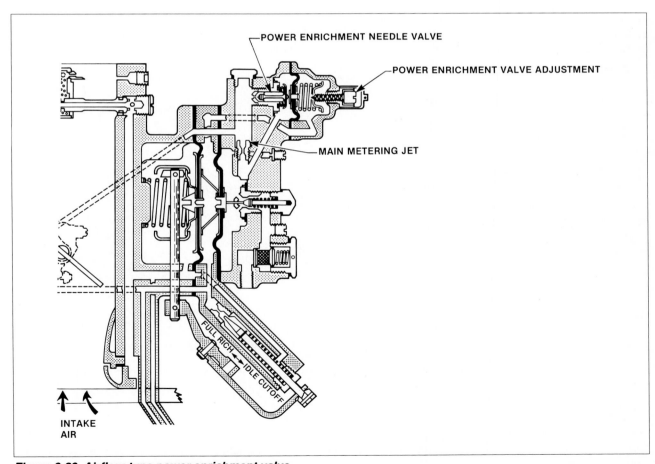

Figure 6-20. Airflow-type power enrichment valve.

Correct any excess play or looseness of control linkages or cables.

When installing carburetors or fuel metering equipment incorporating manual mixture controls that do not have marked positions, adjust the mixture control mechanism to provide an equal amount of spring-back at both the rich and lean end of the control quadrant in the cockpit when the mixture control on the carburetor is moved through the full range. Where mixture control detents are used, rig the control mechanism so that the designated positions on the control quadrant will agree with the corresponding positions on the carburetor or fuel metering equipment.

In all cases check the controls for proper positioning, correct excess play or looseness of control linkage or cables, and safety all controls to eliminate the possibility of loosening from vibration during operation.

2) Adjusting Idle Mixtures

Excessively rich or lean idle mixtures result in incomplete combustion within the engine cylinder, with resultant formation of carbon deposits on the spark plugs and subsequent spark plug fouling. In addition, excessively rich or lean idle mixtures make it necessary to taxi at high idle speeds with resultant fast taxi speeds and excessive brake wear. Each engine must have the carburetor idle mixture tailored for the particular engine and installation if best operation is to be obtained.

Engines which are properly adjusted, insofar as valve operation, cylinder compression, ignition, and carburetor idle mixture are concerned, will idle at the prescribed RPM for indefinite periods without loading up, or spark plug fouling. If an engine will not respond to idle mixture adjustment with the resultant stable idling characteristics previously outlined, it is an indication that some other phase of engine operation is not correct. In such cases, determine and correct the cause of the difficulty.

On all aircraft installations where manifold pressure gauges are used, the manifold pressure gauge will give a more consistent and larger indication of power change at idle speed than will the tachometer. Therefore, utilize the manifold pressure gauge when adjusting the idle fuel/air mixture. Check and adjust the idle mixture and speed on all type reciprocating engines as discussed in the following paragraphs.

Always make idle mixture adjustments with cylinder head temperatures at normal values,

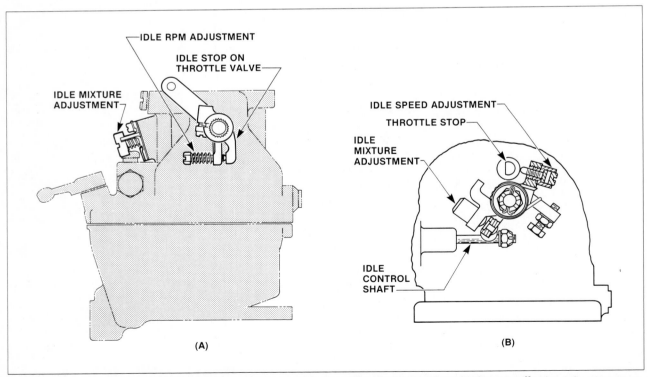

Figure 6-21. (A)—Idle system controls on a float carburetor. (B)—Idle speed and mixture adjustments on a pressure carburetor.

and never with temperatures approaching the maximum allowable.

On an engine having a conventional carburetor, the idle mixture is checked by manually leaning the mixture with the cockpit mixture control. Move the carburetor mixture control slowly and smoothly toward the "idle cutoff" position. At the same time, watch the manifold pressure gauge to determine whether the manifold pressure decreases prior to increasing as the engine ceases firing. The optimum mixture is obtained when a manifold pressure decrease immediately precedes the manifold pressure increase as the engine stops. The amount of decrease will vary with the make and model engine and the installation. As a general rule, the amount of manifold pressure decrease will be approximately one-fourth inch Hg.

On installations that do not use a manifold pressure gauge, it will be necessary to observe the tachometer for an indication of an RPM change. With most installations, the idle mixture should be adjusted to provide an RPM rise prior to decreasing as the engine ceases to fire. This RPM increases will vary from 10 to 50 RPM, depending upon the installation.

If the check of the idle mixture reveals it to be too lean or too rich, increase or decrease the idle fuel flow as required. Then repeat the check. Continue checking and adjusting the idle mixture until it checks out properly. After each adjustment, "clear" the engine by briefly running it at a higher RPM. This prevents fouling of the plugs which might otherwise be caused by incorrect idle mixture.

After adjusting the idle mixture, recheck it several times to determine definitely that the mixture is correct and remains constant on repeated changes from high power back to idle.

3) Idle Speed Adjustment

After adjusting the idle mixture, reset the idle stop to the idle RPM specified in the aircraft maintenance manual. The engine must be warmed up thoroughly and checked for ignition system malfunctioning. Throughout any carburetor adjustment procedures, run the engine up periodically to approximately half of normal rated speed to clear the engine.

Some carburetors are equipped with an eccentric screw to adjust idle RPM. Others use a spring-loaded screw to limit the throttle valve closing. In either case, adjust the screw as required to increase or decrease RPM with the throttle retarded against the stop. Open the throttle to clear the engine; close the throttle and allow the RPM to stabilize. Repeat this operation until the desired idling speed is obtained.

b. Overhaul

There is normally no particular number of hours between overhauls specified by the carburetor manufacturer, but good operating practice dictates that at the time of engine overhaul, the carburetor should also be overhauled. Operating beyond this time can cause poor fuel metering, which could lead to detonation and subsequent damage to a freshly overhauled engine.

As mentioned early in this chapter, the maintenance of pressure carburetors requires a flow bench and other specialized equipment and is performed by specialists in facilities approved by the carburetor manufacturer. For these reasons, the overhaul of pressure carburetors will not be considered here. The float carburetor overhaul can be accomplished with a minimum of investment in special tools and equipment, and is still within the scope of work performed in many aircraft repair facilities.

1) Disassembly

Disassemble the carburetor in a clean work area where all of the parts may be laid out systematically. Have the latest carburetor service and overhaul instructions and follow them in detail.

2) Cleaning

After the carburetor has been disassembled and a preliminary inspection made of all of the parts for wear or breakage, clean the entire unit. First, wash all of the parts in a safety solvent to remove the grease and dirt. Dry the parts with compressed air, and then immerse them in a decarbonizing solution. Carburetor decarbonizer is normally of the water seal or glycerine seal type, in which the water or glycerine floats on top of the active ingredients to prevent evaporation of the highly volatile solvents. When placing the part in a decarbonizer, be sure it is completely covered by the active agent and is below the seal layer.

A word of caution regarding some of the commercially available decarbonizers: Some are more active than others and will attack certain metals used in carburetors, so be sure to check the instructions before using them. Use extreme care that the decarbonizer does not get on your skin or in your eyes. If this should happen, wash the affected areas with running water, and if you get any in your eyes, get medical attention immediately, After the parts have been decarbonized for the appropriate time, remove them, rinse them in hot water and dry them thoroughly with compressed air.

3) Inspection And Repair

After all of the parts are clean, carefully inspect them for any indication of wear of damage. Needle valves and seats should be closely examined for indications of grooves or scratches. The needle valve and seat in some older models of carburetors may be lapped together to facilitate complete sealing, but all of the MSA carburetors require the float valve and seat assembly to be replaced with new units at each overhaul. All parts subject to wear should be checked against a table of limits or else replaced. Be sure to follow the manufacturer's overhaul instructions in detail.

4) Reassembly

When reassembling carburetors, many operations require the use of special tools, and it is poor economy to use anything other than the proper tool for some of these specialized jobs. The use of an incorrect tool may damage a part costing far more than the proper tool.

Most carburetor bodies are made of aluminum alloy castings, and when installing straight plugs or jets, put a drop or two of engine oil on the threads. When installing tapered plugs, insert the plug into the casting for one thread, then put a very small amount of thread lubricant on the second thread of the plug. When you screw the plug into the hole it will squeeze the lubricant between the threads and prevent galling. Use ex-

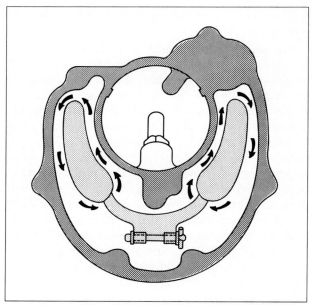

Figure 6-23. After the float level has been adjusted, a test fixture is used to check the side clearance of the float.

treme care to prevent any of the lubricant from getting inside the carburetor, since it is insoluble in gasoline and it may plug up the jets or passages.

Install the needle valve and float, and adjust the float level in the way the manufacturer recommends. After getting the correct float level, check the side clearance of the float in the float chamber. This usually requires a special cutaway float bowl to check to see that a drill rod gauge of specified size will pass completely around the floats without binding. When the float level and side clearance are both correct,

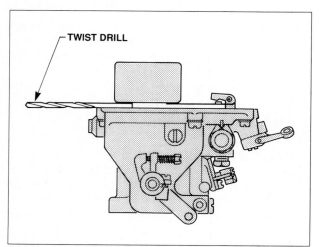

Figure 6-22. Method of measuring the correct float level.

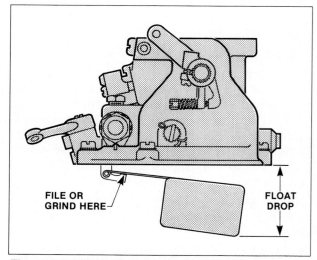

Figure 6-24. Method of measuring the float drop.

check the float drop as specified in the overhaul manual.

Some carburetors have the float mounted in the fuel bowl, and the fuel level must be checked to determine proper adjustment. Level the carburetor body on a flow bench and put the test fuel into the bowl under the recommended pressure. Adjust the level the fuel rises in the bowl before it is shut off by the needle valve. Add or remove shims from under the needle seat until the fuel level is correct. When checking this level, be sure to measure away from the wall of the float bowl, because where the fuel wets the walls, it is higher than it is away from the walls.

5. Fuel Injection Systems

While the pressure carburetor went a long way toward overcoming some of the problems en-countered with float-type carburetors, it still did not adequately solve difficulties associated with uneven fuel/air mixture distribution. This issue has become increasingly important as the horse-power requirements of modern aircraft engines have continued to go up. The modern aircraft engine operates with such high cylinder pressures that an inadvertently lean mixture on an individual cylinder can cause detonation with the possibility of structural damage resulting. Fuel injection systems were developed to overcome these difficulties and assure both accurate metering and proper delivery to each cylinder.

a. Direct Fuel Injection

Some of the larger reciprocating engines in the past used a direct fuel injection system with a master control unit. This was similar to a large pressure carburetor that metered the correct

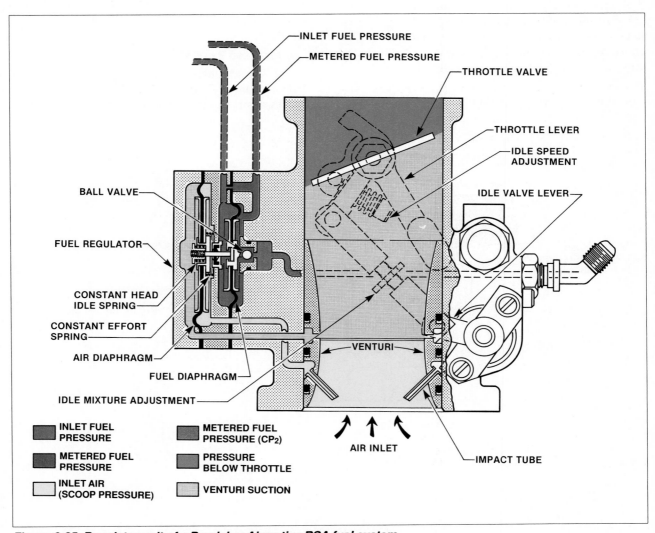

INLET FUEL PRESSURE
METERED FUEL PRESSURE
THROTTLE VALVE
THROTTLE LEVER
IDLE SPEED ADJUSTMENT
IDLE VALVE LEVER
BALL VALVE
FUEL REGULATOR
CONSTANT HEAD IDLE SPRING
CONSTANT EFFORT SPRING
AIR DIAPHRAGM
FUEL DIAPHRAGM
IDLE MIXTURE ADJUSTMENT
VENTURI
AIR INLET
IMPACT TUBE

INLET FUEL PRESSURE
METERED FUEL PRESSURE
INLET AIR (SCOOP PRESSURE)
METERED FUEL PRESSURE (CP₂)
PRESSURE BELOW THROTTLE
VENTURI SUCTION

Figure 6-25. Regulator unit of a Precision Airmotive RSA fuel system.

amount of fuel into two multi-cylindered piston pumps. These pumps forced the metered fuel directly into the combustion chambers of the individual cylinders as timed, high pressure spurts.

Timed injection systems, because of their complexity, have been superseded by the simpler, yet effective, continuous flow systems.

b. Continuous Flow Fuel Injection

Continuous flow fuel injection systems meter the fuel and deliver it the intake port of each cylinder on the engine. There are currently two different types of continuous flow fuel injection systems in use.

1) RSA System

Precision Airmotive produces two very successful and popular fuel metering systems, the RS system and the RSA system. These units were formerly manufactured by Bendix. The RS system uses a side-by-side regulator and a flow of servo fuel to regulate the flow control valve. The more recent system, the RSA, does not use servo fuel, and this is the system we will discuss.

The RSA fuel system is a continuous flow system which meters the fuel by a pressure drop that is proportional to the airflow through the venturi. The regulator unit for this system is seen in figure 6-25.

a) Air Metering Force

The air metering force is similar to that discussed with the Bendix PS pressure carburetor. The impact tubes in the inlet of the throttle body sense the pressure of the air entering the engine, and the venturi senses its velocity. These two forces move the air diaphragm proportional to the amount of air taken into the engine.

b) Fuel Metering Force

Fuel from the engine-driven fuel pump enters the fuel control through the strainer and the mixture control valve. Some of this fuel acts on the fuel diaphragm to cause it to close the ball valve. Fuel for the engine operation flows through the main metering jet and the throttle fuel valve, into the metered fuel chamber of the regulator. This metered fuel opens the ball valve.

c) Metered Fuel Flow

The actual metering is done by the pressure drop across the orifices in the fuel control. In this system, the metering force is determined by

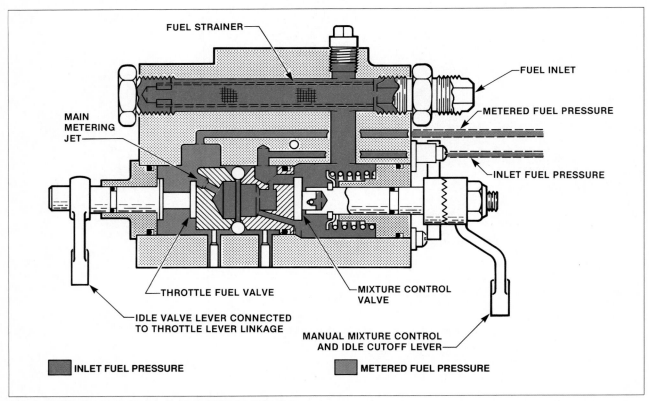

Figure 6-26. Fuel control unit of an RSA fuel system.

the position of the ball valve on its seat. The inlet pressure is held relatively constant by the engine driven fuel pump, and the outlet pressure is controlled by the balance between the fuel and the air metering forces. When the throttle is opened, the total air metering force increases. This moves the air diaphragm to the left, which opens the ball valve and lowers the pressure downstream of the orifice in the metered fuel chamber. The pressure in the inlet fuel pressure chamber is greater than the metered fuel pressure by the amount of pressure dropped across the fuel control, and this tends to close the valve. The balance between the air and the fuel forces therefore holds the valve off its seat a stabilized amount for any given airflow.

d) Flow Divider

After the fuel leaves the regulator, it flows through a flexible hose to the flow divider. This unit (figure 6-26) is located on top of the engine in a central location. The injector nozzles are connected to the flow divider by 1/8-inch stainless steel tubing. A pressure gauge in the cockpit reads the pressure at the outlet of the flow divider. This is actually the pressure drop across the fuel injector nozzles and is directly proportional to the fuel flow through the nozzles. For all flow conditions other than idle, the restriction of the nozzles causes a pressure to build up in the metered fuel lines which influences the fuel metering force. Under idle flow conditions, the opposition caused by the nozzles is so small that the metering would be erratic, and to prevent this, a coil spring holds the flow divider valve closed until metered fuel pressure becomes sufficient to off-seat it.

For idle fuel flow, the flow divider opens only partially and thus serves the double function of creating the downstream pressure for the fuel control, and dividing the fuel to the cylinders for these extremely low flow conditions. When the mixture control is placed in the idle cutoff position, the flow divider cuts off the fuel flow and leaves the fuel lines to the injector nozzles full of fuel.

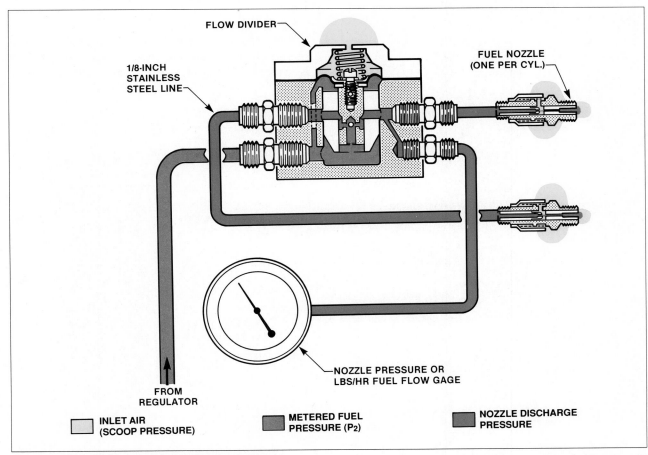

Figure 6-27. Flow divider for an RSA fuel system.

e) Injection Nozzles

This system uses air bleed-type nozzles, which screw into the cylinder head near the intake ports. Each nozzle consists of a brass body which incorporates a metering orifice, an air bleed hole, and an emulsion chamber. Around this body is a fine mesh metal screen and a pressed steel shroud. These nozzles are calibrated to flow within plus or minus two per-cent of each other. They are interchangeable between engines, and between cylinders. An identification mark is stamped on one of the hex flats of the nozzle opposite the air bleed hole. When installing a nozzle in a horizontal plane, the air bleed hole should be positioned as near the top as practical, in order to minimize fuel bleeding from the opening immediately after the engine is shutdown.

f) Idle System

When there is a low airflow through the engine such as is encountered during idling, the air metering forces are not high enough to open the ball valve to provide adequate fuel flow for idling. The air diaphragm is between two springs which hold the ball valve off its seat until the airflow becomes sufficient. The constant head spring we see in figure 6-29 pushes against the air diaphragm and forces the ball valve off its seat. This maintains a constant head of pressure across the fuel control. As the airflow increases, the air diaphragm moves over, compressing the constant head spring until the diaphragm bushings makes solid contact with the ball valve shaft.

Beyond this point, the ball valve acts as though it is directly connected to the diaphragm. A smooth transition between idle and cruise RPM is provided by the use of the constant effort

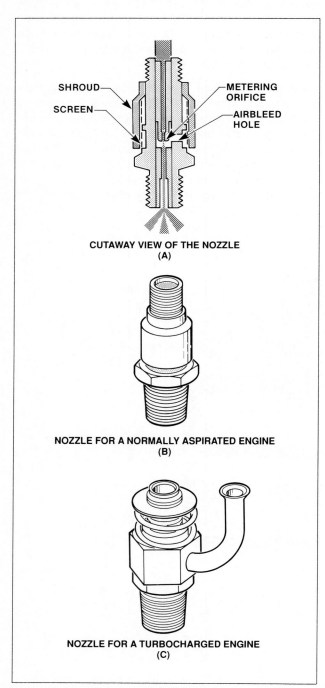

CUTAWAY VIEW OF THE NOZZLE
(A)

NOZZLE FOR A NORMALLY ASPIRATED ENGINE
(B)

NOZZLE FOR A TURBOCHARGED ENGINE
(C)

Figure 6-28. Fuel nozzles for the RSA fuel system.

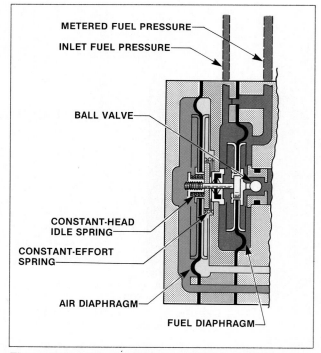

Figure 6-29. Idling springs in an RSA fuel system.

spring working between the air diaphragm and the housing. This spring, in effect, preloads the air diaphragm, giving it an initial loaded position from which to work.

g) Manual Mixture Control

A spring loaded, flat, plate-type valve in the fuel control is moved by a linkage from the cockpit to regulate the amount of fuel that can flow to the main metering jet. When the mixture control is placed in the idle cutoff position, the passage to the main metering jet is completely closed and no fuel can flow to the jet. In the rich position, the opening afforded by the mixture control is larger than the metering jet, and the jet limits the flow. In any intermediate position, the opening is smaller than the main jet, and the mixture control becomes the flow limiting device. (See figure 6-26, page 6-24.)

h) Automatic Mixture Control

A reverse tapered needle attached to a bellows, figure 6-30, varies the airbleed between the two air chambers of the regulator. The bellows contains helium to sense density changes and a small amount of inert oil to dampen vibrations. As the air density decreases, from an increase in altitude or temperature, the pressure inside the bellows causes it to expand. This moves the needle and increases the bleed across the air diaphragm. This decreases the air metering force and leans the mixture.

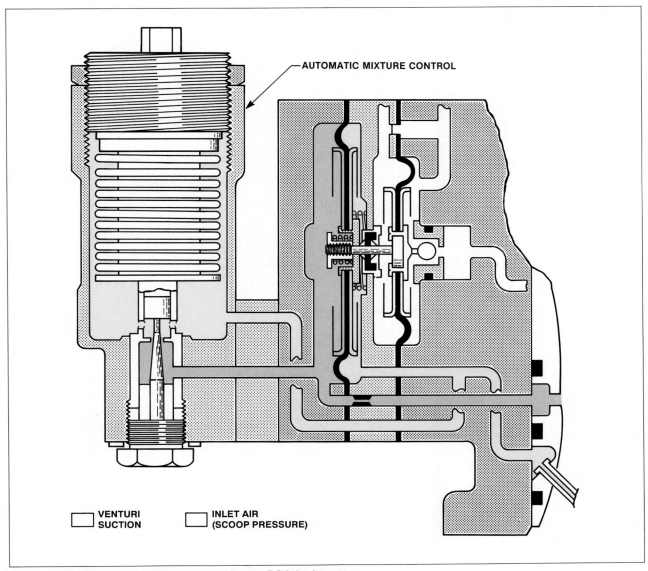

AUTOMATIC MIXTURE CONTROL

VENTURI SUCTION

INLET AIR (SCOOP PRESSURE)

Figure 6-30. Automatic mixture control for an RSA fuel system.

i) Starting Procedure

To start an engine equipped with this injection system, first place the mixture control in the idle cutoff position and open the throttle about ⅛ of the way. Turn on the master switch and the boost pump. Move the mixture control to the full

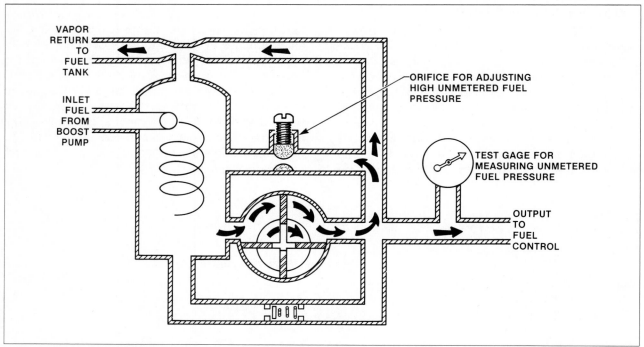

Figure 6-31. Teledyne-Continental fuel pump showing the high, unmetered fuel pressure adjustment.

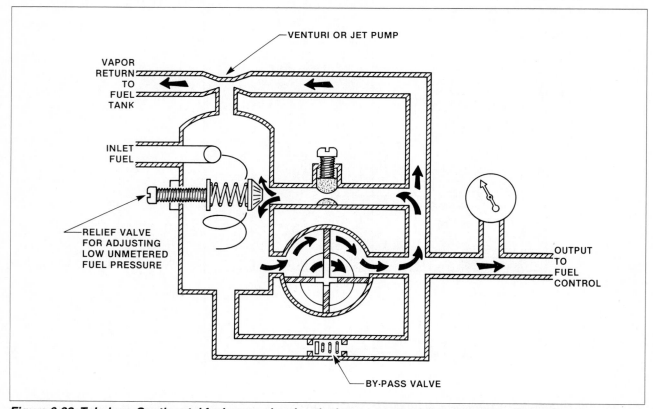

Figure 6-32. Teledyne-Continental fuel pump showing the low, unmetered fuel pressure adjustment.

rich position until there is an indication of flow on the flow meter, and return the mixture control to the idle cutoff position. Turn the ignition ON and engage the starter. As soon as the engine starts, move the mixture control to the full rich position.

2) Teledyne-Continental System

The Teledyne-Continental fuel injection system meters its fuel as a function of the engine RPM, and does not use airflow as a metering force. A special engine-driven fuel pump, which is an integral part of the system, produces the fuel metering pressure.

a) Injection Pump

The pump is the heart of this fuel injection system. It is basically a vane-type, constant displacement pump, with special features that allow it to produce an output pressure that varies with the engine speed.

If a passage containing an orifice by-passes the pump mechanism, figure 6-31, the output pressure will vary according to the speed of the pump, and the size of the orifice will determine the pressure for any given speed. If its size is increased, the output pressure will decrease.

This system works well for flows in the cruise and high power range, but when the fuel flow is low, the orifice does not produce enough restriction to maintain a constant output pressure. To deal with this, an adjustable pressure relief valve is installed in the line. During idle, the output pressure is determined by the setting of the relief valve, and the orifice has no effect. At the high power end of operation, the relief valve is off its seat, and the pressure is determined by the orifice.

All fuel injection systems must have vapor free fuel in their main metering section, and a provision is made in the pump to remove all vapor from the fuel and return it to the tank.

Fuel enters the pump through a chamber where the vapor is swirled out of the liquid and collects in the top. Some fuel from the pump outlet returns to the fuel tank through a venturi, or jet pump, arrangement on top of this chamber. This produces a low pressure which attracts the vapors and returns them to the tank.

A final feature of this pump is a by-pass check valve around the pump, so fuel from the aircraft boost pump may flow to the fuel control for starting. As soon as the engine pump pressure becomes higher than that of the boost pump, the valve closes and the engine pump takes over.

Turbocharged engines have a unique problem during acceleration. If the fuel flow increases

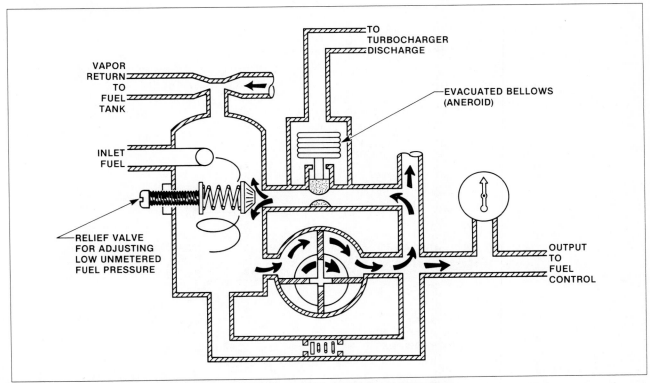

Figure 6-33. Teledyne-Continental fuel pump used with a turbocharged engine.

before the turbocharger has time to build up to speed and increase the airflow proportionally, the engine may falter from an overly rich mixture. Pumps for these engines have the simple orifice replaced with a variable restrictor controlled by an aneroid valve. This unit is illustrated in figure 6-33.

An evacuated bellows is surrounded by upper deck pressure which is actually the turbocharger discharge pressure. This bellows moves a valve which controls the size of the orifice, varying the output fuel pressure proportional to the inlet air pressure.

When the throttle is suddenly opened and the engine speed increases, rather than immediately supplying an increased fuel pressure to the control, the aneroid holds the orifice open until the turbocharger speed builds up and increases the air pressure into the engine. As the inlet air pressure increases, the orifice becomes smaller and the fuel pressure, and therefore the fuel flow, increase.

The drive shaft of this fuel pump has a loose coupling to take care of any slight misalignment between the pump and the engine drive. There is also a shear section in the coupling that will break to protect the pump and the engine if the pump should ever seize.

b) Fuel Control Unit

The diagram in figure 6-34 shows the fuel control used with this type of fuel injection system. Fuel leaves the engine-driven fuel pump at a pressure that is proportional to the engine speed. It then flows through the fuel control filter into the manual mixture control valve. This valve differs from that used in the RSA fuel system, as it acts as a variable selector valve rather than a shutoff valve. When the mixture control is in the idle cutoff position, all fuel is by-passed back to the pump, and none flows to the engine. In the full rich position, all of the fuel flows to the engine. Any intermediate position drops the pressure upstream of the metering orifices by routing some of the fuel back to the pump and some of it to the engine. A metering plug with a precision orifice limits the maximum amount of fuel than can flow into the engine under Full Throttle, Full Rich conditions. The throttle in the cockpit controls both the throttle air valve, similar to that

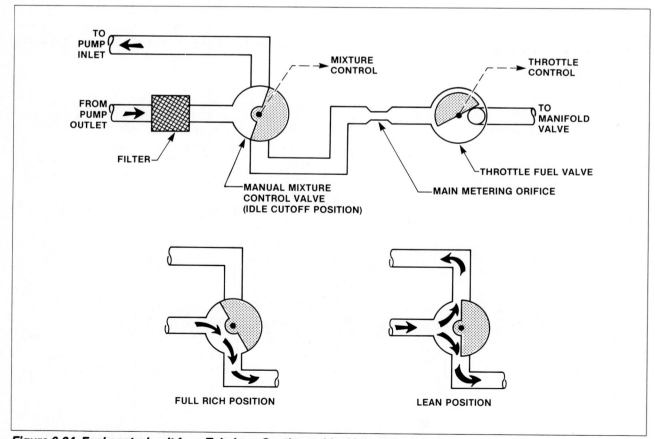

Figure 6-34. Fuel control unit for a Teledyne-Continental fuel injection system.

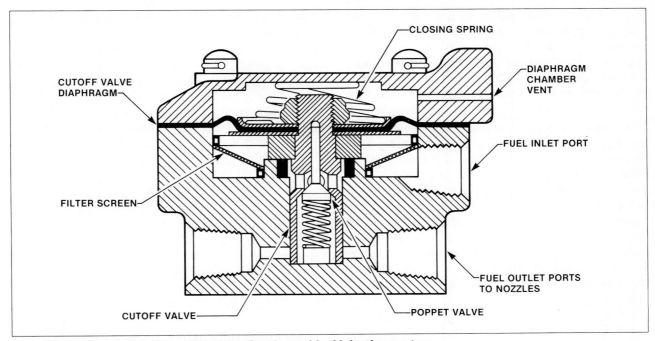

Figure 6-35. Fuel manifold for a Teledyne-Continental fuel injection system.

used in a carburetor, and the throttle fuel valve, which is essentially a variable orifice which determines the amount of fuel that is allowed to flow to the engine for any given fuel pressure.

c) Fuel Manifold Valve

After the fuel leaves the throttle fuel valve, it flows through a flexible fuel line to the manifold valve, figure 6-35, which is usually mounted on top of the engine. This valve serves two basic functions: it distributes the fuel evenly to all of the cylinders, and it provides a positive shutoff of the fuel when the mixture control is put in the idle cutoff position.

When the fuel pressure rises, the diaphragm lifts the valve off its seat, but a spring-loaded poppet valve inside the cutoff valve stays on its seat until the fuel pressure has opened the valve completely so it can do no metering. Then the poppet opens and allows fuel to flow to the nozzles. The opposition caused by this valve provides a constant pressure downstream of the jets for metering at idle. Above idle, the valve is fully open, and offers no opposition. When the mixture control is placed in its idle cutoff position, the fuel pressure drops and the spring closes the manifold valve to provide a positive shutoff of the fuel to the nozzles. If the poppet should become plugged or sticky, erratic or rough idling will result.

The chamber above the diaphragm is vented to static atmosphere to allow unrestricted movement of the valve. It is important that ram air not be allowed into this chamber, so the vent must be open and positioned either toward the side of the engine or to the rear.

d) Injector Lines

The nozzles are connected to the manifold valve by six stainless steel lines, ⅛-inch in diameter, and all the same length. It is very important that lines not be shortened because of their proximity to the manifold valve. The excess line is generally coiled in the center of the run.

e) Injector Nozzles

Possibly the simplest, yet some of the most important components in a fuel injection system are the injector nozzles. The nozzle used with this system is illustrated in figure 6-36. One nozzle in each cylinder provides the point of discharge for the fuel into the induction system. Fuel flows from the manifold valve into the nozzle, through a calibrated orifice into the intake valve chamber of the cylinder head. Air is drawn through a screen into the injector nozzle where it mixes with the fuel and forms an emulsion to aid in vaporization.

There are three sizes of nozzle orifices in use with this system; each is identified by a letter stamped on the nozzle. The A-size nozzle will flow a given amount of fuel for a given pressure. A set of B-size nozzles flows one-half gallon more fuel per hour with the same pressure, and the C-size nozzles flow yet another half-gallon per hour. When the engine was calibrated in its factory run-in, the proper size nozzles were installed and this size should be kept in the engine from then on.

Different models of engines require different styles of nozzles. Some engines require long nozzles to inject the fuel farther into the intake chamber; others function best with short nozzles. The nozzles differ in appearance, but their function is the same. Nozzles used with turbocharged engines have their shrouds vented to the turbocharger side of the throttle valve. If this were not done, increasing the manifold pressure above atmospheric would blow fuel out of the bleed holes.

f) Starting

Starting an engine equipped with a Teledyne-Continental fuel injections system consists mainly of the normal prestart settings of the switches and controls. Turn the fuel on, open the throttle approximately 1/8 of the way, and place the mixture control in the full rich position. Turn the boost pump on HIGH and when fuel flow is indicated on the flowmeter, engage the starter. The engine will start and the boost pump may be turned off.

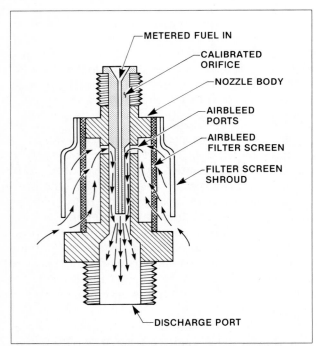

Figure 6-36. Fuel injector nozzle for a Teledyne-Continental fuel injection system.

6. Fuel Injection System Maintenance

At least once each one hundred hours of operation, all of the components in a fuel injection system should be checked for security and integrity of mounting. All lines should be checked to see that they are not chafed of leaking. Leaks would be indicated by the presence of fuel dye stains. All moving parts should be checked for wear, and the ends of the throttle link rods lubricated with a drop of engine oil.

Injector nozzles do not require much service. At intervals established by the manufacturer (about 300 hours of operation) the nozzles should be removed from the engine, soaked in acetone or lacquer thinner, and blown out. A clogged nozzle can usually be located by the presence of fuel dye stain on the cylinder head around the nozzle. Since fuel cannot be drawn into the cylinder through a plugged nozzle, it will escape through the air bleed hole.

Wires, drills, or other cleaning devices should never be used to remove obstructions from the orifice. If soaking does not clear out the obstruction, replace the nozzle. The metal shroud that is pressed over the nozzle to protect the screen should never be removed.

a. Field Adjustments

Very few field adjustments may be made on the continuous flow fuel injection systems. Like the float carburetor, idle speed and mixture adjustments may be made to assure proper operation.

1) RSA Fuel System Adjustments

As with all fuel metering systems, this system controls the idle RPM by limiting the amount of air allowed to flow past the throttle valve, and controls the idle mixture by the amount of fuel allowed to flow to the discharge nozzles.

A spring loaded screw, figure 6-37, contacts a stop on the throttle body to limit the amount the throttle air valve can close. An adjustable length fuel rod connects the throttle air valve to the throttle fuel valve and controls the amount the throttle fuel valve remains open. Adjustment of this length determines the idle mixture ratio and ultimately the idle manifold pressure.

2) Teledyne-Continental System Adjustments

At each one-hundred hour inspection, the low and high unmetered fuel pressure and the high metered fuel pressure must be checked. An accurate fuel pressure gauge is connected into the fuel line between the pump and the fuel control. The engine is started, warmed up, and the idle speed properly set. The pressure indicated on the test gauge should be that specified by the latest manufacturer's service bulletin for the engine being inspected. If it is not within the specified limits, the relief valve must be adjusted to get this pressure.

After the correct pressure is obtained, the idle mixture is checked. The mixture control is pulled slowly to the idle cutoff position and the tachometer watched. There should be an increase of approximately 50 RPM before the engine ceases to run. If the rise is less than this, the mixture is too lean, and the idle mixture linkage should be shortened a bit. If the RPM increases more than is allowed, the mixture is too rich and the rod should be lengthened by turning the idle mixture adjustment to the left. This leans the mixture.

With the unmetered fuel pressure and the idle speed and mixture adjusted, the high unmetered fuel pressure should be checked. The engine is operated at full throttle, maximum RPM, and the test gauge read. This pressure should be within the range specified in the service bulletin. If it is not, the orifice should be adjusted to bring this pressure to the value desired. At this high RPM, every precaution must be taken to operate the engine for the absolute minimum time on the ground.

After the pressures are checked and the test gauge is removed from the system, a flight test should be made to check the high metered fuel pressure on the airplane's own fuel flow gauge. This reading must be made at full throttle, maximum RPM, after the engine has about ten or fifteen minutes at cruise power to stabilize.

b. Overhaul

Like a carburetor, the fuel injection system is normally overhauled at the same time as engine overhaul occurs. The overhaul of all types of fuel injection systems requires specialized tools, flow benches, and specially trained technicians. These requirements generally mean that only certified repair stations licensed to do this work will perform the overhaul.

7. Water Injection System For Reciprocating Engines

There are few of these now being used, but the water injection system is designed to enable more power to be obtained from the engine at

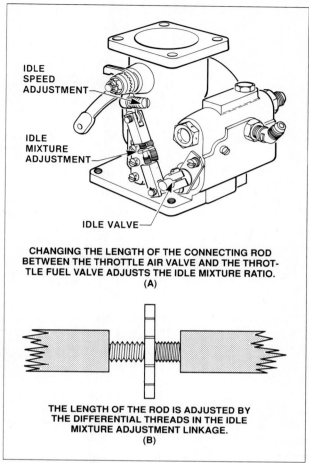

CHANGING THE LENGTH OF THE CONNECTING ROD BETWEEN THE THROTTLE AIR VALVE AND THE THROTTLE FUEL VALVE ADJUSTS THE IDLE MIXTURE RATIO.
(A)

THE LENGTH OF THE ROD IS ADJUSTED BY THE DIFFERENTIAL THREADS IN THE IDLE MIXTURE ADJUSTMENT LINKAGE.
(B)

Figure 6-37. Idle speed and mixture adjustment for an RSA fuel system.

takeoff than is possible without water injection. These systems may also be referred to as ADI or antidetonation injection.

The carburetor (operating at high power settings) delivers more fuel to the engine than it actually needs. A leaner mixture would produce more power; however, the additional fuel is necessary to prevent overheating and detonation. With the injection of the antidetonant fluid, the mixture can be leaned out to that which produces maximum power, and the vaporization of the water-alcohol mixture then provides the cooling formerly supplied by the excess fuel. This system is illustrated in figure 6-38.

Operating on this best power mixture, the engine develops more power even though the manifold pressure and RPM settings remain unchanged. In addition though, the manifold pressure can be increased to the point which would cause detonation without the injection of the water-alcohol mixture. Thus, the increase in

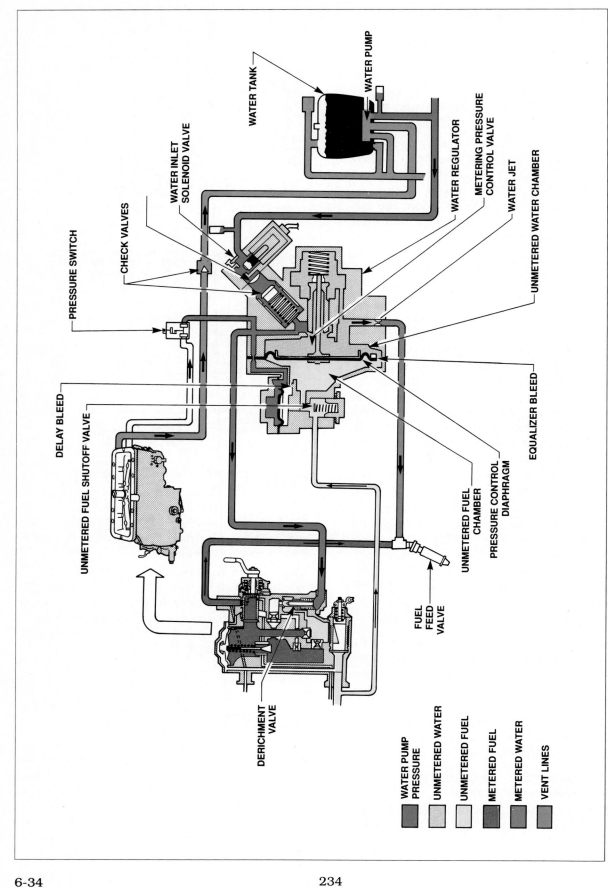

WATER PUMP

WATER TANK

WATER INLET
SOLENOID VALVE

WATER REGULATOR

CHECK VALVES

METERING PRESSURE
CONTROL VALVE

WATER JET

PRESSURE SWITCH

UNMETERED WATER CHAMBER

DELAY BLEED

EQUALIZER BLEED

UNMETERED FUEL SHUTOFF VALVE

UNMETERED FUEL
CHAMBER

PRESSURE CONTROL
DIAPHRAGM

FUEL
FEED
VALVE

DERICHMENT
VALVE

WATER PUMP
PRESSURE

UNMETERED WATER

UNMETERED FUEL

METERED FUEL

METERED WATER

VENT LINES

Figure 6-38. Schematic diagram of a typical ADI system.

234

power and antidetonant injection is twofold: the engine can be operated on the best power mixture, and the maximum manifold pressure can be increased.

C. Turbine Engine Fuel Metering Systems

The turbine engine fuel system functions to supply a precise amount of fuel to the engine in all conditions of ground and air operations. The system must be free of dangerous operational characteristics such as vapor lock. Further, it must be possible to increase and decrease power at will to obtain the thrust required for any operating condition.

This is accomplished by a device called a fuel control, which meters fuel to the combustion chamber. The pilot selects a fuel flow condition using the cockpit control known as the power lever. By placing the lever in a certain position, the pilot tells the fuel control how much thrust is desired. The fuel control monitors several engine operating parameters and, based on those readings, will provide sufficient fuel flow to the engine to produce the desired power, at a flow rate that will not allow the engine operating limits to be exceeded. These automatic features prevent rich or lean flameout and over-temperature or over-speed conditions from occurring.

Lean die-out occurs, as one might expect, from a lessening of fuel in the mixture until combustion is no longer supported. A rich blowout occurs when the force of the fuel flow during low airflow conditions interrupts the normal burning process near the fuel distribution nozzle. This can cause unstable combustion, and the flame will blow away from the nozzle and out of the combustor. At this point combustion ceases and a relight (restart) procedure is required.

1. Turbine Engine Fuels And Additives

Aviation turbine fuels are used for powering turbojet, turboprop, and turboshaft engines. There are currently two types of turbine fuel in use, JET A and JET A-1, which are kerosene types, and JET B, which is a blend of gasoline and kerosene fractions.

Jet A-1 specifies a freeze point of -47°C (-52.6°F) and Jet A a freeze point of -40°C (-40°F).

Jet B, similar to JP-4, is normally used by the military, particularly the Air Force. This fuel has an allowable freeze point of -50°C (-58°F).

Certain aircraft/engine combinations require fuel additives as anti-icing or antimicrobial agents. Anti-icing additives keep entrained water from freezing without the use of fuel heat, except at very low temperatures. Microbial agents kill microbes, fungi, and bacteria which form a slime, and in some cases, a matted waste in fuel systems.

Most often the additives are premixed in the fuel by the distributor. If they are not, the service person must add the agents when fueling the aircraft. A popular brand of a combined anti-icing and antimicrobiological mixture is called PRIST. It is designed to be added during servicing. The type and amount, however, must be determined to maintain the airworthiness of the fuel system in the existing climatic conditions.

For the approved fuel and fuel additives used to service a turbine engine, the technician should check the aircraft operator's manual or Type Certificate Data Sheet.

2. Jet Fuel Controls

The fuel control is an engine driven accessory which can operate by mechanical, hydraulic, electrical, or pneumatic forces in various combinations. Fuel controls are often divided into two basic groups: (1) hydromechanical and (2) electronic.

a. Hydromechanical

Figure 6-39 is a simplified schematic of a hydromechanically operated gas turbine fuel control. It functions to meter fuel as follows:

1) Fuel Metering Section

Movement of the shut-off lever (10) during the engine start cycle allows fuel to flow out to the engine. This shut-off lever is needed because the minimum flow stop (11) prevents the main metering valve (4) from completely closing. The full rearward position of the power lever is the IDLE position, and is against the idle stop. This prevents the power lever from becoming a fuel shut-off. The shut-off lever in this illustration also provides the function of ensuring the correct working pressure buildup within the fuel control during the starting cycle. This is said to prevent roughly metered fuel from entering the engine before its correct time.

Fuel from the supply system is pumped through the main fuel pump (8) to the main metering valve (4). As fuel flows through the orifice created by the taper of the valve, a pressure drop occurs. Fuel from the metering valve to the fuel nozzles is referred to as metered fuel. Fuel in this instance is metered by weight rather

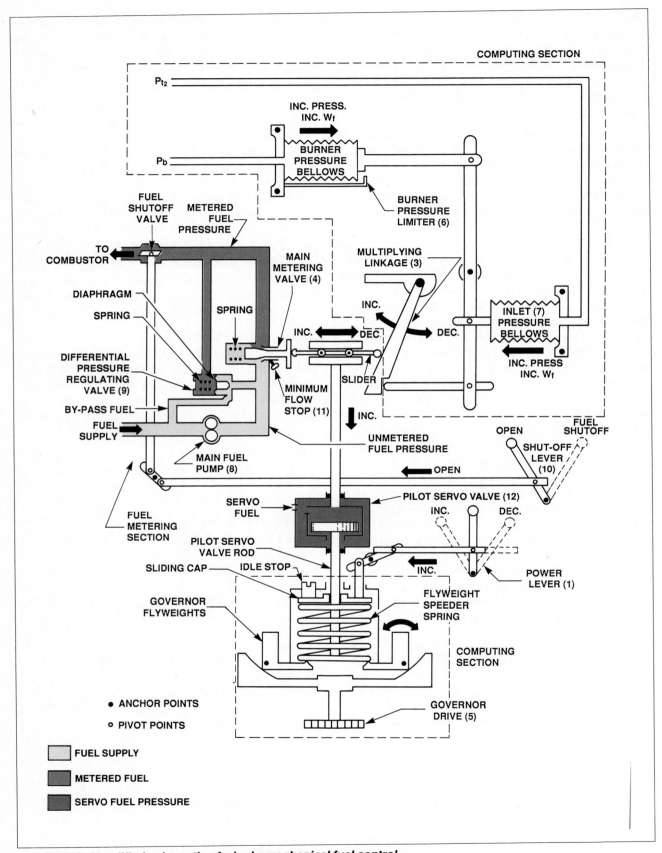

Figure 6-39. Simplified schematic of a hydromechanical fuel control.

than by volume. This is done because the heat potential (Btu per pound) of the fuel is constant regardless of fuel temperature, while Btu's per unit volume is not. Fuel now flows in a correctly metered condition to the combustion section of the engine.

If only one operating condition were needed, only one fuel metering orifice size would be needed, but, aircraft engines obviously must change power settings. A constantly changing fuel bypass is the means by which pressure differential is maintained at a constant value regardless of orifice size. By directing metered fuel to the spring side of the hydraulically operated differential pressure regulator diaphragm, the pressure differential will always return to the value of the spring tension. Because the spring tension is a constant value, the pressure differential across the orifice will also become a constant.

To understand this concept more fully, consider that the fuel pump always delivers fuel in excess of the fuel control's need and the differential pressure regulator control valve continually returns excess fuel back to the pump inlet.

2) Computing Section

During engine operation, forward movement of the power lever (1) causes the spring cap to slide down the pilot servo valve rod (2) and compress the flyweight speeder spring. This action will force the flyweights in at the top, creating an under-speed condition. The pilot servo valve (12) functions to prevent sudden movement as its fluid is displaced top to bottom. If we consider that the multiplying linkage (3) remains stationary during this time, the slider will move down the inclined plane and to the left. As it moves left, the slider will force the metering valve (4) to the left against its spring tension, allowing increased fuel to flow to the engine. With increased fuel flow, the engine will speed up and drive the governor shaft (5) faster. The new flyweight force created will come to equilibrium with the speeder spring force as the flyweights return to an upright position. They are now in position to act at the next speed change.

On many engines, static pressure in the burner can is a useful measure of mass airflow. If mass airflow is known, fuel/air ratio can be more carefully controlled. As burner pressure P_b increases, the burner pressure bellows expands to the right. Excessive movement is restricted by the burner pressure limiter (6). If the pilot servo

valve rod remains stationary, the multiplying linkage will force the roller to the left, opening the metering valve to match fuel flow to the increased mass airflow. This condition could occur in an increased nose down condition, which would increase airspeed, inlet ram air, and engine mass airflow.

An increase in inlet pressure P_{T2} would also cause the inlet pressure bellows N_3 to expand, forcing the multiplying linkage to the left and causing the metering valve to open wider.

b. Electronic

Some engines utilize a system of electronic controls to monitor the engine operation and supply the required control inputs to keep the engine operating within limits. Engine shaft speeds (% RPM) and EGT are continuously monitored during engine operation. Electronic controls are used on some installations only as a limiter. They will only operate as an input if the engine speed or EGT approach the limits of safe operation.

Let us take a brief look at the fuel control system used on the Rolls Royce RB-211 engine, seen in figure 6-40. An analysis of the schematic will show that the control amplifier receives a signal from turbine gas temperature (TGT) and two compressor speed signals N_1 and N_2.

This control operates on a hydromechanical schedule until near full engine power. Then the electronic circuit starts to function as a fuel limiting device.

The pressure regulator in this installation is similar to the pressure regulating valve in the simplified hydromechanical fuel control diagram, except that in this system the bypassing of fuel occurs at the fuel pump outlet rather than the fuel control. Near full power, when predetermined TGT and compressor speed values are reached, the pressure regulator reduces fuel flow to the spray nozzles by returning increased amounts of fuel to the fuel pump inlet. The fuel flow regulator in this control acts as a hydromechanical control, receiving signals from the high speed compressor N_1 and N_2 gas path air pressure (P_1, P_2, P_3) and power lever position.

Full authority digital engine controls (F.A.D.E.C.) take over virtually all of the steady state and transitional controls, and replace most of the hydromechanical and pneumatic elements found in other fuel controls. This system reduces the engine fuel system to a pump and a control valve, an independent shutoff valve, and a few

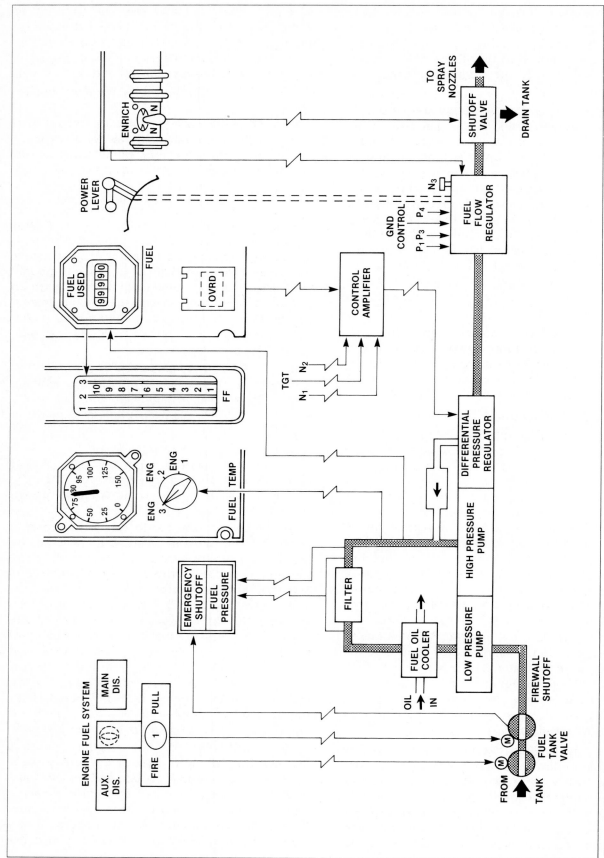

Figure 6-40. Electro-hydromechanical fuel control.

features necessary to keep the engine operating safely in case of a massive electronic failure.

3. Water Injection Systems For Turbine Engines

Water injection in a gas turbine engine is a means of augmenting engine thrust. The maximum thrust produced by a turbine engine depends greatly upon the density or weight of the airflow through the engine. Increases in ambient air pressure or temperature reduces the density of the air, and therefore, the maximum thrust of the engine. Water injection may be used to restore or boost the power output of the engine for takeoff by cooling the airflow with water or a water-methanol mixture. Methanol added to the water acts as an antifreeze and provides an additional source of fuel.

Water may be injected directly into the compressor inlet or into the combustion chamber. Injecting water into the combustion chamber inlet is usually more suitable for engines using an axial flow compressor. This location provides a more even distribution and a greater quantity of the fluid can be injected.

If water alone was sprayed into the engine compressor inlet, it would reduce the turbine inlet temperature. The addition of methanol restores this loss when the methanol is burned in the combustion chamber. This restores power without having to adjust fuel flow.

When the coolant is injected into the combustion chamber inlet it increases the mass flow through the turbine relative to that through the compressor. This reduces the pressure and temperature drop across the turbine and results in an increased tailpipe pressure which means additional thrust. The reduction in turbine inlet temperature allows the fuel control to schedule an increase in fuel flow, providing additional thrust. When methanol is used in the fluid, the turbine inlet temperature will reflect the burning of the methanol in the combustion chamber.

A typical water injection system is shown in figure 6-41. Notice that it contains two independent injection nozzles, one to spray water into the compressor inlet and the other to spray water into the diffuser.

There is a limit to the amount of fluid injection any compressor or combustor can efficiently utilize. In the system shown, full thrust augmentation, when required, necessitates the use of both. On other installations it is common to see injection at only one location, either the compressor or the diffuser.

When ambient temperature is low, however, only the diffuser injection system can be used. Below 40°F at takeoff RPM, there is a danger of ice formation. At low ambient temperatures thrust is usually high enough without water injection. This water injection system is controlled by a cockpit switch which arms the circuit and makes flow into both manifolds possible. When closed, the cockpit switch allows electrical current to flow to the fuel control microswitch. As the power lever reaches takeoff power, the microswitch is depressed and the water pump valve will be powered to open. This will allow compressor bleed air to flow through the air-driven water pump which supplies water under a pressure of 200 - 300 PSIG to the dual manifold. If compressor flow is not needed, a cockpit switch is installed to deactivate its flow valve. The pressure sensing tube to the fuel control is present to alert the control to reset fuel flow higher when water is flowing. This system is not generally needed if water-alcohol is used, because combustion of the alcohol keeps turbine inlet temperature at its required value.

A tank float level circuit will cut off power to the pump when the tank is empty, and will also prevent the system from operating if the circuit is activated with an unserviced water supply. When the water injection system is not in use, the check valve at the diffuser prevents high temperature air from backing up into the water system. Drains are present to drain the lines when the system is not in use, preventing freeze-up. In some installations a bleed air system allows the pilot to purge the system of water after terminating water injection.

4. Jet Fuel Control Maintenance

The repair of the turbine engine fuel control is very limited. The only repairs permitted in the field are the replacement of the control and the required adjustments afterwards. Adjustments are limited to the idle speed and the maximum speed adjustment, commonly called trimming the engine. Both adjustments are made in the normal range of operation.

Trimming is a term applied to idle speed and maximum thrust adjustment made during performance testing. Idle speed adjustment is very similar from one engine to the next. It sets engine idling speed to the manufacturer's best economy and performance range. Idle speed is used during periods of operation when thrust is not required. Depending upon the particular engine, a maximum percent RPM adjustment or maximum EPR (engine pressure ratio) adjust- ment assures the correct maximum thrust is being produced by the engine. This thrust value is referred to as manufacturer's guaranteed rated thrust, sometimes shortened to rated thrust.

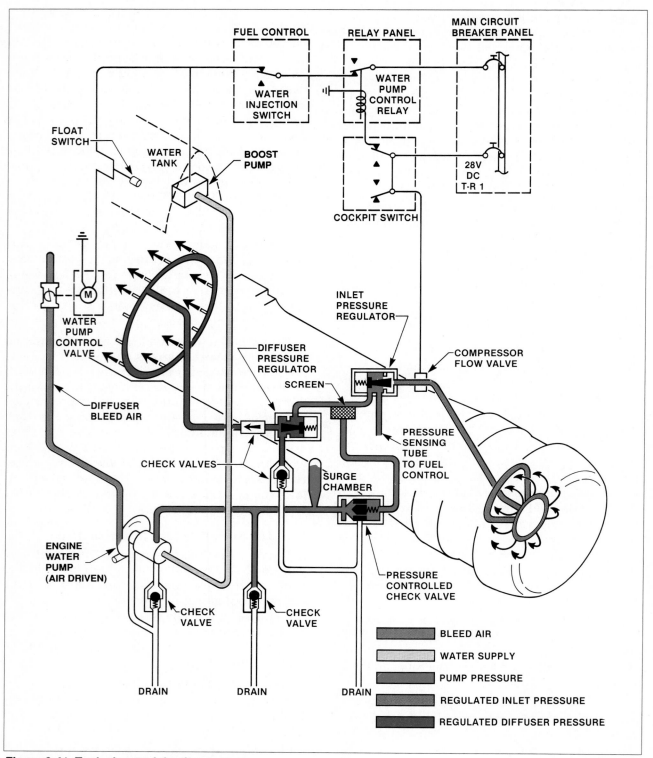

Figure 6-41. Typical water injection system.

Most manufacturer's recommend that in order to stabilize cams, springs, and linkages within the fuel control, all final adjustments must be made in the increase direction. If an over adjustment occurs, the procedure would be repeated by decreasing trim to below target values. Then increase trim back to the desired values.

The trim adjustments are usually accomplished using some sort of adjuster requiring only a screwdriver or wrench to turn. These adjusters are seen in figure 6-42. Adjuster are usually equipped with some sort of friction lock that dispenses with the use of lockplates, locknuts, or lockwire. On some engines provision is made for remote adjusting equipment. The remote control unit makes it possible to make the adjustments during ground test with the cowls closed. The remote unit may be operated from the cockpit.

Another important part of the trim procedure is to check for power lever cushion or spring-back. The technician, before and after the trim run, moves the power lever full forward and releases it. The distance the lever springs back is measured against prescribed tolerances. If out of

limits, adjustment is required. This spring-back assures that the pilot will not only be able to obtain takeoff power but also additional power lever travel for emergencies. If the spring-back is correct, the fuel control will reach its internal stops before the cockpit quadrant reaches its forward stop.

The trim check is accomplished whenever engine thrust is suspect, and after such maintenance tasks as prescribed by the manufacturer. A few of these might include trimming after engine change, fuel control change, or loss of cushion. Trimming is otherwise required due to deterioration of engine efficiencies, as service time takes its toll, and also aircraft linkages stretch to cause misalignment in the cockpit engine control systems.

In conjunction with the trim check, the idle speed is set and then an acceleration check is usually accomplished as an additional check on engine performance. After the trim check is completed, a mark is placed on the cockpit power lever quadrant at the takeoff trim position. The power lever is then advanced from the idle position to takeoff position and the time is measured against a published tolerance. The time, even for a large gas turbine engine is quite low, in the range of 5 to 10 seconds.

D. Turbine Engine Fuel System Components

1. Engine-Driven Fuel Pump

The main fuel pump is an engine driven accessory. As such, when the engine speeds up, the pump also speeds up and delivers more fuel. The pump is designed to deliver a continuous supply of fuel to the fuel control at a quantity which is in excess of the engine needs. After metering the required amount of fuel to the combustor, the fuel control returns the surplus fuel to the fuel pump inlet.

Main fuel pumps are generally spur gear types with single or dual elements, and often a centrifugal boost element. The gear pump is classified as a positive displacement type because it delivers a fixed quantity of fluid per revolution. In this respect it is very similar to a gear type oil pump.

A typical turbine engine fuel pump is shown in figure 6-43. The boost element is geared up to produce the required inlet pressure to the dual high pressure gear elements. Dual elements with shear sections on the drive shaft are designed so

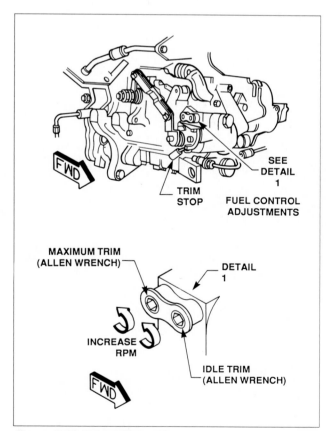

Figure 6-42. Trim adjustment.

that if one section fails, the other will continue to function and provide sufficient fuel for cruise and landing operation. Check valves are present in the outlet to prevent fuel recirculation into an inoperative element. A relief valve is incorporated to provide protection to the fuel system.

Pumps of this type produce the high pressure needed for atomization of fuel in the combustor. Many large gear pumps can produce up to 1,500 psi and a volume of 30,000 pounds per hour.

On some smaller engines the fuel pump provides a mounting base for the fuel control. On others the fuel pump is not a separate unit at all, but rather the pump housing is incorporated into the base of the fuel control.

2. Fuel Heater

Some engines use only the lubrication system oil cooler for heat transfer to the fuel, while others incorporate a separate fuel heater. Fuel heat is supplied to prevent ice crystals from forming due to entrained water. When ice forms, fuel filter clogging occurs which can cause the filter to bypass. This condition allows unfiltered fuel to flow to downstream components. In severe cases, icing can cause flow interruption and engine flameout as ice forms again in the downstream components such as in the fuel control.

On engines where icing is critical, a pressure switch is often installed in the filter by-pass. If the filter ices, the pressure drop will cause a light to come on in the cockpit.

Fuel heat is designed to be used when the fuel temperature approaches 32°F. Fuel heat is either automatically activated three to five degrees Fahrenheit above the freezing point of water, or it is selected by a toggle switch in the cockpit. In this system, fuel on its way to the engine low pressure filter passes through the cores of the heater assembly. The solenoid allows bleed air to pass over the cores to warm the fuel.

Typical operational restrictions are as follows:

(1) Operate for one minute prior to takeoff and operate for one minute in every 30 during flight. Excessive heating can cause vapor lock or heat damage to the fuel control.

(2) Do not operate during takeoff, approach, or go around because of flameout possibilities from vaporization during these critical flight regimes.

On some installations the cycle time is automatically controlled by an electric timer and gate

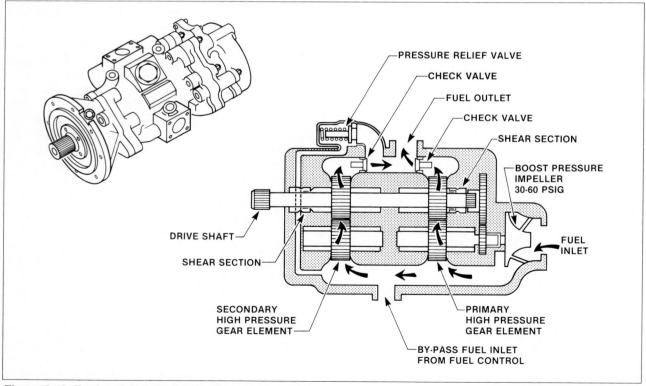

Figure 6-43. Engine-driven fuel pump for a turbine engine.

valve arrangement. To check on the operation, as the system cycles on, the technician can observe gauge indications such as EPR and oil temperature and the fuel filter light as follows:

(1) EPR will usually drop due to compression loss as bleed air flows.

(2) Oil temperature will usually rise as fuel temperature rises within the oil cooler.

(3) If a filter by-pass light is illuminated due to filter icing, the light should extinguish as the system cycles on.

(4) If the fuel by-pass light remains on, the technician would suspect a solid contamination at the fuel filter rather than icing.

In some aircraft, a separate fuel heat system is not installed, because the fuel-oil cooler plus additives in the fuel give sufficient protection against fuel icing. If an air-oil cooler is used, a fuel heat system is generally used.

3. Fuel Filters

Two levels of filtration are generally required in turbine engine fuel systems. A low pressure coarse mesh filter is installed between the supply tank and the engine, and a fine mesh filter between the fuel pump and the fuel control. The fine filter is necessary because the fuel control is a device with many minute passageways and fine tolerances. Filters for this application have a micronic rating of 10 to 200 microns, depending upon the amount of contamination protection needed.

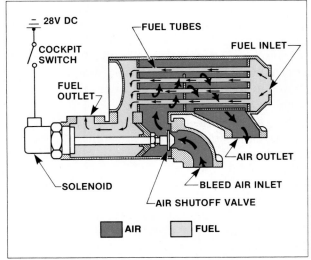

Figure 6-44. Fuel heater for use with a turbo-jet engine.

Several varieties of filtering elements are used in fuel systems. The most common are: the steel mesh, the wafer screen, the steel mesh pleated screen, and cellulose fiber. The cellulose fiber filter has an equivalent micron rating. By way of explanation, a 35 micron filter of the wafer screen type will have square openings with a diameter of 35 microns and will prevent particles larger than 35 microns in diameter from passing through the system. The cellulose element will filter out particles of relatively the same size.

Fuel filter checks are frequent inspection items for the maintenance technician. If water or metal contaminants are present in the filter element or filter bowl, the technician must locate the source of the problem before returning the aircraft to service.

In figure 6-45A a wafer screen, bowl type filter, containing a by-pass valve is illustrated. The by-pass valve will open at 8 to 12 psid. This means that it will open if the downstream pressure differs from the upstream pressure by 8 to 12 psi. This might be the situation if the filter starts to accumulate ice crystals or solid contaminants.

The filter in figure 6-45B contains two filter elements. The pleated mesh element filters the main system fuel on its way to the combustor and has a filtration rating of 40 microns. A by-pass valve relieves at 28 to 32 psid if this element clogs. The cylindrical mesh element is rated at 10 microns and filters fuel being routed to the fuel control to operate the servo mechanisms. The minimal flow in this part of the fuel system permits the use of a very fine filter. This fine filter is needed to protect the highly machined parts of the fuel control and protect against clogging of the numerous small fluid passageways.

4. Fuel Spray Nozzles And Fuel Manifolds

Fuel nozzles, also called fuel distributors, are the terminating point of the fuel system. They are located in the inlet of the combustion liner to deliver fuel in a defined quantity. Fuel cannot be burned in a liquid state. It must first be mixed with air in correct proportions by atomization or vaporization.

a. Atomizing Type Nozzles

This type of nozzle receives fuel from a manifold and delivers it to the combustor in a highly atomized, precisely patterned spray. The cone shaped, atomized spray pattern provides a

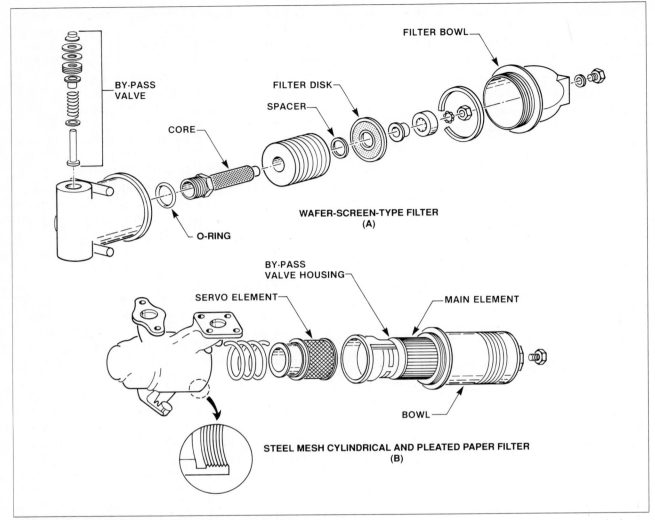

Figure 6-45. Fuel filters for use with turbine engines.

large fuel surface area of very fine fuel droplets. This provides for optimum fuel/air mixing. The most desirable flame pattern occurs at higher compression ratios, and during starting and other off design speeds, the lack of compression allows the flame length to increase. If the spray pattern is also slightly distorted, the flame, rather than being held in the center of the liner, can touch the metal and cause a hot spot or even burn through.

Another problem that occurs to distort the spray pattern is contaminated particles within the nozzle, or carbon buildup outside the nozzle orifice which can cause what is termed hot streaking. That is, an unatomized stream of fuel is present which tends to cut through the cooling air blanket and impinge on the liner or on downstream components such as the turbine nozzle.

Some fuel nozzles are mounted on pads external to the engine, to facilitate removal for inspection. Others are mounted internally and are only accessible when the combustion can is removed. The duplex nozzle shown in figure 6-46B is an externally mounted design; the simplex nozzle shown in figure 6-46A is an internally mounted type.

The simplex design provides a single spray pattern and incorporates an internally fluted spin chamber to impart a swirling motion and reduce axial velocity of the fuel for better atomization as it exits the orifice. The internal check valve present in the simplex nozzle shown here is there to prevent dribbling of fuel from the fuel manifold into the combustor after shutdown. Some fuel systems with simplex nozzles as the main fuel distributors incorporate a second, smaller, simplex nozzle called a primer or starting nozzle, which sprays a very fine atomized mist for improved light off.

There are two common types of duplex fuel nozzles, the single-line and the dual-line.

The duplex nozzle shown, referred to as a single-line duplex type, receives its fuel at one inlet port and becomes a flow divider to distribute fuel through two spray orifices. Often, as

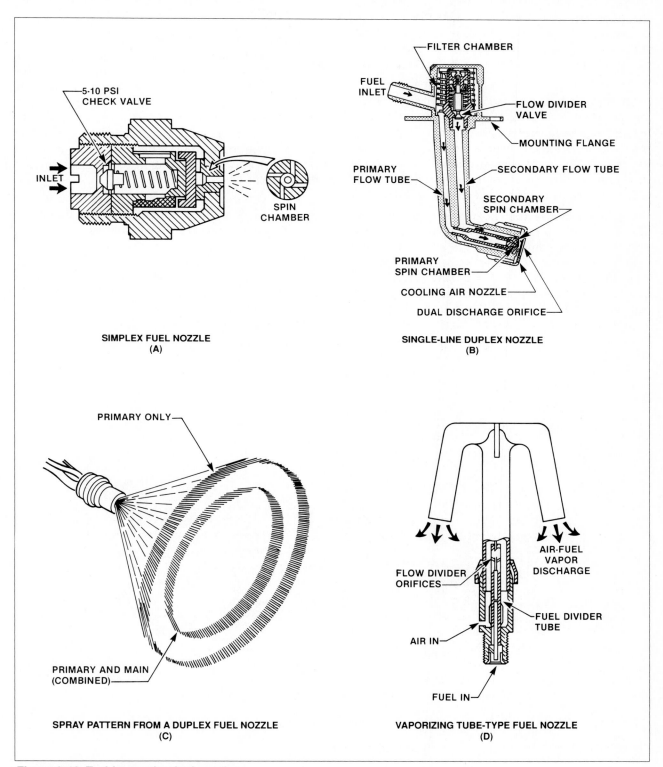

Figure 6-46. Turbine engine fuel nozzles.

shown, the center orifice, called the pilot or primary fuel, sprays at a wide angle during engine start and acceleration to idle. The outer orifice, referred to as main or secondary fuel, opens at a preset fuel pressure to flow along with the pilot fuel. Fuel of much higher volume and pressure, flowing from this outer orifice, causes the spray pattern to narrow so that the fuel will not impinge on the combustion liner at higher power settings.

The duplex nozzles also utilize spin chambers for each orifice. This arrangement provides an efficient fuel atomization and mixture residence time, as it is called, over a wide range of fuel pressures. The high pressure supplied to create the spray pattern gives good resistance to fouling of the orifices from entrained contaminants.

The head of the fuel nozzle is generally also designed with air holes which provide some primary air for combustion, but these holes are mainly used for cooling and cleaning the nozzle head and spray orifices. At times of starting fuel flow only, the cooling airflow is also designed to prevent primary fuel from back-flowing into the secondary orifice and carbonizing. A distortion of

the orifice by carbon buildup around the head of the nozzle can distort the spray pattern. This buildup can be seen on a borescope check on some engines. If severe enough, this could require removal of the nozzles for cleaning.

b. Vaporizing Type Nozzles

This type of fuel nozzle connects to a fuel manifold in an arrangement similar to the atomizing type. But, instead of delivering the fuel directly to the primary air in the combustor, as the atomizing type does, the vaporizing tube premixes the primary air and fuel. Combustor heat surrounding the nozzle causes the mixture to vaporize before exiting into the combustor flame zone.

Some vaporizers have only one outlet and are referred to as a cane-shaped vaporizer. Figure 6-46D shows a dual outlet T-shaped vaporizer. Because vaporizing nozzles do not provide an effective spray pattern for starting, an additional set of small atomizing type spray nozzles may be installed for use during engine start. This system is generally referred to as a primer or starting fuel system. The Olympus engine in the Concord

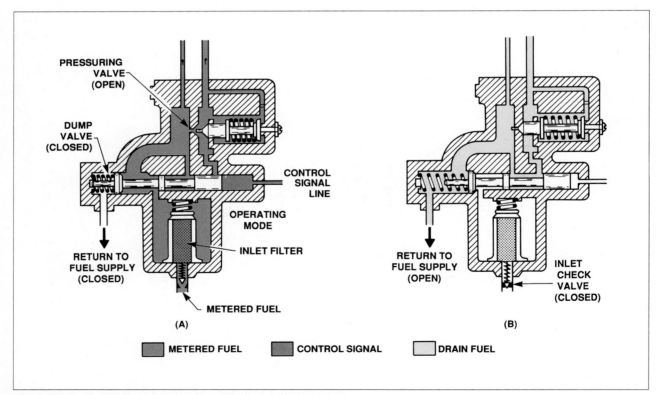

Figure 6-47. Operation of the pressurizing and dump valve.

SST utilizes the vaporizing fuel nozzle and primer fuel nozzle system.

c. Pressurizing And Dump Valve

A pressurizing and dump valve (P&D valve) is often used along with a duplex fuel nozzle of the dual inlet line type. Rather than provide a flow divider in each nozzle, as with the single-line duplex, this arrangement allows for one central flow divider called a pressurizing and dump valve. The term pressurizing refers to the fact that at a preset pressure, fuel flows into the main manifold as well as through the pilot manifold. The term dump refers to the valve's capacity of dumping the entire fuel manifold after shutdown. Manifold dumping is a procedure which sharply cuts off combustion and also prevents fuel boiling as a result of residual engine heat. This boiling would tend to leave solid deposits in the manifold which could clog the finely calibrated passageways.

In figure 6-47 a pressure signal from the fuel control arrives at the P&D valve when the power lever is opened for engine start. This pressure signal shifts the dump valve to the left (view A), closing the dump port and opening the passageway to the manifolds. Metered fuel pressure builds up at the inlet check valve until the spring tension is overcome and fuel is allowed to flow through the inlet filter to the pilot manifold. At a speed slightly above ground idle, fuel pressure will be sufficient to overcome the pressurizing valve spring force, and fuel will also flow to the main manifold.

To shut off the engine, the fuel lever in the cockpit is moved to off. The fuel control pressure signal is then lost, and spring pressure will shift the dump valve back to the right (view B), opening the dump valve port. At the same time, the inlet check valve will close, keeping the metered line flooded and ready for use on the next engine start.

d. Drain Valves

In the past dump fuel had been allowed to spill onto the ground or siphon from a drain tank in flight. However, current FAA regulations prohibit this form of environmental pollution, and now the storage tanks have to be drained by hand. To eliminate the need for hand draining, several types of recycling systems have evolved. One such system returns fuel to the supply tank when the shutoff lever is actuated. Another pushes fuel, which would have formerly been dumped, out of the fuel nozzles by introducing bleed air into the dump port. This prolongs combustion slightly until fuel starvation occurs. Still another plugs the dump port and fuel then drains out of the lower nozzles on shutdown to evaporate in the combustor. This, of course, can only be accomplished where fuel nozzles have no tendency to carbon up internally from residual heat.

5. Fuel Quantity Indicating System

Fuel quantity units vary from one installation to the next. A fuel counter or indicator, mounted on the instrument panel, is electrically connected to a flowmeter installed in the fuel line to the engine.

The fuel counter, or totalizer, utilizes a digital readout to indicate the pounds of fuel used. When the aircraft is serviced with fuel, the counter is manually set to the total of pounds of fuel in all tanks. As the fuel passes through the metering element of the flowmeter, it sends a signal to the fuel counter. This signal actuates the fuel counter mechanism so that the number of pounds of fuel passing to the engine is subtracted from the original reading. Thus, the fuel counter continually shows the total quantity of fuel in the aircraft.

Early totalizer systems operated with electric signals activating a mechanical counter, not unlike an automobile odometer. Newer systems utilize microprocessor technology, and may be integrated with other aircraft systems. The new systems can instantly provide information on fuel used, fuel remaining, current rate of fuel consumption, and coupled with navigation information, can tell the pilot if there is enough fuel to reach the aircraft's destination.

FAR

FAR

33·37 Ignition system

248

Chapter VII
Engine Ignition And Electrical Systems

A. Reciprocating Engine Ignition Systems

The basic requirements for reciprocating engine ignition systems are the same, regardless of the type of engine involved or the make of the components of the ignition system. All ignitions systems must deliver a high-tension spark to each cylinder of the engine, in firing order, at a predetermined number of degrees ahead of the top dead center position of the piston. Automobile engines have the problem of their high rotational speed requiring a great many sparks each second, but aircraft reciprocating engines turn much more slowly than automobile engines and they do not need high speed ignition. However, since aircraft engines operate with such high cylinder pressures, an extremely high degree of reliability is essential.

Aircraft systems are required by Federal Aviation Regulations, Part 33, to have "at least two spark plugs for each cylinder and two separate electrical circuits with separate sources of electric energy, or have an ignition system of equivalent in-flight reliability."

The requirements for two separate sources of electric energy have traditionally been met by using two separate magnetos. The relatively slow turning aircraft engines do not require the complexity of the breakerless ignition systems nor the high energy produced by the capacitor discharge system.

A magneto ignition system produces its initial voltage by two self-contained alternating current generators, which have permanent magnets for their rotating fields. As with any permanent magnet generator, the faster the generator turns, the more voltage it produces. The main problem with the magneto system is that of producing a sufficiently intense spark for starting the engine when the magneto is rotating very slowly. We will see that there are several ways to assist the magneto in producing this spark for starting.

1. Battery Ignition System

To overcome the limitation of a magneto producing a weak spark for starting, some of the ignition systems used with early aircraft engines had a magneto to fire one of the spark plugs in each cylinder and a battery ignition system to fire the other plug. To start the engine, only the battery system was used. A spark was provided with this system that allowed the engine to start and build up sufficient speed for the magneto to produce a hot spark. For all normal operations, both the magneto and the battery system worked

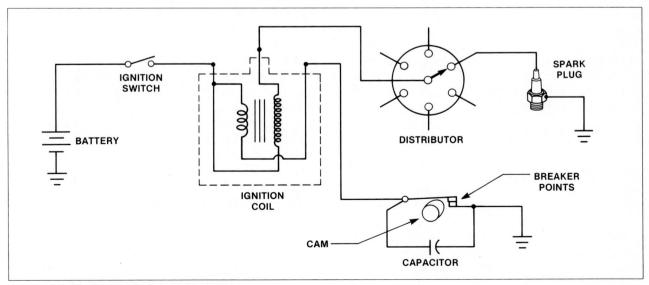

Figure 7-1. Typical battery ignition system.

together. In figure 7-1, we have the schematic of a typical battery ignition system.

When the ignition switch is turned on (closed), and the breaker points are closed, current flows from the battery through the coil and the breaker points to ground. As this current flows, a magnetic field builds up around the turns of wire in the primary winding. The lines of flux in this field expand to the maximum as current flows through the coil. When the breaker points are opened by the cam, the current stops flowing and the magnetic field collapses. As the field collapses, the lines of flux cut across the turns in the secondary winding and induce a high voltage in it.

When the breaker points open, they stop the flow of primary current, and the collapsing magnetic field cuts across the turns of the secondary coil and will induce a high voltage in it. One end of the secondary coil is connected to the primary coil, and the other end is carried outside the coil housing through the high-voltage terminal.

The high tension secondary voltage is carried into the distributor which acts as a selector switch to direct the voltage to the proper spark plug. In the spark plug, the high voltage causes current to flow across the gap and produce the spark needed to ignite the fuel-air mixture.

Inductance is a characteristic of a coil that opposes any change in the rate of flow of current. When the breaker points close, inductance prevents the current reaching its maximum flow rate immediately, and when the points open, inductance tries to keep the current flowing. The amount of voltage induced into the secondary winding is determined by the rate of collapse of the magnetic field around the primary winding. If the current could stop flowing immediately, there would be a higher voltage induced into the secondary winding. To increase the speed with which the current stops flowing, a capacitor is installed in parallel with the breaker points.

When the points open, the current from the battery stops flowing, and the magnetic field around the primary winding begins to collapse. As it collapses, the field cuts across the turns of the windings and induces a voltage in them that causes an induced current to flow. This induced current flows in the same direction as the battery current. If there were no capacitor in the circuit, as the points began to open, the current flow through the points would cause a spark to jump between the points. This spark ionizes the air be-

tween the points and makes it conductive so that current can continue to flow even though the points are open. This flow, in the form of an arc, not only slows down the collapsing of the magnetic field, but it deposits metal from one breaker point to the other and shortens the life of the points.

To speed up the collapse of the field and prevent arcing, a capacitor is installed across (in parallel) the points. As the points begin to open, the electrons see the capacitor as an easy path to ground and they flow into it. By the time the capacitor is charged enough to prevent the flow of electrons into it, the points are opened sufficiently wide that there will be no arcing across them, and the current stops flowing.

2. Magneto Ignition Systems

Modern certificated reciprocating engines for aircraft use magnetos as the source of the sparks to ignite the fuel/air mixture inside the cylinders. In the history of the magneto, there have been several types, some highly efficient and successful, while others met with less than complete success.

a. High And Low Tension

One of the easiest ways to classify aircraft magneto systems is to divide them into high-tension and low-tension systems.

All ignition systems provide a high voltage at the spark plug to jump the gap and ignite the fuel/air mixture. During World War II it was discovered that when high powered reciprocating engine airplanes were flying at high altitudes, the high voltage inside the distributor of the magneto could jump between the distributor electrodes and cause failure of the spark plugs to fire. This caused rough engine operation and loss of power.

Several design changes were made to prevent arcing inside the distributor. Some magneto manufacturers made their distributors physically larger to increase the distance the spark would have to jump. Others pressurized the distributor with compressed air to make it more difficult for the spark to jump. These measures were only partially effective. The most success in overcoming the arcing, or flashover problem, came with the low-tension magneto.

In this system, the coil inside the magneto has only a primary winding. There is another coil with a primary and a secondary winding mounted on the cylinder head, near the spark

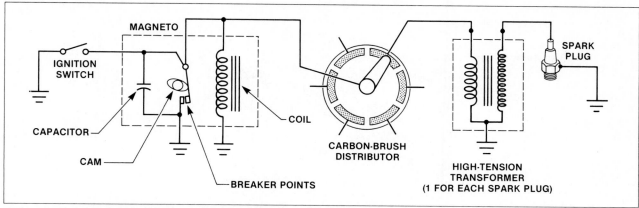

Figure 7-2. Typical low-tension ignition system for an aircraft engine.

plugs. These units are called the high-tension transformers. Electrical current from the magneto is directed by the distributor to the primary winding of this transformer where it induces a high voltage into the secondary winding. This high voltage is carried to the spark plug through a very short lead. There is no flashover in this system, because the only place the high voltage exists is in the transformer, the short spark plug lead, and the spark plug itself.

Low-tension ignition systems were originally built for the large 18 and 28 cylinder radial engines, but in later years this type of ignition system was used on some smaller horizontally opposed engines. Today, turbine powered aircraft do most of the high altitude flying, and this type of magneto has fallen off in popularity.

All of the ignition systems for the currently manufactured certificated reciprocating engines are of the high-tension type. These systems consist of a magneto with a built-in distributor, an ignition harness connecting the distributor to

each of the spark plugs, and the spark plugs themselves.

A high-tension magneto uses a permanent-magnet alternating current generator to produce the primary current. This current flows through the primary winding of the high-voltage step-up coil. A cam-operated set of breaker points interrupts the flow of current through the primary winding of the coil, and the collapse of the magnetic field around the primary winding induces a high voltage in the secondary winding. This high voltage is carried to the distributor rotor by a carbon brush and then to the proper spark plug through the appropriate ignition cable. The ignition switch grounds the primary circuit to stop the magneto from producing sparks.

b. Single And Dual-Type Magnetos

The rotating-magnet magneto is the type of magneto used currently and is the only one we will discuss in detail. It has been with us in several forms for almost sixty years. Today it is available in both single and dual-type systems.

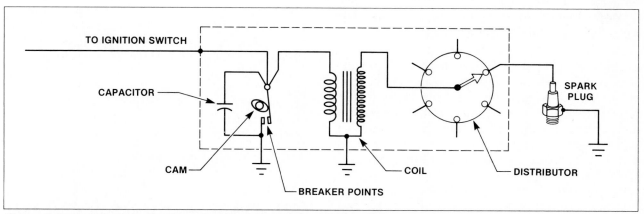

Figure 7-3. Electrical circuit of a typical high-tension aircraft magneto.

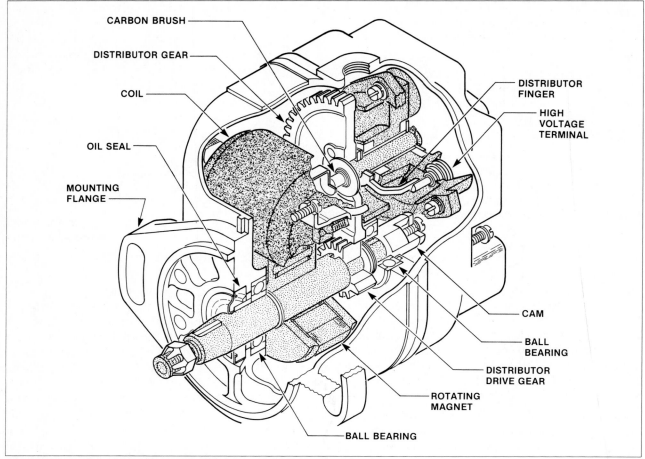

Figure 7-4. A flange-mounted rotating-magnet-type aircraft magneto.

The single magneto consists of a permanent magnet having two, four, or eight poles rotating inside a laminated iron frame. The flux from the magnet flows through the frame and cuts across the primary winding of the magneto coil that is mounted on the frame. The cam which opens the breaker points is attached to the rotating magnet shaft, and the gear that drives the distributor rotor is driven from the magnet shaft. A typical high-tension single-type magneto is seen in figure 7-4.

The Federal Aviation Administration requires that all certificated aircraft engines have an ignition system with two separate sources of electrical energy. A concession has been made in the interpretation of this regulation that allows the use of dual-type magnetos. These magnetos have one housing, one rotating magnet, and one cam, but there are two separate and independent systems that contain all of the other parts of the ignition system. There are two coils, each having its own primary and secondary winding, two capacitors, two sets of breaker points, two dis-

tributors, two sets of ignition leads, and of course, two spark plugs in each cylinder.

3. Magneto Operating Principles

The rotating-magnet magneto has four basic systems we will consider. The mechanical system is that portion of the magneto that includes the housing, the bearings, the oil seals, and all of the non-electrical portions of the magneto. The magnetic system consists of the rotating magnet, the pole shoes, and the core of the magneto coil. The primary electrical system consists of the primary winding of the coil, the breaker points, the capacitor, and the ignition switch. And the secondary electrical system consists of the secondary winding of the coil, the distributor, the ignition harness, and the spark plugs.

a. The Mechanical System

Most magnetos have the rotating magnet supported in ball or needle bearings. Many of the earlier magnetos required that the bearings be preloaded to increase their life. This preloading was accomplished by changing the number of shims behind the bearings. But the more modern magnetos use sealed ball bearings pressed onto the shaft. Whatever type of bearing is used, be sure to follow the procedures specified in the manufacturer's overhaul manual when replacing the bearings or overhauling the magneto.

Most of the magnetos mounted on horizontally opposed engines have the oil seal in the magneto rather than in the engine mounting pad. This seal is normally made of a tough, resilient plastic material held snugly against the magneto shaft with a spring. If there is any indication of oil inside the magneto, the magneto must be removed from the engine and this seal replaced.

Magnetos are mounted on the engine by methods known as base mounting or flange mounting. Base mounted magnetos are bolted rigidly to the engine accessory case, and the rotating magnet is coupled to the engine drive with a vernier coupling. A vernier coupling is a toothed coupling with more teeth on one side than on the other. By disconnecting the coupling and rotating it, the timing between the magneto and the engine can be changed in very small increments. The more common flange mounted magnetos are bolted to the engine with the at-

tachment bolts passing through banana shaped slots in the magneto case, or it may be held tight to the engine with clamps. Either method will allow the magneto to be rotated slightly for fine adjustment of the magneto-to-engine timing.

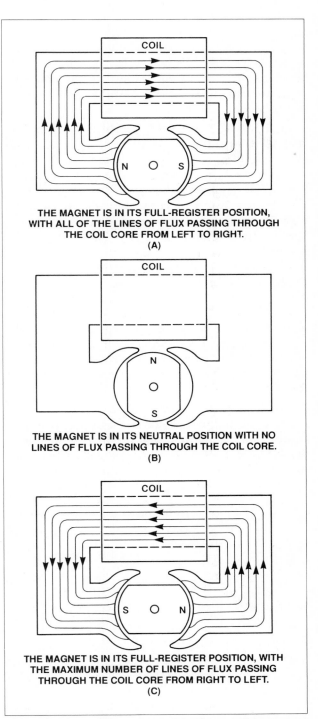

THE MAGNET IS IN ITS FULL-REGISTER POSITION, WITH ALL OF THE LINES OF FLUX PASSING THROUGH THE COIL CORE FROM LEFT TO RIGHT.
(A)

THE MAGNET IS IN ITS NEUTRAL POSITION WITH NO LINES OF FLUX PASSING THROUGH THE COIL CORE.
(B)

THE MAGNET IS IN ITS FULL-REGISTER POSITION, WITH THE MAXIMUM NUMBER OF LINES OF FLUX PASSING THROUGH THE COIL CORE FROM RIGHT TO LEFT.
(C)

Figure 7-6. The magnetic circuit of a rotating-magnet magneto.

Figure 7-5. The Bendix D-3000 dual magneto.

b. The Magnetic Circuit

Most popular magnetos for modern four or six cylinder aircraft engines use a two-pole magnet made of a very high grade, high permeability alloy steel.

The pole shoes for the magnetic circuit are made of laminated steel and are usually cast right into the magneto housing. The core of the magneto coil is also part of the magnetic circuit, and it is wedged tightly against the pole shoe extensions so that it will make a good magnetic path for the flux to flow with a minimum of reluctance.

In figure 7-6, we see the paths the lines of magnetic flux take as they flow through the magnetic circuit of the magneto. In view A, the magnet is in what is called its full register position, with all of the lines of flux from the magnet passing through the coil core from left to right. In view B, the magnet has rotated 90 degrees and there is no flux in the coil core. This is called the neutral position of the magnet. In view C, the magnet is again in its full register position, but this time the lines of flux pass through the coil core from right to left. The magnetic field has expanded to a maximum, collapsed and expanded again to a maximum, only in the opposite direction. The primary winding of the magneto coil is cut by the flux each time the magnetic field expands and collapses and current is induced in the primary winding.

When current flows in a conductor, it produces a magnetic field. The current generated as the field collapses will produce a magnetic field that will try to sustain the collapsing field. And the current generated as the magnetic field builds up will produce a magnetic field that opposes the buildup.

If we complete the primary circuit so current can flow in it, the flux from the magnetic field produced by current flowing in the primary winding combines with the flux caused by the rotating magnet. When these fields combine, the greatest change in flux does not occur when the magnet passes through its neutral position as it does when there is no primary current, but the maximum rate of change occurs a few degrees of magnet rotation beyond the neutral position. If the breaker points are opened when they will cause the greatest change in the resultant flux, the most intense spark will be produced. The point at which the breaker points open is called the E-gap angle. The resultant flux curve of a magneto is shown in figure 7-7.

c. The Primary Electrical Circuit

The primary winding on the magneto coil consists of around 180 to 200 turns of relatively heavy copper wire coated with an enamel insulation. It is wound directly over the laminated iron core that forms a part of the magnetic circuit. The inside end of the primary winding grounds to the iron core and also to a ground lead. The outside end of the primary winding connects to the inside end of the secondary winding and is brought out of the coil through a lead that is connected to the insulated breaker point.

The breaker points are normally held closed by a leaf-type spring and are opened by the cam that is mounted on the end of the rotating magnet shaft. The cam allows the points to close when the magnet is in its full register position. As the magnet moves away from the full register position, the flux through the coil core begins to decrease and a voltage is induced in the primary winding that causes current to flow through the breaker points to ground. This current causes a

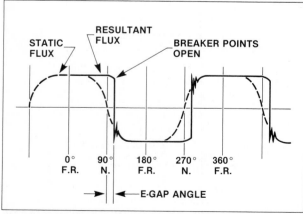

Figure 7-7. Change in flux density as the magnet rotates.

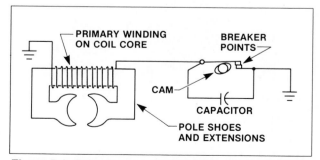

Figure 7-8. The primary electrical circuit of a high-tension magneto.

magnetic field which prevents the flux in the coil core following the static flux curve. The two magnetic fields, the one from the rotating magnet and the one from the primary current, cause the flux to follow the resultant flux curve we saw in figure 7-7.

When the magnet rotates a few degrees beyond its neutral position (the E-gap angle), the cam will open the breaker points and the primary current will stop flowing. This sudden stoppage of the primary current causes the magnetic field in the coil core to collapse. Remember that it is the rate of flux change that determines the amount of voltage induced by a magnetic field, and because this flux change is so fast, a high voltage is induced into the primary winding.

Any time moving contact points interrupt a flow of current, an arc is produced between the points. As the points begin to separate, the resistance increases and the current flowing through the resistance produces heat. This heat becomes so intense that it ionizes the air and current flows through it, causing an arc that not only delays the decrease in current flow, but it also transfers metal from one breaker point to the other and can even weld the points together.

To prevent this arcing, a capacitor is installed in parallel with the points. As the contacts begin to open and the resistance across them begins to increase, the electrons see the capacitor as a low resistance path to ground and flow into it. By the time the capacitor is charged up enough to stop the flow of electrons, the points have opened far enough that no spark can jump across them.

In some modern magnetos, the capacitor serves a dual function. It is in parallel with the breaker points to prevent arcing across them as they open, and it is also in series with the ignition switch to prevent electromagnetic radiation from the primary lead causing radio interference. This type of capacitor serves as a feed-through for the ignition lead. The pigtail inside the magneto connects to the insulated breaker point, and the lead from the ignition switch in the cockpit connects to the capacitor terminal outside of the magneto. The metal case of the capacitor is connected to the outside of the plates in the capacitor, and any radio frequency energy that is induced into the primary lead by the points opening is carried to ground before it can leave the magneto.

d. The Secondary Electrical Circuit

A coil made up of thousands of turns of very fine wire is wound on top of the primary coil in the magneto coil assembly. The inside end of this secondary coil is connected to the outside end of the primary winding, and the outside end is brought out of the coil assembly at a high voltage contact usually on the side of the coil.

A spring loaded carbon brush in the center of the distributor gear presses against the high voltage contact and conducts the high secondary voltage into the distributor rotor. The distributor finger, which is a conductive arm in the rotor, carries the high voltage from the coil to the contact for the proper spark plug lead in the distributor block.

Heavily insulated, shielded spark plug leads carry the high voltage from the distributor to the

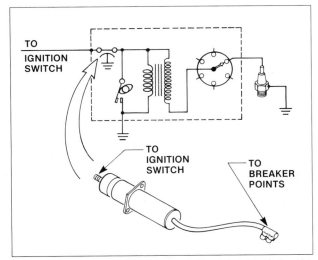

Figure 7-9. A feed-through capacitor used in the primary circuit of some magnetos.

Figure 7-10. The high-tension terminal in a coil of an aircraft magneto.

spark plug. Current flows across the gap in the spark plug and produces the spark that ignites the fuel/air mixture inside the cylinder.

4. Ignition Harness

There may be enough high voltage generated in a magneto to cause an adequate spark to jump the gap in the spark plug, but if this high voltage is not delivered to the spark plug without losses, engine performance will be less than optimum.

Modern communication and navigation equipment must be able to receive signals from ground stations without interference caused by the ignition system. Since all high voltage ignition systems generate extraneous radio frequency (RF) signals, they must be contained within the harness and grounded. Unless this is done, there will be enough energy radiated to interfere with radio reception.

a. Construction

Ignition leads are usually made of stranded copper or stainless steel wire, enclosed in a rubber or silicone insulation. This insulation is covered with a braided metal shield, which is in turn protected by a tough plastic outer covering.

Slick Electro, Inc., produces a very popular ignition harness that, instead of using stranded wire, uses a continuous spiral of wire. This spiral

Figure 7-11. A typical stranded ignition lead.

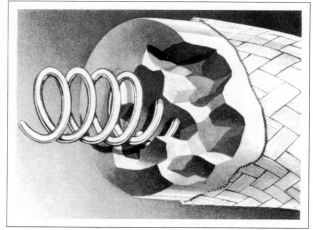

Figure 7-12. The coiled conductor in a Slick Electro ignition lead.

is impregnated with a high voltage silicone rubber insulation.

There have been two sizes of ignition leads used in aircraft engine ignition harnesses, 5mm and 7mm. Practically all of the modern harnesses use the smaller size lead. Many of the older radial engines used unshielded wire run inside separate shielding. When it was necessary to replace a lead, the old lead was pulled from the shielding and a new lead was pulled through in its place. With the more modern installations, the entire lead, shielding and all, is replaced.

Modern ignition harnesses are available with terminal ends to fit either the standard 5/8-24 shielded spark plug or the 3/4-20 all-weather spark plug. Many operators, when having to replace both the spark plugs and the harness at the same time are converting the ignition system to the all-weather configuration.

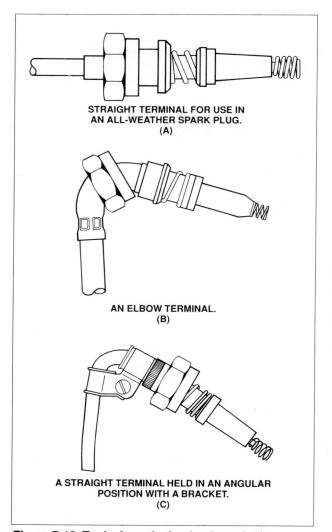

STRAIGHT TERMINAL FOR USE IN
AN ALL-WEATHER SPARK PLUG.
(A)

AN ELBOW TERMINAL.
(B)

A STRAIGHT TERMINAL HELD IN AN ANGULAR
POSITION WITH A BRACKET.
(C)

Figure 7-13. Typical spark plug lead terminals.

The large bend radius required by the older 7mm ignition leads made angled lead terminals important. There are elbows with 70°, 90°, 110°, and 135° bends, so the lead can be installed without straining the terminal end. The smaller leads may also use the angled elbows, but some harnesses are fitted with straight terminals. When it is necessary to have an angle between the lead and the terminal, a bracket is used to hold the lead with an adequate bend radius. The bracket prevents the lead being strained (see figure 7-13).

Some of the older harnesses used a phenolic or a ceramic tube with a coil spring at its end for the terminal connection inside the spark plug. These are called cigarettes. The insulation is cut back from the stranded conductor far enough to allow the wires to stick through the small hole in the end of the terminal. The ends of the wire are fanned out to provide a good electrical contact and to secure the cigarette to the wire. A cigarette is seen in figure 7-14.

Some modern harnesses use silicone rubber for the terminal connectors. In this case the terminal is crimped to the wire rather than spread-

Figure 7-14. A ceramic terminal insulator for an ignition harness.

ing the strands. The springs screw over the end of the terminal, and they may be replaced when they become damaged. The components of this type of lead are illustrated in figure 7-15.

One of the main source of radio interference from a shielded ignition harness comes from improper securing of the shielding at the ends of the leads. Figure 7-16 shows the components used to secure the shielding at the magneto end of an ignition lead. The shielding is secured by clamping it between an outer and an inner ferrule, and the two ferrules are pressed together so the shielding becomes an integral part of the lead, and it is electrically grounded at each end.

b. Installation

Installation of a complete harness for a modern installation has been made very easy and nearly foolproof. Harnesses are generally sold as a kit, which will include the ignition wires for both magnetos preassembled and cut to length for the particular installation. These kits are purchased for a certain make and model of magneto, installed on a particular make and model of engine.

Installation is as simple as removing the old harness, including most of the hardware used to secure and route the wires. Take note of the installation as you will be installing the new hardware included with the harness kit. The new harness is already installed to the proper fitting that will screw onto the distributor of the magneto. The wires are marked on the spark plug terminal ends as to which cylinder and which

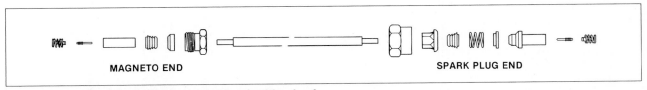

MAGNETO END   SPARK PLUG END

Figure 7-15. The typical components of an ignition lead.

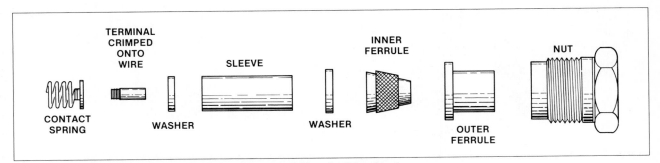

CONTACT SPRING   WASHER   SLEEVE   WASHER   INNER FERRULE   OUTER FERRULE   NUT

TERMINAL CRIMPED ONTO WIRE

Figure 7-16. The components on the magneto end of an ignition lead.

spark plug they are to be installed. This is generally in the form 1T which would indicate cylinder #1, top spark plug.

Install the new harness at the magneto and carefully lay out the wires to the proper cylinders. Secure the harness with the hardware provided, carefully routing wires so as not to touch exhaust system components, or to interfere with engine controls. Finally install the terminals in the spark plugs.

If a single spark plug lead becomes damaged, it can be replaced individually without having to replace the entire harness. The various harness manufacturers furnish detailed information describing the approved methods for installing both the spark plug terminal and the magneto terminal. These instructions must be followed to the letter, and the special tools that are required for this operation must be used.

c. Testing

When troubleshooting an ignition problem, we often blame the magnetos or spark plugs, when the problem is actually somewhere between them, in the harness. If an ignition lead has a high resistance leak to ground, the voltage may leak off to ground before it can build up high enough to jump the gap in the spark plug.

This kind of electrical leakage often occurs only when the harness is hot, making the source of trouble difficult to find with normal troubleshooting procedures.

There are a number of harness testers on the market that will show when a harness has an excessive electrical leakage. These tester place a high voltage on the harness and actually cause it to break down if there is a weak spot

in the insulation. Excessive leakage is then shown by the illumination of an indicator light

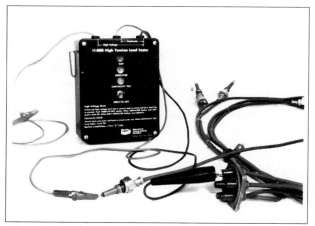

Figure 7-18. Ignition harness test unit.

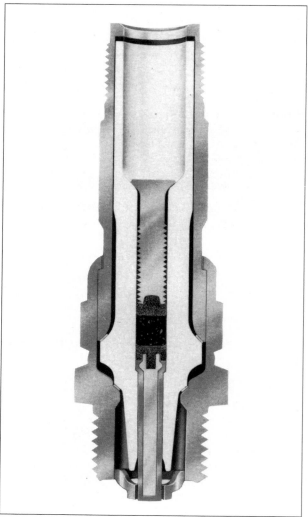

Figure 7-19. A massive-electrode shielded spark plug with 5/8-24 shielding.

Figure 7-17. Typical tools used to install the magneto-end terminals on Slick Electro ignition leads.

or, in the case of one of the more popular testers, by the extinguishing of a spark that is jumping across a visible gap. One of these testers is seen in figure 7-18.

5. Spark Plugs

The function of the spark plug in an ignition system is to conduct a short impulse of high voltage current through the wall of the combustion chamber. Inside the cylinder it provides an air gap across which this impulse can produce an electric spark to ignite the fuel/air charge. While the aircraft spark plug is simple in its construction and operation, it is nevertheless the direct or indirect cause of a great many malfunctions in aircraft engines. But spark plugs provide a great deal of trouble-free operation, considering the adverse conditions under which they operate.

Aviation spark plugs are made in two sizes of shell threads, 14mm and 18mm. With the exception of the Franklin engine, all modern aircraft engines use the 18mm spark plug.

There are two types of shielded spark plugs used in aircraft engines. The older type harness has a 5/8-24 thread on the shield (seen in figure 7-19), and the newer type, called the high altitude or all-weather spark plug. This type uses a 3/4-20 thread on the shield. As you can see in figure 7-20, the ceramic insulator in the all-weather plug does not extend to the top of the shell. This provides room for the resilient grommet on the ignition lead to form a watertight seal that prevents rain from entering the terminal end of the spark plug and causing misfiring.

a. Reach

The length of the threads on the shell classifies a spark plug according to is reach. A short reach plug has ½-inch of threads on its shell, and a long reach plug has 13/16-inch of threads.

The reason for the two different reaches is the physical construction of the cylinder heads into which the spark plug screws. When the recommended spark plug is properly installed in an aircraft engine, the bottom of the threads is flush with the inside of the cylinder head. Figure 7-21 illustrates common problems relating to spark plug reach. If a long reach plug is installed in an engine requiring one with a short reach (view A), or if the correct spark plug is installed without a gasket (view B), the end of the threads will stick out into the combustion chamber. Heat will damage the bottom threads and carbon will fill the thread grooves so that removal of the spark plug will be difficult.

If the reach is too short for the engine (view C), or if two gaskets are used (view D), the threads in the spark plug insert of the cylinder will be exposed and they will fill with carbon. When the correct spark plug is screwed into the hole, it will bottom on the carbon and the correct torque will be reached without the spark plug seating against its gasket. This loose installation will allow hot gases to leak past the threads and will damage the cylinder head.

Some cylinder head temperature gauges take their reading from a gasket-type thermocouple

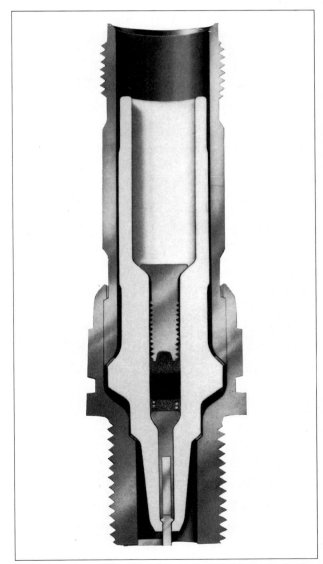

Figure 7-20. A fine-wire electrode shielded spark plug of the all-weather type.

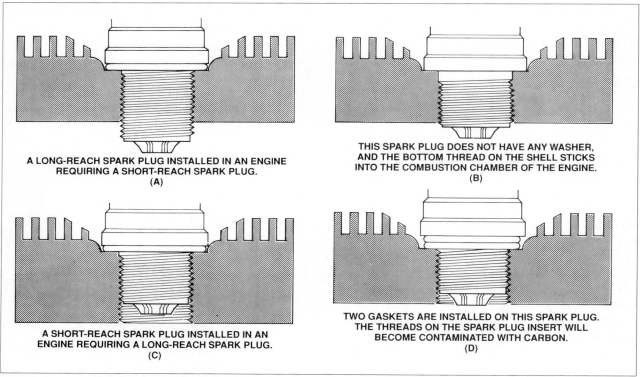

Figure 7-21. Common installation problems pertaining to spark plug reach.

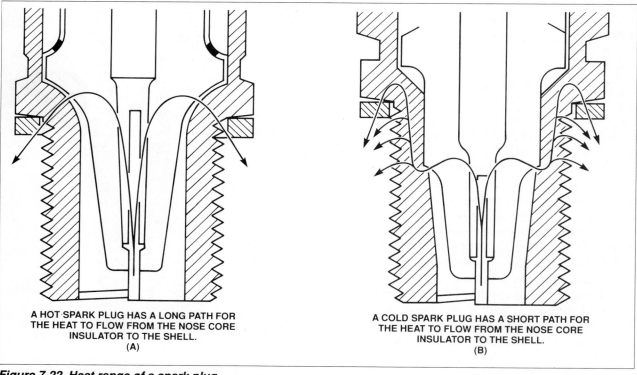

Figure 7-22. Heat range of a spark plug.

pickup under one of the spark plugs. If this type of pickup is used, be sure that no regular gasket is used with the thermocouple gasket.

If a short reach spark plug has been used in a long reach engine, or if two gaskets have been used, before the correct spark plug is installed, you should clean all of the carbon out of the bottom threads by running the correct thread cleaning tool into the hole.

b. Heat Range

The heat range of a spark plug refers to the ability of the insulator and center electrode to conduct heat away from its tip. Hot spark plugs have a long heat path and the tip operates at a high temperature. This type of plug is used in engines whose cylinder temperatures are relatively low. A cold spark plug has a short path for the heat, and are used in hot running, high compression engines.

The heat range of a spark plug has become very important in some of the smaller engines that were designed to operate on 80-octane aviation gasoline and are now, because of availability, forced to use Avgas 100. The higher octane fuel contains from four to eight times as much tetraethyl lead as the fuel they were designed to use, and this extra lead may cause spark plug fouling.

It is important when selecting replacement spark plugs for an engine to choose the correct heat range for the operating conditions. The Type Certificate Data Sheet for the engine will list all of the spark plugs that are approved for the engine. Do not install spark plugs that are not approved for a particular installation.

c. Resistor-Type Spark Plugs

Shielded ignition will reduce radio interference, but may cause accelerated wear of the spark plug electrodes. This is because the shield acts as a capacitor, storing electrical energy that is released when the spark jumps the gap in the spark plug. As this spark tries to die away, the energy that is stored in the capacitance of the ignition harness is returned, and it continues to supply energy to sustain the spark. This long duration spark is not needed since the fuel/air mixture has already been ignited, and it causes the spark plug electrodes to erode faster.

To minimize this problem, modern shielded spark plugs have a resistor of about 1,500 ohms installed inside the spark plug insulator, between the spark plug lead and the center

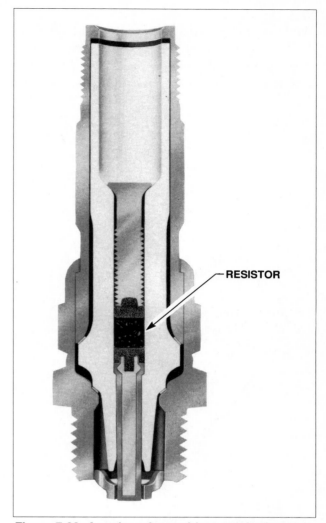

Figure 7-23. A resistor is used in a spark plug to increase the life of the electrodes.

electrode. This resistor reduced the duration of the spark while in no way affecting the production of the initial spark.

d. Servicing

Spark plugs should be removed for inspection and servicing at intervals recommended by the manufacturer. Since the rate of gap erosion varies with different operating conditions, engine models, and type of spark plug, engine malfunction traceable to faulty spark plugs may occur before the regular servicing interval is reached. Normally, in such cases, only the faulty plugs are replaced.

1) Removal

Spark plug servicing begins when the spark plug is removed from the engine. This operation should be done carefully, as it is possible to damage the insulator by improper removal of the lead terminal.

Hold the lead with one hand and loosen the terminal nut with the proper crowfoot or open end wrench. The the terminal nut is unscrewed all of the way, remove the terminal by pulling it straight out. If it is bent to one side there is danger of breaking the insulation inside the spark plug, or the terminal insulator.

Loosen the spark plug from the cylinder using a deep socket wrench. Special six-point sockets are made for removing spark plugs. The socket must be square on the hex of the spark plug, because if it is tilted, even a little, there is a very

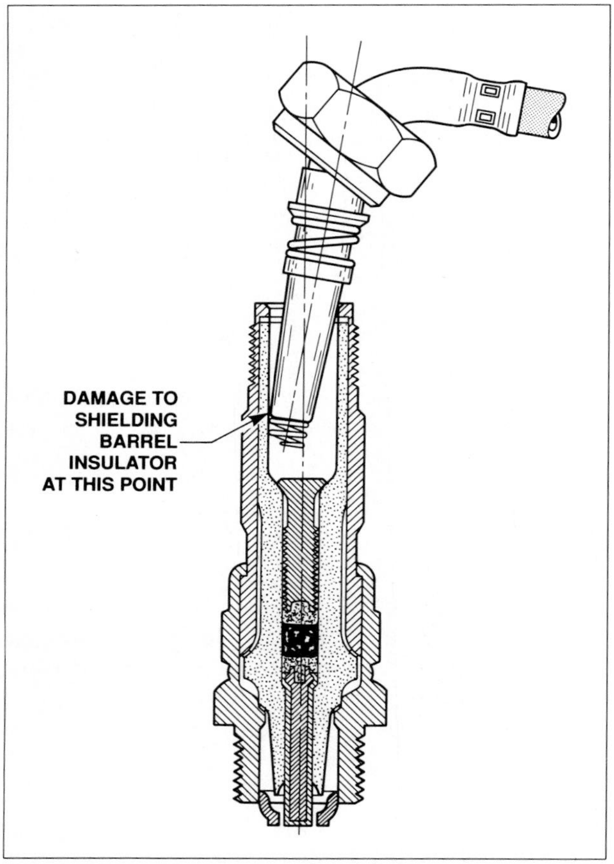

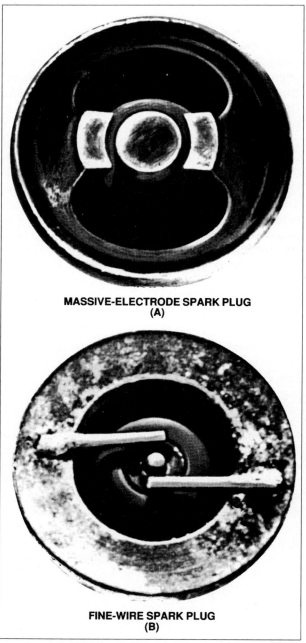

MASSIVE-ELECTRODE SPARK PLUG (A)

DAMAGE TO SHIELDING BARREL INSULATOR AT THIS POINT

Figure 7-24. Improper lead removal technique can lead to damage.

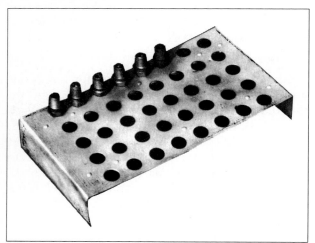

Figure 7-25. Spark plug trays allow the technician to identify where the plug had been installed.

FINE-WIRE SPARK PLUG (B)

Figure 7-26. Appearance of a spark plug that has been operating normally.

real danger of damaging the insulation inside the spark plug.

As the spark plugs are removed from the cylinders, put them in a tray with numbered holes for each spark plug. By using this type of tray, you will know the hole from which each spark plug was removed. Because the spark plugs tell a great deal about the condition of the cylinders, it is important to be able to identify their cylinder of origin. This tray also makes it possible to rotate the spark plugs when they are reinstalled, ensuring more even electrode wear.

2) Visual Inspection

Examine the spark plugs carefully. A spark plug that has been operating normally and that is not worn out, will have an appearance similar to that in figure 7-26. The insulator will be covered with a dull brown deposit and there will not be an excessive amount of build-up on the firing end cavity. If the spark plug is in this condition, it can be cleaned, regapped, tested, and reinstalled in the engine.

If the spark plug has been operating normally but the electrodes are worn to about one-half their original dimensions, the plug should be replaced. Severe erosion of both the center electrode and the ground electrode may indicated fuel metering problems. In a carbureted engine this may indicate an induction air leak, and in a fuel injected engine a partially clogged nozzle may be causing the cylinder to run excessively

Figure 7-28. Excessive lead deposits could indicate improper fuel vaporization or the use of fuel with too high a lead content.

lean. When this type of abnormal wear is found, further investigation is called for.

When the inside of the firing end cavity is filled with a hard clinker-like deposit, it indicates that the spark plug has been subject to lead fouling. All of these deposits must be removed and the spark plug cleaned, gapped, and tested before reinstallation.

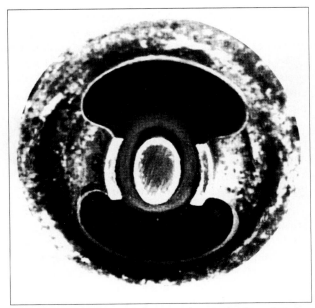

Figure 7-27. A massive-electrode spark plug showing excessive wear.

Figure 7-29. Black, sooty deposits indicate that the engine has been operating with too rich an idle mixture.

If all of the spark plugs shown this kind of fouling, you should check into the possibility of installing a set of spark plugs with a hotter heat range, if they are approved for the particular installation.

Carbon fouling shows up as a soft, black, sooty deposit in the spark plug. It is caused by operating with an excessively rich idling mixture, and from excessive ground idling. A leaking primer may also cause this condition.

Oil fouling is caused by an excessive amount of oil leaking into the cylinder, either from work or broken piston rings, or from a valve guide that has excessive clearance. This type of fouling requires a careful inspection of the engine and the damage must be repaired before the aircraft can be returned to service.

If there is a hard glaze on the nose insulator of a spark plug, there is a good possibility that there is a leak around the induction system filter and that sand has gotten into the engine. This glaze is non-conductive at low temperatures, but becomes conductive at high temperatures. Silicon glaze is very difficult to remove, and because it is non-conductive a low temperatures a spark plug may test good, and fail in the engine when it is hot.

Examine the terminal barrel insulation for cracks. If any are found the spark plug must be discarded. Check the insulation in the firing end cavity. If any cracks are found, discard the plug.

3) Cleaning

Degrease the spark plugs using safety solvent or other approved methods. After the spark plug is clean, dry it with compressed air.

Use a vibrator-type cleaning tool with the proper cutter blade to remove all of the lead

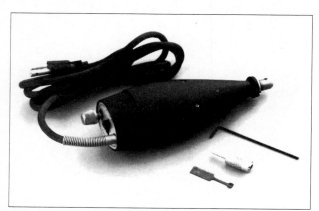

Figure 7-30. This hand-held vibrating cleaning tool makes fast work of removing lead deposits.

Figure 7-31. This combination spark plug cleaner and tester is typical of those used in aircraft maintenance shops.

deposits from the firing end cavity. Hold the plug over the cutter blades, and with the blades vibrating, lightly work the plug back and forth over the blades so that all of the lead deposits will be loosened. Do not force the plug against the cutters; just allow them to chip away at the deposits.

After all of the lead deposits are broken out of the firing end cavity, very lightly blast the cavity with an abrasive blast. Put the spark plug in the proper sized adapter in the cleaning machine, and wobble it in a circular motion while blasting. Only blast for a few seconds, as little as five seconds of abrasive blasting can erode the electrodes of a fine-wire spark plug as much as two or three hundred hours of operation.

Use only the proper medium in the spark plug cleaner, and replace it after cleaning 75 to 100 spark plugs. Follow the instructions of the manufacturer of the cleaning machine for the type of abrasive, and air pressure to be used.

After the firing end of the spark plug has been abrasive-blasted, blow it out with a blast of clean air to remove all of the cleaning medium. Carefully inspect the plug with a lighted magnifying glass to check the condition of the insulator and electrodes, and to be sure that every bit of the abrasive is out of the cavity.

Clean the terminal-end of the cavity with a cleaning tool and one of the approved insulator cleaning compounds. Make sure that all of the residue from the cleaning compound is removed using the method recommended by the manufacturer of the compound.

Clean the threads at both ends of the spark plug with a steel brush. Inspect them, and remove any damaged portions of the threads with a fine triangular file.

4) Gapping

Setting the proper gap between the center and ground electrodes of a spark plug is one of the most important parts of spark plug servicing, and you must use the proper equipment to do a satisfactory job.

For massive-electrode spark plugs, screw the plug into the proper gapping tool and carefully move the ground electrode over so it will be parallel to the center electrode and the correct distance away. This distance is measured with a feeler gauge. Be sure to position the ram of the gap adjusting tool so the ground electrode will be parallel to the center electrode, rather than angling over to it. If it is not parallel, the gap will widen as soon as a very small portion of the ground electrode wears away.

It is not recommended that a gap be widened if it has been inadvertently closed too much, as damage to the nose ceramic or to the electrode can result.

Fine-wire spark plugs are easier to gap than those using massive-electrodes. Extreme caution must be observed, however, as both platinum and iridium are extremely brittle and can be broken if they are improperly handled. Use a special gapping tool and move the ground electrodes over until they are the correct distance away from the center electrode. Do not move the ground electrodes too far, as they should never be moved back.

5) Testing

After the spark plugs have been cleaned and gapped, they should be tested. The spark plug

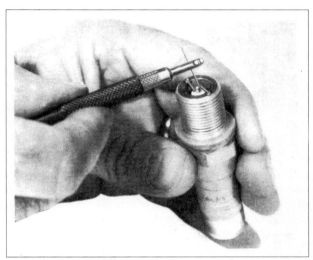

Figure 7-33. The use of the gapping tool to measure the gap in a fine-wire spark plug.

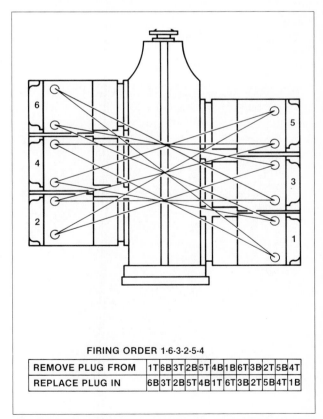

FIRING ORDER 1-6-3-2-5-4

REMOVE PLUG FROM	1T	6B	3T	2B	5T	4B	1B	6T	3B	2T	5B	4T
REPLACE PLUG IN	6B	3T	2B	5T	4B	1T	6T	3B	2T	5B	4T	1B

Figure 7-34. When replacing the spark plugs after they have been serviced, rotate them to the next cylinder in firing order, and from top to bottom.

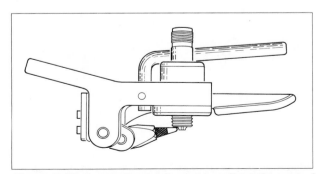

Figure 7-32. A gapping tool used to adjust the gap of massive-electrode spark plugs.

manufacturers sell equipment for this purpose. Spark plug testing is accomplished by screwing the spark plug into the tester and applying air pressure at the value specified for the spark plugs gap being used. When the test switch is depressed, a spark should jump the gap consistently.

6) Installation

The spark between the electrodes of an aircraft spark plug acts in much the same way as the arc used for welding. Metal is taken from one electrode and deposited on the other. In spark plugs, we are mainly concerned with the metal that is removed. We can extend the service life of a spark plug by minimizing the amount of erosion caused the metal transfer.

When a spark plug fires positively, the ground electrode will be worn away more severely than the center electrode, but when it fires negatively, the center electrode will be worn most severely.

Horizontally opposed engines have an even number of cylinders, and will fire the spark plugs with the same polarity each time. To even out the wear on the spark plugs, each time they are removed they should be replaced in the cylinder next in the firing order from the one where it was removed. Additionally, the spark plugs

should be swapped, bottom for top. If a plug was removed from the bottom position, it should be replaced in the top hole of the cylinder next in the firing order. This rotation pattern may be seen in figure 7-34.

Before replacing the spark plugs, the threads on the shell should be treated with an anti-seize compound. Spark plug manufacturers generally will supply the type of compound recommended. Very sparingly apply a bit of this compound to the second thread from the firing end. Never put any on the first thread, as there is a possibility that the compound may run down onto the electrodes and foul them. No anti-seize compound should be used on the barrel terminal threads.

Install the spark plugs using new copper gaskets. The spark plug should screw all of the way down to the gasket using just your fingers. If it does not, there is a possibility that there is carbon in the threads of the adapter and they should be cleaned out with the proper spark plug thread clean-out tool.

When all of the spark plugs have been screwed into the cylinder heads and all are resting on their gaskets, use a properly calibrated torque wrench and, putting a smooth and even pull on the wrench, tighten the spark plugs to the torque recommended in the aircraft service manual.

When all of the spark plugs have been installed and properly torqued, you should install the spark plug leads. Wipe the lead terminal sleeve with a clean lint-free cloth moistened (not wet) with acetone or MEK. Slip the terminal sleeve straight into the spark plug barrel and

Figure 7-35. When replacing spark plugs apply a small amount of anti-seize compound to the second thread on the shell.

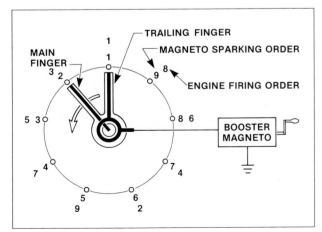

Figure 7-36. The high voltage from a booster magneto is distributed to the spark plugs through a trailing finger on the distributor rotor.

tighten the nut finger-tight, and then about one-eighth of a turn more with a properly fitting wrench.

6. Auxiliary Systems For Starting

One of the main problems with using magnetos as the source of electrical energy for aircraft engine ignition is the fact that they do not produce a hot spark when they turn at a very slow speed. This requires some form of auxiliary system to provide the spark for starting the engine. This spark must not only have a high intensity, but it should occur later than the normal spark. It should occur about the time the piston reaches top center so the maximum pressure will be built up inside the cylinder just after the piston passes over top center and starts on the way down. This will prevent the engine kicking back when it is being started. Kickbacks can damage the starter.

There are a number of systems that have been used for supplying this hot and late spark for starting. We will consider some of them, and we

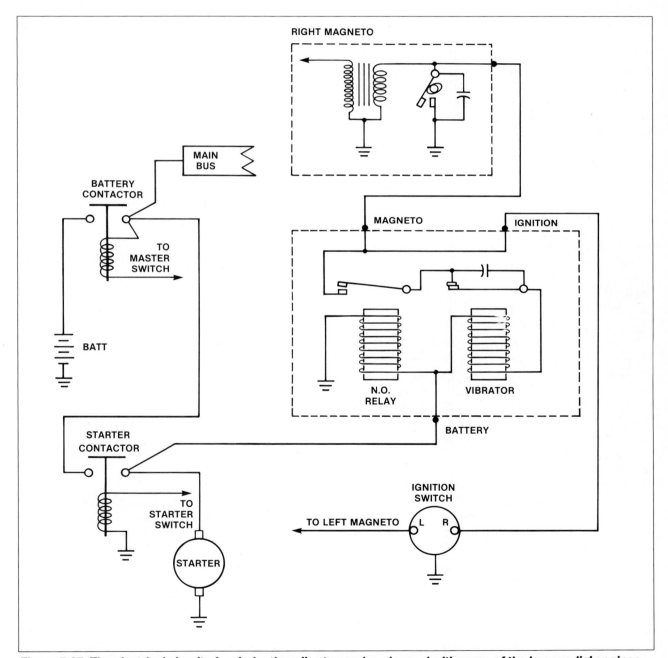

Figure 7-37. The electrical circuit of an induction vibrator such as is used with some of the large radial engines.

will discuss in some detail the two systems that are most popular today.

a. Booster Magnetos

A system that was quite popular up through World War II was the booster magneto. A separate magneto, usually mounted inside the cockpit and turned with a hand crank, was used to supply the spark for starting. Its output went into the distributor where it was directed to the proper spark plug through a trailing finger. This finger conducted the high voltage to the cylinder next in firing order to the one that was being supplied by the normal magneto. In a nine-cylinder radial engine whose firing order is 1-3-5-7-9-2-4-6-8, for example, when the magneto was in position to fire cylinder number three, the booster magneto was sending a hot spark to cylinder number one. The piston in cylinder number one had already started down, and the expanding gases caused by this late ignition gave it the needed push to allow the engine to build up enough speed for the regular magneto to take over. The booster magneto was used only until the engine started running properly.

b. Induction Vibrators

The booster magneto worked quite well for small single-engine airplanes, but larger multi-engine airplanes used a form of induction vibrator. The starter rotates the engine fast enough that kickback is not a problem, and the auxiliary spark is delivered to the spark plugs through the regular distributor finger.

A battery operated vibrator, similar to a buzzer, produces a pulsating direct current any time the engine starter switch is held in the ENGAGE position, and the ignition switch is in the right-magneto position. This pulsating DC goes into the primary coil of the magneto. As long as the breaker points are closed, this pulsating DC goes to ground and does nothing inside the magneto. But as soon as the points open, the current must pass through the primary winding of the coil to get to ground. This pulsating current in the primary coil induces a high voltage into the secondary winding and produces a hot spark at the spark plug.

c. "Shower Of Sparks" Ignition System

This is a modern version of the induction vibrator that is used with many of the horizontally opposed engines installed on modern general aviation aircraft.

This system works essentially the same as the induction vibrator system we have just described, except that the magnetos used with this system have an extra set of breaker points in parallel with the normal points. These points are called the retard points and they are timed so that they open later than the normal points.

In figure 7-38A, we have a typical electrical circuit for the Bendix "Shower of Sparks" ignition system. The right magneto used in this system is of standard construction, but the left magneto has two sets of breaker points operated by the same cam.

The advance set of points operates in exactly the same way as the points in the right magneto. They are in parallel with the capacitor and are connected to the LEFT terminal of the ignition switch, and they are in the ignition circuit at all times. The retard points are connected to the LR (left-retard) terminal of the ignition switch. This portion of the switch is normally open and is closed only when the ignition switch is held in the START position (figure 7-38B).

A starting vibrator is used with this system to produce pulsating direct current from the DC supplied by the aircraft battery. You will notice in figure 7-38B that when the ignition switch is held in the Start position, current from the battery flows through both the contacts and the coil of the starting vibrator. It then flows through the BO and the LR contacts in the ignition switch, and to ground through both the retard and the advance set of breaker points in the left magneto. As soon as the current flows in the vibrator coil, a magnetic field is produced that pulls the contacts open and interrupts the flow of current so the spring can close the contacts and current will again flow through the coil.

This continual making and breaking of the current causes pulsating direct current to flow through the magneto breaker points. The capacitor in parallel with the vibrator contacts prevents the points arcing as they interrupt the flow of current. Electrons flow into the capacitor as the contacts begin to open rather than flowing across the contacts and causing a spark. By the time the capacitor is charged to the battery voltage, the contacts are open far enough that no spark can jump the gap.

When the ignition switch is placed in the Start position, the right magneto is grounded so its

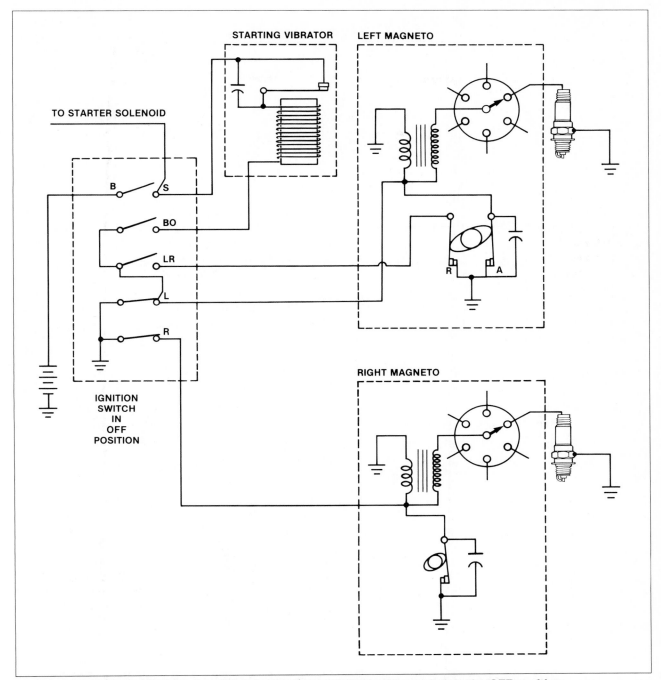

Figure 7-38A. The Bendix "Shower of Sparks" system with the ignition switch in the OFF position.

normally advanced timing cannot cause a spark that could cause the engine to kick back. The starter is energized so the engine will begin turning and the pulsating DC from the starting vibrator flows to ground through both sets of breaker points in the left magneto.

As the crankshaft turns, the advance points in the left magneto open, and now all of the pulsat-

ing DC must flow to ground through the retard points. The crankshaft continues to rotate, and about 20 or so degrees after the advance points open, the piston reaches the top of its stroke and the retard points open. Now, with both sets of points open, the pulsating DC can get to ground by flowing through the primary coil of the left magneto. When this pulsating current flows

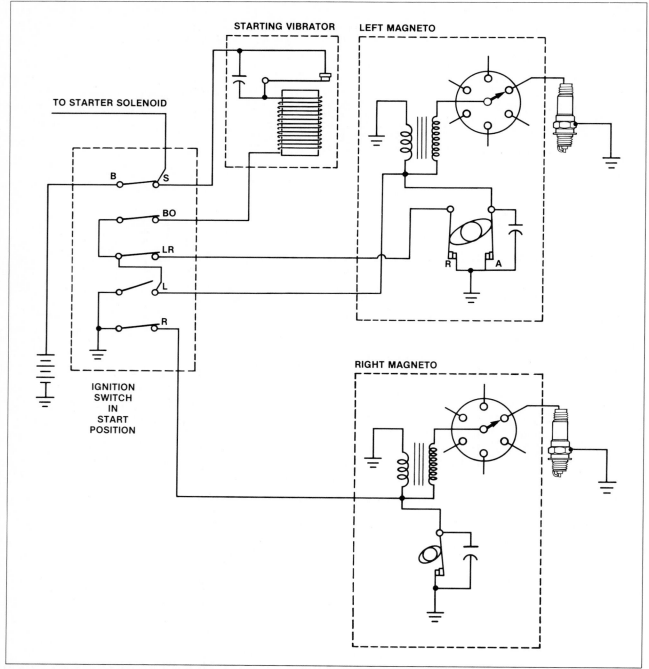

Figure 7-38B. The Bendix "Shower of Sparks" system with the ignition switch in the START position.

through the primary coil, it induces a high voltage into the secondary winding, and as long as both sets of breaker points are open, a "shower of sparks" will jump across the spark plug that is connected to the distributor terminal being supplied by the distributor rotor. This procedure continues, distributing to each cylinder

hot and late ignition until the engine is running and the ignition switch is returned to the BOTH position.

When the ignition switch is placed in the BOTH position (figure 7-38C), all of the contacts are open. The starter solenoid is de-energized, the starting vibrator gets no more current, the retard breaker points are out of the left magneto circuit, and the primary of neither magneto is grounded.

When the ignition switch is not held in the spring loaded Start position, it functions as any other ignition switch. In the OFF position, both magnetos are grounded. In the RIGHT position, the left magneto is grounded and the primary circuit of the right magneto is open. In the LEFT position, the right magneto is grounded and the primary circuit for the left magneto is open. In the BOTH position, the primary circuit for both magnetos are open.

d. Impulse Couplings

The vast majority of four and six-cylinder horizontally opposed aircraft engines use an

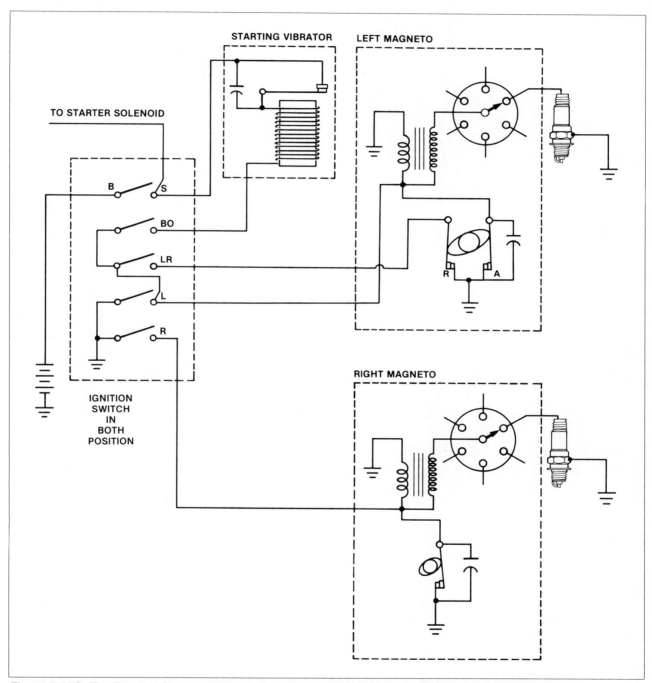

Figure 7-38C. The Bendix "Shower of Sparks" system with the ignition switch in the BOTH position.

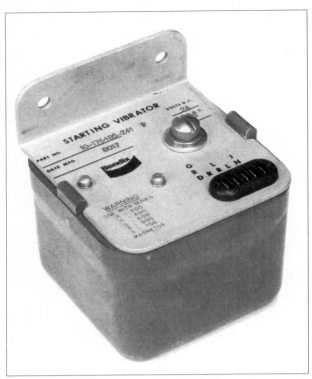

Figure 7-39. Starting vibrator, such as is used with the Bendix "Shower of Sparks" system.

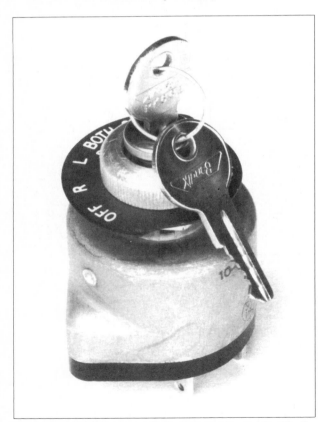

Figure 7-40. Ignition switch such as is used with the Bendix "Shower of Sparks" system.

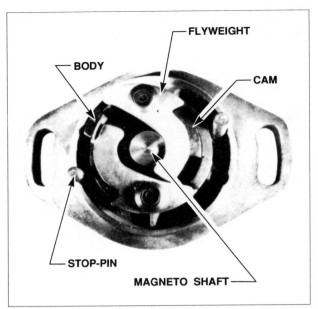

Figure 7-41. An impulse coupling that mechanically provides a hot and late spark for starting an aircraft engine.

impulse coupling on one or both magnetos to produce a hot and late spark for starting the engine.

An impulse coupling is a small spring-loaded coupling between the magneto shaft and the engine drive gear. When the engine is not running but is turned over by hand or by the starter, flyweights in the impulse coupling contact a stop pin in the magneto housing. This pin holds the magnet shaft still as the engine continues to rotate. By the time the engine has rotated far enough for the piston to reach top center, a projection on the body of the impulse coupling wedges the flyweight off of the stop pin and the spring spins the magneto shaft fast enough to produce a hot and late spark.

This action takes place for every spark the magneto produces until the engine starts running and turning fast enough for centrifugal force on the flyweights to hold them away from the stop pin. Then the impulse coupling acts as a straight coupling for the magneto.

7. Magneto Timing

Ignition timing requires that the following four conditions occur at the same instant: (1) The piston in the number one cylinder must be a prescribed number of degrees before top dead center on the compression stroke, (2) the rotating magnet of the magneto must be in the E-gap position, (3) the breaker points must be just opening and, (4) the distributor finger must be aligned with the electrode serving the number one cylinder. If any one of these conditions is out of synchronization, the ignition system is said to be "out of time".

a. Internal Timing

When we install a magneto on an engine, there are two types of timing that must be considered: the internal timing of the magneto and the timing of the magneto to the engine. Internal timing is the adjustment of the breaker points so that they will stop the flow of primary current at exactly the moment the magnetic field around the coil will produce the greatest flux change, the E-gap position.

We can position the magnet in most magnetos by allowing the magnet to find its own neutral position. It has a natural tendency to "pull in" to the neutral position, and you can easily feel when this happens. Attach a timing scale to the magneto housing and clamp a pointer over the cam end of the rotating magnet shaft. Set the pointer to the zero mark on the scale.

Rotate the magnet shaft in the normal direction of its rotation until the pointer aligns with the number of degrees for the E-gap angle specified by the manufacturer. Clamp the magnet in this position with a rotor holding tool.

Connect the magneto timing light across the breaker points until the timing light shows that the breaker points have just opened.

Figure 7-43. *The rotating magnet is held in the E-gap position with a special rotor holding tool.*

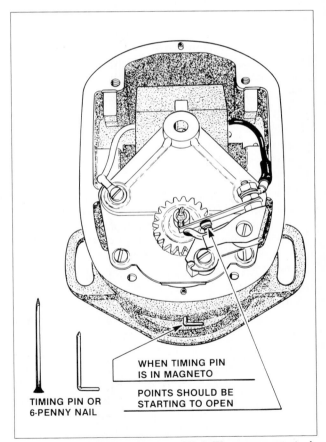

WHEN TIMING PIN IS IN MAGNETO

POINTS SHOULD BE STARTING TO OPEN

TIMING PIN OR 6-PENNY NAIL

Figure 7-44. *The magnet in a Slick Electro magneto is held in the correct position for timing by inserting a timing pin through a hole in the housing into a matching hole in the shaft of the rotating magnet.*

Figure 7-42. *Bendix magnetos are put in the correct firing position using a pointer on the rotating magnet shaft and a calibrated scale attached to the magneto housing.*

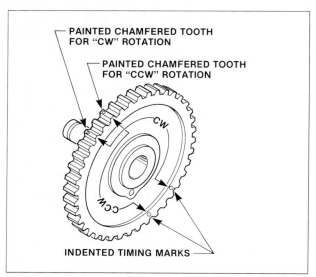

PAINTED CHAMFERED TOOTH FOR "CW" ROTATION

PAINTED CHAMFERED TOOTH FOR "CCW" ROTATION

CW

CCW

INDENTED TIMING MARKS

Figure 7-45. A magneto distributor gear showing the marks used to properly time the distributor to the magneto.

Magnetos produced by Slick Electro have a timing hole in the housing and the rotor shaft through which you can insert a timing pin, or a six penny nail. This pin holds the magnet in the correct position, a few degrees beyond the neutral position.

The position of the magnet when the points open is the most important part of internal timing, but we must also be sure that the points close when the magnet is near the full register position. This is done by making certain that the maximum point opening is within the tolerance allowed by the manufacturer.

Remove the timing pin or loosen the rotor holding tool, and rotate the magnet until the cam follower is on the highest point of the cam lobe; then measure the clearance between the breaker points. The manufacturer's specifications will list the minimum and maximum clearance. If the clearance does not fall within this tolerance when the E-gap is correctly adjusted, the breaker point assembly will need to be replaced.

The distributor gear is meshed with the drive gear by aligning the timing mark on the distributor gear with the dot or the chamfered tooth on the drive gear. The same distributor gear may be used on magnetos that rotate either clockwise or counterclockwise. To establish the direction of rotation there are two marks on the gear. Align the "CW" or "RH" mark with the marked tooth of the drive gear if the magneto shaft turns in a clockwise direction as viewed from the drive end. When the distributor gear is properly meshed

with the drive gear, a painted tooth or a mark on the face of the gear is visible in the timing hole of many of the Bendix magnetos to indicate that the distributor is in the proper position to fire number one cylinder.

b. Magneto-To-Engine Timing

Magneto to engine timing is based on having the magneto in the firing position for cylinder number one, and installing it on the engine which has been rotated until cylinder number one is in the proper position for the ignition event.

Put the engine in the position to fire cylinder number one. Locate the compression stroke by removing one of the spark plugs in cylinder number one, and with your finger over the spark plug hole, rotate the engine until you feel air blowing out the hole. This shows that the piston is moving up with both valves closed. Using a timing device (Time-Rite Indicator or timing protractor) or the timing marks on the engine case, accurately position the piston the correct number of degrees before top dead center, as specified by the engine manufacturer.

Now, with the engine in position for cylinder number one to fire, hold the magneto with its magnet in the E-gap position and the distributor ready to fire cylinder number one, and slip the magneto drive into the mounting cavity on the accessory section of the engine. Some engines drive the magnetos through rubber cushions that are held in pressed steel cushion retainers set into the magneto drive gear. In other engines the magneto drive gear meshes directly with an accessory drive gear. Whatever system the engine uses, be sure that you follow the magneto installation procedures in detail as they are provided by the manufacturer.

Secure the magneto to the engine with the appropriate nuts or clamps, but do not tighten them yet. Connect a timing light across the breaker points and, with your hand or a soft mallet, gently tap the magneto to rotate it until the timing light indicates that the breaker points are just opening. Now, you can tighten the nuts or clamps.

Install the second magneto and time it so that its breaker points open at the correct time. Most of the more modern engines have the ignition from both magnetos occur at the same time, but some engines have staggered timing.

With both magnetos installed and timing lights connected across both sets of breaker points, turn the crankshaft backwards, enough for both sets of points to close. Rotate the crankshaft in the direction of normal rotation until the timing lights indicate that both sets of breaker points have opened. If the engine uses synchronized timing, the lights should indicate both sets of points opening at the same time. If they do not, loosen the hold-down nuts or clamps of the magneto that is not properly timed and gently tap the magneto until it has rotated in its mount enough for its points to open at the correct time.

If the magneto is equipped with an impulse coupling, it must be disengaged before the magneto can be timed to the engine. When installing the magneto, trip the flyweights and hold the impulse coupling in the running position. After the magneto is installed, but before you connect the timing light, back the crankshaft up until the coupling engages, and then rotate it ahead until the impulse coupling snaps. Then carefully rotate the crankshaft backwards until the breaker points close, but not enough to re-engage the impulse coupling. Now proceed with the timing as described above.

Some of the Slick Electro magnetos must be "sparked out" to be sure that the magneto is in the proper position for installation. Hold the number one spark plug lead about 1/16-inch from the magneto frame and rotate the drive until the impulse coupling snaps and a good healthy spark jumps from the number one lead to the case. This indicates that the magneto is in the position to have just fired the spark plug in cylinder number

one. Rotate the magneto back until you can insert the timing pin in the hole in the housing and the rotating magnet shaft. Now, the magneto is in the correct position for installation.

8. Ignition System Maintenance

Each preflight run-up requires that the magnetos be checked for proper operation. This is indicated by a uniform drop in RPM when operating on either magneto independently. To perform a proper magneto check, the engine must be warmed up to the proper oil and cylinder head temperature, and the propeller must be in the low pitch, high RPM position. Advance the throttle to the recommended speed, and then move the ignition switch from the BOTH to the RIGHT position, and watch the tachometer for the amount of RPM drop. Then place the switch back in the BOTH position and allow the engine RPM to stabilize; then place the switch in the LEFT position and again watch the RPM.

The RPM drop on either single magneto should be about equal, and within the limits established by the manufacturer. When operating on a single magneto, the engine should still run smoothly and evenly.

If the RPM drop is smooth, but is more than the manufacturer recommends, there is a good possibility that the engine is operating with either a too rich or a too lean mixture. A sharp drop in the RPM is an indication of one or more fouled spark plugs, a defective ignition lead, or the magneto being out of time.

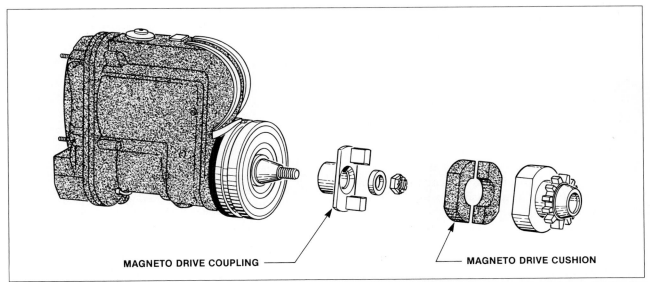

MAGNETO DRIVE COUPLING ——⌐   ⌐—— MAGNETO DRIVE CUSHION

Figure 7-46. Many modern magnetos are driven through a rubber drive cushion that is held in a slot in the accessory gear.

275

If there is no drop when making the magneto check, there is a possibility that the magneto switch is malfunctioning or there is a P-lead loose from the magneto. In either case, the magneto is "hot" when the switch is off, and this must be corrected immediately. To check for this condition, idle the engine and turn the switch to the OFF position. If the engine does not die immediately, one of the conditions listed above are present. If the engine dies, do not turn the switch back on, as this could cause a backfire and damage the engine.

When a magneto is operating, there are two components whose normal wear can shift the magneto timing. The plastic cam follower and the breaker points are subject to wear that will affect timing. Cam follower wear causes the timing to drift late, or retard the spark. Breaker point wear will cause a shift in timing to the early side, or become more advanced. One popular series of magnetos have been designed so that the wear of the cam follower and the breaker point erosion should essentially balance each other and the timing should drift only a minimum amount during the life of the magneto.

When either the breaker points or the cam follower wear enough to cause the magneto-to-engine timing to be off, the only proper way to correct this is to remove the magneto and re-time it internally. After correcting the internal timing drift caused by points or cam follower wear, be sure to check the maximum amount of breaker point opening. If both the correct position of opening and the maximum amount of opening cannot be obtained, the breaker assembly must be replaced.

The breaker points in a magneto are subject to the most difficult operating conditions in the magneto, and any failure on their part can prevent the magneto operating.

On modern magnetos the breaker assembly is a single unit and when there is a problem with the points it is the practice to replace the entire assembly. This assembly consists of the two breaker points, the cam follower with its felt lubricating pad, and the mounting bracket. The points themselves are now almost all made of tungsten.

Examine the points for condition. Normal points should have a smooth, flat surface with a dull gray, sandblasted, or frosted appearance over the area where electrical contact is made. After a time of operation some metal transfer will occur and minor irregularities will develop on the surface of the points. This is not harmful if the pits and mounds are small.

No attempt should ever be made to file or otherwise treat the surface of breaker points. If they appear oily, they can be cleaned by pulling a piece of clean craft paper through them.

The felt pad that supplies oil to the cam follower should be checked for the proper amount of oil. It should leave your fingers oily when it is squeezed. If it does not, it should be oiled according to the recommendations in the manufacturer's service information.

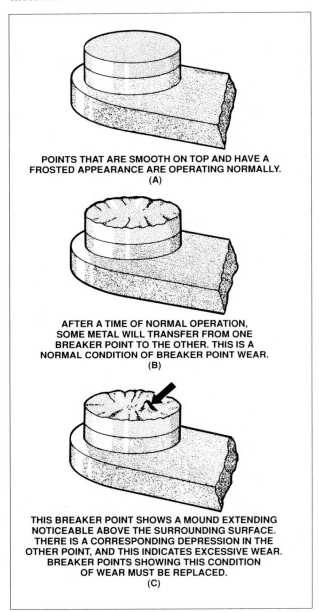

POINTS THAT ARE SMOOTH ON TOP AND HAVE A FROSTED APPEARANCE ARE OPERATING NORMALLY.
(A)

AFTER A TIME OF NORMAL OPERATION, SOME METAL WILL TRANSFER FROM ONE BREAKER POINT TO THE OTHER. THIS IS A NORMAL CONDITION OF BREAKER POINT WEAR.
(B)

THIS BREAKER POINT SHOWS A MOUND EXTENDING NOTICEABLE ABOVE THE SURROUNDING SURFACE. THERE IS A CORRESPONDING DEPRESSION IN THE OTHER POINT, AND THIS INDICATES EXCESSIVE WEAR. BREAKER POINTS SHOWING THIS CONDITION OF WEAR MUST BE REPLACED.
(C)

Figure 7-47. Conditions of the breaker points in a magneto.

Magnetos, like most engine accessories, should operate without problems during the entire service life of the engine. When the engine is overhauled, it is normal to overhaul or replace the magnetos. Magneto overhaul may be performed in most well equipped maintenance facilities, or exchange units may be obtained from the magneto manufacturer, or a repair station certified for magneto overhaul.

9. Engine Analyzer

The engine analyzer is an adaptation of the laboratory oscilloscope. It may be either a portable or a permanently mounted instrument, whose function it is to detect, locate and identify engine operating abnormalities. These may included those caused by a faulty ignition system, detonation, sticking valves, poor fuel injection, or the like. The need for a more positive means of detecting and locating operational troubles became evident with the introduction of the larger, more complex reciprocating engines used on transport-type and military aircraft.

These units are generally associated with large aircraft that are no longer a major part of the active fleet. The typical airborne analyzer unit installation weighs approximately 45.5 pounds. There are, however, some portable units that may be used on all sizes of reciprocating engines.

Figure 7-48 illustrates six typical engine analyzer patterns. Although training is required before one can accurately interpret the meaning of each signal, the configuration of the signals in the illustration shows that every malfunction presents a distinctive and recognizable picture.

B. Turbine Engine Ignition Systems

Since turbine ignition systems are operated only for a brief period during the starting cycle, they are, as a rule, more trouble-free than the typical reciprocating engine ignition systems. Modern gas turbine engine ignition systems are generally of the high-intensity, capacitor-discharge type.

The main ignition system is used primarily during ground starting and is then turned off. A secondary function of this system is to provide a stand-by protection against in-flight flameout.

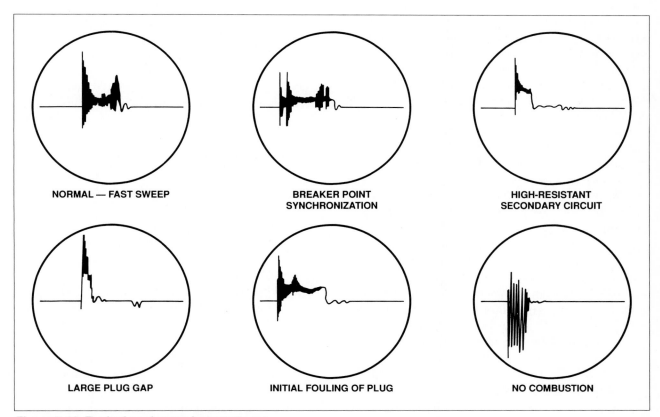

NORMAL — FAST SWEEP

BREAKER POINT SYNCHRONIZATION

HIGH-RESISTANT SECONDARY CIRCUIT

LARGE PLUG GAP

INITIAL FOULING OF PLUG

NO COMBUSTION

Figure 7-48. Typical engine analyzer patterns.

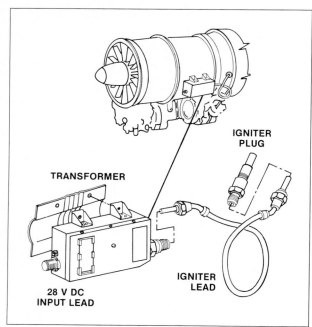

Figure 7-49. One unit of a dual ignition system for a turbine engine.

On some newer installations, a pressure sensitive device in an auto-relight system will turn on the main ignition automatically whenever engine internal pressures drop to a certain value. Another popular configuration is the continuous duty system. This system generally contains a separate, low power discharge to one or both igniter plugs which can be selected by the pilot. This system can be operated for as long as the need remains for a self-relight capability in flight.

Turbine engine ignition systems require special handling by the technician to assure safety of maintenance personnel and to prevent damage to the engine systems. These "high intensity" ignition systems are capable of a lethal charge of electricity, and their handling should be "dead serious".

(1) Ensure that the ignition switch is off before performing any maintenance on the systems. Some systems have a time requirement before the system is safe to work on.

(2) To remove an igniter plug, disconnect the transformer input lead, wait the time prescribed by the manufacturer, and then disconnect the igniter lead and ground the center electrode to the engine. The igniter lead and plugs are now safe to remove.

(3) Exercise great caution in handling damaged transformer units. Some contain radioactive material on the air gap points. This is used

to calibrate the discharge point to a preset voltage.

(4) Ensure proper disposal of unserviceable igniter plugs. The materials used in their manufacture may require special handling.

(5) Before a firing test of igniters is performed, ensure that the combustor is not fuel-wetted, to prevent fire or explosion.

(6) Do not energize the system for troubleshooting if the igniter plugs are removed. Serious overheating of the transformers can result.

Turbine engine ignition systems carry a joule rating. A joule is defined as watts multiplied by time. One joule per second equals one watt. The time factor for plug firing is very short, in the millionths of a second. Some ignition systems of the high voltage type are rated as high as 20 joules with 2,000 amps output. This power is possible from the physically small generating system because of the very short duration of the spark.

1. Types Of Turbine Engine Ignition Systems

There are two common classifications of capacitor ignition systems, the high-tension (voltage) and the low-tension (voltage).

With either the high or low tension system, two ignitor plugs are usually incorporated in the engine combustor. The typical system consists of two transformers (exciter units), two ignition leads, and two igniter plugs. The two sets may be housed separately or as one unit, with two output leads.

a. Low-Tension DC Input Systems

Figure 7-50 shows the low tension output, DC input system. Note that only one igniter plug is fired by this circuit. Two identical circuits are usually included in a single transformer unit to supply power to the two igniter plugs that most engines require.

Sequence of events:

(1) With the cockpit switch open, a permanent magnet will hold the points closed by attraction of the point armature.

(2) When the cockpit switch is closed, current flows through the battery negative side, up through the primary coil, across the points, and to the battery positive terminal.

(3) As electromagnetic force builds, the points are pulled open, stopping the current flow. This action is repeated approximately 200

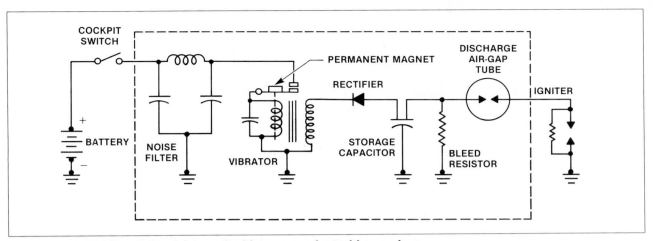

Figure 7-50. The low tension DC input ignition system for turbine engines.

times per second, producing a pulsating DC voltage. As the points open, there is a tendency for the current to jump the point gap. A capacitor across the points prevents this arcing by offering a path of least resistance for this current flow.

(4) When the current first flows through the closed points, bottom to top of the primary coil, a pulse is produced in the secondary coil. This pulse attempts to flow in the opposite direction, from the bottom of the secondary coil out of the ground, and up through the capacitor to the top side of the secondary coil. But, the rectifier blocks current flow in this direction. The current path is also blocked by the discharge tube which is an open circuit at this time.

(5) A second stronger pulse occurs when the points open and the primary field collapses into the secondary, creating a voltage of greatly increased value. Secondary current flows in the opposite direction, from the top of the coil and through the rectifier, to allow electrons to store on the top plate of the storage capacitor. The current path is completed as free electrons are pushed from the bottom plate of the capacitor, out of the ground, to the bottom side of the secondary coil. The half-wave rectifier or blocking diode is used to change secondary coil induced alternating current to direct current.

(6) After repeated cycles, a charge will build on the negative (top) side of the storage capacitor, sufficient to overcome the gap in the discharge tube. The initial current

surge ionizes the air cap (making it conductive) and allows the capacitor to discharge fully to the igniter plug.

(7) In a low voltage system, the igniter plug is referred to as a self-ionizing or shunted-gap-type plug. The firing end of the plug contains a semi-conductor material which bridges the gap between the center electrode and the ground electrode. The plug fires when the current flows from the storage capacitor through the center electrode, the semi-conductor, the outer casing, then back to the positive plate of the capacitor. As the current flows initially through the semi-conductor, heat builds up creating an increased resistance to current flow. The air gap also becomes heated sufficiently to ionize and the current takes the path of least resistance across the ionized gap, fully discharging the capacitor and creating a high energy capacitive discharge spark.

(8) The bleed resistor is present in the circuit to allow the capacitor to bleed off its charge when the system is de-energized. It also protects the circuit from overheating if power is turned on when no igniter plug is installed.

b. High Tension AC Input Systems

A high tension AC input ignition system for turbine engines is seen in figure 7-51. This system uses 115 volt alternating current, operating at 400 hertz applied to the primary side of the transformer. Because the system uses AC, the vibrator is not required. This eliminates the problems associated with the use of vibrating contacts.

7-31

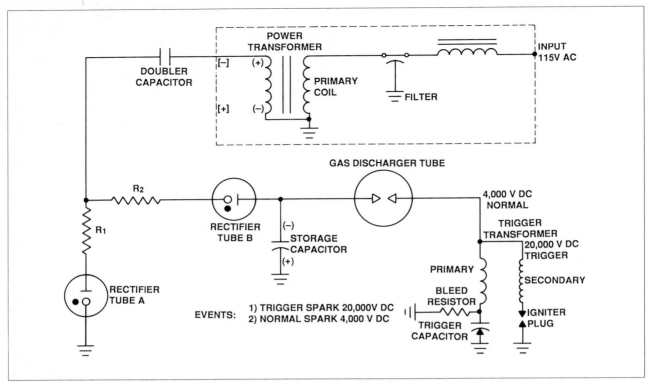

Figure 7-51. A high tension AC input ignition system used for turbine engines.

Sequence of events:

(1) During the first half cycle, the primary coil produces approximately 2,000 volts in the secondary coil and current flows from the bottom (-) side of the coil and out at the ground. Current then flows into the ground at rectifier tube "A" through the resistor (R_1), through the doubler capacitor, and back to the top (+) side of the secondary coil. This leaves the left side of the doubler capacitor charged at 2,000 volts. Rectifier tube "B" blocks any other current path during this half cycle.

(2) During the second half cycle, the primary coil produces another 2,000 volts in the secondary coil. The current flows from the top side of the coil and charges the right side of the doubler capacitor to 2,000 volts. The doubler now has a total charge of 4,000 volts and current flows through resistor (R_2), through rectifier tube B, through the storage capacitor, out of the ground, and returning to the bottom (+) side of the secondary coil. Rectifier tube "A" blocks current flow from the doubler capacitor and R_1 to ground ensuring current flow to the storage capacitor.

(3) Repeated pulses charge the storage capacitor to a point where the air gap in the discharge tube ionizes. When this occurs, current flows through the trigger transformer primary coil, the trigger capacitor, the ground, and back to the bottom side (+) of the storage capacitor.

This action induces a voltage into the secondary coil of the trigger transformer, at approximately 20,000 volts, sufficient to ionize the igniter plug air gap and complete a path back to the storage capacitor. The trigger spark which occurs by action of the trigger transformer and capacitor, creates a low resistance path and allows both the trigger capacitor and the storage capacitor to fully discharge at the igniter plug, creating a second high intensity spark.

The high tension spark created by this type system is needed to blast carbon deposits from the igniter plug electrodes, also to vaporize fuel globules at the firing end sufficiently to ignite the fuel/air mixture in the combustor either on the ground or in flight.

2. Igniter Plugs

Igniter plugs for gas turbine engines differ considerably from the spark plugs used on

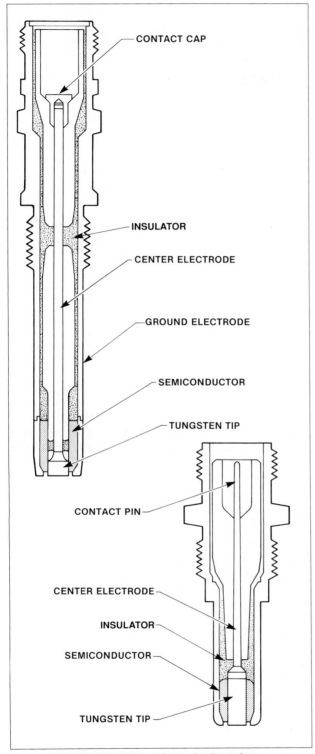

Figure 7-52. Typical low voltage igniter plugs.

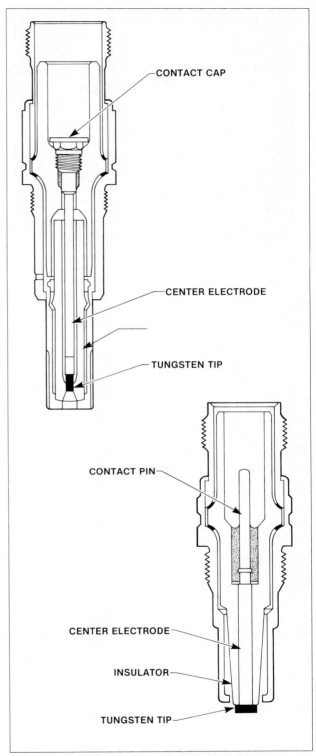

Figure 7-53. Typical high voltage igniter plugs.

reciprocating engines. The gap at the igniter plug tip is much wider and the electrode is designed to withstand a much higher intensity spark. The igniter plug is also less susceptible to fouling be-

cause the high energy spark removes carbon and other deposits each time the spark plug fires. The construction material is also different, in that the turbine igniter is made of a very high

281

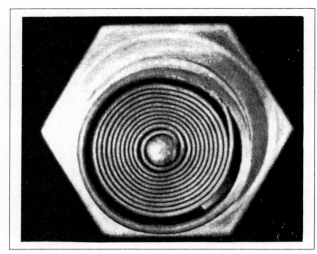

Figure 7-54. Glow-plug type turbine igniter.

quality, nickel-chromium alloy for its corrosion resistance and low coefficient of heat expansion. For this reason, it is many times more expensive than a spark plug.

a. Types Of Igniter Plugs

Many varieties of igniter plugs are available, but usually only one will suit the needs of a particular engine. The igniter plug tip must protrude properly into the combustor in each installation. On long ducted fan engines it must be long enough to mount on the outer case, pass through the fan duct, and penetrate the combustor.

Igniters for high and low tension systems are not interchangeable and care should be taken to be sure the manufacturer's recommended igniter plug is used.

Some smaller engines incorporate a glow plug type igniter rather than a spark igniter. The glow plug is a resistance coil of very high heat value and is said to be designed for extremely low temperature starting. A typical system is seen in some models of the Pratt & Whitney PT6 engine.

The glow plug is supplied with approximately 2,000 volts DC to turn the coil yellow hot. The coil is very similar in appearance to an automobile cigarette lighter. Air directed up through the coil mixes with fuel dipping from the main fuel nozzle. This is designed to occur when the main nozzle is not completely atomizing its discharge during engine start. The influence of the airflow on the dripping fuel acts to create a hot streak or torch-type ignition. After the fuel is terminated, the air source serves to cool the igniter coil all the time the engine is being operated.

b. Cleaning And Servicing Igniters

High voltage igniter plugs may usually be cleaned on the outer case with a soft brush and solvent and the ceramic portion cleaned with a felt swab and solvent. The electrode tip may be cleaned with solvent, but abrasive grit cleaning is never permitted. After cleaning, dry air is used to

1. NO IGNITER SPARK WITH THE SYSTEM TURNED ON		
POSSIBLE CAUSE	CHECK FOR	REMEDY
IGNITION RELAY	CORRECT POWER INPUT TO TRANSFORMER UNIT	CORRECT RELAY PROBLEMS, REFER TO STARTER-GENERATOR CIRCUIT
TRANSFORMER UNIT	CORRECT POWER OUTPUT, OBSERVING IGNITION SYSTEM CAUTIONS	REPLACE TRANSFORMER UNIT
HIGH TENSION LEAD	CONTINUITY OR HIGH RESISTANCE SHORTS WITH OHMMETER AND MEGER-CHECK UNIT	REPLACE LEAD
IGNITER PLUG	1. CRACKED INSULATOR OR DAMAGED SEMICONDUCTOR	REPLACE PLUG
	2. HOT ELECTRODE EROSION	REPLACE PLUG
2. LONG INTERVAL BETWEEN SPARKS		
POSSIBLE CAUSE	CHECK FOR	REMEDY
POWER SUPPLY	WEAK BATTERY	RECHARGE BATTERY
3. WEAK SPARK		
POSSIBLE CAUSE	CHECK FOR	REMEDY
IGNITER PLUG	CRACKED CERAMIC INSULATION	REPLACE PLUG

Figure 7-55. Troubleshooting turbine engine ignition systems.

blow off the remaining solvent and the plug is ready for inspection.

Inspection of this type plug generally consists of a visual inspection and a measurement check with a technician's scale or suitable depth micrometer. After the visual check an operational check is performed. The operational check should follow the guidelines established by the engine manufacturer.

The self-ionizing, or shunted-gap igniter plugs used with low tension systems are generally cleaned only on their outer casing. The semiconductor material at the firing end is easily damaged and manufacturers seldom permit any type of cleaning, regardless of the carbon buildup.

Measurement checks are not usually accomplished on these plugs, as quite often the semiconductor material consists of only a very thin coating over a ceramic base material. Operational checks are similar to those used with high tension systems.

If glow plug heater coils have carbon buildup which appears to fuse the coils together, the coil end can be immersed in carbon remover to soften the deposit. Brushing with a soft nylon brush or fiber brush then generally removes the softened carbon. Finally, the coil is rinsed in warm water and blown dry with an air blast. Operational checks of glow plugs will be specified by the engine manufacturer.

3. Ignition System Inspection And Maintenance

Maintenance of the typical turbine engine ignition system consists primarily of inspection, test, troubleshooting, removal and installation.

Logical troubleshooting procedures should be used when hunting for a problem in a turbine engine ignition system. The chart in figure 7-55 outlines the procedures to use when the system produces no spark, the spark is weak, or when there is too long an interval between sparks.

C. Powerplant Electrical Installation

The satisfactory performance of any modern aircraft depends to a very great degree on the continuing reliability of electrical systems and subsystems. Improperly or carelessly installed or maintained wiring can be a source of both immediate and potential danger. The continued proper performance of electrical systems depends upon the knowledge and technique of the technician who installs, inspects, and maintains the electrical wire and cable of the electrical systems.

In this section we are concerned with the installation of the wiring and circuit components that are primarily used in the electrical systems that relate directly to the powerplant portion of a modern aircraft.

The electrical installation in an aircraft consists of a source of electrical energy and a load to use the energy. Between the source and the load, there must be conductors of sufficient size to carry all of the current without overheating or without producing an excessive voltage drop. There must also be adequate circuit protection devices to assure that the proper amount of current is available at the load when it is needed and to assure that excessive current cannot flow in the circuit. Excessive current can damage electrical equipment and produce enough heat to create a fire hazard.

1. Wire

When the wire for an electrical system is chosen, there are several factors that must be considered:

(1) The wire must be of sufficient size that the current flowing through it will not produce enough heat to damage the insulation.

(2) The wire must be large enough that its resistance will not cause the current flowing through it to produce a voltage drop which will lower the voltage at the load beyond the allowable limit.

(3) The wire and its terminals must be sufficiently strong and installed in such a way that vibrations will not cause the wire to break.

(4) The insulation on the wire must have sufficient electrical strength to prevent electrical leakage, and it must be strong enough mechanically that it is not likely to be damaged by abrasion.

(5) The wire must be as light in weight as is consistent with the other requirements.

a. Wire Type

Because of the vibration inherent in all aircraft, the wiring between the components must be of the stranded type, but the wire used inside electrical and electronic components where vibration is no problem is usually solid. Installation and servicing of this type of wiring is done by electronic specialists and is not considered to be part of the electrical system servicing done by A&P technicians.

The majority of the wire used in an aircraft electrical system is stranded copper wire that meets specifications MIL-W-5086. This wire is made up of strands of annealed copper that are covered with a very thin coating of tin to prevent the copper oxidizing. The wire is covered with an insulation of polyvinylchloride or nylon and, in some instances, with a glass cloth braid. The insulation on most of the MIL-W-5086 wire will withstand 600 volts, but one type of this wire (Type IV) has an insulation that has a dielectric strength of 3,000 volts.

MIL-W-5086 wire is used in aircraft installations in sizes from AN-0000, called four aught, to AN-22. Smaller size wire is available and is used in some electronic equipment, but because of its low physical strength it is not used in airframe or powerplant wiring installations.

When large amounts of electrical current must be carried for long distances in an aircraft, a weight saving is accomplished by using MIL-W-7072 aluminum wire instead of copper. Aluminum wire can carry about two thirds as much current as the same size copper, and it weighs only about one third as much.

Aluminum wire has two basic limitations. It requires special techniques for installing the terminals, and it is easily crystallized by vibration; so breakage is a problem. But, when aluminum wire is properly terminated and protected from vibration, it makes an effective weight-saving installation.

The insulation used on MIL-W-7072 aluminum wire is the same as that used on MIL-W-5086 copper wire.

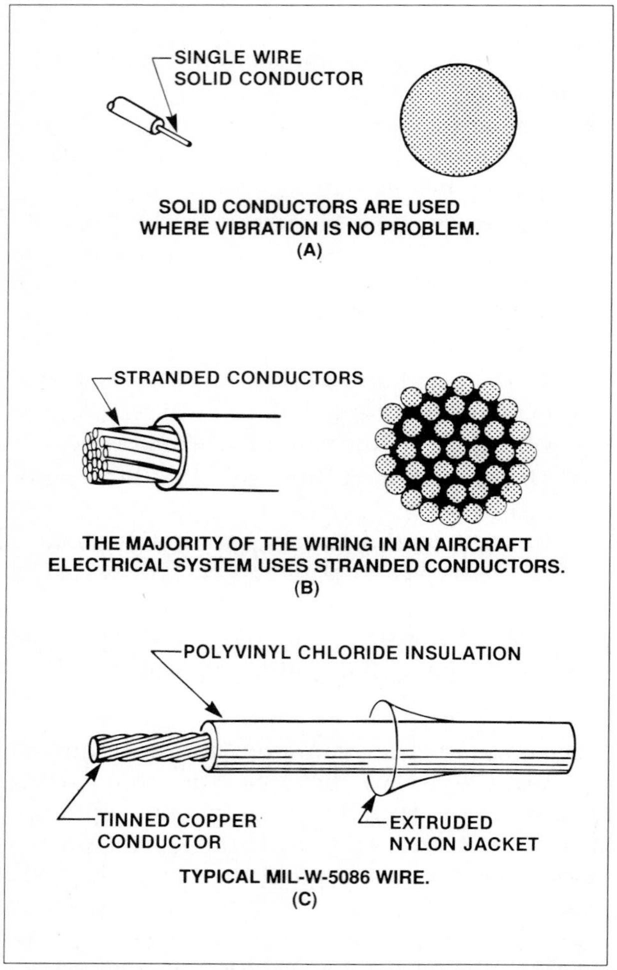

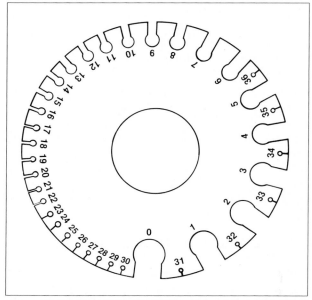

Figure 7-57. The American Wire Gage is used to indicate the size of electrical wire. The width of the parallel slot is the diameter of the wire.

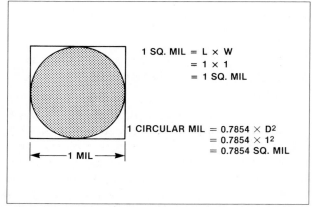

Figure 7-58. The circular mil is used to measure the area of a round conductor.

Figure 7-56. Typical wire used for aircraft electrical system installation.

A handy rule of thumb for replacing copper wire with aluminum wire is to always use an aluminum wire that is two wire gauge numbers larger than the copper wire it is replacing. Remember when using this rule that the larger the number, the smaller the wire. If we want to replace a piece of four-gauge copper wire with aluminum, we must use at least a two-gauge wire.

Because of the small amount of weight that can be saved with the smaller size wires, and because of the danger of the wire breaking from vibration, aluminum wire of sizes smaller than six-gauge is not approved for use in aircraft electrical systems.

b. Wire Size

Wire size is measured according to the American Wire Gage (AWG) system, with the smaller numbers used to identify the larger wire. A wire gauge, similar to the one in figure 7-57, can be used to measure the size of solid conductors. The width of the slot is the size of the wire, and the circular cutout at the end of the slot is merely for clearance, not for measuring.

The amount of current a wire can carry is determined by its cross-sectional area, and rather than square units being used for this measurement, the circular mil is used to express the conductor area: One circular mil is the area of a conductor whose diameter is one mil, or one thousandth of an inch.

The area of a circle is 0.7854 times the square of its diameter so, as we see in figure 7-58, the area of a round conductor in circular mils is 0.7854 times its area in square mils. A 20-gauge wire whose diameter is 32 mils has a area of 1,024 circular mils, but this area is only 804.2 square mils.

Diameter	=0.032 inch, or 32 mils
Area	=1,024 circular mils
	= 804.2 square mils

NOMINAL SYSTEM VOLTAGE	ALLOWABLE VOLTAGE DROP VOLTS	
	CONTINUOUS OPERATION	INTERMITTENT OPERATION
14	0.5	1.0
28	1.0	2.0
115	4.0	8.0
200	7.0	14.0

Figure 7-59. The allowable voltage drops for typical aircraft electrical systems.

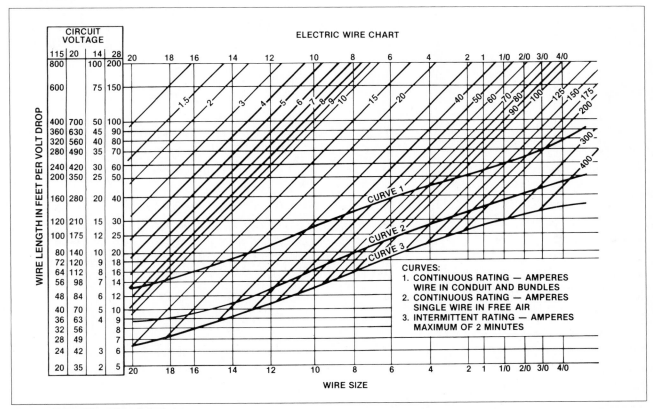

Figure 7-60. Electric wire chart.

When we replace a wire in an aircraft electrical system, we must use the same size and type of wire as was originally used; but if we are making an original installation, we must choose a wire of a size that will carry the current without overheating and will not produce more than the allowable voltage drop for the length of the wire used and for the current it carries.

In figure 7-59, we have the allowable voltage drop for both intermittent and continuous operation in 14, 28, 115, and 200-volt systems. If we install a cowl flap motor in a 28-volt system, we must use a wire large enough that it will not cause more than a two-volt drop between the bus and the motor. We are allowed two volts because a cowl flap motor is an intermittent load. If we were installing a fuel boost pump that operates continually, we would be allowed only a one-volt drop.

In the wire chart in figure 7-60, we can find the wire size we must use when we know whether the load is continuous or intermittent, when we know the voltage of the system and the length of the wire, and when we know if the wire is routed by itself or if it is in a bundle with other wires. Let's take the example of a 28-volt boost pump motor that draws six amps continuously: The wire must be 40 feet long, and we will run it in a bundle with other wires.

To find the size wire we need, first locate the diagonal line that represents six amps and follow it down until it intercepts the horizontal line representing 40 feet in the 28-volt column. This intersection takes place between the 16 and 14-gauge wire size vertical lines. We should use the larger of the two wires, and so we will choose a 14-gauge wire. Notice that this intersection is above all three of the condition curves, which means that we can safely run six amps of current in this size wire without it overheating, and there will be only a one-volt drop in the 40 feet of wire.

You will notice that there are four columns of figures for the circuit voltages. This is in keeping with the information we have in figure 7-59. A 28-volt system is allowed a one-volt drop, a 14-gauge system can only have a half-volt drop, and the length of wire for the allowable voltage drop is only one half of that allowed for a 28-volt system. A 115-volt system is allowed a four-volt

WIRE SIZE SPECIFICATION MIL-W-5086	SINGLE WIRE IN FREE AIR MAXIMUM AMPERES	WIRE IN CONDUIT OR BUNDLED MAXIMUM AMPERES	MAXIMUM RESISTANCE OHMS/1000 FT. (20°C)	NOMINAL CONDUCTOR AREA CIRCULAR MILLS	FINISHED WIRE WEIGHT POUNDS PER 1,000 FEET
AN—20	11	7.5	10.25	1,119	5.6
AN—18	16	10	6.44	1,779	8.4
AN—16	22	13	4.76	2,409	10.8
AN—14	32	17	2.99	3,830	17.1
AN—12	41	23	1.88	6,088	25.0
AN—10	55	33	1.10	10,443	42.7
AN—8	73	46	.70	16,864	69.2
AN—6	101	60	.436	26,813	102.7
AN—4	135	80	.274	42,613	162.5
AN—2	181	100	.179	66,832	247.6
AN—1	211	125	.146	81,807	
AN—0	245	150	.114	104,118	382
AN—00	283	175	.090	133,665	482
AN—000	328	200	.072	167,332	620
AN—0000	380	225	.057	211,954	770

Figure 7-61. Current-carrying capacity of copper electrical wire.

WIRE SIZE SPECIFICATION MIL-W-7072	SINGLE WIRE IN FREE AIR MAXIMUM AMPERES	WIRE IN CONDUIT OR BUNDLED MAXIMUM AMPERES	MAXIMUM RESISTANCE OHMS/1000 FT. (20°C)	NOMINAL CONDUCTORAREA CIRCULAR MILLS	FINISHED WIRE WEIGHT POUNDS PER 1,000 FEET
AL—6	83	50	0.641	28,280	....
AL—4	108	66	.427	42,420	....
AL—2	152	90	.268	67,872	....
AL—0	202	123	.169	107,464	166
AL—00	235	145	.133	138,168	204
AL—000	266	162	.109	168,872	250
AL—0000	303	190	.085	214,928	303

Figure 7-62. Current-carrying capacity of aluminum electrical wire.

drop, so the length of wire is four times that in the 28-volt column. And in a 200-volt system we are allowed seven volts, so a wire 280 feet long would be needed before the voltage drop caused by six amps of current would be excessive for this system.

The three condition curves allow us to determine whether or not we can run the wire in a bundle or if it must be run by itself. If the intersection of the diagonal current line and the vertical line representing the wire gauge falls above curve 1, the wire is satisfactory from the current standpoint to be routed in a bundle, even when the current flows through it continuously. For example, a 14-gauge wire can carry up to 17 amps continuously in a bundle.

Between 17 and 29 amps can be carried in a 14-gauge wire continuously if the wire is routed by itself in free air so that the heat can be carried away from it. Between 29 and 32 amps can be carried in a 14-gauge wire if the flow is intermittent, with a maximum duration of flow of two minutes. A 14-gauge wire should not carry more than 32 amps of current under any conditions, as this much current will overheat it.

The information we find in this chart is verified in the table of figure 7-61. Figure 7-62 gives us the same information on the current carrying capability, resistance, area, and weight of MIL W-7072 aluminum wire.

c. Wire Marking

There are so many wires in a modern airplane that troubleshooting an electrical system malfunction would be greatly hindered if some way were not used to identify each of the wires.

Many of the aircraft manufacturers have their own system for identifying wires, but one stand-

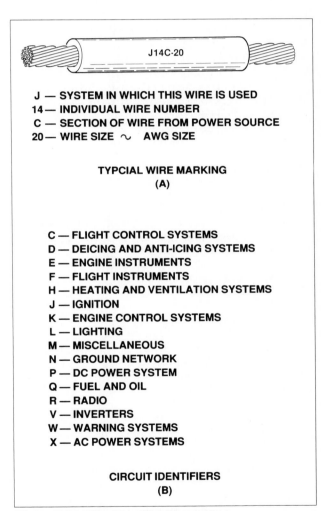

J — SYSTEM IN WHICH THIS WIRE IS USED
14 — INDIVIDUAL WIRE NUMBER
C — SECTION OF WIRE FROM POWER SOURCE
20 — WIRE SIZE ∿ AWG SIZE

TYPCIAL WIRE MARKING
(A)

C — FLIGHT CONTROL SYSTEMS
D — DEICING AND ANTI-ICING SYSTEMS
E — ENGINE INSTRUMENTS
F — FLIGHT INSTRUMENTS
H — HEATING AND VENTILATION SYSTEMS
J — IGNITION
K — ENGINE CONTROL SYSTEMS
L — LIGHTING
M — MISCELLANEOUS
N — GROUND NETWORK
P — DC POWER SYSTEM
Q — FUEL AND OIL
R — RADIO
V — INVERTERS
W — WARNING SYSTEMS
X — AC POWER SYSTEMS

CIRCUIT IDENTIFIERS
(B)

Figure 7-63. Wire identification system.

ard identification system is shown in the example in figure 7-63. The wire is stamped about every 12 to 15 inches along its length with the number J14C-20. From this identification we know that this wire is in the magneto circuit (the letter J tells us this). It is wire number 14 in this system, and it is the third individual segment of this wire from the magneto. We know this from the letter C. The -20 indicates that it is a 20-gauge wire. If the wire went to ground, it would have the letter N at the end of the identification.

```
A — ARMAMENT                              L — LIGHTING
B — PHOTOGRAPHIC                              LA—CABIN
C — CONTROL SURFACE                           LB—INSTRUMENT
    CA — AUTOMATIC PILOT                      LC—LANDING
    CC — WING FLAPS                           LD—NAVIGATION
    CD — ELEVATOR TRIM                        LE—TAXI
D — INSTRUMENT (OTHER THAN FLIGHT OR          LF—ROTATING BEACON
    ENGINE INSTRUMENT)                        LG—RADIO
    DA — AMMETER                              LH—DEICE
    DB — FLAP POSITION INDICATOR              LJ—FUEL SELECTOR
    DC — CLOCK                                LK—TAIL FLOODLIGHT
    DD — VOLTMETER                        M — MISCELLANEOUS
    DE — OUTSIDE AIR TEMPERATURE              MA—COWL FLAPS
    DF — FLIGHT HOUR METER                    MB—ELECTRICALLY OPERATED SEATS
E — ENGINE INSTRUMENT                         MC—SMOKE GENERATOR
    EA — CARBURETOR AIR TEMPERATURE           MD—SPRAY EQUIPMENT
    EB — FUEL QUANTITY GAUGE & TRANSMITTER    ME—CABIN PRESSURIZATION EQUIPMENT
    EC — CYLINDER HEAD TEMPERATURE            MF—CHEM O₂ — INDICATOR
    ED — OIL PRESSURE                     P — DC POWER
    EE — OIL TEMPERATURE                      PA—POWER CIRCUIT
    EF — FUEL PRESSURE                        PB—GENERATOR CIRCUITS
    EG — TACHOMETER                           PC—EXTERNAL POWER SOURCE
    EH — TORQUE INDICATOR                 Q — FUEL & OIL
    EJ — INSTRUMENT CLUSTER                   QA—AUXILIARY FUEL PUMP
F — FLIGHT INSTRUMENT                         QB—OIL DILUTION
    FA — BANK AND TURN                        QC—FENGINE PRI MER
    FB — PITOT STATIC TUBE HEATER & STALL     QD—MAIN FUEL PUMPS
         WARNING HEATER                       QE—FUEL   VALVES
    FC — STALL WARNING                    R — RADIO (NAVIGATION & COMMUNICATIONS)
    FD — SPEED CONTROL SYSTEM                 RA—INSTRUMENT LANDING
    FE — INDICATOR LIGHTS                     RB—COMMAND
G — LANDING GEAR                              RC—RADIO DIRECTION FIND
    GA—ACTUATOR                               RD—VHF
    GB—RETRACTION                             RE—HOMING
    GC—WARNING DEVICE (HORN)                  RF—MARKER BEACON
    GD—LIGHT SWITCHES                         RG—NAVIGATIONI
    GE—INDICATOR LIGHTS                       RH—HIHG FREQUENCY
H — HEATING, VENTILATING & DEICING            RJ—INTERPHONE
    HA — ANTI-ICING                           RK—UHF
    HB — CABIN HEATER                         RL—LOW FREQUENCY
    HC — CIGAR LIGHTER                        RM—FREQUENCY MODULATION
    HD — DEICING                              RP—AUDIO SYSTEM & AUDIO AMPLIFIER
    HE — AIR CONDITIONERS                     RR—DISTANCE MEASURING EQUIPMENT (DME)
    HF — CABIN VENTILATION                    RS—AIRBORNE PUBLIC ADDRESS SYSTEM
J — IGNITION                              S — RADAR
    JA — MAGNETO                          U — MISCELLANEOUS ELECTRONIC
K — ENGINE CONTROL                            UA—IDENTIFICATION — FRIEND OR FOE
    KA — STARTER CONTROL                  W — WARNING & EMERGENCY
    KB — PROPELLER SYNCHRONIZER               WA—FLARE RELEASE
                                              WB—CHIP DETECTOR
                                              WC—FIRE DETECTION SYSTEM
                                          X — AC POWER
```

Figure 7-64. Circuit function and specific circuit code letter identification for electric wiring.

A two-letter identification code is used by one popular aircraft manufacturer, and this code is shown in figure 7-64. A wire in the ignition circuit would have the two-letter identification JA.

Wire bundles can be marked by using pressure sensitive tape around the bundle with the number marked on it or with a piece of polyvinylchloride sleeving with the bundle number stamped on it. This sleeving is tied around the bundle. Bundles are marked near the points at which they enter and leave a compartment.

2. Wiring Installation

There are two basic types of wiring installation used in aircraft: open wiring and wiring in a conduit. In open wiring, the wires are installed without any type of protective covering. It is fast and easy to install and it makes servicing of the wiring simple, but it has a definite disadvantage in wheel wells and engine nacelles as it provides no protection from abrasion or from heat.

Polyvinylchloride tubing, which is usually called spaghetti, is often used to enclose a bundle of wires to protect them from abrasion and moisture. This is not considered as conduit and it must be used with caution where the wires are subjected to a great deal of hard usage.

Wire bundles, whether run in the open or inside tubing, should be tied together every three to four inches with a double wrap of waxed linen or nylon lacing cord, secured with a clove hitch and a square knot. The bundles should be securely clamped to the structure, using clamps lined with a non-metallic cushion.

The bundles should be supported from the structure of the aircraft and not from any fluid line. If a wire bundle is to run parallel to any line carrying a liquid fluid such as fuel, oil, or hydraulic fluid, the wire bundle should be routed above the fluid line so that a leak will not drip fluid onto the wires. If it is at all possible, the wires should be at least six inches above the fluid lines.

Wire bundles should not be run any closer than three inches to any control cable, and if there is any possibility that the wire could ever touch the cable, some form of mechanical guard must be installed that will keep the wire bundle and the cable separated.

When the wire bundles are to pass through a hole in a bulkhead in the aircraft structure, the bundle should be clamped to a bracket to hold it centered in the hole. If there is less than ¼-inch

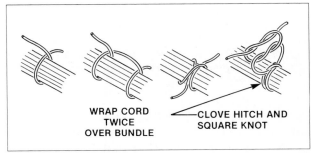

WRAP CORD TWICE OVER BUNDLE — CLOVE HITCH AND SQUARE KNOT

Figure 7-66. Method of making a spot tie on an electrical wire bundle.

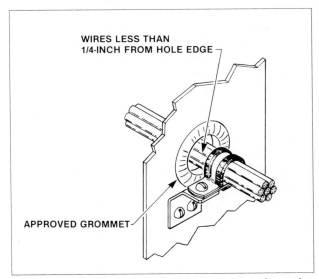

WIRES LESS THAN 1/4-INCH FROM HOLE EDGE

APPROVED GROMMET

Figure 7-67. When wire bundles must pass through a bulkhead or frame, they must be supported with a cushion clamp, and a grommet must be installed in the hole to protect the wires from chafing.

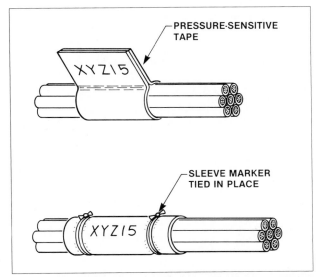

PRESSURE-SENSITIVE TAPE

XYZ15

SLEEVE MARKER TIED IN PLACE

XYZ15

Figure 7-65. Methods of identifying wire bundles in an aircraft electrical installation.

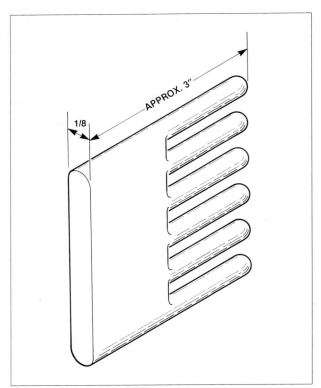

Figure 7-68. A plastic comb such as this is a handy tool for keeping the wires straight when making up a wire bundle.

between the wire bundle and the edge of the hole, the hole should have a rubber grommet installed, to protect the wire from being cut if it should contact the metal.

When making up a wire bundle, first connect one end of the wires to the terminal strips or into the connector; then arrange the wires into the neatest and most compact bundle you can form. Be generous with the use of spot ties as you form the bundle. When all of the wires are in the bundle, use a spot tie every three to four inches along the run of the bundle. Keep all of the wires parallel by using a plastic comb such as the one in figure 7-68.

If the bundle is to be encased in polyvinylchloride tubing, you must, of course, put the bundle in the tubing before the final end is connected. New tubing resists the wire bundle sliding through it and you can make the job easier if you blow a spoonful of talcum through the tube to help the wire slide through. One easy way of putting a long wire bundle through vinyl tubing is to blow one end of a piece of lacing cord through the tube with compressed air and then tie the end of the bundle to the lacing cord and pull it through the tubing.

Some wire bundles are laced, rather than secured with spot ties. But, lacing is not a good practice for wires installed in the aircraft structure and especially in the powerplant area, since a break in the lacing will loosen the bundle. Individual spot ties made with lacing cord or with nylon straps such as the patented TY-RAP are much better than lacing for holding wire bundles together.

Wire bundles may be enclosed in either rigid or flexible metal conduit when they pass through an area where they are likely to be chafed or crushed.

The inside diameter of the conduit must be about 25% larger than the maximum diameter of the wire bundle it encloses, and when you are figuring the size of the conduit to use for a wire bundle, you must remember that the nominal diameter of a conduit is its outside diameter; so you must subtract twice the wall thickness of the conduit from its outside diameter in order to find its inside diameter.

The conduit must be supported by clamps from the aircraft structure, and there must be a ⅛-inch drain hole at the lowest point in each run of the conduit, so that any moisture that condenses inside the conduit can drain out.

When the conduit is made up, all sharp edges and burrs must be removed and all of the bends must be made using a bend radius that will not cause the tube to kink, to wrinkle or to be excessively flattened.

3. Wiring Termination
a. Terminals

When wires are to be attached to studs on a terminal strip, they are terminated with a crimp-

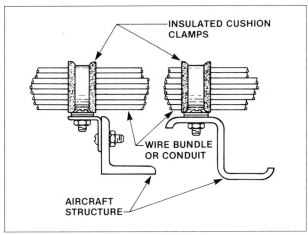

Figure 7-69. Methods of supporting a wire bundle from the aircraft structure.

on solderless terminal. In the smaller sizes, that is for wires up through ten-gauge, these terminals are preinsulated with the color of the insulator identifying the size of wire they fit. Terminals with red insulation are used on wire sizes 22 through 18, blue insulation is used on terminals for 16 and 14-gauge wire, and yellow terminals fit 12 and 10-gauge wire. Wires larger than 10-gauge use uninsulated terminals, and after the terminal is crimped in place, a piece of vinyl tubing is slid over the barrel of the terminal, and it is tied in place with lacing cord.

To install a terminal, the insulation on the wire is stripped back enough to allow the end of the wire to extend through the barrel of the terminal when the end of the insulation is against the

barrel. When the terminal is crimped with the proper tool, the joint between the wire and the terminal will be as strong as the wire itself.

There are two basic types of hand-operated crimping tools. The small type shown in figure 7-72 is used only for occasional repair work, but the ratchet type is preferred, as it assures that all crimps will have the proper amount of pressure applied.

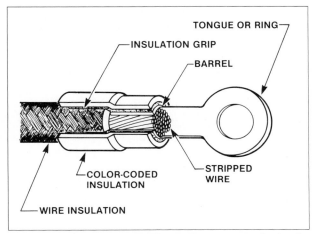

Figure 7-70. Preinsulated solderless terminals for aircraft electrical wire.

Figure 7-72. Combination crimping tool and wire stripper for installing solderless terminals.

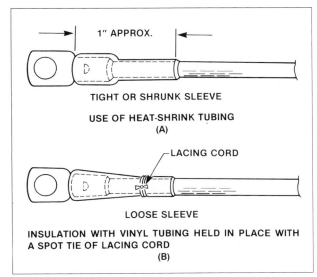

Figure 7-71. Methods of insulating solderless terminals on an electrical wire.

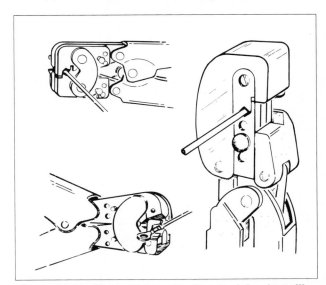

Figure 7-73. Heavy-duty crimping tool for installing preinsulated solderless terminals on aircraft wires.

The handles on the ratchet-type crimping tool will not release until the jaws have moved close enough together to properly compress the terminal barrel. Only ratchet-type crimping tools are used in aircraft production shops, and these tools are periodically calibrated to assure that every terminal installed with them will be properly compressed.

Terminals on wires of 0-gauge through 0000-gauge are usually installed with pneumatic squeezers that exert enough pressure on the terminal barrel to produce a joint that is as strong as the wire itself.

Aluminum wire presents some special problems when installing the terminals. Aluminum wire oxidizes when it is in contact with the air, and the oxide is an electrical in-sulator. To assure a good electrical connection between the wire and the terminal, the inside of the aluminum terminal is partially filled with a compound of petrolatum (petroleum jelly) and zinc dust that will grind the oxide film from the wire when the terminal is compressed. The petrolatum will then cover the aluminum and prevent the oxygen in the air from causing new oxides to form.

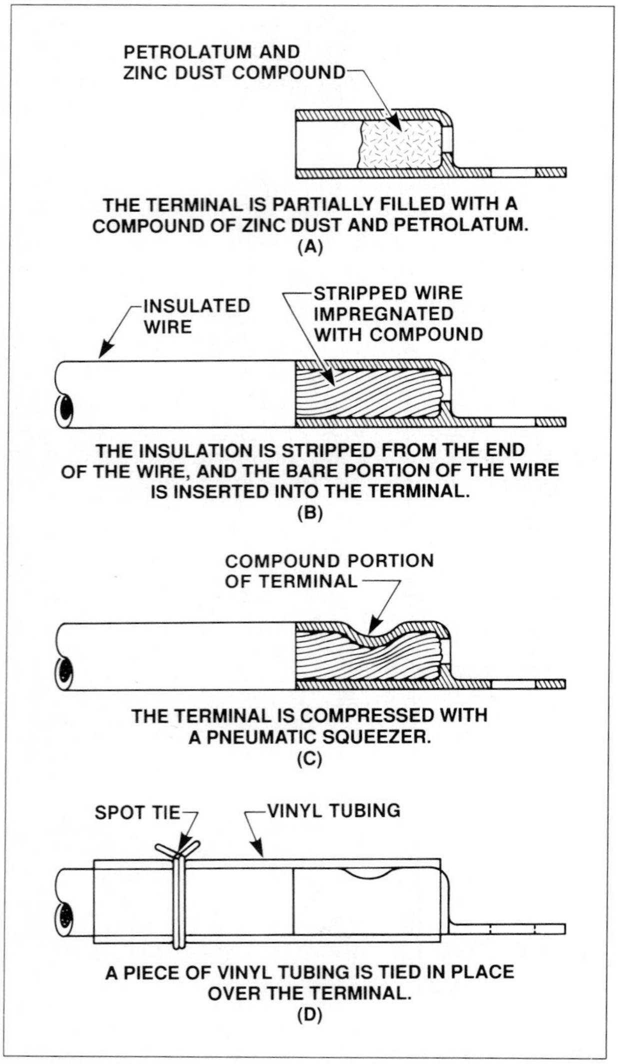

b. Terminal Strips

Most of the terminal strips in an aircraft electrical system are of the barrier type and are made of a strong paper-base phenolic compound. The smallest terminal stud allowed for electrical power systems is a number ten, and many of the circuits in the powerplant portion of the electrical system are electrical power circuits.

When attaching the terminal end of wires to the terminal strips, fan the wires out from the bundles so they will align with the terminal studs and stack the terminals on the studs as shown in figure 7-75. Notice that the ring is not in the cen-

PETROLATUM AND
ZINC DUST COMPOUND

THE TERMINAL IS PARTIALLY FILLED WITH A
COMPOUND OF ZINC DUST AND PETROLATUM.
(A)

INSULATED WIRE

STRIPPED WIRE
IMPREGNATED
WITH COMPOUND

THE INSULATION IS STRIPPED FROM THE END
OF THE WIRE, AND THE BARE PORTION OF THE WIRE
IS INSERTED INTO THE TERMINAL.
(B)

COMPOUND PORTION
OF TERMINAL

THE TERMINAL IS COMPRESSED WITH
A PNEUMATIC SQUEEZER.
(C)

SPOT TIE   VINYL TUBING

A PIECE OF VINYL TUBING IS TIED IN PLACE
OVER THE TERMINAL.
(D)

Figure 7-74. *Installation of a wire terminal on large-gauge aluminum wire.*

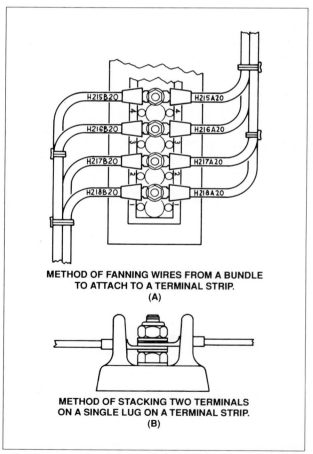

METHOD OF FANNING WIRES FROM A BUNDLE
TO ATTACH TO A TERMINAL STRIP.
(A)

METHOD OF STACKING TWO TERMINALS
ON A SINGLE LUG ON A TERMINAL STRIP.
(B)

Figure 7-75. *Electrical wires attached to a terminal strip.*

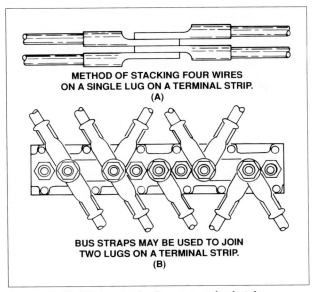

Figure 7-76. Wires stacked on a terminal strip.

ter of the terminal, but is to one side of the wire so there is a correct way of stacking them.

There should never be more than four terminals on any one stud. If it is necessary to connect more than four wires to one point, you can join two or more studs with cadmium-plated copper bus straps and use enough studs to connect all of the wires.

c. Junction Boxes

Most of the junction boxes installed in the powerplant section of an aircraft are made of aluminum alloy or of stainless steel and are mounted in such a way that they minimize the possibility of water getting into the box and causing electrical shorts or corrosion. Most of the junction boxes in the powerplant area are mounted vertically so that any washers or nuts dropped during servicing will not fall under the

wires where they could cause a short and maybe even a fire.

The power should always be off of the aircraft when you are working in an electrical junction box, but since this is not always possible, you must use extreme care that you do not short circuit any of the terminals with your tools. Be sure to remove your rings and wrist watch, as it is possible to short accidentally between two terminals and get a severe burn.

d. Connectors

Wiring used to connect portions of an aircraft electrical system that are not removed for servicing is normally done with wires connected to the studs on a terminal strip. But if the equipment is likely to be removed for servicing, it is connected with one of the AN or MS connectors. The individual wires are soldered into the pots in the ends of the contacts, or in some of the newer type of connectors, tapered pins are crimped onto the end of the wires, and the pins are wedged into tapered holes in the end of the contact.

To install a soldered connector to a wire bundle, first disassemble the connector and slip the wire clamp, the coupling ring, and assembly nut over the bundle. These components, naturally, cannot be installed after the connector is soldered in place.

Strip the insulation from about one-half inch of the end of the wire with a wire stripper. Do not use a knife to strip the insulation from the wire because of the danger of nicking some of the strands; nicked strands are sure to break and increase the resistance of the joint.

Slip a piece of vinyl tubing about one inch long over the end of the wire and solder the wire into the solder pot. To properly solder the wire in the pot, first fill the pot with solder and then heat it

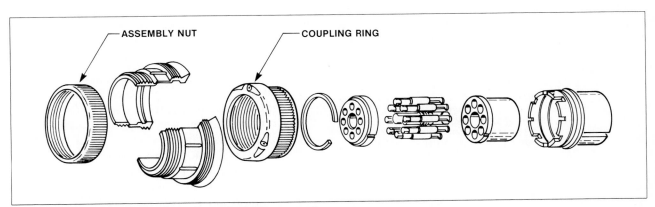

Figure 7-77. An exploded view of a typical MS connector.

with a soldering iron until the solder melts. Then insert the wire into the molten metal. Remove the soldering iron and hold the wire still until the

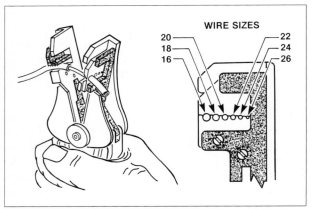

Figure 7-78. *This type of wire stripper will not nick the strands of wire when the insulation is removed.*

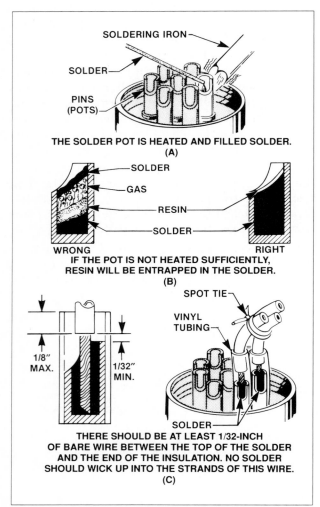

Figure 7-79. *Proper method of attaching wires into the solder pots on an MS connector.*

solder solidifies—the solder is hard when it loses its shiny appearance and looks frosted. If the wire is moved before the solder solidifies, it will have a granular appearance and the joint will have a high resistance.

When all of the wires are soldered into the pots, inspect the connector for the condition of the solder, looking especially for any solder that may bridge any of the contacts or for too much, or too little, solder. The solder in a properly soldered connection should completely fill the pot and have a slightly rounded top. The solder must not wick up into the strands of the wire, and there must be about 1/32-inch of bare wire between the top of the solder pot and the end of the insulation. Slip the vinyl tubing down over the solder pot and tie the wires together with a spot tie of lacing cord to prevent the insulation tubing slipping up and leaving the contacts uninsulated. Reassemble the connector and clamp the wires in the wire clamp.

4. Wire Bundle Routing And Clamping

The wiring harnesses that are installed in an aircraft at the factory are made on a jig board, and they are preformed with all of the bends they will have when they are installed. This provides the neatest and most secure installation. If a number of wires in a bundle have been damaged and must be repaired, it is usually a good idea to order a complete new harness from the factory and install it in exactly the same way the damaged harness was installed. But, if you are making an original installation, there are some considerations you should follow:

(1) If possible, limit the number of wires in a single bundle. Since it is possible for a single fault to damage all of the wires in a bundle, it is better to use more than one bundle than to risk a fault disabling several circuits.

(2) Do not bundle ignition wires, shielded wires, or wires that are not protected with either a fuse or a circuit breaker with other wires.

(3) Any time you have extra pins or sockets in a connector, put spare wires in them, because if one wire becomes damaged, it is much easier to switch from a damaged wire to one of the spares than it is to run a new wire in the bundle. Use a wire of the maximum size the contact will support, and number it with the number of the contact to which it is connected. Be sure to label it as a spare and include this wire on the wiring

diagram for the installation, showing that a spare wire is available.

(4) Clamp the bundle to the aircraft structure using insulated cushion clamps, and when the bundle must make a bend, be sure to use a bend radius that does not cause the wires on the inside of the bend to bunch up. A good rule of thumb is to use a bend radius of about ten times the diameter of the bundle.

(5) The bundle should be run tight enough that there is not more than about one-half inch of slack between the support points when normal hand pressure is put on the wires between the supports. But there must be sufficient slack after the last support that will allow you to replace the terminal if need be, and enough slack to prevent vibration or shifting of the equipment putting strain on the wires.

(6) Wiring installations in the engine compartment are often subjected to high temperatures, and any wires that pass through hot, or potentially hot, areas should have high-temperature insulation.

5. Bonding And Shielding

Because of the large amount of radio and electronic equipment carried in a modern airplane, it is important that all of the electromagnetic fields radiating from any motors or wires carrying alternating current be intercepted and grounded. And, the electrical charges that build up on any components must be carried to the main aircraft ground before they become high enough to cause a spark as they pass from the component to ground.

There are two basic ways to prevent electromagnetic interference; bonding and shielding.

a. Bonding

Bonding consists of electrically connecting all components in the aircraft together so there will be no insulated components on which electrical charges can build up. In the airframe section, all of the control surfaces are connected to the main aircraft structure with braided bonding straps so the resistance of the control hinge will not insulate the surface from the main structure. In the powerplant portion of an aircraft, we must bond all of the shock-mounted components to the main structure with bonding straps.

Any electrical component that uses the aircraft structure as the return path for its current must be bonded to the structure. Use bonding straps that are large enough to carry all of the return current without producing a voltage drop in excess of that allowed by the aircraft manufacturer. A rule of thumb that will usually keep the bonding straps large enough is to be sure that the resistance between any component and the aircraft structure is no more than three milliohms (0.003 ohms).

The bonding braid must be long enough that it will not interfere with the free movement of the component, and it must be of a material that will not produce an electrode potential difference with the structure that could cause corrosion.

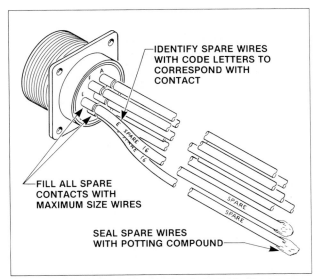

IDENTIFY SPARE WIRES WITH CODE LETTERS TO CORRESPOND WITH CONTACT

FILL ALL SPARE CONTACTS WITH MAXIMUM SIZE WIRES

SEAL SPARE WIRES WITH POTTING COMPOUND

Figure 7-80. If there are spare contacts in the connector, solder spare wires into them and route the spares with the bundle.

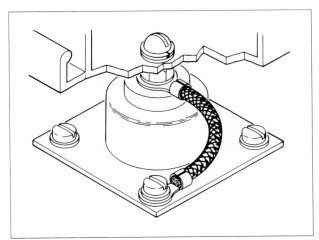

Figure 7-81. A bonding strap of adequate electrical capacity should be used to jump any insulated shock mount.

Aluminum alloy jumpers are usually used to bond aluminum alloy components together, and cadmium-plated copper jumpers are used for steel components.

Aircraft engines are mounted in rubber shock mounts, and a large flow of current from the starter must return through the engine mount to the main aircraft structure. Be sure there is a heavy bonding strap between the engine side of the mount and the airframe side. If this strap is missing or broken, there is a danger of fire, as fluid lines such as the fuel lines and primer lines must carry all of the return current from the starter.

b. Shielding

Shielding is used in an aircraft electrical system to intercept the radiated electrical energy, from either wires carrying alternating current or wires in the ignition system that have radio frequency energy from the spark superimposed over the direct or alternating current they carry.

Shielding is a braid of tin-plated or cadmium plated copper wire around the outside of the insulation. This braid is connected to ground through a crimped-on ground lead.

Shielding is used to prevent electromagnetic radiation from the wire, but in the wiring for some of the sensitive electronic components, the wires are shielded to keep electromagnetic radiation out of them. The shielding used on most of the components in the powerplant system of an aircraft may be grounded at both ends, but the shielding on the wires in some electronic circuits are grounded at only one end to prevent current flowing in the shielding and causing electromagnetic interference.

6. Circuit Protection

Conductors should be protected with circuit breakers or fuses located as close as possible to the electrical power source bus. Normally, the manufacturer of the electrical equipment specifies the fuse or circuit breaker to be used when installing the equipment.

The circuit breaker or fuse should open the circuit before the conductor emits smoke. To accomplish this, the time/current characteristics of the protection device must fall below that of the associated conductor. Circuit-protector characteristics should be matched to obtain the maximum utilization of the equipment operated by the circuit.

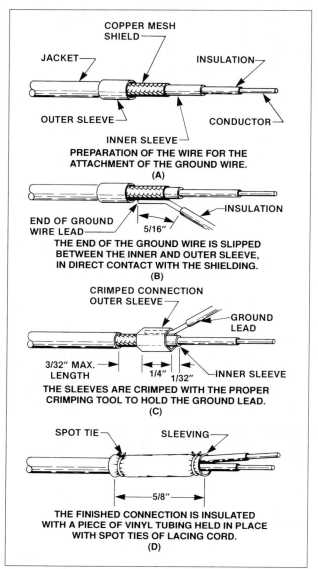

Figure 7-82. Attachment of ground lead to a shielded wire, using a crimped-on sleeve.

Figure 7-83 shows an example of the chart used in selecting the circuit breaker and fuse protection for copper conductors. This limited chart is applicable to a specific set of ambient temperatures and wire bundle sizes, and is presented as an example only.

All re-settable circuit breakers should open the circuit in which they are installed regardless of the position of the operating control when an overload or circuit fault exists. Such circuit breakers are referred to as "trip-free." Automatic re-set circuit breakers automatically re-set themselves periodically. They should not be used as circuit protection devices in aircraft.

WIRE AN GAUGE COPPER	CIRCUIT BREAKER AMPERAGE	FUSE AMP.
22	5	5
20	7.5	5
18	10	10
16	15	10
14	20	15
12	30	20
10	40	30
8	50	50
6	80	70
4	100	70
2	125	100
1		150
0		150

Figure 7-83. Wire and circuit protector chart.

7. Switches And Relays

A specifically designed switch should be used in all circuits where a switch malfunction would be hazardous. Such switches are of rugged construction and have sufficient contact capability to break, make, and carry continuously the connected load current. Snap-action design is generally preferred to obtain rapid opening and closing of contacts regardless of the speed of the operating toggle or plunger, thereby minimizing contact arcing.

The nominal current rating of the conventional aircraft switch is usually stamped on the switch housing. This rating represents the continuous current rating with the contacts closed. Switches should be derated from their nominal current rating for the following types of circuits:

(1) High rush-in circuits—Circuits containing incandescent lamps can draw an initial current which is 15 times greater than the continuous current. Contact burning or welding may occur when the switch is closed.

(2) Inductive circuits—Magnetic energy stored in solenoid coils or relays is released and appears as an arc as the controlled switch is opened.

(3) Motors—Direct current motors will draw several times their rated current during starting, and magnetic energy stored in their field coils is released when the control switch is opened.

NOMINAL SYSTEM VOLTAGE	TYPE OF LOAD	DERATING FACTOR
24 V.D.C.	LAMP	8
24 V.D.C.	INDUCTIVE (RELAY-SOLENOID)	4
24 V.D.C.	RESISTIVE (HEATER)	2
24 V.D.C.	MOTOR	3
12 V.D.C.	LAMP	5
12 V.D.C.	INDUCTIVE (RELAY-SOLENOID)	2
12 V.D.C.	RESISTIVE (HEATER)	1
12 V.D.C.	MOTOR	2

Figure 7-84. Switch derating factors.

The chart in figure 7-84 is typical of those available for selecting the proper nominal switch rating when the continuous load current is known. This election is essentially a derating to obtain reasonable switch efficiency and service life.

Hazardous errors in switch operation can be avoided by logical and consistent installation. Two position "on-off" switches should be mounted so that the "on" position is reached by an upward or forward movement of the toggle. When the switch controls movable aircraft elements, such a landing gear or flaps, the toggle should move in the same direction as the desired motion. Inadvertent operation of a switch can be prevented by mounting a suitable guard over the switch.

Relays are used as switching devices where a weight reduction can be achieved or electrical controls can be simplified. A relay is an electrically operated switch and is therefore subject to dropout under low system voltage conditions. The above discussion of switch ratings is generally applicable to relay contact ratings.

D. Generator Systems

Energy for the operation of most electrical equipment in an airplane depends upon the electrical energy supplied by a generator. A generator is any machine which converts mechanical energy into electrical energy by electromagnetic induction. Generators designed to produce alternating current are called AC generators; generators which produce direct-current energy are called DC generators.

For airplanes equipped with direct-current electrical systems, the DC generator is the regular source of electrical energy. One or more DC generators, driven by the engine(s), supply electrical energy for the operation of all units in the electrical system, as well as energy for charging the battery. In most cases only one generator is driven by each engine, but in some large airplanes, two generators may be driven by a single engine. Aircraft equipped with alternating-current systems use electrical energy supplied by AC generators, also called alternators.

1. Direct Current Power Systems

Most light aircraft use only a DC power system. If there is any need for alternating current it may be supplied by a small inverter. These aircraft will use a DC generator to supply power for the electrical system, and to charge the battery.

a. Types Of DC Generators

There are three types of DC generators: series-wound, shunt-wound, and shunt-series or compound-wound. The difference in type depends on the relationship of the field winding to the external circuit.

1) Series-Wound

The field winding of a series generator is connected in series with the external circuit, called the load (figure 7-85). The field coils are composed of a few turns of large wire; the magnetic field strength depends here more on the current flow than the number of turns in the coil.

Series generators have very poor voltage regulation under changing load, since the greater the current through the field coils to the external circuit, the greater the induced EMF and the greater the terminal voltage. Therefore, when the load is increased, the voltage increases; likewise, when the load is decreased, the voltage decreases.

The output voltage of a series-wound generator may be controlled by a rheostat in parallel with the field windings, as shown in A of figure 7-85. Since the series-wound generator has such poor regulation, it is never employed as an airplane generator. Generators in airplanes have field windings which are connected either in shunt or in compound.

2) Shunt-Wound

A generator having a field winding connected in parallel with the external circuit is called a shunt generator and is shown in figure 7-86. The field coils of a shunt generator contain many turns of a small wire; the magnetic strength is

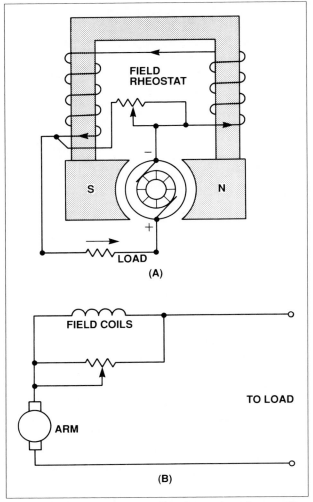

Figure 7-85. Diagram and schematic of a series-wound generator.

derived from the large number of turns rather than the current strength through the coils.

If a constant voltage is desired, the shunt-wound generator is not suitable for rapidly fluctuating loads. Any increase in load causes a decrease in the terminal or output voltage, and any decrease in the load causes an increase in the terminal voltage. This is because the armature and the load are connected in series, and all current flowing in the external circuit passes through the armature winding. Because of the resistance in the armature winding, there is a voltage drop (IR drop = current × resistance). As the load increases, the armature current increases and the IR drop in the armature increases. The voltage delivered to the terminals is the difference between the induced voltage and the voltage drop; therefore there is a decrease in terminal voltage. This decrease in voltage causes a decrease in field strength, because the current in the field coils decreases in proportion to the decrease in terminal voltage; with a weaker field, the voltage is further decreased.

When the load decreases, the output voltage increases accordingly, and a larger current flows in the windings. This action is cumulative, so the output voltage continues to rise to a point called field saturation, after which there is no further increase in output voltage.

The terminal voltage of a shunt generator can be controlled by means of a rheostat inserted in series with the field winding as shown in A of figure 7-86. As the resistance is increased, the field current is reduced; consequently, the generated voltage is reduced also. For a given setting of the

field rheostat, the terminal voltage at the armature brushes will be approximately equal to the generated voltage minus the IR drop produced by the load current in the armature; thus, the voltage at the terminals of the generator will drop as the load is applied. Certain voltage-sensitive devices are available which automatically adjust the field rheostat to compensate for variations in load. When these devices are used, the terminal voltage remains essentially constant.

The output and voltage-regulation capabilities of shunt-type generators make them suitable for light to medium duty use on aircraft. While once popular, these units have largely been replaced by DC alternators.

3) Compound-Wound

A compound-wound generator combines a series winding and a shunt winding in such a way that the characteristics of each are used to advantage. The series field coils are made of a relatively small number of turns of large copper conductor, either circular or rectangular in cross section, and are connected in series with the armature circuit. These coils are mounted on the same poles which the shunt field coils are mounted and, therefore, contribute a magneto-motive force which influences the main field flux of the generator. A diagrammatic and a schematic illustration of a compound-wound generator is shown in figure 7-87.

If the ampere-turns of the series field act in the same direction as those of the shunt field, the combined magneto-motive force is equal to the sum of the series and shunt field components. Load is added to a compound generator in the same manner in which load is added to a shunt generator, by increasing the number of parallel paths across the generator terminals. Thus, the decrease in total load resistance with added load is accompanied by an increase in armature-circuit and series-field circuit current.

The effect of the additive series field is that of increased field flux with increased load. The extent of the increased field flux depends on the degree of saturation of the field as determined by the shunt field connection. Thus, the terminal voltage of the generator may increase or decrease with load, depending on the influence of the series field coils. This influence is referred to as the degree of compounding.

Changes in terminal voltage with increasing load depends upon the degree of compounding. A flat-compound generator is one in which the no-

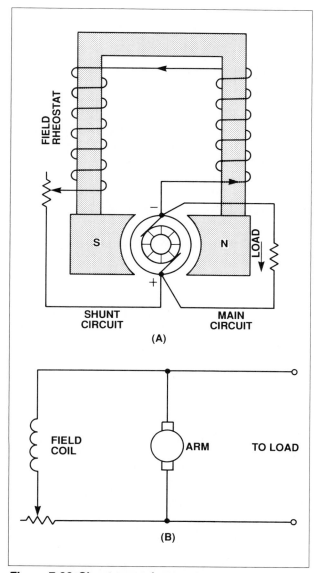

Figure 7-86. Shunt-wound generator.

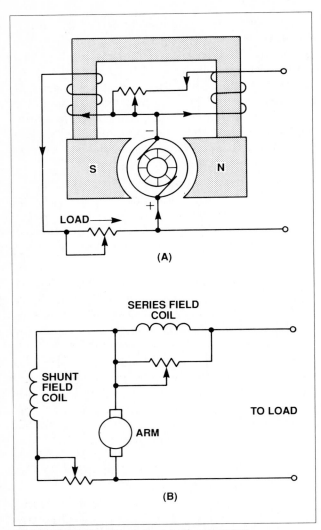

Figure 7-87. Compound-wound generator.

Differential generators have somewhat the same characteristics as series generators in that they are essentially constant-current generators. However, they generate rated voltage at no load, the voltage dropping materially as the load current increases. Constant-current generators are ideally suited as power sources for electric arc welders and are used almost universally in electric arc welding.

If the shunt field of a compound generator is connected across both the armature and the series field, it is known as a long-shunt connection. If the shunt field is connected across the armature alone, it is called a short-shunt connection. These connections produce essentially the same generator characteristics.

A summary of the characteristics of the various types of generators discussed is shown graphically in figure 7-88.

b. DC Alternators

DC alternators do exactly the same thing as DC generators. They produce alternating current and convert it into direct current before it leaves the device. The difference being that in an alternator, field current is taken into the rotor through brushes which ride on smooth slip rings. The AC load current is produced in the fixed windings of the stator, and after it is rectified by six solid-state diodes it is brought out of the alternator through solid connections.

Two of the limitations of DC generators for aircraft installations are the limited number of pairs of poles that can be used, and the fact that

load and full-load voltages have the same value. The under-compound generator has a full-load voltage less than the no-load value, and an over-compound generator has a full-load voltage which is higher than the no-load value.

Compound generators are usually designed to be over-compounded. This feature permits varied degrees of compounding by connecting a variable shunt across the series field. Such a shunt is sometimes called a diverter. Compound generators are used where voltage regulation is of prime importance.

If the series field aids the shunt field, the generator is said to be cumulative-compounded (B of figure 7-87). If the series field opposes the shunt field, the generator is said to be differentially compounded.

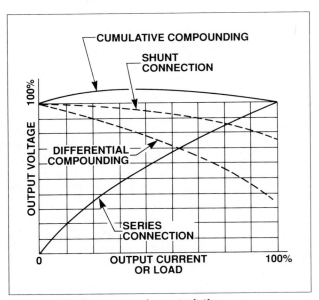

Figure 7-88. Generator characteristics.

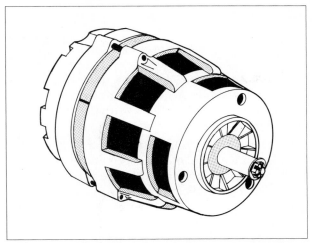

Figure 7-89. DC alternators are used in almost all of the modern aircraft that require a low or medium amount of electrical power.

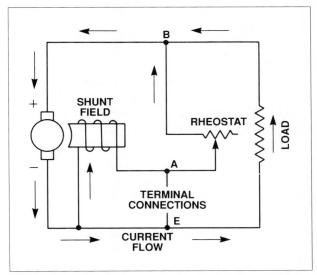

Figure 7-90. Regulation of generator voltage using a field rheostat.

the load current is produced in the rotating member and must be brought out of the generator through the brushes.

DC alternators solve these two problems, and since they produce three-phase AC and convert it into direct current with built-in solid-state rectifiers, their output at low engine speed allows them to keep the battery charged even when the aircraft is required to operate on the ground with the engine idling—as it must often do when waiting for clearance to takeoff.

c. Voltage Regulation

Efficient operation of electrical equipment in an airplane depends on a constant voltage supply from the generator. Among the factors which determine the voltage output of a generator, only one, the strength of the field current, can be conveniently controlled. To illustrate this control refer to the diagram in figure 7-90, showing a simple generator with a rheostat in the field circuit.

If the rheostat is set to increase the resistance in the field circuit, less current flows through the field winding and the strength of the magnetic field in which the armature rotates decreases. Consequently, the output of the generator decreases. If the resistance in the field circuit is decreased with the rheostat, more current flows through the field windings, the magnetic field becomes stronger, and the generator produces a greater voltage.

This principle may be further developed by the addition of a solenoid which will electrically connect or remove the field rheostat from the circuit

as the voltage varies. This arrangement is illustrated in figure 7-91. With the generator running at normal speed and switch K open, the field rheostat is adjusted so that the terminal voltage is about 60 percent of normal. Solenoid S is weak and contact B is held closed by the spring. When K is closed, a short circuit is placed across the field rheostat. This action causes the field current to increase and the terminal voltage to rise.

When the terminal voltage rises above a certain critical value, the solenoid's downward pull exceeds the spring tension and contact B opens, reinserting the field rheostat in the field circuit. This additional resistance reduces the field current and lowers terminal voltage.

When the terminal voltage falls below a certain value, the solenoid armature contact B is closed

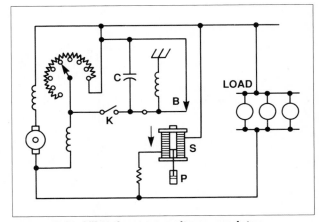

Figure 7-91. Vibrating-type voltage regulator.

again by the spring, the field rheostat is now shorted, and the terminal voltage starts to rise. Thus, an average voltage is maintained with or without load changes.

The dashpot P provides smoother operation by acting as a dampener to prevent hunting. The capacitor C across contact B eliminates sparking.

1) Regulators For DC Generators

Certain light aircraft employ a three-unit regulator for their generator systems. This type of regulator includes a current limiter and a reverse current cutout in addition to a voltage regulator. A three-unit regulator is seen in figure 7-92.

The action of the voltage regulator unit is similar to the vibrating-type regulator described above. The second of the three units is a current regulator to limit the output current of the generator. The third unit is a reverse-current cutout that disconnects the battery from the generator. If the battery is not disconnected, it will discharge through the generator armature when the generator voltage falls below that of the battery. When this occurs the battery will attempt to drive the generator as a motor. This action is called "motoring" the generator and, unless it

is prevented, it will discharge the battery in a short time.

Vibrating-type regulators cannot be used with generators which require a high field current, since the contacts will pit or burn. Heavy-duty generator systems require a different type of regulator, such as the carbon-pile voltage regulator.

The carbon-pile voltage regulator depends on the resistance of a number of carbon disks arranged in a pile or stack. The resistance of the carbon stack varies inversely with the pressure applied. When the stack is compressed under appreciable pressure, the resistance in the stack is less. When the pressure is reduced the resistance of the carbon stack increases because there is more air space between the disks, and air has a high resistance.

Pressure on the carbon pile depends upon two opposing forces: a spring and an electromagnet. The spring compresses the carbon pile, and the electromagnet exerts a pull which decreases the pressure.

Whenever the generator voltage varies, the pull of the electromagnet varies. If the generator volt-

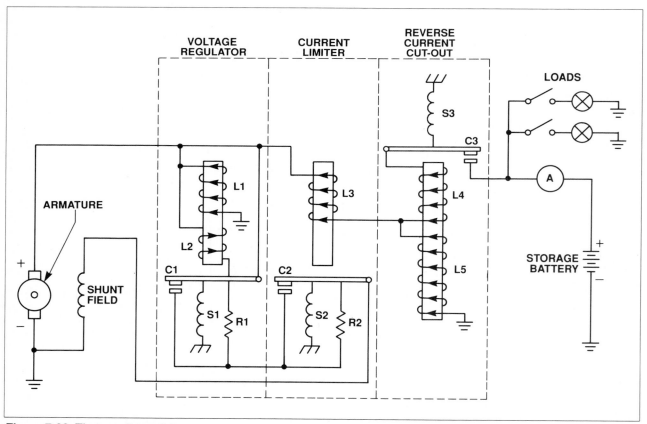

Figure 7-92. Three-unit regulator.

302

age rises above a specific amount, the pull of the electromagnet increases, decreasing the pressure exerted on the carbon pile and increasing its resistance. Since this resistance is in series with the field, less current flows through the field winding, there is a corresponding decrease in field strength, and the generator voltage drops. On the other hand, if the generator output drops below the specified value, the pull of the electromagnet is decreased and the carbon pile places less resistance in the field winding circuit. In addition, the field strength increases and the generator output increases. A small rheostat provides a means of adjusting the current flow through the electromagnet coil. Figure 7-93 shows a typical 24-volt voltage regulator with its internal circuits.

2) Regulators For DC Alternators

The voltage produced by a DC alternator is controlled in exactly the same way it is controlled in a generator, by varying the field current. When the voltage rises above the desired value, the field current is decreased and when the voltage drops too low, the field current is increased.

This action may be accomplished in low-output alternators with vibrator-type controls which interrupt the field current by opening the con-

tacts. A much more efficient means of voltage control has been devised which uses a transistor to control flow of field current.

The transistorized voltage regulator utilizes both vibrating points and transistors for voltage control. The vibrating points operate in exactly the same way they do in a normal vibrator-type voltage regulator, but instead of the field current flowing through the contacts, only the transistor base current flows through them. This is so small compared with the field current which flows throughout the emitter-collector portion of the transistor that there is no arcing at the contacts. A simplified schematic of this circuit is shown in figure 7-94.

The transistorized voltage regulator is a step in the right direction, but semi-conductor devices may be used to replace all of the moving parts and a completely solid-state voltage regulator may be built. These units are very efficient, reliable, and generally have no serviceable components. If the unit is defective it will be removed and replaced with a new one.

Alternator control requirements are different from those of a generator for several reasons. An alternator uses solid-state diodes for its rectifier and since current cannot flow from the battery

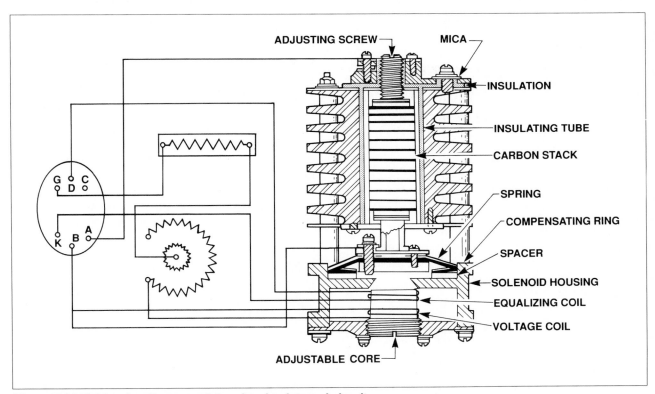

Figure 7-93. A 24-volt voltage regulator showing internal circuits.

into the alternator, there is no need for a reverse-current cutout relay. The field of an alternator is excited from the system bus, whose voltage is limited either by the battery or by the voltage regulator, so there is no possibility of the alternator putting out enough current to burn itself out, as a generator with its self-excited field can do. Because of this there is no need for a current limiter. There must be one control with an alternator, however, that is not needed with a generator, and that is some means of shutting off the flow of field current when the alternator is not producing power. This is not needed in a generator since its field is excited by its own output. An alternator uses either a field switch or a field relay.

Most modern aircraft alternator circuits employ some form of over-voltage protection to remove the alternator from the bus if it should malfunction in such a way that its output voltage rises to a dangerous level.

d. Generator Maintenance

Because of the relative simplicity and durable construction generators will operate many hours without a hint of trouble. The routine inspection and service at each 100-hour or annual inspection interval is generally all that is required. Generator overhaul is often accomplished at the same time as engine overhaul, minimizing aircraft down time and increasing the likelihood of trouble free operation when the aircraft is placed back in service.

1) Routine Inspection And Servicing Of DC Generators

The 100-hour and/or annual inspection of the generator should include the following items:

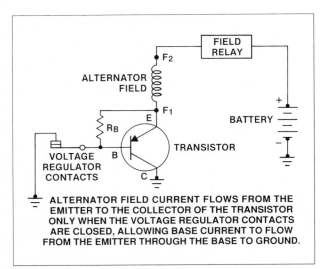

ALTERNATOR FIELD CURRENT FLOWS FROM THE EMITTER TO THE COLLECTOR OF THE TRANSISTOR ONLY WHEN THE VOLTAGE REGULATOR CONTACTS ARE CLOSED, ALLOWING BASE CURRENT TO FLOW FROM THE EMITTER THROUGH THE BASE TO GROUND.

Figure 7-94. Transistorized voltage regulator.

(a) Inspect the generator for security of mounting, checking the mounting flange for cracks and looseness of mounting bolts.

(b) Inspect the mounting flange area for oil leaks.

(c) Inspect generator electrical connections for cleanliness and security of attachment.

(d) Remove the band covering the brushes and commutator. Use compressed air to blow out accumulated dust. Inspect the brushes for wear, and freedom of movement. Check the tension of the brush springs, using a spring scale.

(e) Inspect the commutator for cleanliness, wear, and pitting.

(f) Inspect the area around the commutator and brush assemblies for any particles of solder. This indicates that overheating has occurred, and the generator should be removed.

If a DC generator is unable to keep the aircraft battery charged, and if the ammeter does not show the proper rate of charge, you should first check the aircraft electrical system that is associated with the battery and with the generator. Physically check every connection in the generator and battery circuit and electrically check the condition of all of the fuses and circuit breakers. Check the condition of all ground connections for the battery, battery contactor, and the generator control units. When you have determined that there is no obvious external problem and the generator armatures does turn when the engine is cranked, you should next determine which is at fault, the generator or the generator control.

One of the easiest ways of determining which unit is not operating is to connect a voltmeter between the G terminal of the voltage regulator and ground to check the voltage output of the generator. Because this check requires that the generator be turning it must be accomplished with the engine running, or on an appropriate test stand. In either case, observe the proper safety precautions. Even if the field winding is open, or the voltage regulator is malfunctioning, the generator should produce residual voltage—that is, the voltage produced by the armature cutting across the residual magnetic field in the generator frame. This should be about one or two volts.

If there is no residual voltage, it is possible that the generator need only have the residual magnetism restored. Residual magnetism is restored by an operation known as "flashing the field." This is accomplished by momentarily passing current through the field coils in the same way that it normally flows.

The method of accomplishing this task varies with the internal connections of the generator, and with the type of voltage regulator used. Be certain to follow the specific instructions of the equipment manufacturer as failure to do so could result in damage to the generator and/or voltage regulator.

If the generator produces residual voltage but no output voltage, the trouble could lie with the generator or with the regulator. To determine which, operate the engine at a speed high enough for the generator to produce an output, and bypass the voltage regulator with a jumper wire. Again, this connection will vary with the type of generator and regulator being used, and this operation should be performed in accordance with the manufacturer's recommendations.

If the generator produces voltage with the regulator shorted, the problem is with the voltage regulator. Be sure that the regulator is properly grounded, as a faulty ground connection will prevent its functioning properly.

It is possible to service and adjust some vibrator-type generator controls but, because of the expense of the time involved and the test equipment needed to do the job properly, most servicing is done by replacing a faulty unit with a new one.

If the generator does not produce an output voltage when the regulator is bypassed, remove the generator from the engine and overhaul it or replace it with an overhauled unit.

2) DC Alternator Service And Maintenance

If an alternator fails to keep the battery charged, you should first determine that all of the alternator and battery circuits in the electrical system are properly connected and that there are no open fuses or circuit breakers. There should be battery voltage at the B terminal of the alternator and at the Batt or (+) terminal of the voltage regulator.

It is extremely important in an alternator installation that the battery be connected with the proper polarity, and that anytime an external power source is connected to the aircraft it must have the correct polarity. Connecting a battery or APU with the poles reversed can burn out the rectifying diodes.

The solid-state diodes in an alternator are quite rugged and have a long life when they are proper-

ly used, but they can be damaged by excessive voltage or by reverse current flow. For this reason an alternator must never be operated without being connected to an electrical load, as the voltage can rise high enough to destroy the diodes.

Alternators receive their field current from the aircraft bus and do not depend upon residual magnetism to get them started. Since there is no need for residual magnetism, alternators must NEVER have their field flashed, or polarized, as this action is sometimes called.

To aid in systematic troubleshooting, some manufacturers have made test equipment available that can be plugged into the aircraft electrical system between the voltage regulator and the aircraft system to indicate by use of indicator lights whether the trouble is in the voltage regulator, the over-voltage sensing circuit, or in the alternator field or output circuit. By using this type of test equipment, much time can be saved and unnecessary replacement of good components can be avoided. If systematic troubleshooting indicates that the alternator is at fault, it can be disassembled and repaired.

There are basically two problems that prevent an alternator from producing electrical power. The most likely is a shorted or open diode in the rectifying circuit and there is a possibility of an open circuit in the field.

To check for a shorted circuit, measure the resistance between the B terminal of the alternator and ground. Set the ohmmeter on the $R \times 1$ scale and measure the resistance. The reverse the ohmmeter leads and measure the resistance again. With one measurement, the batteries in the ohmmeter forward bias the diodes and you should get a relatively low resistance reading. When you reverse the leads, the batteries reverse bias the diodes and you should get an infinite or a very high reading. If you do not get an infinite or very high reading, one or more of the diodes are shorted.

You cannot detect an open diode with this type of ohmmeter test, because the diodes are connected in parallel and the ohmmeter cannot detect one diode that is open when it is in parallel with other diodes that are good. But, if the alternator does not produce sufficient output voltage and everything else appears in good condition, you should disconnect the diodes from the circuit and test them individually with an ohmmeter. A good diode will have an infinite or

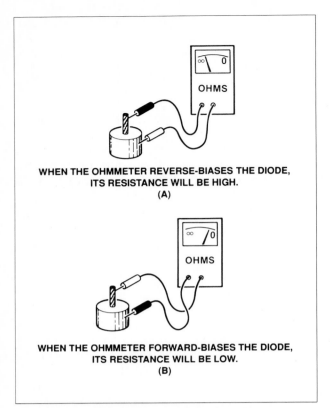

WHEN THE OHMMETER REVERSE-BIASES THE DIODE,
ITS RESISTANCE WILL BE HIGH.
(A)

WHEN THE OHMMETER FORWARD-BIASES THE DIODE,
ITS RESISTANCE WILL BE LOW.
(B)

Figure 7-95. Method of checking an alternator rectifier diode.

very high resistance in one direction and a relatively low resistance when the ohmmeter leads are reversed. An open diode will give a high resistance reading with both positions of the ohmmeter leads, and the diode will have to be replaced.

3) Generator Overhaul

Generator overhaul is normally accomplished at any time the generator has been determined to be inoperative, or at the same time as the aircraft's engine is overhauled. The generator overhaul may be accomplished in some aircraft repair facilities, but is nowadays more often the job of an FAA Certified Repair Station licensed for that operation.

Detailed instruction concerning the steps involved in the overhaul of generators was covered in the General Section Textbook of this series.

2. Alternating Current Power Systems

Direct current is normally used as the main electrical power for aircraft, because it can be stored and the aircraft engines can be started using battery power. Large aircraft require elaborate ground service facilities and require external power sources for starting, they can take

advantage of the weight saving provided by using alternating current for their main electrical power.

Alternating current has the advantage over direct current in that its voltage can be stepped up or down. If we need to carry current for a long distance, we can pass the AC through a step-up transformer to increase the voltage and decrease the current. The high voltage AC can be conducted to the point it will be used through a relatively small conductor, and at its destination it is passed through a step-down transformer where its voltage is lowered and its current is stepped back up to the value we need.

It is an easy matter to convert AC into DC when we need direct current to charge batteries or to operate variable speed motors. All we need to do is pass the AC through a series of semiconductor diodes. This changes the AC into DC with relatively little loss.

a. AC Generating Systems

Alternators are classified in several ways in order to distinguish properly the various types. Ones means of classification is by the type of excitation system used. In alternators used on aircraft, excitation can be affected by one of the following methods.

(1) A direct-connected, direct-current generator. This system consists of a DC generator fixed on the same shaft with the AC generator. A variation of this system is a type of alternator which uses DC from the battery for excitation, after which the alternator is self-excited.

(2) By transformation and rectification from the AC system. This method depends on residual magnetism for initial AC voltage buildup, after which the field is supplied with rectified voltage from the AC system.

(3) Integrated brushless type. This arrangement has a direct-current generator on the same shaft with an alternating-current generator. The excitation circuit is completed through silicon rectifiers rather than a commutator and brushes. The rectifiers are mounted on the generator shaft and their output is fed directly to the alternating-current generator's main rotating field.

Another method of classification is by the number of phases of output voltage. Alternating current generators may be single-phase, two-phase, three-phase, or even six-phase and more. In the electrical systems of aircraft, the three-phase alternator is by far the most common.

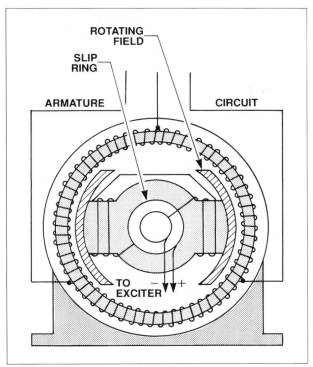

Figure 7-96. Alternator with stationary armature and rotating field.

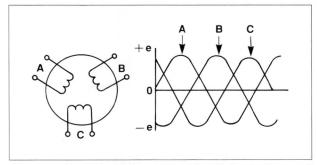

Figure 7-97. Simplified schematic of three-phase alternator with output waveforms.

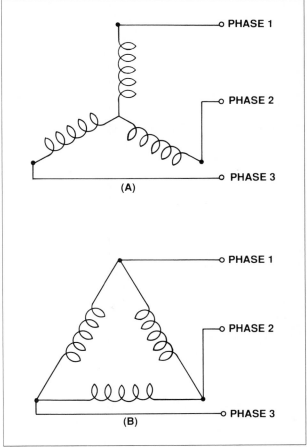

Figure 7-98. Schematic diagrams of Y and delta connections.

Still another means of classification is by the type of stator and rotor used. From this standpoint, there are two types of alternators: the revolving-armature type and the revolving-field type. The revolving-armature alternator is similar in construction to the DC generator, in that the armature rotates through a stationary magnetic field. The revolving-armature alternator is found only in alternators of low power rating and generally is not used.

The revolving-field type of alternator (figure 7-96) has a stationary armature winding (stator) and a rotating-field winding (rotor). The advantage of having a stationary armature winding is that the armature can be connected directly to the load without having sliding contacts in the load circuit. The direct connection to the armature circuit makes possible the use of large cross-section conductors, adequately insulated for high voltage.

b. Phase Rotation

A three-phase or polyphase circuit, is used in most aircraft alternators, instead of a single or two-phase alternator. The three-phase alternator has three single-phase windings spaced so that the voltage induced in each winding is 120° out of phase with the voltage in the other two windings.

A simplified schematic diagram, showing each of the three phases, is illustrated in figure 7-97. The rotor is omitted for simplicity. The waveforms of the voltage are shown to the right of the schematic. The three voltages are 120° apart and are similar to the voltages that would be generated by three single-phase alternators, whose voltages are out of phase by 120°. The three phases are independent of each other.

Rather than having six leads from the three-phase alternator, one of the leads from each phase may be connected to form a common junction. The stator is then called Y or star-connected, and is illustrated in A of figure 7-48. The common lead may or may not be brought out of the alternator. If it is brought out it is called the neutral lead.

A three-phase stator can also be connected so that the phases are connected end-to-end as shown in B of figure 7-98. This arrangement is called a delta connection.

c. Alternator Maintenance

Maintenance and inspection of alternator systems is similar to that of DC systems. Proper maintenance of an alternator requires that the unit be kept clean and that all electrical connections are tight and in good repair. Because alternators and their drive systems differ in design and maintenance requirements, no attempt will be made here to detail those procedures. Specific information may be found in the manufacturer's service publications and in the maintenance program approved for the particular aircraft.

ENGINE STARTING SYSTEMS

A. Reciprocating Engine Starting Systems

The earliest aircraft engines were started by hand "propping" them. The mechanics swung the propeller by hand to pull the engine through one or two compression strokes, and if everything was as it should be, the engine started. Cold weather made the oil heavy, and the engines were hard to start. As the engines grew larger and the propellers longer, the procedure for starting became more difficult, and several methods were devised to replace the hand-cranking procedure.

1. Inertia Starters

One of the first types of starters coupled to the crankshaft was the hand inertia starter. In this type of starter, a relatively heavy flywheel is spun

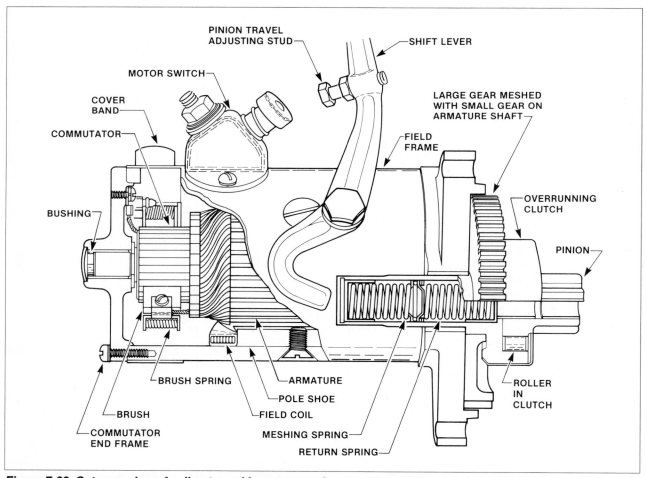

Figure 7-99. Cutaway view of a direct-cranking starter using an over-running clutch.

7-60

7-60   308

with a hand crank through a step-up gear arrangement. When the flywheel is spinning at a high rate of speed with lots of kinetic energy stored in it, the crank is removed, and the engage handle is pulled to extend a ratchet-type jaw out of the starter to engage with a similar ratchet on the rear end of the crankshaft. A torque-overload clutch is used between the flywheel and the jaws to prevent the sudden engagement damaging either the engine or the starter. With the jaws engaged, the energy stored in the flywheel turns the engine over enough to get it started.

Hand inertia starters were soon improved by mounting an electric motor on the back of the starter to spin the flywheel. When the flywheel was up to speed, the motor was de-energized and the engage handle pulled to engage the flywheel to the engine. In case the aircraft battery was run down, there were provisions on these starters to use a hand crank to drive the flywheel. This combination electric and hand inertia starter was pretty much the standard starter for large engines up until well into World War II.

2. Direct-Cranking Starters

The most widely used starting system on all types of reciprocating engines utilizes the direct-cranking electric starter. This type of starter provides instant and continual cranking when energized. The direct-cranking electric starter consists basically of an electric motor, reduction gears, and an engaging and disengaging mechanism.

a. Starters For Low Horsepower Engines

Many of the small horizontally opposed aircraft engines use a form of direct-cranking electric starter similar to the one in figure 7-99. This starter uses a small series-wound electric motor with a small gear on the end of its shaft. This small gear meshes with a large gear that is part of an over-running clutch. These starters may be engaged either by a hand-pulled cable or with a solenoid that operates the shift lever.

When the shift lever is pulled, it compresses the meshing spring and forces the pinion to mesh with the starter gear inside the accessory case of the engine. When the pinion and the starter gear are fully meshed, further movement of the shift lever closes the starter motor switch, and the starter cranks the engine. When the engine starts, the over-running clutch allows the pinion to spin without doing any damage, and as soon as the toggle is released or the solenoid is

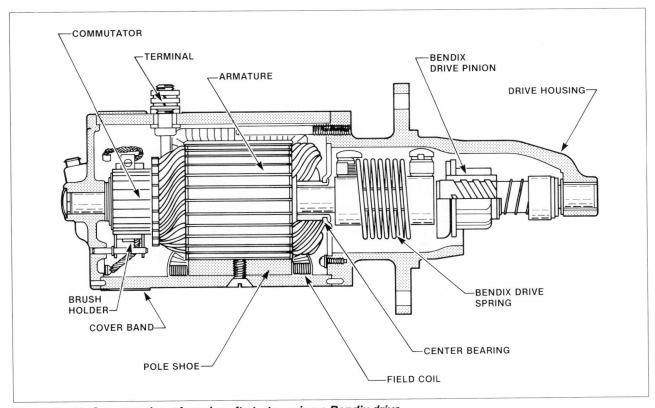

Figure 7-100. Cutaway view of an aircraft starter using a Bendix drive.

de-energized, the return spring pulls the pinion away from the starter gear.

The popular series of Avco-Lycoming horizontally opposed engines that have the large diameter starter gear just behind the propeller use a direct cranking electric starter similar to the ones used on automobile engines. These starters are driven through a Bendix drive.

When the starter switch is closed, the series-wound electric motor spins the pinion through the Bendix drive spring. The drive pinion fits loosely over the drive shaft, and as the armature spins, the pinion moves forward on the helical splines, and it engages the teeth on the periphery of the engine starter gear. The starter then cranks the engine. As soon as the engine starts and the starter gear begins to spin the Bendix drive pinion, the pinion is forced back along the helical splines, and it disengages from the starter gear.

Some of the new generation of Teledyne-Continental aircraft engines use a starter mounted on the side of the accessory case, and it cranks the engine through a right-angle worm-gear-type adaptor.

In figure 7-101, we see the way this system works. The series-wound electric motor drives the starter worm gear, which meshes with the worm wheel. The clutch spring is attached to the worm wheel, and when the worm wheel turns, the spring tightens around a knurled drum on the starter shaft gear, and the starter gear, which is meshed with the crankshaft gear, cranks the engine. As soon as the engine starts, the starter shaft turns faster than the worm wheel, and the spring releases the knurled drum. The generator drive pulley is mounted on the end of the starter gear shaft, and with the clutch spring disengaged, the shaft serves as the generator drive shaft.

b. Starters For High Horsepower Engines

In a typical high-horsepower reciprocating engine starting system, the direct-cranking electric starter consists of two basic components: a motor assembly and a gear section. The gear section is bolted to the drive end of the motor to

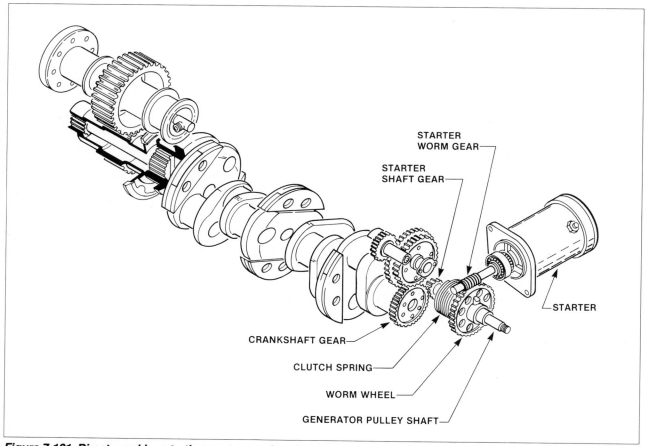

Figure 7-101. *Direct-cranking starting system such as is used on some modern Teledyne-Continental aircraft engines.*

form a complete unit. This type of starter is seen in figure 7-102.

The motor assembly consists of the armature and motor pinion assembly, the bell end assembly, and the motor housing assembly. The motor housing also acts as the magnetic yoke for the field structure.

The starter motor is a non-reversible, series interpole motor. Its speed varies directly with the applied voltage and inversely with the load.

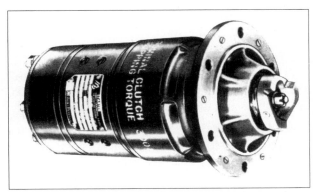

Figure 7-102. Direct-cranking starter for a large aircraft engine.

The starter gear section, shown in figure 7-103, consists of a housing with an integral mounting flange, planetary gear reduction, a sun and integral gear assembly, a torque-limiting clutch, and a jaw and cone assembly.

When the starter circuit is closed, the torque developed in the starter motor is transmitted to the starter jaw through the reduction gear train and clutch.

The starter gear train converts the high speed low-torque of the motor to the low-speed high-torque required to crank the engine.

B. Turbine Engine Starting Systems

Gas turbine engines are generally started by a starter power input to the main gearbox which in turn rotates the compressor. On the dual axial compressor gas turbine, the starter rotates the high speed compressor system only. On free turbine, turboprop, or turboshaft engines, again the compressor rotor system only is rotated by the starter through the accessory gearbox. The usual starting sequence is to energize the starter and then at 5 to 10% rotor speed, to energize ignition

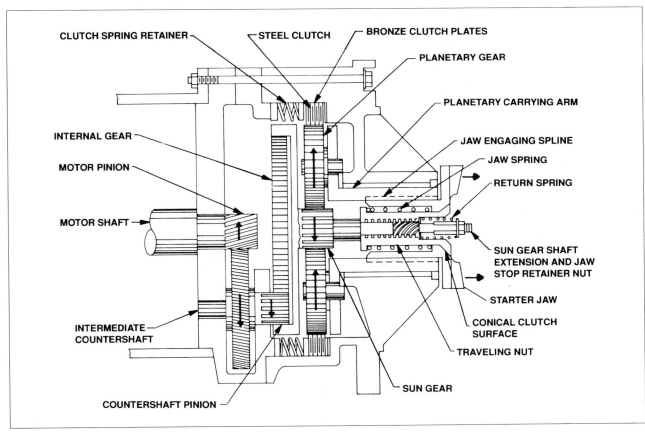

Figure 7-103. Starter gear section.

and open the fuel lever. A normal light-off will usually occur in 10 seconds or less. If light-off does not occur within 10 seconds the start would generally be aborted to investigate the malfunction. Such problems as low starting power, weak ignition, or air in the fuel lines can cause starting problems.

Compressor rotation by the starter provides the engine with sufficient air for combustion and also aids the engine in self-accelerating to idle speed after combustion occurs. Neither the starter nor the turbine wheel have sufficient power on their own to bring the engine from rest to idle speed, but when used in combination, the process takes place smoothly in approximately 30 seconds on the typical engine. The start is often automatically terminated by a speed sensor device after self-accelerating speed is reached; at this point turbine power is sufficient to take the engine up to idle. If the engine is not assisted to the correct speed, a hung (stagnated) start may occur. That is, the engine stabilizes at or near

the point of starter cutoff. To remedy this situation, the engine must be shut down for investigation of the problem. Any attempt to accelerate by adding fuel will quite often result in a hot start as well as a hung start, because the engine is operating with insufficient airflow to support further combustion.

Turboprop and turboshaft engines are started either in low pitch to reduce drag on the rotor and provide more speed and airflow or they are configured with a free-turbine driving the propeller, which allows for a low drag acceleration in that the compressor rotor system only is being turned by the starter.

1. Electric Starters

Electric starting systems for gas turbine aircraft are of two general types: (1) Direct-cranking electrical systems and (2) starter-generator systems.

a. Direct-Cranking Starters

Direct-cranking electric starters are not in wide use on flight engines because the combina-

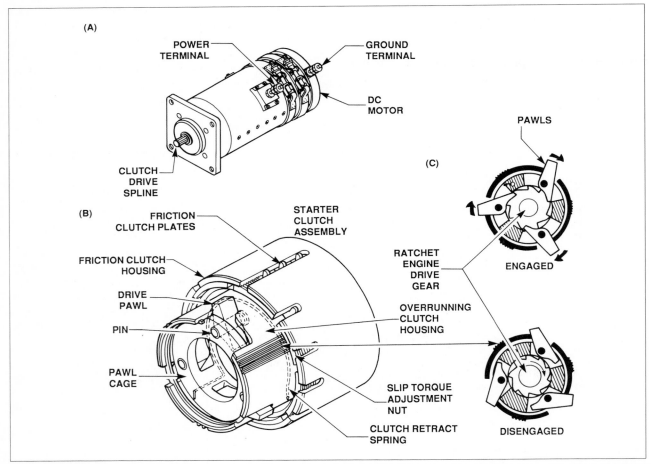

Figure 7-104. (A)—Direct cranking starter for a turbine engine. (B)—Starter clutch assembly. (C)—Overrunning clutch action.

tion starter-generator is more feasible for small engines. Also, large engines require such high starting power that starter weight becomes a problem. However, electric starters are widely used on auxiliary and ground power units, and some small flight engines.

Most electric starters contain an automatic release clutch mechanism to disengage the starter drive from the engine drive. Figure 7-104 shows a clutch assembly that performs two functions. Its first function is to prevent the starter from applying excessive torque to the engine drive. At approximately 130 inch pounds of torque, small clutch plates within the clutch housing slip around and act as a friction clutch. This setting is adjustable. During starting, the friction clutch is designed to slip until engine speed and starter speed increase to develop less than the slip torque setting.

The second function of the clutch assembly is to act as an overrunning clutch. This pawl and ratchet-type mechanism contains three pawls which are spring loaded to the disengage position (figure 7-104C). When the starter is rotated, inertia causes the pawls to move inward to engage a ratchet-type engine drive gear. This occurs because the pawl cage assembly, which floats within the pawl clutch housing, tries to remain stationary when the armature starts to drive the clutch housing around. However, the pawl clutch housing quickly forces the pawls inward by a bumping action, overcoming the retracting spring force. When engine speed approaches idle, its speed exceeds that of the starter and the pawls slip out of the tapered slots of the engine drive gear and throw outward, via force of the retracting spring. This overrunning feature prevents the engine driving the starter to burst speed.

b. Starter-Generator Systems

The combination starter-generator is most widely utilized on corporate size jet aircraft due to the weight saving feature of one engine accessory taking the place of two. Because of its dual purpose, the drive mechanism differs from the electric starter. The starter-generator has a drive spline which stays permanently engaged to the engine.

1) Starter-Generator Circuits

An analysis of the example diagram will be made easier by tracing the circuit shown in figure 7-106 in the following steps:

(1) Master switch closed (up) allows either battery power or external power to reach the fuel valve, the throttle relay coil, the fuel pumps, and the ignition relay contactor.

(2) Battery and start switch closed (up) allows bus power to illuminate the cockpit light, to close the ignition relay, and to close the motor relay. Ignition occurs at this time.

(3) Closing the motor relay in turn allows the undercurrent relay to close and the starter to operate.

(4) The battery and start switch can be released and current will continue to flow to the relays via the emergency stop lead. However, as engine speed increases and less than 200 amperes of current is flowing, the undercurrent relay opens to shut down the starter and ignition circuit operation.

(5) Pulling the emergency stop button will open the ignition circuit at the same point as the undercurrent relay. This button can be used if a malfunction occurs and the relay contacts stick closed or if continuous high ampere draw from a false start prevents normal cutout.

(6) An external power receptacle door microswitch prevents both external power and battery power on the bus at the same time. Some aircraft installations provide no battery start capability or require that battery starting only be used in emergencies to increase service life of the battery.

Figure 7-105. DC aircraft starter-generator used on a gas turbine engine.

2) Starter-Generator Maintenance

The procedures listed on the chart in figure 7-107 are typical of those used to repair malfunctions in a starter-generator system. These procedures are presented as a guide only. The appropriate manufacturer's service instructions and the latest maintenance directives should always be consulted for the aircraft involved.

2. Air Turbine Starters

The air turbine starter was developed as a high power-to-weight ratio device. It has only one-fifth the weight of a comparable electric starter. This starter is used almost exclusively on commercial aircraft and is also becoming an optional accessory on some corporate jets.

A low pressure, high volume air source of approximately 40 psig at 50-100 pound/minute is supplied to this starter from an on board auxiliary power unit (APU), a ground power unit, or from the air bleed source of an operating main engine. Air enters the starter inlet and passes through a set of turbine nozzle vanes to change pressure to velocity and impinge at high kinetic

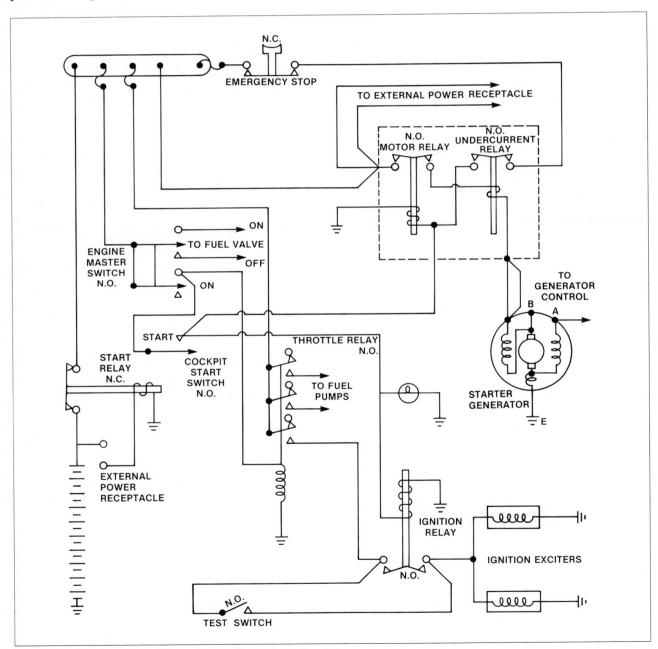

Figure 7-106. Circuit for a typical aircraft starter-generator.

PROBABLE CAUSE	ISOLATION PROCEDURE	REMEDY
Engine Does Not Rotate During Start Attempt:		
Low supply voltage to the starter.	Check voltage of the battery or external power source.	Adjust voltage of the external power.
Power switch is defective.	Check switch for continuity.	Replace switch.
Ignition switch in throttle quadrant.	Check switch for continuity.	Replace switch.
Start-lockout relay energized.	Check position of generator control switch.	Place switch in "OFF" position.
Battery series relay is defective.	With start circuit energized, check for 48 volts DC across battery seriesrelay coil.	Replace relay if no voltage is present.
Starter relay is defective.	With start circuit energized, check for 48 volts DC across starter relay coil.	Replace realy if no voltage is present.
Defective starter.	With start circuit energized, check for proper voltage at the starter.	Replace realy if voltage is not present.
Start lock-in relay defective.	With start circuit energized, check for 28 volts DC across the realy coil.	Replace relay if voltage is not present.
Start drive shaft in component drive gearbox is sheared.	Listen for sounds of starter rotation during an attempted start. If the starter rotates bu the engine does not, the drive shaft is sheared.	Replace the engine.
Engine Starts But Does Not Accelerate To Idle:		
Insufficient starter voltage.	Check starter terminal voltage	Use larger capacity ground power unit or charge batteries.
Engine Fails To Start When Throttle Is Placed In Idle:		
Defective ignition system	Turn on system and listen for spark-igniter operation.	Clean or replace spark igniters, or replace exciters, or leads to igniters.

Figure 7-107. Starter-generator system troubleshooting procedures.

energy levels on the turbine blades. The exhaust air exits overboard through a cowl fairing. The air supply is shut off automatically by a centrifugal cutout switch which closes the inlet air supply valve.

The turbine rotates upwards of 60 to 80 thousand RPM and is geared down 20 to 30 times. An integral oil supply provides lubrication of the gear train. The oil level and magnetic drain plug are frequent inspection items for the maintenance technician.

On shutdown, at approximately 30% engine speed, the pawls of the overrunning clutch on this type starter re-engage sufficiently for restarting if it should be required. This procedure can damage some starters and must only be accomplished within the manufacturer's recommended limits.

Safety features usually incorporated in this starter include a drive shaft shear point, which will break at a predetermined gear train induced torque force if the clutch does not release and the engine drives the starter above design speed. Another safety feature to prevent the starter from reaching burst speed if inlet air does not terminate on schedule, is that the stator nozzle airflow becomes choked and turbine wheel speed stabilizes in an overspeed condition. After either of these malfunctions occurs, a special inspection of the magnetic drain plug is generally required.

The illustration shows that the overrunning clutch, called a sprag clutch assembly, is different from the one previously mentioned for electric starters. The clutch in this installation is in a driveshaft housing which stays permanently engaged to the engine gearbox drive. The pawls are forced inward by small leaf springs to engage the sprag clutch ratchet. At a preset engine speed, the pawls experience sufficient G force to throw outward, disengaging the drive shaft assembly from the sprag clutch ratchet. The sprag clutch ratchet and starter gear-train coast to a halt and the drive shaft housing containing the pawls will continue to rotate at engine gearbox speed. A clicking sound heard during coast-down on this type starter is not a malfunction, but rather the result of the pawls riding on the ratchet.

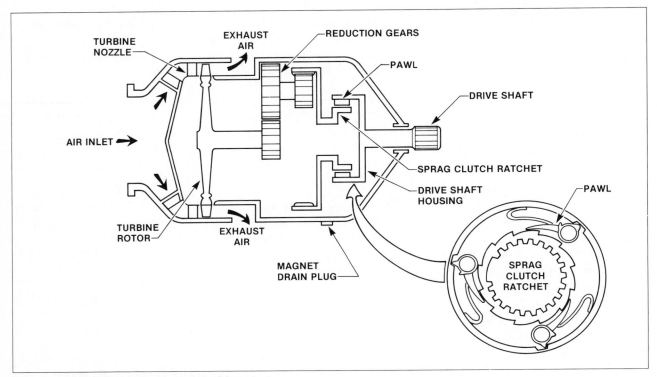

Figure 7-108. Schematic of an air turbine starter.

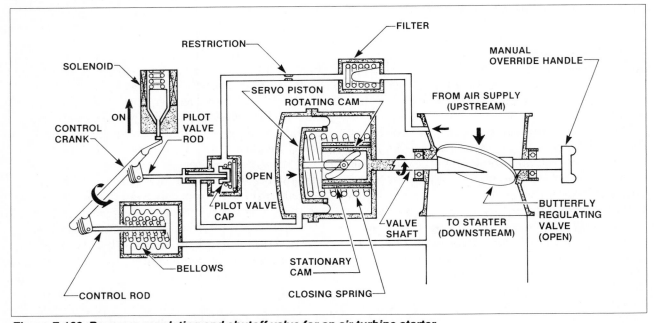

Figure 7-109. Pressure regulating and shutoff valve for an air turbine starter.

a. Starter Pressure-Regulating And Shutoff Valve

The starter air valve is installed in the inlet air line to the starter. It consists of a control head and a butterfly valve and is powered open electrically by means of a cockpit switch.

In figure 7-109, the solenoid is energized upward by the cockpit start switch, and the following events occur:

TROUBLE	PROBABLE CAUSE	REMEDY
Starter does not operate (no rotation)	No air supply	Check air supply.
	Electrical open in cutout switch	Check switch continuity. If no continuity, remove starter and adjust or replace switch.
	Sheared starter drive coupling	Remove starter and replace drive coupling.
	Internal starter discrepancy	Remove and replace starter.
Starter will not accelerate to normal cutoff speed	Low starter air supply	Check air source pressure.
	Starter cutout switch set improperly	Adjust rotor switch actuator.
	Valve pressure regulated too low	Replace valve.
	Internal starter malfunction	Remove and replace starter.
Starter will not cut off	Low air supply	Check air supply.
	Rotor switch actuator set too high	Adjust switch actuator assembly.
	Starter cutout switch shorted	Replace switch and bracket assembly.
External oil leakage	Oil level too high	Drain oil and reservice properly.
	Loose vent, oil filler, or magnetic plugs	Tighten magnetic plug to proper torque. Tighten vent and oil filler plugs as necessary and lockwire.
	Loose clamp band assembly	Tighten clamp band assembly to higher torque.
Starter runs, but engine does not turn over	Sheared drive coupling	Remove starter and replace the drive coupling. If couplings persist in breaking in unusually short periods of time, remove and replace starter.
Starter inlet will not line up with supply ducting	Improper installation of starter on engine, or improper indexing of turbine housing on starter	Check installation and/or indexing for conformance with manufacturer's installation instructions and the proper index position of the turbine housing specified for the aircraft.
Metallic particles on magnetic drain plug	Small fuzzy particles indicate normal wear	No remedial action required.
	Particles coarser than fuzzy, such as chips, slivers, etc., indicate internal difficulty	Remove and replace starter.
Broken nozzle vanes	Large foreign particles in air supply	Remove and replace starter and check air supply filter.
Oil leakage from vent plug assembly	Improper starter installation position	Check installed position for levelness of oil plugs and correct as required in accordance with manufacturer's installation instructions.
Oil leakage at drive coupling	Leaking rear seal assembly	Remove and replace starter.

Figure 7-110. Air turbine starter system troubleshooting guide.

(1) The control crank rotates counterclockwise, pushing the control rod to the right and extending the bellows fully. The butterfly type regulating valve being closed permits this because no pressure is present in the sensing line at this time.

(2) The control crank also forces the pilot valve rod and cap to the right against a spring tension.

(3) Air that had been blocked in the filtered inlet line flows past the cap to the servo piston and opens the butterfly valve.

(4) As pressure builds in the downstream supply line, the sensing line takeoff directs air to partially compress the bellows. As this occurs, the pilot valve rod off-seats, allowing servo piston air to vent to atmosphere.

(5) When downstream air pressure reaches a preset value, the amount of air flowing to the servo piston through the restrictor equals the amount of air being bled to atmospheric, and the system is in a state of equilibrium. This feature is present to protect the starter if inlet air pressure is set too high.

(6) When a predetermined starter drive speed is reached, the centrifugal cutout flyweight switch de-energizes the solenoid and the butterfly returns to a closed position.

(7) The manual override handle is present to manually rotate the butterfly open and closed if corrosion or icing is causing excessive friction within the system. After freeing the restriction to movement, the valve must operate normally or be replaced.

b. Air Turbine Starter Maintenance

The troubleshooting procedures listed in figure 7-110 are applicable to air turbine starters equipped with a combination pressure-regulating and shutoff valve. These procedures should be used as a guide only, and are not intended to supplant the manufacturer's instructions.

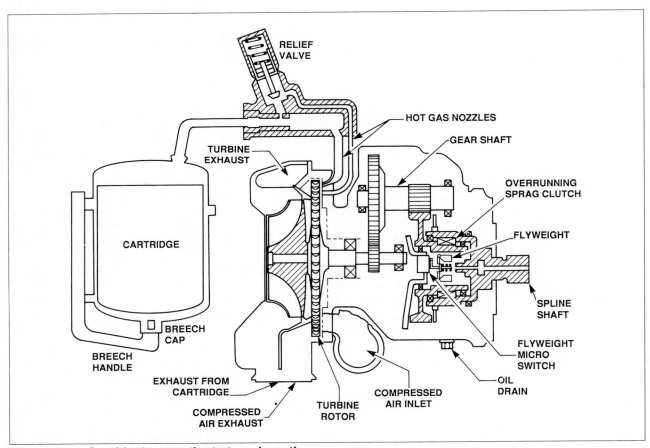

Figure 7-111. Cartridge/pneumatic starter schematic.

3. Cartridge/Pneumatic Turbine Starter

Many other starting systems have been developed in the past for military and commercial engines. They are not in common use in either general or commercial aviation.

The cartridge-pneumatic starter is an accessory gearbox mounted starter which can use either an explosive charge or a low pressure, high volume air source similar to the air turbine starter.

To accomplish a cartridge start, a cartridge is first placed in the breech cap. The breech is then closed on the breech chamber by means of the breech handle and rotated a part-turn to engage the lugs between the two breech sections. This rotation allows the lower section of the breech handle to drop into a socket and completes the cartridge ignition circuit. Until the ignition circuit is completed, it is impossible to fire the cartridge.

The cartridge is ignited by applying voltage through the connector at the end of the breech handle. Upon ignition, the cartridge begins to generate gas. The gas is forced out of the breech to the hot gas nozzles which are directed toward the buckets on the turbine rotor, and rotation is produced. Gas emerging from the opposite side of the turbine wheel enters an exhaust ring in the exhaust duct, where it is collected and passed out of the starter via the overboard exhaust collector.

The cartridge/pneumatic starter can also be operated by compressed air from a ground cart, or by engine cross-bleed air. The air passes into the nozzle ring and is directed against the buckets of the turbine rotor by vanes placed around the ring. Rotation is thus produced in essentially the same manner as during a cartridge start.

4. Fuel/Air Combustion Turbine Starter

This is an accessory gearbox mounted starter which utilizes a high pressure (3,000 psi) air source and a combustion process. It is very similar to a small gas turbine engine. Operation of this starter is, in most installations, fully automatic; actuation of a single switch causes the starter to fire and accelerate the engine from rest to starter cutoff speed.

The fuel/air combustion starter was developed primarily for short-flight, air-carrier type aircraft. The installed combustion starter provided quick starting at air terminals without ground starting equipment.

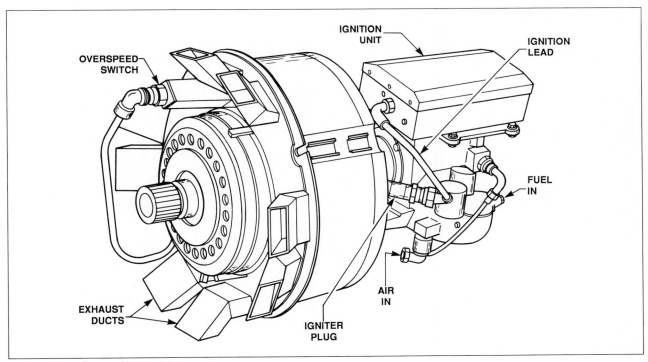

Figure 7-112. Fuel/air combustion starter.

5. Turbine Driven Auxiliary Power Unit

The auxiliary power unit is generally mounted in the rear of the airplane, and an air manifold which runs through the entire ship interconnects the APU, the ground service connection, the engine bleed air ports and the starter inlets. A common procedure for this system is to start one engine from a ground or on-board starting unit and then to start the remaining engine(s) from the bleed air source of the operating engine.

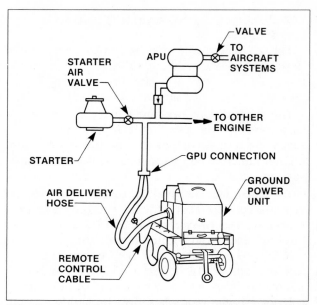

Figure 7-113. Air turbine starting system with on-board APU and ground power connections.

Chapter VIII
Engine Lubrication And Cooling Systems

The primary purpose of a lubricant is to reduce friction between moving parts. Because liquid lubricants (oils) can be circulated readily, they are used universally in aircraft engines.

A. Requirements And Characteristics Of Reciprocating Engine Lubricants

While its primary purpose is to reduce friction, engine lubricating oil also serves to provide cooling, seal and cushion, protect against corrosion, and clean. We will examine here each of these functions and the properties that must exist in an acceptable engine lubricating oil.

1. Functions Of Lubricating Oils

a. Reduces Friction

If we could microscopically examine the surfaces of the metal parts inside an aircraft engine, we would find that they are not perfectly smooth, but are made up of peaks and valleys. When two parts with surfaces such as these are rubbed together, there is friction that will soon wear away the metal.

In order to reduce this friction, a film of oil is placed between the moving parts. This oil wets the surfaces, fills in the valleys and holds the metal surfaces apart. The movement is now between layers of the oil rather than the metal surfaces, and the oil slides over itself with very little friction.

The viscosity of an oil is a measure of its fluid friction, and the amount of clearance between the moving parts determines the viscosity of the oil that is needed to prevent the film breaking away and allowing the metal-to-metal contact that causes wear.

b. Provides Cooling

The lubricating oil is in intimate contact with the moving parts of an aircraft engine, and it absorbs some of the heat from the combustion process. This heated oil then flows through the system to the oil cooler where the heat is given up to the outside air as it passes through the core of the cooler.

c. Seals And Cushions

The viscous nature of oil—that is, its ability to wet the surface it contacts—makes oil a good sealing agent between moving parts. The oil film on the cylinder walls and around the piston forms a tight seal in the cylinder, and the thin film of oil between the rocker arm and its bushing takes up much of the hammering shock from the valve action.

d. Protects Against Corrosion

When metal remains uncovered in the presence of moisture or some of the chemicals that contaminate the air, rust and other forms of surface corrosion will attack the metal. This is especially true of metal surfaces such as cylinder walls and crankshafts which have been hardened by the nitriding process. A film of oil covering these surfaces will prevent oxygen reaching the metal and causing it to corrode.

e. Cleans

Dirt, dust, carbon and water all enter the oil, and the ability of an oil to hold these contaminants

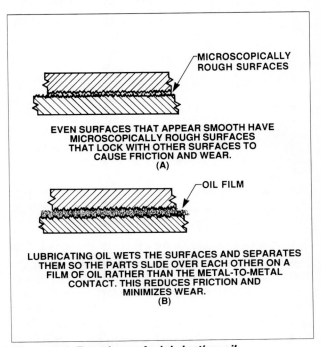

MICROSCOPICALLY ROUGH SURFACES

EVEN SURFACES THAT APPEAR SMOOTH HAVE MICROSCOPICALLY ROUGH SURFACES THAT LOCK WITH OTHER SURFACES TO CAUSE FRICTION AND WEAR.
(A)

OIL FILM

LUBRICATING OIL WETS THE SURFACES AND SEPARATES THEM SO THE PARTS SLIDE OVER EACH OTHER ON A FILM OF OIL RATHER THAN THE METAL-TO-METAL CONTACT. THIS REDUCES FRICTION AND MINIMIZES WEAR.
(B)

Figure 8-1. Functions of a lubricating oil.

8-1

until they can be trapped in the filter helps keep the inside of the engine clean and reduces abrasive wear.

2. Requirements Of Engine Lubricants

Several factors must be considered in determining the proper grade of oil to use in a particular engine. The operating load, rotational speeds and operating temperatures are the most important. The conditions encountered in the various types of engines will determine the grade of lubricating oil to be used.

a. Viscosity

While there are several important properties which a satisfactory engine lubricant must possess, its viscosity is the most important. The resistance of an oil to flow is known as its viscosity. An oil which flows slowly is viscous, or has a high viscosity. If it flows freely, it has a low viscosity. The viscosity of oil is measured using an instrument known as the Saybolt Universal Viscosimeter. The number of seconds required for 60 cubic centimeters of the oil to flow through a calibrated orifice at a specific temperature is known as the Saybolt Seconds Universal viscosity or S.S.U.

The oil used in reciprocating engines has a relatively high viscosity because of:

(1) Large engine operating clearances due to the relatively large size of the moving parts, the different materials used, and the different rates of expansion of the various materials.

(2) High operating temperatures.

(3) High bearing pressures.

b. Viscosity Index

Unfortunately the viscosity of oil is affected by temperature. It is not uncommon for some grades of oil to become practically solid in cold weather. This increases drag and makes circulation almost impossible. Other oils may become so thin at high temperature that the oil film is broken, resulting in rapid wear of the moving parts.

Viscosity index is a measure of the change in viscosity of an oil with a given change in temperature. The index itself is based on the viscosity changes with temperature of two reference oils. One oil is rated at 100, and the other is rated at zero. The smaller the change in the viscosity for a given temperature change, the higher the viscosity index.

c. Gravity API

Specific gravity is a comparison of the weight of a substance to the weight of an equal volume of distilled water at a specified temperature. As an example, water weighs approximately 8 pounds to the gallon; an oil with a specific gravity of 0.9 would weigh 7.2 pounds to the gallon.

The American Petroleum Institute has formulated a measurement of the specific gravity of oils which is an expansion of the regular specific gravity scale. A conversion chart must be used to relate any API number to its corresponding specific gravity.

d. Color

The color of an oil is rated by comparing its color with an American Society of Testing and Materials (ASTM) color chart. The reference 1.00 on the chart is pure white, and 8.00 is a red, darker than claret wine.

e. Cloud Point And Pour Point

Cloud point and pour point also help to indicate suitability. The cloud point of an oil is the temperature at which its wax content, normally held in solution, begins to solidify and separate into tiny crystals, causing the oil to appear cloudy or hazy. The pour point of an oil is the lowest temperature at which it will flow or can be poured.

f. Flash Point And Fire Point

Flash point and fire point are determined by laboratory tests that show the temperature at which a liquid will begin to give off ignitable vapors (flash) and the temperature where there are sufficient vapors to support a flame (fire). These points are established for engine oils to determine that they can withstand the high temperatures encountered in an engine.

g. Carbon Residue

A given amount of oil is placed in a stainless steel receptacle and is heated to an accurately controlled high temperature until it is evaporated. The container is weighed before and after the test, and the amount of carbon residue left in the container is expressed as a percent of the weight of the sampled material.

3. Engine Oil Classification System

Generally, commercial aviation oils are classified numerically, such as 80, 100, 120, etc., which is an approximation of the viscosity. If the actual Saybolt values were used to designate the viscosity of oil, there probably would be several hundred grades of oil. To simplify the selection of oils, they are often classified under a Society of Automotive Engineers (SAE) system, which divides all oils into seven groups (SAE 10 to 70) according to viscosity at either 130 or 210°F.

SAE ratings are purely arbitrary and bear no direct relationship to the Saybolt or other ratings. The letter "W" indicates that the oil, in addition to meeting the viscosity requirements at the testing temperature specifications, is a satisfactory oil for winter use in cold climates.

Although the SAE scale has eliminated some confusion in the designation of lubricating oils, it must not be assumed that this specification covers all the important viscosity requirements. An SAE number indicates only the viscosity (grade) or relative viscosity; it does not indicate quality or other essential characteristics. It is well known that there are good oils and inferior oils that have the same viscosities at a given temperature and, therefore, are subject to classification in the same grade. The SAE letters on an oil container are not an endorsement or recommendation of the oil by the Society of Automotive Engineers.

Although each grade of oil is rated by an SAE number, depending upon its specific use, it may be rated with a commercial aviation grade number or an Army and Navy specification number. The characteristics of aviation lubricating oils are detailed in figure 8-2.

B. Reciprocating Engine Lubrication Systems

Reciprocating engine oil systems may be roughly divided into two types: (1) dry-sump systems and (2) wet-sump systems. Because the dry sump system will introduce all of the components involved in the lubricating system, we will deal with it in detail and then supplement the information with the differences encountered in the wet-sump systems.

1. Dry-sump Lubricating Systems

Many reciprocating aircraft engines have pressure dry-sump lubrication systems. The oil supply in this type of system is carried in a tank. A pressure pump circulates the oil through the engine, scavenger pumps then return it to the tank as quickly as it accumulates in the engine sumps. The need for a separate supply tank is apparent when considering the complications that would result if large quantities of oil were carried in the engine crankcase. On multi-engine aircraft, each engine is supplied with oil from its own complete and independent system.

Although the arrangement of the oil systems in different aircraft varies widely and the units of which they are composed differ in construction details, the functions of all such systems are the same. The principal units in a typical reciprocating engine dry-sump system installed on a horizontally opposed engine are illustrated in figure 8-3.

2. Wet-sump Lubricating Systems

Most modern aircraft engines use a wet-sump lubricating system in which all of the oil is carried in a sump which is part of the engine itself. The wet-sump system is simple and reliable, and is suitable for use on the smaller reciprocating engines used today. The main disadvantages of the wet-sump system are:

	AN 1065 AVIATION 65 SAE 30	AN 1080 AVIATION 80 SAE 40	AN 1100 AVIATION 100 SAE 50	AN 11120 AVIATION 120 SAE 60
VISCOSITY S.S.U. @ 100°F S.S.U. @ 130°F S.S.U. @ 210°F	443 215 65.4	676 310 79.2	1,124 480 103.0	1,530 630 123.2
VISCOSITY INDEX	116	112	108	107
GRAVITY API	29.0	27.5	27.4	27.1
COLOR ASTM	1.5	4.5	4.5	5.5
POUR POINT °F	−20	−15	−10	−10
POUR POINT DILUTED °F	−70	−70	−70	−50
FLASH POINT °F	450	465	515	520
CARBON RESIDUE % W	0.11	0.23	0.23	0.40

Figure 8-2. Characteristics of aircraft engine lubricating oils.

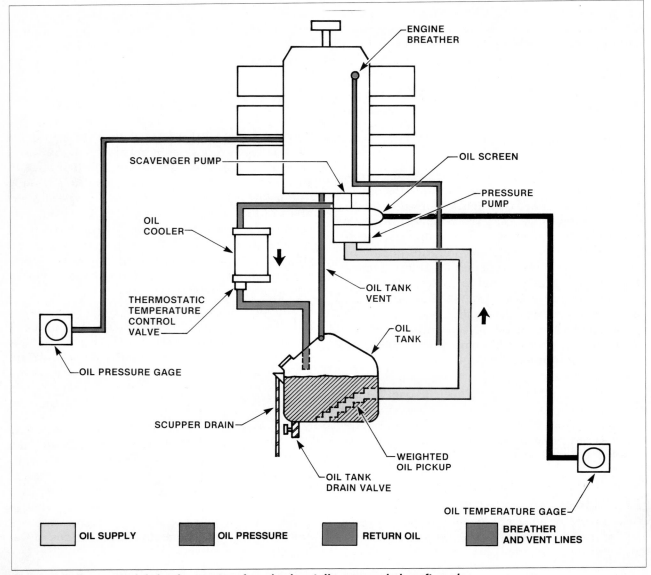

Figure 8-3. Dry-sump lubrication system for a horizontally opposed aircraft engine.

(1) The oil supply is limited by the sump (oil pan) capacity.

(2) Provisions for cooling the oil are more difficult to arrange because the system is a self-contained unit.

(3) Oil temperatures are likely to be higher on large engines because the oil supply is so close to the engine and is continuously subjected to the operating temperatures.

3. Lubricating System Components

a. Oil Tanks

Dry-sump engines carry their oil in an external reservoir which must have a capacity compatible with the amount of fuel carried, plus a margin that will provide for adequate circulation and cooling.

Oil tanks are generally constructed of aluminum alloys. The oil tank is placed close enough to the engine and high enough above the oil pump inlet to ensure gravity feed. The tank filler neck is positioned to provide sufficient room for expansion and for foam to collect. The filler cap or cover is marked with the word "OIL" and the tank capacity. A scupper drain in the filler cap well disposes of any overflow caused by the filling operation. Oil tank vent lines are provided to ensure proper tank ventilation in all attitudes of flight. These lines are usually connected to the engine crankcase to prevent loss of oil through the vents. This indirectly vents the tanks to the atmosphere through the crankcase breather.

Some oil tanks have a built-in hopper (figure 8-4), or temperature accelerating well, that extends from the oil return fitting on top of the oil tank to the outlet fitting in the bottom of the tank. In some systems, the hopper tank is open to the main oil supply at the lower end; other systems have flapper-type valves that separate the main oil supply from the oil in the hopper.

By separating the circulating oil from the surrounding oil in the tank, less oil is circulated. This hastens the warming of the oil when the engine is started. A hopper tank also makes oil dilution practical because only a relatively small volume of oil will have to be diluted.

Oil dilution is a system installed on some reciprocating engines to aid in cold weather starting. Before the engine is shut down, and while the oil is still hot, fuel from the carburetor is directed into the engine oil pump inlet where it mixes with

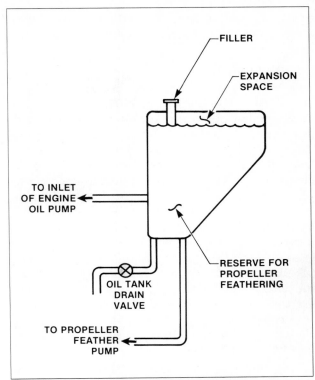

Figure 8-5. Typical dry-sump oil tank for an engine equipped with a Hydromatic feathering propeller.

the oil and dilutes it. The amount of dilution is determined by the anticipated outside air temperature, and is controlled by the length of time that the oil dilution solenoid is held open. When the engine is started the next day, the diluted oil flows freely through the engine and assures proper lubrication. When the oil warms up, the gasoline evaporates from it and leaves the engine through the crankcase breather, and the oil returns to its original condition.

Oil tanks used with engines equipped with Hamilton-Standard Hydromatic propellers feed the pressure pump through a standpipe which sticks into the oil tank for a few inches. The tank outlet to the propeller feathering pump is taken from the bottom of the tank. With this arrangement, if an oil line should break and all of the engine oil be pumped overboard by the engine's oil pump, there will still be enough oil in the tank to feather the propeller.

Most aircraft oil systems are equipped with the dipstick-type quantity gauge, often called a bayonet gauge. Some systems may also have an oil quantity indicating system that shows the quantity of oil during flight. One type consists essentially of an arm and float mechanism that rides the level of the oil and actuates an electric transmitter

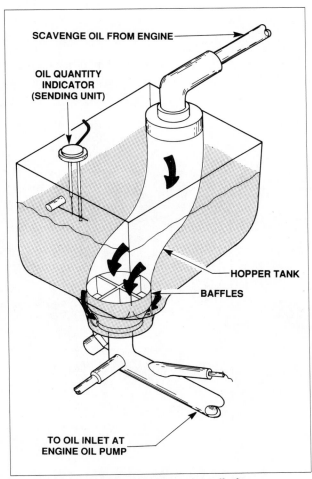

Figure 8-4. Oil tank with hopper installation.

on top of the tank. The transmitter is connected to a cockpit gauge, which indicates the quantity of oil in gallons.

b. Oil Pump

As oil enters the engine (figure 8-6), it is pressurized by a gear-type pump. This is a positive displacement pump that consists of two meshed gears that revolve inside a housing. Oil entering the gear chamber is "picked up" by the gear teeth, trapped between them and the sides of the gear chamber, and is carried around the outside of the gears. The clearance between the teeth and housing is small. The pump inlet is located on the left, in the illustration, and the discharge port is connected to the engine's system pressure line. One gear is attached to a drive shaft that extends from the pump housing to an accessory drive shaft on the engine. Seals are used to prevent leakage around the drive shaft. As the lower gear is rotated counterclockwise, the driven (idler) gear turns clockwise. The oil is discharged from the pressure port into the oil screen passage.

The pressurized oil flows to the oil filter, where any solid particles suspended in the oil are separated from it, preventing possible damage to moving parts of the engine. Oil under pressure then opens the oil filter check valve mounted in the top of the filter. This valve is closed by a light spring loading of 1 to 3 pounds when the engine is not operating.

The by-pass valve, located between the pressure side of the oil pump and the oil filter, permits unfiltered oil to by-pass the filter and enter the engine when the oil filter is clogged or during a cold engine start. The spring loading on the by-pass valve allows the valve to open before the oil pressure collapses the filter, or in the case of cold, congealed oil, it provides a low-resistance path around the filter. It is felt that dirty oil in an engine is better than no lubrication at all.

c. Oil Filters

Solid contaminants and sludge pumped through an aircraft engine lubricating system can clog the oil passages and damage the bearing surfaces, so provisions must be made to remove as much of it as possible. There are two ways this may be done: by a full-flow filter, through which all of the engine oil must flow each time it circulates through the engine, or with a by-pass filter that filters only a portion of the oil each time it circulates, but which eventually gets all of the oil. By-pass filters can be made much finer because, if they should clog and prevent oil flowing through

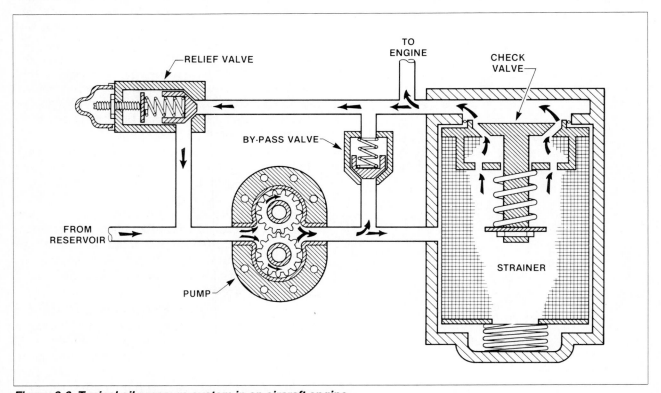

Figure 8-6. Typical oil pressure system in an aircraft engine.

them, they will not starve the engine of oil (see figure 8-7.)

1) Edge Filtration

A long, flat spiral with a wedge-shaped cross section forms the filtering element for an edge-type filter. The oil flows from the outside of the element into the center, and any contaminants collect on the outside where the slots are the smallest. Since the cross section of the spiral is wedge-shaped, if a contaminant should be small enough to pass through, it will not clog the filter. Some edge-type filters are cleaned with a built-in blade that is rotated to scrape off the contaminants that collect on the outside of the element. A familiar name associated with edge-type filtration is the Cuno filter. An edge-type filter is seen in figure 8-8.

2) Depth Filtration

Depth filters consist of a matrix of fibers that are closely packed to a depth of about one inch. The oil flows through this mat and the contaminants are trapped in the fibers. Depth-type filters are more efficient than edge-type because they hold so

much more contamination. One disadvantage, however, is that it is possible for the high pressure oil flowing through it to find a weak spot and channel through, causing the filter to lose a great deal of its effectiveness (see figure 8-9).

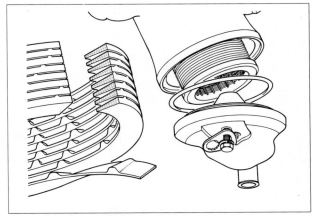

Figure 8-8. Edge filtration-type oil filter.

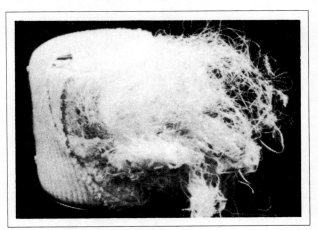

Figure 8-9. Depth-type oil filter.

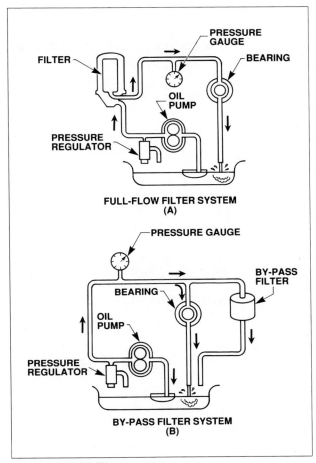

Figure 8-7. Oil filter systems.

FILTER
PRESSURE GAUGE
BEARING
OIL PUMP
PRESSURE REGULATOR
FULL-FLOW FILTER SYSTEM
(A)

PRESSURE GAUGE
BEARING
BY-PASS FILTER
OIL PUMP
PRESSURE REGULATOR
BY-PASS FILTER SYSTEM
(B)

Figure 8-10. Screen-type surface filtration oil strainer.

ENLARGED VIEW OF THE FIBERS IN THE FILTER
ELEMENT
(A)

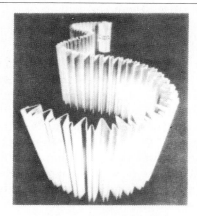

PLEATED FILTER ELEMENT
(B)

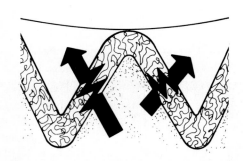

METHOD OF TRAPPING SEDIMENT IN THE FILTER
ELEMENT
(C)

THE PLEATED FILTER ELEMENT IS ASSEMBLED
AROUND A SHEET STEEL CORE
(D)

FILTER ELEMENT
(E)

SPIN-ON-TYPE OIL FILTER
(F)

METHOD OF OPENING A SPIN-ON-TYPE OIL FILTER FOR INSPECTION OF CONTAMINANTS
(G)

Figure 8-11. Semi-depth type oil filters.

3) Surface Filtration

Standard equipment on almost all aircraft engines is a woven wire-mesh oil screen that is useful for trapping some of the larger contaminants that flow through the engine. Particles of contamination larger than the size of the screen openings are trapped on the surface, and the smaller particles pass through. To get better filtering, the size of the wire mesh must be decreased, but when this is done, the cleaning process becomes quite complex and the advantage of simplicity is lost. As a result, this type of filter is often supplemented by a more efficient type (see figure 8-10).

4) Semi-depth Filtration

The most popular filter in common use for the general aviation fleet is a disposable, semi-depth filter made up of resin-impregnated fibers. These fibers are formed into a long sheet and folded in a pleated fashion. All of the oil that flows in the system must pass through the filter element, and in doing so the contaminants are trapped within its fibers. There is so much uniform surface area that there is little tendency for the oil to channel through. The pleated material is assembled around a sheet steel core, and either fitted in a heavy sheet steel case which is an integral part of the filter, or may be made so that it can be installed inside a housing which is part of the engine.

When this type of filter is removed from the engine at inspection time, it is cut open and inspected for the presence of any metal particles that might indicate an impending engine failure. Sealed, spin-on type filters are opened with a special roller-type can cutter that removes the top of the container without introducing any metal particles that might make examination more difficult (see figure 8-11).

d. Oil Pressure Relief Valve

Almost all pumps used in aircraft engine lubrication systems are of the constant-displacement type, and provision must be made to relieve some of the oil back to the inlet side of the pump. This is necessary to keep the pressure constant as the engine RPM changes. In figure 8-12 we see the operating principle of a simple pressure relief valve. Oil from the discharge side of the pump flows into the lubricating passage, which is connected by a spring-loaded valve back into the inlet side of the pump. As long as the pressure is below that for which the relief valve is set, the valve remains on its seat. When the pressure rises above that value, the valve will move off its seat, and oil will be returned to the inlet side of the pump, holding the system pressure constant. An adjustment screw, locked with a jam nut and covered with a protective cap, is used to change the oil pressure.

Some of the larger engines require a very high oil pressure to force cold oil through the bearings during starting and warm-up. But when the oil warms up and becomes thinner, this high pressure would cause excessive oil consumption, so a compensated oil pressure relief valve is used. This valve will hold the pressure high until the oil warms up, and then automatically lower it to the normal operating range.

This is accomplished by using two springs to hold the valve on its seat when the oil is cold. When the oil warms up, a thermostatically-operated valve opens a passage and allows oil to flow beneath a piston, relieving the force on the high-pressure spring. Normal operating pressure is maintained by the force of the low-pressure spring-along. This valve is illustrated in figure 8-13.

e. Oil Pressure Gauge

Oil pressure is measured at the outlet of the engine-driven pump and is indicated on a gauge on the pilot's instrument panel. This gauge warns of possible engine failure caused by an exhausted oil supply, failure of the oil pump, burned-out bearings, ruptured oil lines or other causes that may be indicated by a loss of oil pressure.

One type of oil pressure gauge uses a Bourdon-tube mechanism that measures the difference between oil pressure and cabin (atmospheric) pressure. To prevent gauge fluctuations and keep the loss of oil to a minimum if the line to the instrument should break, a small orifice, about a number 60-drill size, is installed in the fitting where the gauge line attaches to the oil pressure gallery in the engine. One disadvantage of this system is that in cold weather the oil in the long tube running between the engine and the cockpit gauge may congeal and cause a false reading of low-

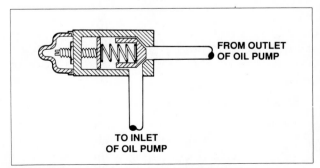

Figure 8-12. Simple oil pressure relief valve.

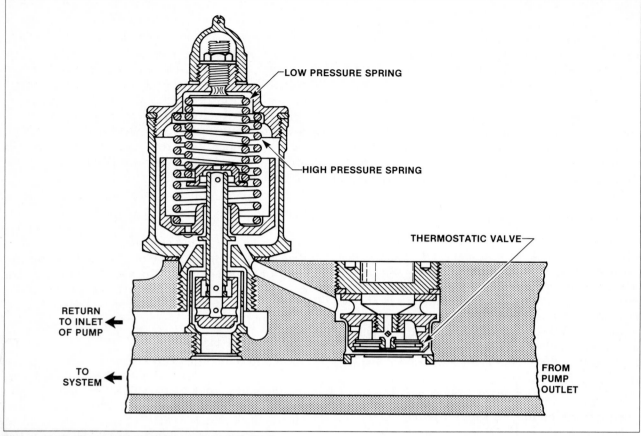

Figure 8-13. Compensated oil pressure relief valve.

or no-oil pressure. This error may be kept to a minimum by filling the line to the cockpit gauge with a very light machine oil.

The trend is toward electrical transmitters and indicators for oil-pressure indicating systems in all aircraft. In this type of indicating system, the oil pressure being measured is applied to the inlet port of the electrical transmitter, where it is conducted to a diaphragm assembly by a capillary tube. The motion produced by the diaphragm's expansion and contraction is amplified through a lever and gear arrangement. The gear varies the electrical value of the indicating circuit, which, in turn, is reflected on the cockpit indicator. This type of indicating system replaces long fluid-filled tubing lines with an almost weightless piece of wire.

f. Oil Temperature Regulator

As discussed previously, the viscosity of the oil varies with its temperature. Since the viscosity affects its lubricating properties, the temperature at which oil enters the engine must be held within close limits. Generally, the oil leaving an engine

must be cooled before it is recirculated. Obviously, the amount of cooling must be controlled if the oil is to return to the engine at the correct temperature. The oil temperature regulator, located in the return line to the tank of a dry-sump system, provides this controlled cooling.

As the name implies, this unit regulates the temperature by either cooling the oil or passing it on to the tank without cooling, depending upon the temperature at which it leaves the engine. The regulator consists of two main parts: (1) a cooler and (2) an oil control valve. The cooler transfers the heat from the oil to the air, while the control valve regulates the flow of oil through the cooler.

g. Indicating Oil Temperature

The oil temperature measurement read on the instrument panel is the temperature of the oil as it enters the engine. On dry-sump engines, the temperature pickup bulb is often located in a special fitting between the oil tank and the pump. On wet-sump engines, it is usually installed inside the oil screen immediately after the pump. Temperature may be measured electrically, by measuring the change in resistance of a special temperature probe, or mechanically by measuring the pressure of a gas sealed inside a bulb held in the oil. The pressure of the gas varies in proportion to its temperature.

h. Oil Cooler

The cooler (figure 8-14) consists of a core enclosed in a double-walled shell. The core is built of copper or aluminum tubes with the tube ends formed to a hexagonal shape and joined together in the honeycomb effect. The ends of the copper tubes of the core are soldered, whereas aluminum tubes are brazed or mechanically joined. The tubes touch only at the ends so that a space exists between them along most of their lengths. This allows oil to flow through the spaces between the tubes while the cooling air passes through the tubes.

The space between the inner and outer shells is known as the annular or by-pass jacket. Two paths are open to the flow of oil through a cooler. From the inlet it can flow halfway around the by-pass jacket, enter the core from the bottom, and then pass through the spaces between the tubes and out to the oil tank (view B of figure 8-14). This is the path the oil follows when it is hot enough to require cooling. As the oil flows through the core, it is guided by baffles, which force the oil to travel back and forth several times before it reaches the core outlet. The oil can also pass from the inlet completely around the by-pass jacket to the outlet without passing through the core (view A of figure 8-14). Oil follows this by-pass route when the oil is cold or when the core is blocked with thick, congealed oil.

i. Flow Control Valve

The flow control valve determines which of the two possible paths the oil will take through a cooler. There are two openings in a flow control valve which fit over the corresponding outlets at the top of the cooler. When the oil is cold, a bellows within the flow control contracts and lifts a valve from its seat. Under this condition, oil entering the cooler has a choice of two outlets and two paths. Following the path of least resistance, the oil flows around the jacket and out past the thermostatic valve to the tank. This allows the oil to warm up quickly and, at the same time, heats the oil in the core. As the oil warms up and reaches its operating temperature, the bellows of the thermostat expands and closes the outlet from the by-pass jacket. The oil must now flow through the core into an opening in the base of the control valve, and

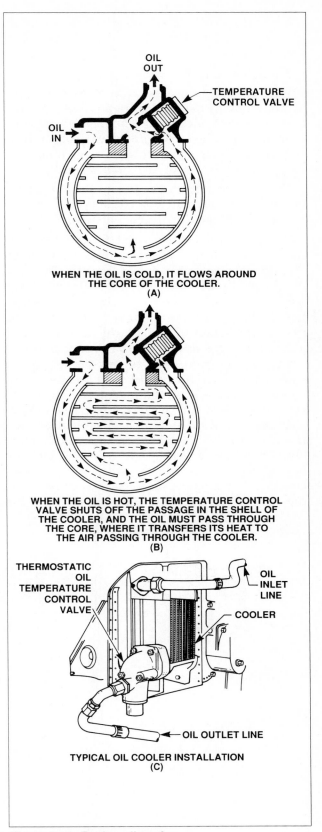

Figure 8-14. Engine oil cooler.

to the tank. No matter which path it takes through the cooler, the oil always flows over the bellows of the thermostatic valve.

j. Surge Protection Valves

When oil in the system is congealed, the scavenger pump may build up a very high pressure in the oil return line. To prevent this high pressure from bursting the oil cooler or blowing off the hose connections, some aircraft have surge protection valves in the engine lubrication systems.

One type of surge valve (figure 8-15) is incorporated in the oil cooler flow control valve; another type is a separate unit in the oil return line.

The surge protection valve incorporated in a flow control valve is the more common type. Although this flow control valve differs from the one just described, it is essentially the same except for the surge protection feature. The high pressure operation condition is shown in figure 8-15, where the high oil pressure at the control valve inlet has forced the surge valve (C) upward. Note how this movement has opened the surge valve and, at the same time, seated the poppet valve (E). The closed poppet valve prevents oil from entering the cooler properly; therefore, the scavenge oil passes directly to the tank through outlet (A) without passing through either the cooler bypass jacket or the core. When the pressure drops to a safe value, the spring forces the surge and poppet valves downward, closing the surge valve (C) and opening the poppet valve (E). Oil then passes from the

control valve inlet (D), through the open poppet valve and into the bypass jacket. The thermostatic valve, according to oil temperature, then determines oil flow either through the bypass jacket to port (H) or through the core to port (G). The check valve (B) opens to allow the oil to reach the tank return line.

k. Airflow Controls

By regulating the airflow through the cooler, the temperature of the oil can be controlled to fit various operating conditions. For example, the oil will reach operating temperature more quickly if the airflow is cut off during engine warm-up. Two methods have been used to accomplish this task: one method employs shutters installed on the rear of the oil cooler, and the other uses a controllable flap on the air-exit duct.

Control of the airflow may be accomplished manually or automatically. The oil cooler air-exit is opened and closed automatically by an electrically operated actuator. Automatic operation of the actuator is determined by electrical impulses received from a controlling thermostat inserted in the oil pipe leading from the cooler to the oil supply tank.

C. Internal Lubrication Of Reciprocating Engines

The lubricating oil is distributed to the various moving parts of a typical internal-combustion engine by one of the three following methods: (1)

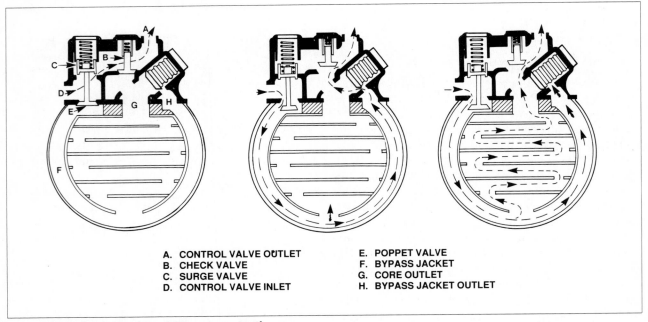

A. CONTROL VALVE OUTLET
B. CHECK VALVE
C. SURGE VALVE
D. CONTROL VALVE INLET

E. POPPET VALVE
F. BYPASS JACKET
G. CORE OUTLET
H. BYPASS JACKET OUTLET

Figure 8-15. Control valve with surge protection.

pressure, (2) splash or (3) a combination of pressure and splash.

The pressure-lubrication system is the principal method of lubricating aircraft engines. Splash lubrication may be used in addition to pressure lubrication on aircraft engines, but is never used by itself; hence, aircraft-engine lubrication systems are always either the pressure type or the combination pressure-and-splash type, usually the latter.

The advantages of pressure lubrication are:

(1) Positive introduction of oil to the bearings.

(2) Cooling effect caused by the large quantities of oil which can be (pumped) circulated through a bearing.

(3) Satisfactory lubrication in various attitudes of flight.

Figure 8-16 shows the various methods of lubrication used in a typical modern horizontally opposed aircraft engine.

D. Lubrication System Maintenance Practices

In this section we will discuss the maintenance practices associated with a typical horizontally opposed engine installation. The system discussed will be similar to the one shown diagrammatically in figure 8-3, and in perspective in figure 8-17. The maintenance operations covered are those associated with the regular oil change and inspection interval.

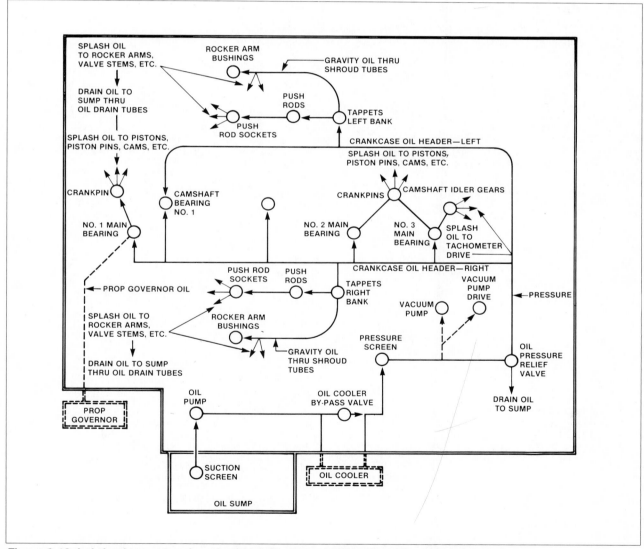

Figure 8-16. Lubrication system for a horizontally opposed aircraft engine utilizing a wet sump.

1. Oil Changes And Servicing

Oil, in service, is constantly exposed to many harmful substances that reduce its ability to protect moving parts. The main contaminants are:

(1) Gasoline.

(2) Moisture.

(3) Acids.

(4) Dirt.

(5) Carbon.

(6) Metallic particles.

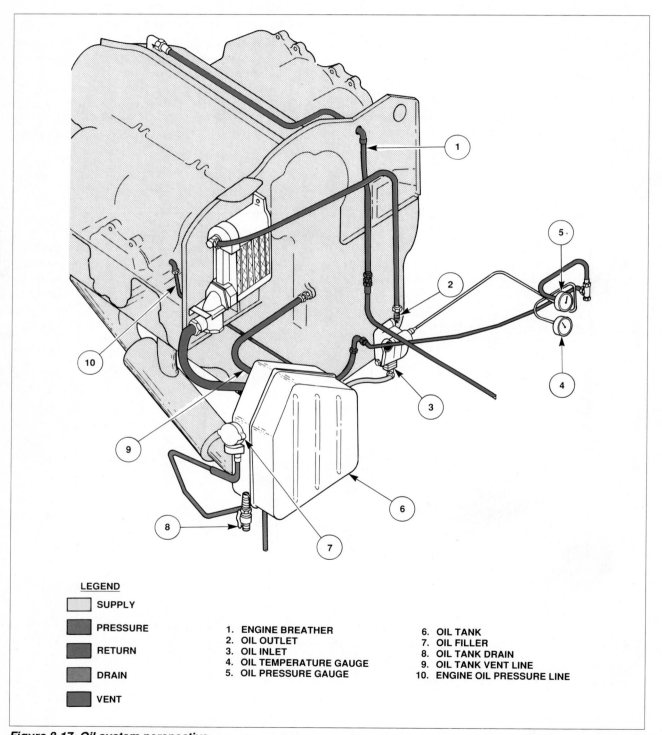

LEGEND

▢	SUPPLY
▨	PRESSURE
▤	RETURN
▥	DRAIN
▦	VENT

1. ENGINE BREATHER
2. OIL OUTLET
3. OIL INLET
4. OIL TEMPERATURE GAUGE
5. OIL PRESSURE GAUGE

6. OIL TANK
7. OIL FILLER
8. OIL TANK DRAIN
9. OIL TANK VENT LINE
10. ENGINE OIL PRESSURE LINE

Figure 8-17. Oil system perspective.

Because of the accumulation of these harmful substances, common practice is to drain the entire lubrication system at regular intervals and refill with new oil. The time between oil changes varies with each make and model aircraft and engine combination.

The first operation is that of draining the used oil. This is usually accomplished immediately after the pre-inspection run-up. At this time the oil is warm and will flow easily and quickly. It is at this time than an oil sample for spectrometric oil analysis programs (SOAP) will be taken. The method of obtaining the sample will be specified in the literature provided with the SOAP kit.

To be effective, the oil analysis samples must be taken at the recommended intervals. This program will indicate trends in the presence of metals in the oil sample, but the data is nearly meaningless if a single sample is observed. It is only through regular sampling, and processing by the same laboratory, that accurate data can be compiled and trends indicated.

Most light aircraft provide an oil drain similar to that shown in figure 8-18. On some aircraft, the normal ground attitude of the aircraft may prevent the tank from draining completely. If the amount of the undrained oil is excessive, the aft portion of the tank can be raised slightly after the tank straps have been loosened to complete the drainage.

After all necessary service to the lubrication system has been accomplished, the oil tank may be refilled with the proper grade of oil. The grade of oil used may vary with the anticipated ambient temperatures. Heavier grade oils will be used in the warm summer months, while a lower viscosity oil may be prescribed for cold weather operations.

After the oil tank has been filled, the engine should be run for at least two minutes. Then the oil level should be checked, and if necessary, sufficient oil should be added up to the proper level on the dipstick. At this time, also inspect the areas around the oil drain plug, oil filter, oil screen and temperature bulbs for leaks.

a. Straight Mineral Oil

MIL-L-6028B is a straight mineral oil that has been used for many years as a chief lubricant for aircraft engines. It has one main limitation, that being its tendency to oxidize when it is exposed to elevated temperatures when it is aerated.

The use of straight mineral oil is, today, associated with new or newly overhauled engines during their break-in period, and radial engines.

b. Ashless-dispersant Oils

By far the most important oil in use today is the ashless-dispersant, or AD oil. It does not have the carbon forming restrictions of straight mineral oil, nor does it form ash deposits, as detergent oils did.

Ashless-dispersant oil does not contain any ash-forming additives, but rather uses additives of the dispersant-type which, instead of allowing the sludge-forming materials to join together, causes them to repel each other and stay in suspension until they can be picked up by the filters.

It is interesting to note that most engine manufacturers recommend that their new engines be operated on straight mineral oil for the first fifty hours, or at least until oil consumption stabilizes, and then switched to AD oil. The reason for this is that the AD oil has so much better lubricating properties that it does not allow enough wear to properly seat the piston rings.

c. Synthetic Oil

The concept of synthetic oil for reciprocating engines is relatively new, and engine manufacturers have not as yet resolved all of the problems, nor have they issued a blanket endorsement for their use. This does not infer any condemnation; it merely indicates that sufficient data has not yet been obtained, nor has field evaluation been completed.

Additive synthetic oils appear to have the advantage over mineral oils with respect to engine cleanliness. Oil oxidation at high temperatures, with its resultant deposits, has proven in laboratory tests to be less than that produced with either straight mineral or ashless-dispersant oil. The wear characteristics of synthetic oil appears

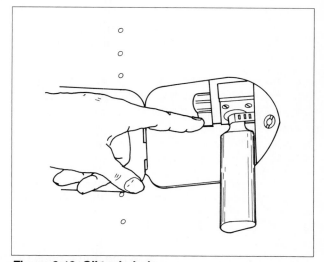

Figure 8-18. Oil tank drain.

to be about the same as those of ashless-dispersant oil and superior to straight mineral oil.

One of the problems with synthetic oil is its more pronounced softening effects on rubber products and resins. One manufacturer requires a more frequent replacement of the inter-cylinder drain lines when synthetic oil is used. Pleated paper oil filters must be examined more closely to be sure that the oil does not dissolve the resins and allow the filter to collapse.

2. Oil Tank

Oil tanks of the sort seen in figure 8-19 may occasionally need to be removed for cleaning or repair. The following steps illustrate the ease with which this operation can be accomplished.

After disconnecting the oil inlet and vent lines (figure 8-19), the scupper drain hose and bonding wire can be removed.

The securing straps fitted around the tank can now be removed, as shown in figure 8-20. Any safety wire securing the clamp must be removed before the clamp can be loosened, and the strap disconnected.

The tank can now be lifted out of the aircraft. The tank is reinstalled by reversing the sequence used in the tank removal.

3. Oil Cooler

The oil cooler seen in figure 8-21 is the honeycomb type. With the engine operating and an oil temperature below 150°F, an oil cooler by-pass valve opens, allowing oil to by-pass the core. This valve begins to close when the oil temperature reaches approximately 150°F. When the oil temperature reaches 185°F, the valve is closed completely, diverting all oil flow through the cooler core.

Oil coolers are normally removed and thoroughly cleaned during engine overhaul. Accumulated sludge may result in the blocking of portions of the cooler and reduce effectiveness. The oil cooler by-pass valve and surge valve, when installed, should be removed and cleaned at the same time as the cooler.

With the cooler removed from the engine, and cleaned, it should be inspected for cracks and other damage. Pay particular attention to welded or soldered seams which are subject to damage from excessive oil pressures. When reinstalling the cooler, new gaskets must be used.

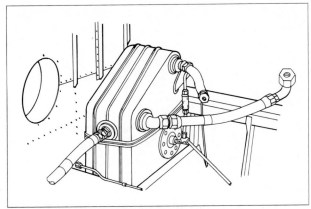

Figure 8-19. Disconnecting oil lines.

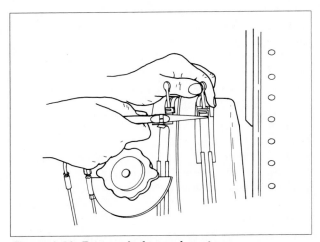

Figure 8-20. Removal of securing straps.

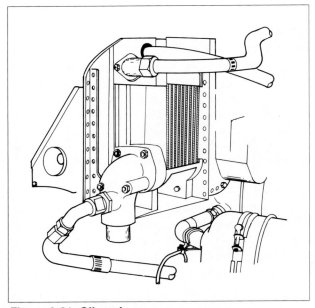

Figure 8-21. Oil cooler.

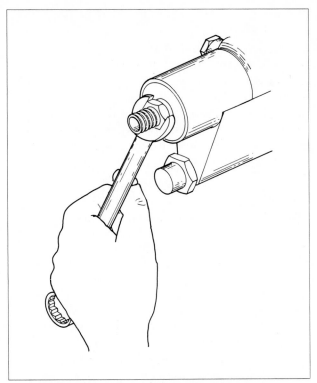

Figure 8-22. Removing oil temperature bulb.

4. Oil Temperature Bulbs

Most oil temperature bulbs are mounted in the pressure oil screen housing. They relay an indication of engine oil inlet temperature to the oil temperature indicator mounted on the instrument panel. Temperature bulbs can be replaced by removing the safety wire and disconnecting the wire leads from the temperature bulb; then remove the temperature bulb, using the proper wrench, as illustrated in figure 8-22.

5. Pressure And Scavenge Oil Screens

Sludge will accumulate on the pressure and scavenge oil screens (figure 8-23) during engine operation. These screens must be removed and cleaned at the intervals specified by the manufacturer.

Typical removal procedures include removing the safety devices and loosening the oil screen housing or cover plate. A suitable container should be provided to collect the oil that will drain from the filter housing or cavity. The container must be clean so that the oil collected in it can be examined for foreign particles. Any contamination already present in the container will give a false indication of the engine condition. This could result in a premature engine removal.

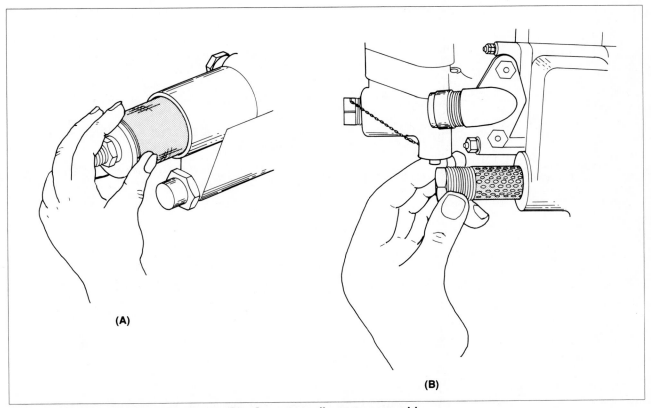

(A)

(B)

Figure 8-23. (A)—Oil pressure screen. (B)—Scavenge oil screen assembly.

After the screens are removed, they should be inspected for contamination and for the presence of metal particles that may indicate engine internal failure. The screen must be cleaned prior to reinstallation in the engine.

6. Oil Filter Replacement

Oil filter replacement and inspection is normally accomplished at the same time intervals established for other lubricating system maintenance.

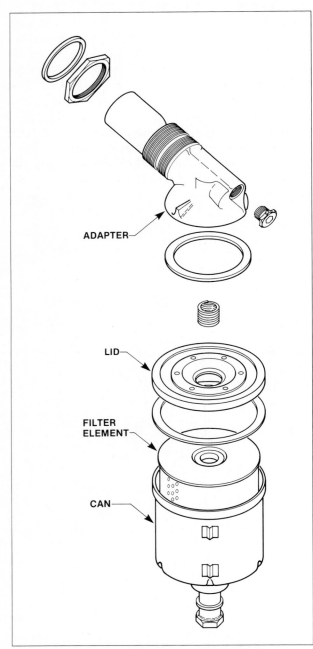

Figure 8-24. Typical installation of a full-flow type oil filter.

The procedures followed will be determined by the type of filtration system used.

Generally this involves the removal of the soiled filter, opening and inspecting it for metal particles, and the installation of a clean filter.

When reinstalling a filter, use new O-rings and gaskets, and tighten the filter housing or cover retaining nuts to the torque value specified in the applicable maintenance manual. Filters should be safetied as required.

7. Oil Pressure Relief Valve Adjustment

An oil pressure relief valve limits oil pressure to the value specified by the engine manufacturer. Oil pressure setting may vary from 35 psi to 90 psi depending upon the installation. The oil pressure must be high enough to ensure adequate lubrication of the engine and accessories at high speeds and powers. On the other hand, the pressure must not be too high, since leakage and damage to the oil system may result.

The oil pressure is adjusted by removing a cover nut, loosening a locknut, and turning the adjusting screw (see figure 8-25). Turn the adjusting screw clockwise to increase the pressure, and counterclockwise to decrease the pressure.

Make the pressure adjustments while the engine is idling and tighten the adjustment screw locknut after each adjustment. Check the oil pressure reading while the engine is running at the RPM specified in the manufacturer's maintenance manual. The oil pressure reading should be between the limits prescribed by the manufacturer.

E. Turbine Engine Lubrication Systems

The lubrication system of a turbine engine supplies oil to the various moving parts within the

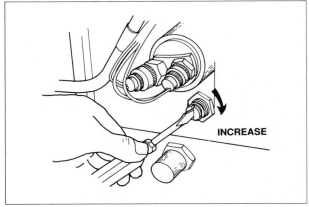

Figure 8-25. Oil pressure relief valve adjustment.

engine which are subjected to friction loads and heating from the gas path. The oil is supplied under pressure along the main rotor shaft and to the gearboxes to reduce friction, to cool, and to clean. It is then returned by a scavenging system to the oil storage tank to be used again and again. Oil consumption is low in gas turbine engines as compared to piston engines, and this accounts for the relatively small oil storage tanks used. They can be as small as 3 to 5 quarts on business jet size engines, and 20 to 30 quarts on large transport type engines. The oil is not exposed to great quantities of combustion products and is kept fairly clean by filtration. Heat, however, is a problem which can cause rapid oil decomposition, and for this reason temperature is accurately controlled by automatic cooling devices and is carefully monitored by the flight crew.

1. Requirements For Turbine Engine Lubricants

There are many requirements for turbine engine lubricating oils, but because of the small number of moving parts and the complete absence of reciprocating motion, the lubrication problems are less complex in the turbine engine than in the reciprocating engine. Because of the absence of reciprocating motion, plus the use of ball and roller bearings, the turbine engine uses a less viscous lubricant. The turboprop engine, while using essentially the same type of oil as the turbojet, must use a higher viscosity product because of the increased bearing pressures introduced by the highly loaded propeller reduction gearing.

The many requirements for lubricating oils are met in the synthetic oils developed specifically for turbine engines. The desirable characteristics of these synthetic lubricants are as follows:

(1) Low volatility—to prevent evaporation at high altitudes.

(2) Anti-foaming quality—for more positive lubrication.

(3) Low lacquer and coke deposits—keeps solid particle formation to a minimum.

(4) High flash point.

(5) Low pour point.

(6) Excellent film strength qualities of cohesion and adhesion—a characteristic of oil molecules that allows them to stick together under compression loads and adhere to surfaces under centrifugal loads.

(7) Wide temperature range—in the order of –60°F to +400°F; engine preheating is not required to approximately –40°F.

(8) High viscosity index—meaning that the oil will tend to retain its viscosity when heated to operating temperatures.

Its principal disadvantage is that it tends to blister or remove paint wherever it is spilled. Painted surfaces should be wiped clean with a petroleum solvent after spillage.

a. FAA Requirements

The following is a list of minimum requirements for a turbine engine oil system as established by the FAA in FAR Parts 23, 25 and 33:

(1) The word "OIL" must be stenciled in the area of the oil tank filler opening.

(2) A means must be provided wherein it is impossible to inadvertently fill the oil tank expansion space.

(3) An oil tank expansion space of 10% must be provided.

(4) An oil tank scupper must be provided to carry spilled oil to a drain point on the engine.

(5) The oil filter must be of a type through which all of the system oil flows.

b. Viscosity

Viscosity is a measure of an oil's pourability, and multi-viscosity oils are designed to flow sufficiently for quick lubrication at low temperatures, yet remain thick enough for good lubrication at higher temperatures.

SAE numbers are not used to identify turbine oils, but they do make synthetic oil viscosity more understandable by comparison. Instead of an SAE rating, synthetics have a Kinematic Viscosity Rating in centistokes.

The centistoke value (metric viscosity measurement) can be seen on some container labels of synthetic lubricants. A rough equivalent to SAE values is: 3cSt. oils are approximately equal to SAE-5, 5cSt. oils are approximately equal to SAE 5W10 multi-viscosity oils, 7cSt. oils are approximately equal to SAE 5W20 multi-viscosity oils.

c. Viscosity Index

Viscosity index is a means of testing the viscosity change when a liquid lubricant is heated to two different temperatures. The quality of synthetic lubricants is determined in this way.

d. Types Of Synthetic Lubricants

Synthetic lubricants are, by their makeup, multi-viscosity, similar to automotive grades SAE-5 to SAE-20. They are a blend of certain diesters, which are themselves man-made (synthesized) extracts of mineral, vegetable and animal oils. Synthetic oils are not compatible with, and cannot be mixed with, mineral based oils. In addition, most manufacturers recommend that different brands or types of synthetic oils not be mixed, or mixed only within strict guidelines of same-type and certain compatible brands.

There are two different types of synthetic lubricants being used in turbine engines today: Type-1 (MIL-L-7808) and Type-2 (MIL-L-23699). Type-2 is the most recent synthetic to be developed and is used in most of the more modern engine designs. Engines originally designed to use Type-1 oil are still using this oil.

Two common reminders one sees in oil company materials concerning synthetic lubricants are as follows:

WARNING: Synthetic turbine lubricants contain additives which are readily absorbed through the skin *and are considered highly toxic. Excessive and/or prolonged exposure to the skin should be avoided.*

CAUTION: Silicone based grease, such as is sometimes used to hold O-rings in place during assembly, can cause silicone contamination to the lube system. This contamination can cause engine oil to foam and result in oil loss through oil tank vents and also lead to engine damage from oil pump cavitation and insufficient lubrication.

2. Wet Sump Lubrication Systems

The wet sump oil system for turbine engines is the oldest design, but is rarely seen in modern flight engines. Components of a wet sump system are similar to a dry sump system, except for the location of the oil supply. The dry sump carries its oil in a separate tank, whereas the wet sump oil is contained integrally in an engine sump.

Figure 8-26 shows an engine with a wet sump lubrication system, where the oil is contained in its accessory gearbox. The bearings and drive gears within are lubricated by a splash system. The remaining points of lubrication receive oil from a gear-type pressure pump, being directed from oil jets in a liquid stream.

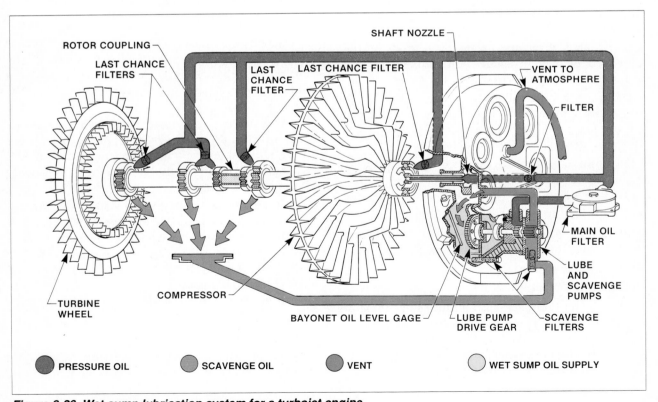

Figure 8-26. Wet sump lubrication system for a turbojet engine.

Most wet sump engines do not incorporate a pressure relief valve and are known as full flow, or variable pressure systems. With this system, the pressure pump size is determined by the flow required at maximum engine speed. The use of this system allows the incorporation of smaller pressure and scavenge pumps because the amount of oil recirculated by the pressure relief valve at high engine speeds is not present.

Scavenged oil is returned to the sump by a combination of gravity flow from the bearings, and suction created by a gear-type scavenge pump located within the pump housing.

The vent line is present to prevent over-pressurization of the gearbox from air seeping past main bearing seals and finding its way to the gearbox via the scavenge system.

3. Dry Sump Systems

Most gas turbine engines utilize a dry sump lubrication system consisting of pressure, scavenge and breather vent subsystems.

The main oil supply is carried in a tank mounted either integrally with the engine, or externally on the engine or in the aircraft. A smaller supply is contained in a gearbox sump which also houses the oil pressure pump, oil scavenge pump, oil filter and other lubricating system components. Another small amount of oil is residual within the oil system lines, sumps and components.

a. System Components

1) Oil Tank

The oil supply reservoir is usually constructed of sheet aluminum or stainless steel, and is designed to furnish a constant supply of oil to the engine during all authorized flight attitudes. In most tanks, a slight pressurization of the oil tank is desired to ensure a positive flow of oil to the pump inlet and suppress foaming in the tank, which in turn prevents pump cavitation. This buildup is accomplished by running the tank overboard vent line through an adjustable relief valve to maintain a positive pressure of approximately 3 to 6 psig.

Some dry sump oil tanks are of the integral type. Whereas the sheet metal type is a separate assembly located outside of the engine, the integral oil tank is formed by space provided within the engine. Sometimes it is in the propeller reduction gearbox that houses the oil, and sometimes it is a cavity between major engine cases.

The distinction between the wet sump and dry sump is that the wet sump is located in the main

gearbox at the lowest point within the engine, facilitating splash lubrication. The dry sump is seldom located at the low point on the engine and usually gravity flows oil to the main oil pump inlet.

Figure 8-27 shows an illustration of a dwell chamber, sometimes referred to as a deaerator. This unit provides a means of separating entrained air from the scavenge oil. The tank shown is of typical capacity for a business jet, approximately four quarts, three of which are usable. The location of the outlet in this example keeps one quart as residual oil and provides a low point for sediment to collect until drained. Other tanks would have a similar arrangement, or perhaps a standpipe.

Today many oil tanks are configured with a pressure remote filling capability. An oil pumping cart can be attached to the tank, and the oil hand pumped into the tank until full. The oil filler cap is usually removed during this operation to prevent overservicing. The hand filling method is, however, still the most common. The scupper shown in figure 8-27 is present to catch oil that is spilled during servicing and to route this spillage through a tube drain location at the bottom of the engine.

In place of a dipstick, some oil tanks incorporate a sight gauge to satisfy the FAR requirements for a visual means of checking oil level. However, these

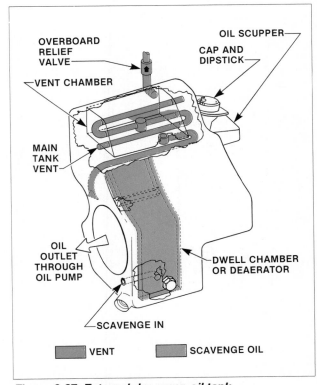

Figure 8-27. External dry sump oil tank.

glass indicators tend to cloud over after prolonged use, and many operators have gone back to the dipstick. Both of these methods of checking oil level are illustrated in figure 8-28.

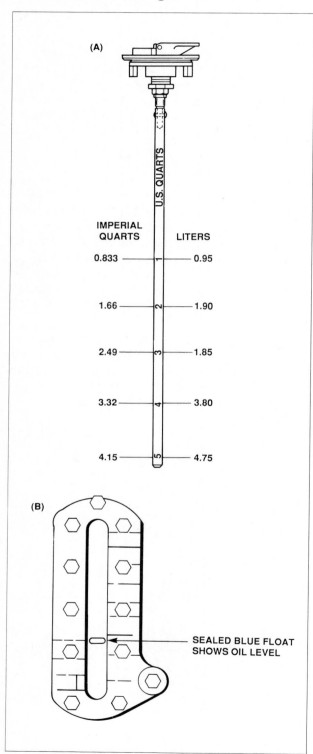

Figure 8-28. (A)—Oil tank dipstick and cap. (B)—Oil tank sight gauge.

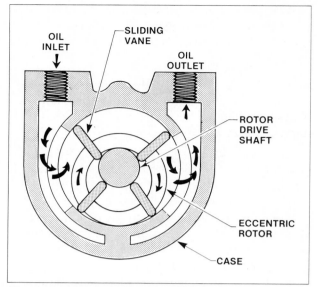

Figure 8-29. Sliding-vane-type oil pump.

2) Oil Pumps

The function of the oil pump is to supply oil under pressure to the parts of the engine that require lubrication. Many oil pumps consist not only of a pressure element, but one or more scavenge elements as well—all in a single housing. In all types of pumps, the scavenge elements have a greater pumping capacity than the pressure element to prevent oil from collecting in the bearing sumps.

The three most common types of oil pumps are the vane, gerotor, and gear-types; the gear-type being the most commonly used. All are classed as positive displacement pumps, as they deposit a fixed quantity of oil in the outlet each revolution.

a) Vane Pump

The pump in figure 8-29 could be a single element or one element of a multiple pump. Multiple pumps of this type generally contain one pressure element and one or more scavenging elements, all of which are mounted on a common shaft. The drive shaft mounts to an accessory gearbox drive pad and all pumping elements rotate together. Pumping action takes place as rotor drive shaft and eccentric rotor, which are actually one rotating piece, drive the sliding vanes around. The space between each vane pair floods with oil as it passes the oil inlet opening and carries this oil to the oil outlet. As the space diminishes to a zero clearance, the oil is forced to leave the pump. The downstream resistance to flow will determine the pump output pressure.

Vane pumps are considered to be more tolerant of debris in the scavenge oil. They are lighter in weight than the gerotor or gear-type pumps.

b) Gerotor Pump

Another form of constant-displacement pump used for lubrication systems is the gerotor (gear-rotor) pump, a special form of gear pump. In figure 8-30, we see a six-tooth spur gear driven from an engine accessory drive. This gear rides inside a rotor which rotates freely in the housing. A seven-tooth internal gear is cut inside the rotor, and as the drive gear is turned, it turns the rotor. In view A, the two marked teeth are meshed and there is a minimum of space between them. As the two gears rotate, the volume between the teeth increases as you follow the marked teeth in views A, B and C. A plate with two kidney shaped openings covers the gears, forming a seal for their ends. As the gears rotate beneath the inlet port, the volume between the teeth continually increases, and as they rotate beneath the outlet port, as seen in views D and E, the volume decreases, moving the

fluid out into the system. Gerotor pumps may be designed to pump relatively large volumes of fluid without having to be excessively thick.

c) Gear Pump

The gear-type pump takes in inlet oil and rotates in a direction which allows oil to move between the gear teeth and the pump inner case until the oil is deposited in the outlet. The idler gear seals the inlet from the outlet, preventing fluid backup, and also doubles the capacity per revolution. This pump may also incorporate a system relief valve in its housing which returns unwanted oil to the pump inlet. Figure 8-31 shows a dual pump with a pressure and scavenge element.

3) Oil Filters

Oil filters are an important part of the lubrication system since they remove foreign particles that collect in the oil.

a) Contaminants In Oil

Contaminants found in the oil system filters come primarily from the following sources:

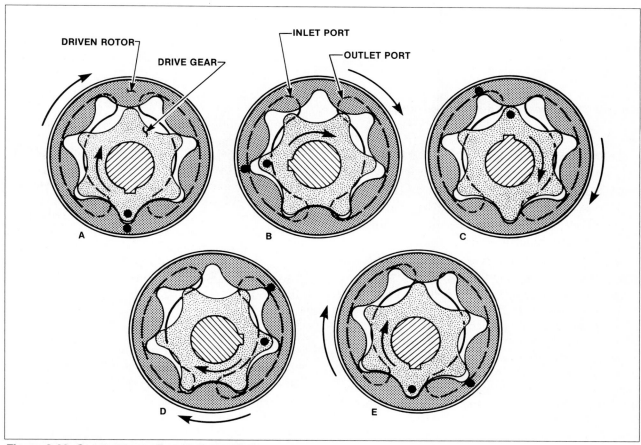

Figure 8-30. Gerotor-type oil pump operation.

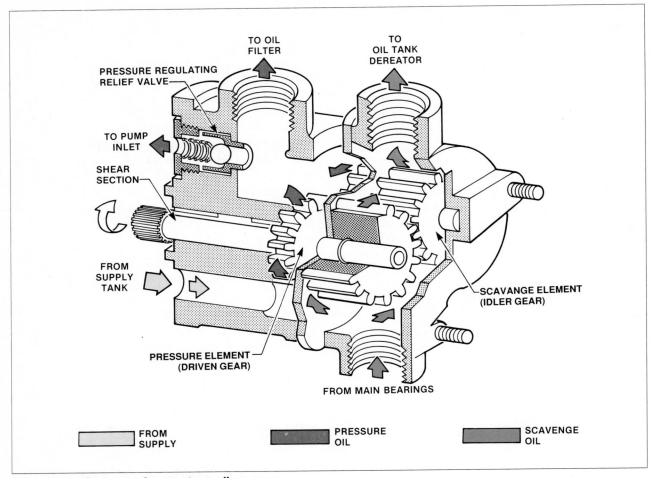

Figure 8-31. Cutaway of a gear-type oil pump.

(1) Products of decomposition of the oil itself, usually seen as small black specks of carbon.

(2) Metallic particles from engine wear and corrosion in oil wetted areas of the engine.

(3) Airborne contaminants entering through the main bearing seals.

(4) Dirt and other foreign matter introduced into the oil supply during servicing.

The contaminants which are seen in filter bowls or on the filter screens are always a matter of concern. Usually, the determination as to whether the engine requires maintenance or whether it is airworthy is a matter of professional judgment based on long experience of a person who has seen cases of normal and abnormal levels of contamination. If a spectrometric oil analysis program has been followed, a read-out of the various metals present in the latest oil sample can be compared to earlier test results. This may yield valuable information affecting the decision-making process of whether or not there is sufficient cause to perform maintenance on the engine.

Another common observation of engine oil is to see it turn dark brown or even blackish, but with little or no contaminants present. This is a chemical reaction to excessive heat causing oil decomposition. The cause of the overheat could be anything from low oil service to serious engine overheating and must be thoroughly analyzed.

b) Filter Ratings

The term "micron" is derived from the international system of measurement and represents a size or distance equal to one millionth part of a meter, or approximately .000039 of an inch.

To get an idea of micronic size, the human eye cannot readily distinguish objects smaller than about 40 microns. A white blood cell measures about 25 microns, and red blood cells about 8 microns.

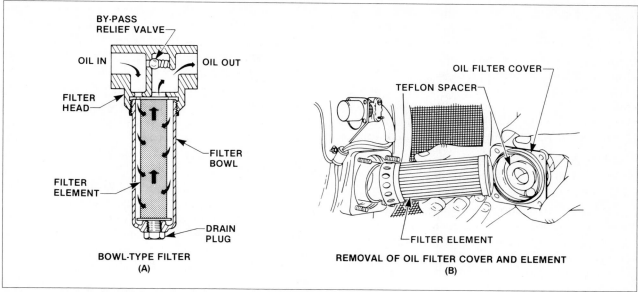

Figure 8-32. Turbine engine oil filters.

c) Types Of Filters

The more common types of main system filters are: (1) disposable laminated paper or fiber, (2) cleanable screen, and (3) screen and spacer types.

All three have micronic ratings in that they are designed to prevent passage of micronic-size contaminant particles into the system.

Figure 8-32A is an illustration of an in-line bowl-type filter which could be either disposable or cleanable. A typical rating for this filter is 20 microns. This means that it will filter out particles larger than 20 microns in diameter.

Observe that oil fills the bowl, then forces its way through the filtering element to the core, exiting at the port near the spring side of the by-pass relief valve. On a cold morning when oil is highly viscous, or if filter clogging restricts oil flow through the element, the by-pass will open, allowing unfiltered oil to flow out to the engine.

An observation of the paper disposable and screen mesh filters would reveal that most are heavily pleated. This is to provide a maximum surface area for filtration. The screen type has a micronic rating actually measurable in microns. The paper, or fiber-type, has an equivalent micronic rating.

Figure 8-32B is a filter which fits into a gearbox annulus and provides the exact same service as the bowl type.

The screen and spacer type filter, more common to Pratt & Whitney engines, is one that can be disassembled for inspection and cleaning. This

filter usually fits into an annulus provided in the main accessory gearbox. The filter configuration is a series of wafer-thin screens between spacers which allows oil to flow in the inward direction.

The filters illustrated are generally thought of as being located in the pressure subsystem of the engine. Some engines also provide filtration for the scavenge subsystems which route oil from the engine back to the supply tank.

4) Oil Pressure Relief Valve Systems

An oil pressure relief valve is included in the pressure oil line to limit the maximum pressure within the system. This valve is especially important if an oil cooler is incorporated in the system, since oil coolers are easily ruptured because of their thin-wall construction. The relief valve is preset to relieve pressure and by-pass the oil back to the inlet side of the pump whenever the pressure exceeds the preset limit.

5) Oil Jets

Oil jets (or nozzles) are located in the pressure lines adjacent to, or within, the bearing compartments and rotor shaft couplings. The oil from these nozzles is delivered in the form of an atomized spray. Some engines use an air-oil mist spray which is produced by routing high-pressure bleed air from the compressor to the oil nozzle outlet. This method is considered adequate for ball and roller bearings; however, the solid oil spray method is considered the better of the two methods.

The oil jets are easily clogged because of the small orifice in their tips; consequently, the oil must be free of any foreign particles. There are fine-mesh screens, called "last chance" filters for straining the oil just before it passes from the spray nozzles onto the bearing surfaces. If these filters in the oil jets become clogged, bearing failure usually results, since nozzles are not accessible for cleaning except during engine overhaul. To prevent damage from clogged oil jets, main oil filters are checked frequently for contaminants.

6) Lubrication System Vents

Vents, or breathers, are lines or openings in the oil tanks or accessory cases of engines.

The vent in an oil tank keeps the pressure within the tank from rising above, or falling below, that of the outside atmosphere. However, as was previously discussed, the vent line may be used to pressurize the tank to ensure positive flow to the oil pump inlet.

In the accessory case, the vent (or breather) is a screen-protected opening which allows accumulated air pressure within the accessory case to escape to the atmosphere. The scavenged oil carries air into the accessory case and this air must be vented; otherwise, the pressure buildup within the accessory case would stop the flow of oil draining from the bearing, thus forcing this oil past the rear bearing oil' seal and into the compressor housing. Oil leakage could, of course, cause any

of several results, the least of which would be the use of too much oil. A more serious result would occur if oil leakage were great enough to cause burning in the combustion area, which could cause turbine failure because of a hot-spot.

The screened breathers usually are located in the front center of the accessory case to prevent oil leakage through the breather when the aircraft is in unusual flight attitudes. Some breathers may have a baffle to prevent oil leakage during flight maneuvers.

A vent which leads directly to the bearing compartment may be used in some engines. This vent equalizes pressure around the front bearing surface so that the lower pressure at the first compressor stage will not cause oil to be forced past the bearing rear oil seal into the compressor.

7) Check Valves

Check valves are sometimes installed in the oil supply lines of dry-sump oil systems to prevent reservoir oil from seeping (by gravity) through the oil pump elements and high-pressure lines after shutdown. Check valves, by stopping flow in an opposite direction, prevent accumulations of undue amounts of oil in the accessory gearbox, compressor rear housing and combustion chamber. Such accumulations could cause excessive loading of the accessory drive gears during starts,

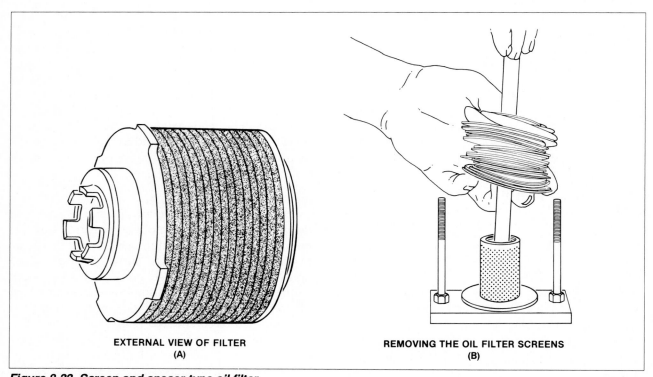

EXTERNAL VIEW OF FILTER
(A)

REMOVING THE OIL FILTER SCREENS
(B)

Figure 8-33. Screen and spacer-type oil filter.

contamination of the cabin pressurization air or internal oil fires.

The check valves usually are the spring-loaded, ball-and-socket type, constructed for free flow of pressure oil. The pressure required to open these valves will vary, but the valves generally require from 2 to 5 psi to permit oil to flow to the bearings.

8) Pressure And Temperature Gauges

Oil system indicators generally consist of oil temperature, oil pressure, and in some installations, warning lights for low oil pressure and for filter bypass.

The cockpit pressure gauge will more likely tap into the oil system, downstream (output side) of the main oil filter, to indicate the actual pressure being delivered to the engine. Many aircraft are also configured with a low-pressure warning light. When power is turned on in the aircraft, this light will illuminate. Then as oil pressure builds in the system during starting, the light will go out at a preset value, equal to the low or "red line" limit for the cockpit oil pressure gauge. Figure 8-34 shows this warning light.

If the warning light does not go out after start-up, or if it comes back on during operation, the operator should look at the oil pressure gauge to confirm the extent of the low pressure situation, and then take appropriate action.

The location of the temperature sensor in the lubrication system seems to be of little significance. Manufacturers place the sensor in either the pressure subsystem or the scavenge subsystem. This is possible because gas turbine-engine oil systems have a high flow rate, circulating at the rate of two to five times the oil tank capacity per minute, causing temperatures to stabilize throughout the entire lubrication system very rapidly. As a result, the cockpit is supplied with a quick and reliable oil temperature indication.

However, some manufacturers state that placing the sensor in the scavenge subsystem is preferable because it gives a slightly quicker indication of high friction heat buildup from failing parts, such as bearings and gears. The more common of the two locations, however, is in the pressure subsystem to show the temperature of the oil entering the engine.

9) Thermostatic Bypass Valve

Thermostatic bypass valves are included in oil systems using an oil cooler. Although these valves may be called by different names, their purpose is always to maintain proper oil temperature by vary-ing the proportion of the total oil flow passing through the oil cooler.

10) Oil Coolers

Oil coolers are used in the lubricating system of turbine engines to reduce the temperature of the oil to a degree suitable for recirculation through the system.

The location of the oil cooler in the system may be used to identify the type of oil system as a hot-tank or cold-tank system. In the hot-tank system the oil cooler is located in the pressure subsystem. With this arrangement, the oil has less entrained air and maximum heat exchange occurs. This allows the use of a smaller cooler. The cold-tank system locates the oil cooler in the scavenge subsystem. This allows the oil to return to the supply tank in a cooled condition.

Two basic types of oil coolers may be encountered. One uses air as the cooling medium, the other fuel. In some installations, both fuel-cooled and air-cooled coolers are used on the same engine.

The air-cooled oil cooler normally is installed at the forward end of the engine. It is similar in construction and operation to the air-cooled oil coolers used on reciprocating engines.

Figure 8-35 illustrates a fuel/oil heat exchanger which is designed to cool the oil and to preheat the fuel for combustion. Fuel flowing to the engine

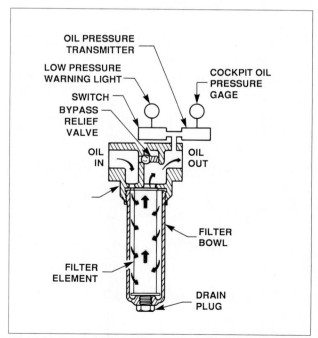

Figure 8-34. Oil filter with oil pressure transmitter and low oil pressure switch.

must pass through this heat exchanger; however, there is a thermostatic valve which controls the oil flow. The oil may bypass the cooler if no cooling is needed. The fuel/oil heat exchanger consists of a series of joined tubes with an inlet and outlet port. The oil enters the inlet port, moves around the fuel tubes, and exits at the outlet port.

The fuel/oil heat exchanger has the advantage of allowing the engine to retain its small frontal area. Because the cooler is mounted on the engine, it offers little or no drag.

4. Turbine Engine Lubrication System Maintenance

Maintenance of gas turbine lubrication systems consists mainly of adjusting, removing, cleaning and replacing various components.

a. Servicing And Oil Changes

Before servicing an engine's oil system, the technician should refer to the engine or aircraft type certificate data sheets, or operations manual for the correct oil type.

A partial list of typical synthetic lubricants the maintenance technician is likely to see is as follows:

Type-1 (MIL-L-7808)	Type-2 (MIL-L-23699)
Aeroshell 300	Aeroshell 500 or 700
Mobil Jet I	Mobil Jet II
Stauffer I	Stauffer II
Castrol 3c	Castrol 205
Enco 15	Enco 2380
Exxon 15	Exxon 25
Exxon 2389	Exxon 2380
Caltex 15	Caltex 2380
Shell 307	Texaco 7388, Starjet-5
Exxon 274	Caltex Starjet-5
	Chevron jet-5
	Sinclair type-2

From this list it can easily be seen that no standard identification system is currently in use.

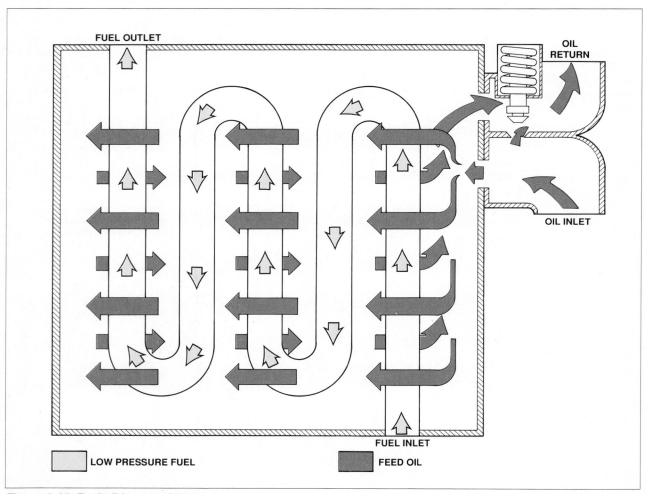

FUEL OUTLET

OIL RETURN

OIL INLET

FUEL INLET

LOW PRESSURE FUEL

FEED OIL

Figure 8-35. Fuel/oil heat exchanger.

In fact, not all oil companies include the type number or MIL Spec on the oil can label. If needed, the technician would have to refer to oil company literature for these specifications.

Synthetic oil for turbine engines is usually supplied in one quart containers to minimize the chance of contaminants entering the lubrication system. Ground personnel should pay careful attention to cleanliness during servicing to maintain the integrity of the lubricant. If the oil is supplied in cans with metal tops, the use of a clean service station-type oil spout is recommended instead of can openers which tend to deposit metal slivers in the oil.

If bulk oil is used, rather than quart containers, filtering with a 10-micron filter or smaller is generally required.

In the event of inadvertent mixing of incompatible lubricants, many manufacturers require the oil system to be drained and flushed before refilling. Also when changing to another approved oil, a system drain and flush would more likely be required if the oils are not compatible.

Draining is usually accomplished at the oil tank, the accessory gearbox sump, the main oil filter, and other low points in the lube system. Flushing generally means reservicing and draining after motoring the engine over with the starter and no ignition.

After final reservice, the engine will generally be run for a short period of time to resupply the lines, sumps, etc., with the residual oil normally held within the system.

If a new oil has been used, the placard stencil near the filler opening or metal oil identification tag, whichever is used, should be changed accordingly.

Another important consideration when servicing the oil system is to ensure that servicing is accomplished within a short time after shutdown. Manufacturers normally require this in order to prevent overservicing (overfilling the system). Overservicing may occur on some engines which have the tendency to allow oil in the storage tank to seep into lower portions of the engine after periods of inactivity.

An important consideration after oil servicing is recording the amount of oil added. A steady oil consumption within allowable limits provides a valuable trend analysis of engine wear at main bearing and seal locations.

Oil consumption of turbine engines is very low. Many business jet-sized engines require only one quart of oil each 200 to 300 flight hours. A typical oil change interval is 300 to 400 flight hours, or 6 months on a calendar interval.

On larger engines—the engines of wide-bodied jets, for instance—one could expect to add no more than 0.2 quart per hour. By comparison, an 18-cylinder radial engine could consume as much as 20 quarts per operating hour and still be considered airworthy.

Many airlines do not establish oil change intervals. The reason being that in the average 20 to 30 quart capacity oil tank, normal replenishment will automatically change the oil at regular 50 to 100 hour intervals.

b. Oil Pressure Adjustments

To adjust oil pressure, first remove the adjusting screw acorn cap on the oil pressure relief valve. Then loosen the locknut and turn the adjusting screw clockwise to increase, or counterclockwise to decrease, the oil pressure. The target values for oil pressure are supplied by the engine manufacturer, and must be followed exactly. The adjustment is usually made while the engine is idling, and the value confirmed with the engine operating at approximately 75% of normal rated thrust. This may make it necessary to perform several adjustments

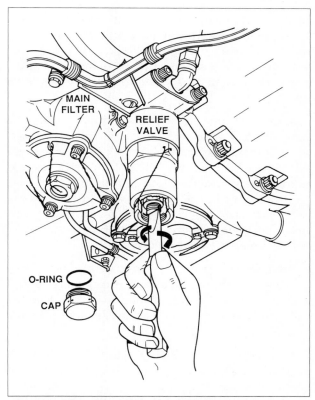

Figure 8-36. Engine oil pressure relief valve adjustment.

before the desired pressure is obtained. When the proper pressure setting is achieved, the adjusting screw locknut is tightened, and the acorn cap is installed with a new gasket, tightened, and secured with lockwire.

c. Oil Filter Maintenance

The oil filter should be removed at every regular inspection. It should be disassembled, cleaned, and any worn or damaged filter elements replaced. The inspection, cleaning or replacement will be dictated by the type of filter element used. Filter maintenance must be accomplished in accordance with the appropriate manufacturer's instructions.

Traditional methods of hand cleaning filters in solvent are still commonly used and acceptable. However, several cleaning devices that induce high frequency sound waves, called "ultrasonic" cleaning, or high frequency "vibrator cleaners" are also available. These units will do a more complete job of removing all of the contaminants from the filtering elements. One type of these units is illustrated in figure 8-37.

d. Scavenge System

The scavenge subsystem removes oil from the bearing compartments and gearboxes by suction from the scavenge pump elements. The entrained air that accumulates in the oil increases its volume and necessitates the use of a much higher capacity scavenge subsystem than the pressure subsystem.

Many scavenge subsystems contain permanent magnet chip detectors which attract and hold ferrous metal particles which would otherwise be circulated back to the oil tank and the engine pressure subsystem. If introduced into the pressure subsystem, the particles could cause excessive wear or damage to the engine. Chip detectors are a point of frequent inspection to detect early signs of main bearing failure.

As a general rule, the presence of small fuzzy particles or grey metallic paste is considered satisfactory and the result of normal wear. Metallic chips or flakes are an indication of serious internal wear or malfunction.

An indicating type of chip detector may be used to give a cockpit warning of the presence of foreign material. When debris bridges the gap between the magnetic positive electrode and the ground electrode (shell), a warning light is activated in the cockpit. When the light illuminates, the flight crew

will take whatever action is warranted, depending upon the other engine instrument readings.

A newer type of chip detector is the electric pulsed chip detector, which can discriminate between small wear-particles, considered non-failure related, and larger particles, which can be an indication of bearing failure, gearbox failure or other potentially serious engine malfunction. This system is seen in view C of figure 8-38.

The pulsed detector is designed with either one or two operating modes: manual only, or manual and automatic. In the manual mode, each time the gap is sufficiently bridged, regardless of the particle size, the warning light will illuminate. The operator may then initiate the pulse; electrical energy will discharge across the gap-end of the chip detector in an attempt to separate the debris from the hot center electrode. This procedure is called burn-off. If the light goes out and stays out, the operator will consider the bridging a result of a non-failure related cause. If the light does not go out, or repeatedly comes on after being cleared, the operator will take appropriate action.

In the automatic mode, if the gap is bridged by small debris, a pulse of electrical energy discharges across the gap. The resulting burn-off prevents a cockpit warning light from illuminating by opening the circuit before a time-delay relay in the circuit activates to complete the current path to ground. If the debris is a large particle, it will remain in place after the burn-off cycle is completed and the warning light will be illuminated when the time-delay relay closes.

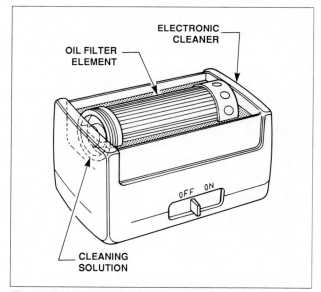

Figure 8-37. Fluid vibrator-type oil filter cleaner.

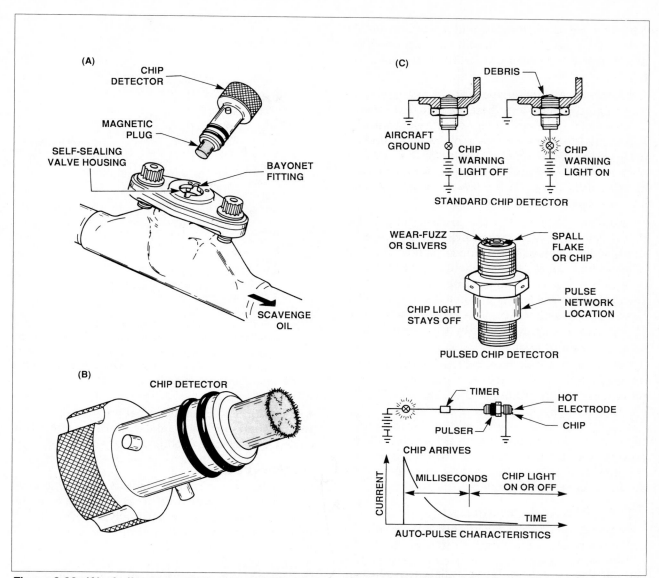

Figure 8-38. (A)—In-line type scavenge magnetic oil chip detector (non-indicating). (B)—Chip detector showing accumulation of ferrous particles. (C)—Comparison between standard, pulsed and auto-pulse detectors.

F. Reciprocating Engine Cooling Systems

The reciprocating engine is a form of heat engine, which means that it converts heat energy into mechanical energy. But it is an extremely inefficient converter, and only changes about one-third of the energy into useful work. Every gallon of aviation gasoline we burn releases about 80,000 BTU of heat energy that does not do any useful work, and all of this heat must be disposed of or it will destroy the engine.

About one-half of this heat is carried out through the exhaust system, and most of the rest is absorbed by the oil or by the metal of the engine.

This heat must be transferred into the air through the cooling system.

Liquid cooled aircraft engines pass water through jackets around the cylinders to absorb the heat from the cylinder walls and cylinder heads. The heated water is then carried outside of the engine into a radiator where air passing through the coils absorbs the heat.

Liquid-cooled engines have been the standard for automotive and industrial engines for years, but have fallen in and out of favor for aircraft use. Early aircraft engines used liquid cooling, and then with advances in design and construction, the air-cooled aircraft engine became the standard. Over the years various models of liquid-cooled engines

351

have been used on aircraft, and are still available today. Because of their limited use on production model aircraft, we will not detail their construction.

Rather than transferring heat from the engine into a liquid coolant and then carrying this coolant to an external radiator where the heat could be transferred into the air, some of the early engine designers put fins on the outside of the cylinder barrels and heads and let them stick out into the air. The air flowing over the fins absorbed the heat and effectively cooled the cylinders.

Air cooling is good, but the penalty imposed by the increased drag is a high price to pay, and as the speed of airplanes continued up above the 120 mile per hour mark, some method of reducing drag was needed. The Townend ring, or speed ring, cowling was developed to enclose the cylinder heads of a radial engine in a streamlined cover. This minimized drag caused by turbulent airflow over the cylinder heads.

As both speed and power increased, the need for more efficient cooling with less drag became apparent. By the beginning of the 1930's the NACA cowling brought in pressure cooling for radial engines. The engine is enclosed in a streamlined cowling that completely covers all portions of the powerplant. Baffles seal the area between the cylinder heads and the cowling and all of the spaces between the cylinders.

1. Baffles And Deflectors

Inter-cylinder baffles cover part of the rear side of the cylinders so air flowing through the fins is forced into the area at the back center of the cylinders, an area that is insufficiently cooled on installations without baffles. The speed of the aircraft forces air into the forward side of the engine and through baffles to provide effective

Figure 8-39. The Townend ring used on the Boeing P26A fighter reduced the drag by smoothing out the airflow over the cylinder heads.

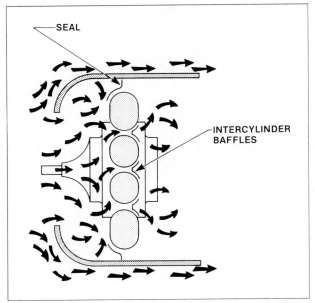

Figure 8-40. The cylinder heat-to-cowling seal and inter-cylinder baffles force cooling air from the forward side of the engine through the cylinder fins in an engine housed in a NACA cowling to remove the maximum amount of heat.

cooling and low drag for radial engines. Even the two-row and four-row radial engines are effectively cooled by pressure cooling.

2. Cowl Flaps

In order to control the amount of cooling, cowl flaps may be installed at the rear of the cowling. The cowl flaps may be manually, electrically, or hydraulically operated, and are actuated by a cockpit control. When these flaps are open, the air flowing past them creates a low-pressure area behind the cylinders. This will increase the pressure drop across the cylinders and, in turn, increase the air flowing through the fins. The increased flow will aid in cooling during ground operations, takeoff and climb. When the airspeed is high and the need for cooling is decreased, the cowl flaps can be closed to decrease the airflow through the cylinders, and to eliminate the drag caused by the open cowl flaps.

Horizontally opposed engines, such as the one seen in figure 8-41, make very effective use of pressure cooling. Air enters the front of the engine through openings in the cowling. Here the ram air pressurizes the area above the engine, and then it flows through the cylinders to the space below, and out through the cowl flaps at the rear of the lower cowl. Small aircraft may not utilize cowl flaps, but rather a lip on the lower cowling which

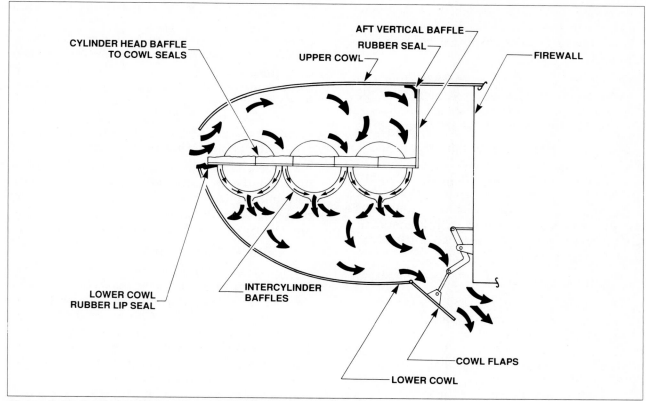

Figure 8-41. Cooling airflow in a pressure cooling system for a horizontally opposed engine installation.

creates a pressure drop to assist the airflow across the cylinders.

3. Augmentor Systems

Augmentor tubes may be used on some aircraft to augment, or increase, the airflow through the cylinders. Like the cowl flaps, they are a method used to create a low pressure area at the lower rear of the cowling in order to increase the airflow through the cylinder cooling fins.

In an augmentor system, the exhaust gases from the engine are routed into a collector and discharged into the inlet of a stainless steel augmentor tube. The flow of high-velocity exhaust gases creates an area of low pressure at the inlet of the augmentor tube, and draws air from above the engine through the cylinder fins. The combination of exhaust gases and cooling air exits at the rear of the augmentor tube. This system is illustrated in figure 8-42.

4. Inspection And Maintenance

The inspection and maintenance of the cooling system components is a part of any 100 hour/annual inspection program, and comprehensive repair or replacement of baffles and seals should be accomplished during engine installation following overhaul.

Remember that sheet metal components of engine cowling and baffles are subject to constant vibration. This environment tends to work-harden the metal at a rate considerably faster than other components on the aircraft. Work-hardening will make the metal brittle and increase the likelihood of fatigue cracking.

a. Cowling

Of the total ram airflow approaching the airborne engine nacelle, only about 15 to 30% enters the cowling to provide engine cooling. The remaining air flows over the outside of the cowling. Therefore the external shape of the cowling must be faired in a manner that will permit the air to flow smoothly over the cowl with a minimum loss of energy. This smoothness must be considered when accomplishing any repairs to cowling, or adjusting alignment of cowl panels and access doors.

Cowling panels must be inspected for scratches, dents and tears in the panels. This type of weakness in the panel structure increases drag by disrupting airflow, and contributes to the starting of corrosion. Internal construction of the cowling panels should be examined to see that reinforcing ribs are not cracked, and that the air seal is not damaged.

The cowling panel latches should be inspected for pulled rivets and loose or damaged handles. The safety locks should be checked for damaged rivets and the condition of the safety spring.

Support brackets should be inspected for security of mounting and cracks. The cowl flap hinges and cowl flap hinge bondings should be checked for security of mounting and for breaks and cracks. These inspections are visual checks and should be performed frequently to ensure that the cowling is serviceable and is contributing to efficient engine cooling.

b. Cylinder Cooling Fins

The cooling fins are of the utmost importance to the cooling system, since they provide a means of transferring the cylinder heat to the air. Their condition can mean the difference between adequate or inadequate cylinder cooling. The fins are inspected at each regular inspection.

Fin area is the total area (both sides of the fin) exposed to the air. During inspection, the fins should be examined for cracks and breaks. These cracks can be filed or even sometimes stop drilled to prevent further cracking. Rough or sharp corners on fins can be smoothed out by filing, and this action will eliminate a possible source of new cracks. However, before re-profiling cylinder cooling fins, consult the manufacturer's service or overhaul manual for the allowable limits.

The definition of fin area becomes important in the examination of fins for broken areas. It is a determining factor for cylinder acceptance or removal. In each specific case, the applicable manufacturer's instructions should be consulted.

c. Cylinder Baffles And Deflectors

The baffles and deflectors normally are inspected during regular engine inspection, but they should be checked whenever the cowling is removed for any purpose. Checks should be made for cracks, dents, or loose hold-down studs. Cracks or dents, if severe enough, would necessitate repair or removal and replacement of these units. However, a crack that has just started can

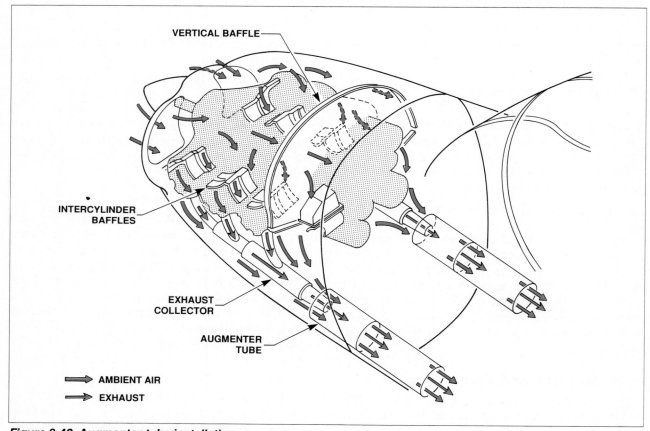

Figure 8-42. Augmentor tube installation.

Figure 8-43. Bayonet-type cylinder head temperature probe.

be stop-drilled, and dents can be straightened, permitting further service from these baffles and deflectors.

The inter-cylinder baffles and the aft vertical baffle all have plastic, rubber or leather strips to provide an air seal between the baffles and the cowling to prevent an air loss in these critical areas. It is vital, when installing the cowling, to pay special attention to these seals to ensure that they are all in good condition and that they all point in the direction shown in the aircraft manufacturer's service manual.

d. Cowl Flap Installation And Adjustment

During cowl flap installation, adjustments are made to ensure the correct "open and close" tolerances of the cowl flaps. This tolerance is of the utmost importance. If the cowl flap is permitted to open too far, the air exiting the engine section is increased in velocity, thus permitting too great a cooling of the cylinders. Also, if the cowl flaps are not adjusted to open the desired amount, the cylinder head temperature may be higher than allowable limits under certain operating conditions. For each engine installation, the cowl flaps are set for tolerances that will permit them to open and close a correct amount, keeping the cylinder head temperature within allowable limits.

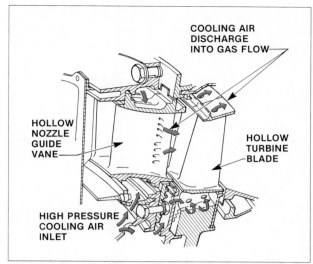

Figure 8-45. The hollow turbine nozzle guide vanes and turbine blades are cooled by a flow of high-pressure bleed air.

5. Cylinder Temperature Indicating Systems

This system usually consists of an indicator, electrical wiring and a thermocouple. Cylinder head temperature monitoring systems may be limited to a single cylinder (usually the one determined to normally have the highest temperature), or may monitor all cylinders. Indicators on multiple-cylinder systems may read the temperature selected by a rotary-type switch, or may include circuitry to electronically scan all cylinders and give a warning if any one exceeds prescribed temperature limits.

The thermocouple consists of a junction of two dissimilar metals, generally iron and constantan, connected by wire to the indicating system. The

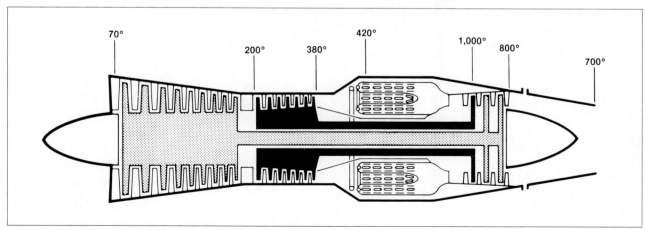

Figure 8-44. Typical temperatures in a twin-spool turbojet engine.

thermocouple end that connects to the cylinder may be either the bayonet or gasket type. To install the bayonet type, the knurled knob is pushed down and turned clockwise until it is snug. In removing this type, the nut is pushed down and turned counterclockwise until released. The gasket type fits under the spark plug and replaces the normal spark plug gasket.

When installing a thermocouple lead, remember not to cut off the lead because it is too long, but coil and tie up the excess. The thermocouple lead is designed to produce a given amount of resistance. If the length is reduced, an incorrect temperature reading will result.

G. Turbine Engine Cooling Systems

Turbine engines, like reciprocating engines, release heat energy from the fuel and convert it into useful work. And, like the reciprocating engine, they are terribly inefficient. Much of the heat that is released must be disposed of before it can damage the lightweight components of the engine.

1. Turbine Engine Cooling Requirements

The burning process in a gas turbine engine is continuous, and nearly all of the cooling air must be passed through the inside of the engine. If only

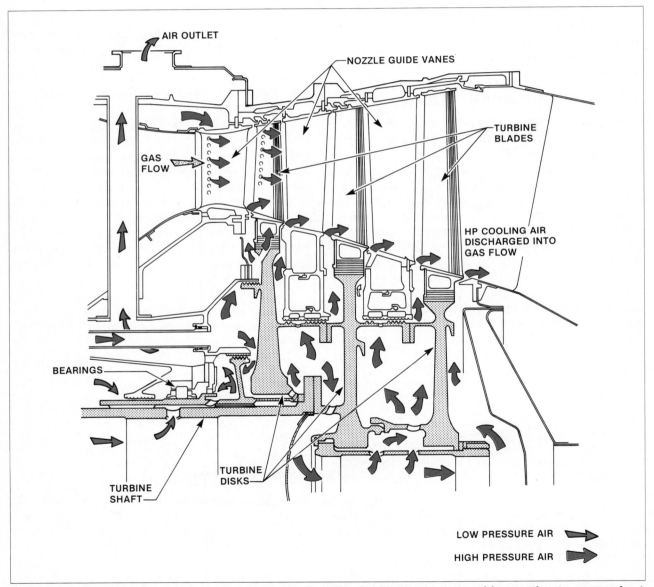

Figure 8-46. High pressure air flows up the face of the disks in this three-stage turbine section to remove heat. Low-pressure air flows around the turbine bearings to remove heat.

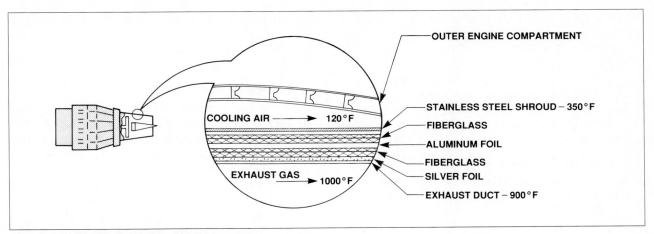

Figure 8-47. Insulation blanket construction.

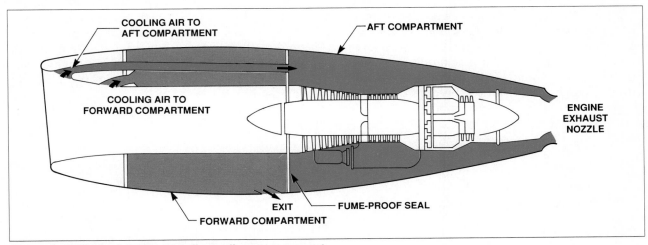

Figure 8-48. Typical engine nacelle cooling arrangement.

enough air were admitted to the engine to provide the ideal air/fuel mixture ratio of 15:1, internal temperatures of the engine would increase to more than 4,000 °F. In practice, a large amount of air in excess of the ideal ratio is admitted to the engine. This large surplus of air cools the hot sections of the engine.

Figure 8-44 illustrates the approximate engine outer-case (skin) temperatures encountered in a properly cooled twin-spool turbojet engine. Because of the effect of cooling, the temperatures of the outside of the case are considerably less than those encountered within the engine.

Internal engine and accessory unit cooling is one of the functions of the internal air system of the gas turbine engine. The internal air system is defined as those airflows which do not directly contribute to the engine thrust.

The burner cans, or combustors, where the energy of the fuel is released, are made of thin material that cannot withstand the continual high temperature of the burning gases. To protect them, a film of high-velocity cooling air is directed along the inner walls of the combustors. Airflow and fuel nozzle spray patterns are adjusted to center the flame in the combustor to avoid contact with the metal components.

The hottest point within the engine is at the nozzle guide vanes for the first stage turbine. On many engines, high-pressure bleed air from the compressor flows through hollow nozzle guide vanes and the hollow turbine blades. This removes some of their heat and discharges it into the exhaust. The more efficient the cooling at this point, the higher the turbine inlet temperatures may be and the higher the thermal efficiency of the engine.

In addition to the cooling air passing through the hollow nozzle guide vanes and hollow turbine blades, bleed air may also be directed to the face of the turbine disk and then discharged into the exhaust system. Air from the low-pressure compressor may flow through the hollow turbine shaft to remove heat from the compressor and turbine bearings. This air, after performing its cooling function, is discharged to the outside air through an air outlet. Figure 8-46 illustrates the path of both high-pressure and low-pressure cooling air in the turbine section.

2. Engine Insulation Blankets

To reduce the temperature of the structure in the vicinity of the exhaust duct and to eliminate the possibility of fuel or oil coming into contact with the hot parts of the engine, it is sometimes necessary to provide insulation on the exhaust duct or other external areas of the engine.

A typical insulation blanket and the temperatures obtained at various locations are shown in figure 8-47. This blanket contains fiberglass as the low-conductance material and aluminum foil as the radiation shield. The blanket is suitably covered so that it does not become oil-soaked.

Insulation blankets have been rather extensively used on some engine installations, but are not employed if the installation permits the more desirable air-cooling method.

3. Nacelle Cooling

The engine exterior and the engine nacelle may be cooled by passing air between the case and the shell of the nacelle (figure 8-48). The engine compartment frequently is divided into two sections. The forward section is built around the engine-air-inlet duct; the aft section is built around the engine. A fume-proof seal is provided between the two sections. The advantage of such an arrangement is that fumes from possible leaks in the fuel and oil lines contained in the forward section cannot become ignited by contact with the hot sections of the engine. In flight, ram air provides ample cooling of the two compartments. On the ground, air circulation is provided by the effect of reduced pressure at the rear of the engine compartment, produced by gases flowing from the exhaust nozzle.

Chapter IX
Engine Fire Protection Systems

A. Principles Of Fire Protection Systems

The powerplant, its related systems, and necessary connections are a natural fire hazard area. Fuel and oil are available in large quantities, and often under pressure. The exhaust system encloses high temperature gases and flames, vibration acting on the lightweight construction of engine components make fluid and exhaust leaks possible and, compounding these problems, the high-velocity air flowing through the engine compartment can carry explosive fumes into areas of high temperature.

1. Classes Of Fires

In order to understand the way an aircraft fire protection system operates, we should be familiar with the classifications of fires as they are listed by the National Fire Protection Association.

Class A fires are those in which solid combustible materials such as wood, paper, or cloth burn. Aircraft cabin fires are examples of Class A fires.

Class B fires have as their fuel, combustible liquids such as gasoline, engine oil, turbine fuel, hydraulic oil, and many of the solvents used in aviation maintenance. This is the type of fire generally encountered in an engine nacelle.

Class C fires are those which involve electrical equipment. Special care must be exercised because of the dangers from the electricity as well as those from the fire itself.

Class D fires involve some burning metal, such as magnesium. The use of the wrong type of fire extinguisher can intensify a Class D fire rather than extinguish it. Wheel and brake fires may fall into this category.

2. Requirements For Overheat And Fire Protection Systems

Overheat and fire protection systems on modern aircraft do not rely on observation by crew members as a primary method of fire detection . An ideal fire protection system will include as many as possible of the following features:

(1) A system which will not cause false warnings, under any flight or ground operating conditions.

(2) Rapid indication of a fire, and accurate location of the fire.

(3) Accurate indication that the fire is out.

(4) Indication that the fire has re-ignited.

(5) Continuous indication for the duration of the fire.

(6) Means for electrically testing the detector system from the aircraft cockpit.

(7) Detectors which resist exposure to oil, water, vibration, extreme temperatures, and maintenance handling.

(8) Detectors which are light in weight and easily adaptable to any mounting position.

(9) Detector circuitry which operates directly from the aircraft power system without inverters.

(10) Minimum electrical current requirements when not indicating a fire.

(11) Each detector system should actuate a cockpit light indicating the location of the fire, and an audible alarm system.

(12) A separate detection system for each engine.

There are a number of overheat and fire detection systems that satisfy these requirements, and a single aircraft may utilize more than one type.

B. Reciprocating Engine Fire Protection Systems

A complete fire protection system will include both a fire detection and a fire extinguishing system.

To detect fires or overheat conditions, detectors are placed in various zones to be monitored. Fires are detected in reciprocating engine aircraft by using one or more of the following:

(1) Overheat detectors.

(2) Rate-of-temperature-rise detectors.

(3) Flame detectors.

(4) Observation by crew members.

1. Reciprocating Engine Fire Zones

The powerplant area has been divided into fire zones based on the volume and the smoothness of the airflow. These classifications allow us to match the type of detection and extinguishing system to the fire conditions. Do not confuse these classifications with the NFPA fire types discussed earlier.

Class A fire zones have large quantities of air flowing past regular arrangements of similarly shaped obstructions. The power section of a reciprocating engine where the air flows over the cylinders is a Class A fire zone.

Class B fire zones have large quantites of air flowing past aerodynamically clean obstructions. Heat exchanger ducts and exhaust manifold shrouds constitute Class B fire zones in a reciprocating engine installation.

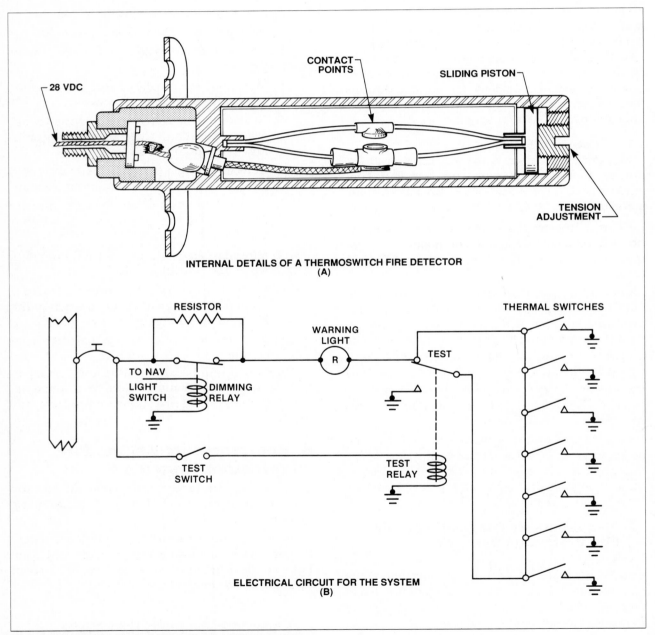

Figure 9-1. Thermoswitch-type fire detection system.

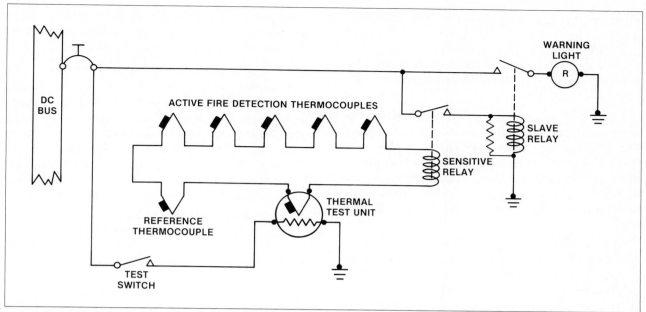

Figure 9-2. Thermocouple-type fire detection system.

Class C fire zones have a relatively small airflow through them. The compartment behind the firewall of a reciprocating engine is considered to be a Class C fire zone.

Class D fire zones are areas that have little or no airflow. Wheel wells and the inside of a wing structure are Class D fire zones.

Class X fires zones are in the powerplant portion of an aircraft that have large volumes of air flowing through them at an irregular rate. These are the most difficult of all areas to protect from fire. The amount of extinguishing agent required for adequate protection of a Class X fire zone is normally twice that required for other zones.

2. Types Of Fire Detection Systems

There are a number of fire detection systems that are able to detect the presence of a fire before it is visible to the flight crew. We will discuss a few basic types that are popular for detecting fires or overheat conditions in the powerplant portion of a modern aircraft.

a. Thermal Switch Type

The thermal switch fire detection system is a spot-type system that uses a number of thermally activated switches to warn of a fire. This system is illustrated in figure 9-1. The switches are wired in parallel with each other, and the entire group of switches are connected in series with the indicator light. If any detector reaches the temperature to which it is adjusted, it will com-

plete the circuit to ground and turn on the warning light.

The spot detector sensors operate using a bimetallic thermoswitch that closes when heated to a high temperature. A detector may be adjusted by heating its case to the required temperature and turning the adjusting screw in or out until the contacts just close.

The entire circuit can be tested by closing the test switch which actuates the test relay and grounds the end of the conductor that ties all of the detectors together. This turns on the warning light.

b. Thermocouple Type

This system operates on the rate-of-temperature-rise principle, rather than operating when a specific temperature is reached. This system will not give a warning when an engine overheats slowly, or a short circuit develops. The thermocouple fire detection system may also be known as the Edison fire detection system, after its manufacturer. In figure 9-2 we see the basic circuit of this type of system. The system consists of a relay box, warning lights, and thermocouples. The wiring system of these units may be divided into the following circuits: (1) The detector circuit, (2) the alarm circuit, and (3) the test circuit.

The relay box contains two relays, the sensitive relay and a slave relay, and the thermal test unit. Such a box may contain from one to eight

361

9-3

identical circuits, depending on the number of potential fire zones. The relays control the warning lights. In turn, the thermocouples control the operation of the relays. The circuit consists of several thermocouples in series with each other and the sensitive relay.

The thermocouple is constructed of two dissimilar metals such as chromel and constantan. The point where these metals are joined, and will be exposed to the heat of a fire, is called a hot junction. A metal cage surrounds each thermocouple to give mechanical protection without hindering free movement of air to the hot junction.

In a typical thermocouple system installation, the active thermocouples are placed in locations where fire is most likely to occur, and one thermocouple, called the reference thermocouple, is placed in a location that is relatively well protected from the initial flame. The temperature of the reference thermocouple will eventually reach that of the other thermocouples, and there will be no fire warning if everything heats up uniformly as it does in normal operation. But, if a fire should occur, the active thermocouples will get hot much sooner than the reference thermocouple, and the difference in temperature will produce a current in the thermocouple loop. This current flows through the coil of the sensitive relay. Anytime the current is greater than 4 milliamperes (0.004 ampere), the sensitive relay will close. The slave relay is energized by current through the contacts of the sensitive relay, and the warning light is turned on by the current through the contacts of the slave relay.

A test circuit includes a special test thermocouple in the loop with the other thermocouples. This test thermocouple and an electric heater are mounted inside the relay housing, and when the test switch on the instrument panel is closed, current flows through the heater and heats up the test thermocouple. This causes current to flow to the thermocouple loop, and the fire warning light will illuminate.

The total number of thermocouples used in individual detector circuits depends on the size of the fire zone and the total circuit resistance. The total resistance usually does not exceed 5 ohms. As shown in the circuit diagram (figure 9-2), the circuit contains a resistor connected across the terminals of the slave relay. This resistor is used to absorb the coil's self induced voltage. This is to prevent arcing across the

points of the sensitive relay. The contacts of the sensitive relay are so fragile that they would burn or weld if arcing were permitted.

c. Continuous-Loop Detector Systems

A continuous-loop detector or sensing system permits more complete coverage of a fire hazard area than any type of spot-type temperature detectors. The continuous-loop system works on the same basic principle as the spot-type fire detectors, except that instead of using individual thermal switches the continuous-loop system has sensors in the form of a long inconel tube.

These are overheat systems, using heat sensitive units that complete an electrical circuit at a certain temperature. There is no rate-of-heat-rise sensitivity in a continuous-loop system. Two

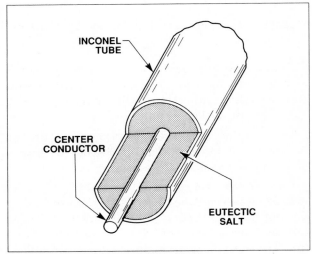

Figure 9-3. Fenwall sensing element.

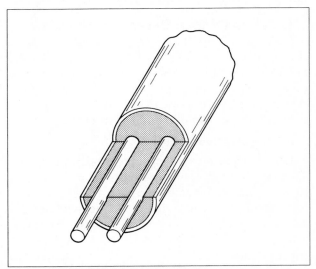

Figure 9-4. Kidde sensing element.

widely used types of continuous-loop systems are the Fenwall and the Kidde systems.

1) Fenwall System

The Fenwall system (figure 9-3), uses a single wire surrounded by a continuous string of ceramic beads in an inconel tube. The beads in this system are wetted with a eutectic salt which possesses the characteristics of suddenly lowering its electrical resistance as the sensing element reaches its alarm temperature.

At normal temperatures, the eutectic salt core material prevents electrical current from flowing. In case of fire or overheat condition, the core resistance drops and current flows between the signal wire and ground, energizing the alarm system.

The Fenwall system uses a magnetic amplifier control unit. This system is non-averaging but will sound an alarm when any portion of its sensing element reaches the alarm temperature.

2) Kidde System

In the Kidde continuous-loop system (figure 9-4), two wires are imbedded in a special ceramic core within an inconel tube. One of the wires is welded to the case at each end and acts as an internal ground. The second wire is a hot lead (above ground potential) that provides an electrical current signal when the ceramic core material changes its resistance with a change in temperature.

The Kidde sensing elements are connected to a relay control unit. This unit constantly measures the total resistance of the full sensing loop. The system senses the average temperature, as well as any hot spot.

Both systems continuously monitor temperatures in the affected compartments, and both will automatically reset following a fire or over-

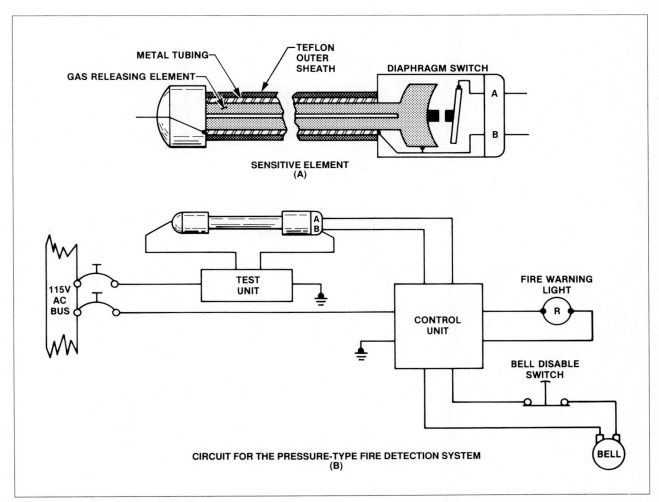

Figure 9-5. Lindberg fire detection system.

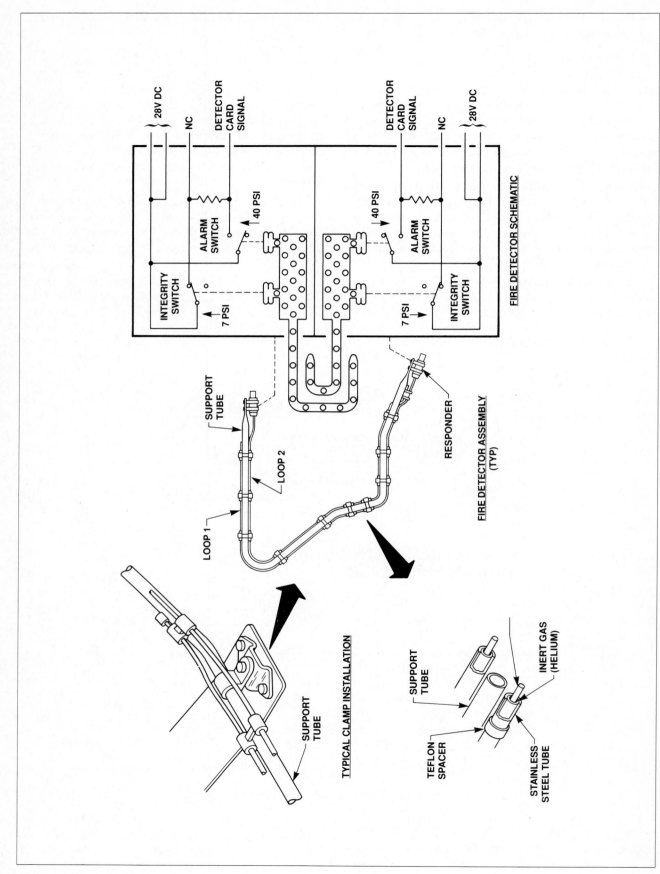

Figure 9-6. Systron-Donner fire detector system (Boeing).

heat alarm, after the overheat condition is removed or the fire is extinguished.

d. Pressure-Type Sensor Responder Types

The continuous-loop fire detection system initiates a fire warning signal when any portion of the continuous loop reaches a temperature for which the loop element is designed. The pressure-type sensor responder system actuates when any portion of the element reaches a temperature that would signal a fire condition, or when a large portion of the element is exposed to a lower temperature, as could happen in an overheat condition that could cause structural damage, or precede a fire.

The sensitive element of this system consists of a sealed gas-filled tube containing an element that absorbs gas at a low temperature and releases it as the temperature rises. The tube is connected to a pressure switch that will close when the gas pressure in the tube reaches a predetermined value.

Two slightly different types of this system may be found in use, the Lindberg system and the Systron-Donner system.

1) Lindberg System

The Lindberg fire detection system (figure 9-5), is a continuous-element type detector consisting of a stainless steel tube containing a discreet element. This element has been processed to absorb gas in proportion to the operating temperature set point. When the temperature rises (due to a fire or overheat condition) to the operating temperature set point, the heat generated causes the gas to be released from the element. Release of the gas causes the pressure in the stainless steel tube to increase. This pressure rise mechanically actuates the diaphragm switch in the responder unit, activating the warning lights and an alarm bell.

To test this system, low-voltage AC is sent through the outer sheath of the element. When this current heats the sheath to the required temperature, the element will release gas and the pressure on the diaphragm will close the contacts and initiate the fire warning. When the test switch is released, the detector element will cool off, the contacts will open, and the fire warning will stop.

2) Systron-Donner System

The sensing element of the Systron-Donner system contains a titanium center wire, which is the gas absorption material. This material contains hydrogen gas. The center wire is wrapped with an inert metal tape for protection and the turns of the tape will allow release of the hydrogen gas from the wire when temperatures reach the established level. This wrapped wire is installed in a stainless steel tube and is surrounded with helium gas under pressure.

The helium gas provides the averaging or overheat function of the sensor. Because the pressure of the helium gas will increase as temperatures rise, it will exert an increasing pressure on the pneumatic switch at the end of the sensor. At a preselected value, the switch will close and signal an overheat condition.

If a fire exists, the localized high temperature will cause a large quantity of hydrogen gas to be released from the titanium wire. This will cause an increase in the total gas pressure in the tube, and will actuate the pneumatic switch. This action is known as the discrete function of the sensor.

When the fire is extinguished and the sensor begins to cool, the hydrogen gas will once again be absorbed by the titanium wire, gas pressure will reduce, and the pneumatic switch will reopen. The system is again ready to indicate overheat or fire conditions.

Test circuits, which include a pressure warning switch, will indicate the operational condition of the system. If helium gas pressure is lost, the test circuit warns the flight crew that the system is not operational.

C. Turbine Engine Fire Protection Systems

Several general failures or hazards can result in overheat conditions or fires peculiar to turbine engine installations, because of their operating characteristics. The two major types of turbine failure can be classified as either thermodynamic or mechanical.

Thermodynamic causes are those which upset the proportion of air used to cool combustion temperatures to the levels which turbine metals can tolerate. When the cooling cycle is upset, turbine blades can melt, causing a sudden loss of thrust. The rapid buildup of ice on inlet screens or inlet guide vanes can result in severe over-temperature in the turbine section, causing turbine blades to melt, or to be severed and thrown outward. Such failures can result in a severed tail cone and possible penetration of the aircraft structure, tanks, or equipment near the turbine wheel. In general, most thermodynamic failures are caused by ice, excess air bleed or leakage, or faulty controls which permit compressor stall or excess fuel.

Mechanical failures, such as fractured or thrown blades, can also lead to overheat conditions or fires. Thrown blades can puncture the tail cone creating an overheat condition. Failure of forward stages of multi-stage turbines usually is much more severe. Penetration of the turbine case by failed blades is a possible fire hazard, as is the penetration of lines and components containing flammable fluids.

A high flow of fuel through an improperly adjusted fuel nozzle can cause burn-through of the tail cone in some engines. Engine fires can be caused by the burning fluids that occasionally run out through the exhaust pipe.

1. Turbine Engine Fire Zones

Because turbine engine installations differ markedly from reciprocating engines, the fire zone system used for reciprocating engines cannot be used.

A possible fire zone in a turbine engine installation is any area in which an ignition source, together with combustibles, combustible fluid line leakage, or combustible mixtures, may exist. The following engine compartments usually are protected:

(1) Engine power section, which includes the burner, turbine, and tailpipe.

(2) Engine compressor and accessory section, which includes the compressor and all the engine accessories.

(3) Complete powerplant compartments, in which no isolation exists between the engine power section and the accessory section.

2. Types Of Fire Or Overheat Detectors

Turbine powered aircraft will utilize the same types of engine fire and overheat detectors discussed earlier for reciprocating engine installations. The complete aircraft fire protection system of most large turbine powered aircraft will incorporate several of these detection methods.

3. Ground Fire Protection

The problem of ground fires has increased in seriousness with the increased size of turbine engine powered aircraft. For this reason, a central ground connection to the aircraft's fire extinguishing system has been provided on some aircraft. Such systems provide a more effective means of extinguishing ground fires and eliminate the necessity of removing and recharging the aircraft-installed fire extinguisher cylinders. These systems usually include a means for operating the entire system from one place, such as the cockpit or at the location of the fire extinguishing agent supply on the ground.

On aircraft not equipped with a central ground connection to the aircraft fire extinguisher system, means are usually provided for rapid access to the compressor, tailpipe, or burner compartments. Thus, many aircraft systems are equipped with spring-loaded or pop-out access doors in the skin of the various compartments.

Internal engine tailpipe fires that take place during engine shutdown or false starts can be blown out by motoring the engine with the starter. If the engine is running, it can be accelerated to rated speed to achieve the same result. If such a fire persists, a fire extinguisher agent can be directed into the tailpipe. It should be remembered that excessive use of CO_2 or other agents that have a cooling effect can shrink the turbine housing on the turbine and cause the engine to disintegrate.

D. Extinguishing Systems And Agents

There are three requirements for a fire: (1) there must be fuel that can be burned, (2) there must be oxygen to unite with the fuel and, (3) there must be sufficient heat to raise the temperature of the fuel to the point where it will combine with the oxygen. To extinguish a fire, any one of these three components can be taken away and the fire will go out. Extinguishing systems may be designed to generate an atmosphere that will dilute the oxygen levels to a point where the fire can no longer be sustained, to reduce the temperature below the ignition point, or a combination of these factors.

1. Fire Extinguishing Agents

The fixed fire extinguisher systems used in most engine fire protection systems are designed to dilute the atmosphere with an inert agent that will not support combustion. Many systems use perforated tubing or discharge nozzles to distribute the extinguishing agent. The newer high-rate-of-discharge (HRD) systems may use open-end tubes to deliver a quantity of extinguishing agent in 1 or 2 seconds.

a. Carbon Dioxide

Carbon dioxide (CO_2) is a colorless, odorless gas that is about one and one-half times as heavy as air. It is liquified by compressing and cooling it, and then is stored in steel cylinders. When it is released into the atmosphere, it expands and cools to a temperature of about -110°F, and becomes a white solid that resembles snow. When it changes from this solid into a gas, it does not pass through the liquid state, but goes directly from a solid to a gas.

From a standpoint of toxicity and corrosion hazards, carbon dioxide is the safest agent to use, and is especially recommended for use on Class B and Class C fires. It was for many years the most widely used extinguishing agent. If handled improperly, it can cause mental confusion and suffocation. Because of its variation in vapor pressure with temperature, it is necessary to store CO_2 in stronger containers than are required for most other agents.

b. Halogenated Hydrocarbons

The most effective extinguishing agents are the compounds formed by replacement of one or more of the hydrogen atoms in the simple hydrocarbons methane and ethane, by halogen atoms. The probable extinguishing mechanism of these agents is a "chemical interference" in the combustion process. This may be termed "chemical cooling" or "energy transfer blocking". This extinguishing mechanism is much more effective than oxygen dilution and cooling.

These agents are identified through a system of "halon numbers" which describe the chemical makeup of the agent. The first digit represents the number of carbon atoms in the compound molecule; the second digit, the number of fluorine atoms; the third digit, the number of chlorine atoms; the fourth digit, the number of bromine atoms; and the fifth digit, the number of iodine atoms, if any. If there is no iodine present the fifth digit does not appear. For example Bromotrifluoromethane $C F_3 B_r$, is referred to as Halon 1301, or sometimes by the trade name Freon 13.

A number of these agents have been used in the past, and many are no longer in production. Some early halon extinguishing agents produced toxic gases when exposed to fire. For example, carbon tetrachloride (Halon 104) was the first generally accepted agent of the halogenated family,

and was very popular for electrical hazards. When exposed to heat, the vapors of this compound form deadly phosgene gas.

Because of changing regulations, and developing environmental impact data, the aviation technician should keep abreast of current developments pertaining to the use of halogenated hydrocarbons as fire extinguishing agents. Halon fire extinguishing agents may be found in both portable extinguishers and installed systems on aircraft.

2. Fire Extinguishing Systems

A complete fire protection system consists of a fire detection and a fire extinguishing system. In an aircraft, it is very important that any fire extinguisher available be of the proper type to fight the class of fire that is likely to occur. There are two basic categories into which installed extinguishing systems are placed: (1) conventional systems, and (2) high-rate-of-discharge (HRD) systems. These systems may also be identified by the type of extinguishing agent used. Conventional systems are usually associated with the use of carbon dioxide, and HRD systems by the use of halogenated hydrocarbons.

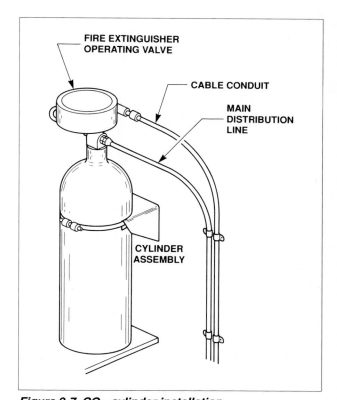

Figure 9-7. CO_2 cylinder installation.

a. Conventional Systems

Conventional system is a term applied to those fire extinguishing installations first used in aircraft. Still used in some older aircraft, the systems are satisfactory for their intended use, but are not as efficient as newer designs.

This fire extinguisher system is designed around a cylinder (figure 9-7) that stores the carbon dioxide under pressure, and a remote control valve assembly in the cockpit to distribute the extinguishing agent to the engines. The gas is distributed through tubing from the CO_2 cylinder valve to the control valve assembly in the cockpit, and then to the engines via tubing installed in the fuselage and wing tunnels. The tubing terminates in perforated loops which encircle the engines.

To operate this type of engine fire extinguisher system, the selector valve must be set for the engine which is on fire. An upward pull on the T-shaped control handle located adjacent to the engine selector valve actuates the release lever in the CO_2 cylinder valve. The compressed liquid in the CO_2 cylinder flows in one rapid burst to the outlets in the distribution line of the affected engine. Contact with the air converts the liquid into "snow" and gas which smothers the flame.

Other CO_2 systems may use multiple bottles to enable the system to deliver the extinguishing agent twice to any of the engines. Each bank of CO_2 bottles is equipped with a red thermo-safety discharge indicator disk, set to rupture at or above a preselected pressure (about 2,650 psi). If the ambient temperature raises the pressure of the bottles to this value the disk will rupture, discharging the bottles overboard. Each bank of bottles is also equipped with a yellow system-discharge indicator disk. Mounted adjacent to the red disk. the yellow disk indicates which bank of bottles has been emptied by a normal discharge.

b. High-Rate Discharge Systems

High-rate-of-discharge (HRD) is the term applied to the highly effective systems most currently in use. Such HRD systems provide discharge rates through high pressurization, short feed lines, large discharge valves and outlets. The extinguishing agent is usually one of the halogenated hydrocarbons (halon) sometimes

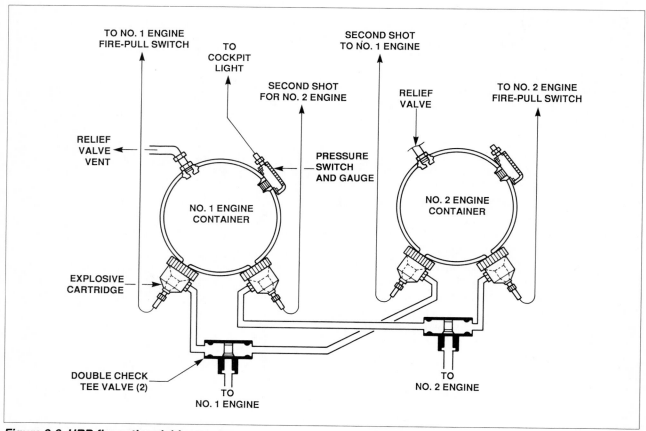

Figure 9-8. HRD fire extinguishing system.

boosted by high-pressure dry nitrogen. Because the agent and pressurizing gases are released into the fire zone in such a short period of time, the zone is temporarily pressurized and interrupts the ventilating air flow. The few, large-sized outlets are carefully located to produce high velocity swirl effects for best distribution.

The extinguishing agent is contained in a pressurized steel container, as seen in figure 9-8. A bottle pressure gauge is provided to indicate readiness of the system. The container is equipped with two discharge valves, which are operated by electrically discharge cartridges. These two valves provide the main and reserve controls, which release and route the extinguishing agent to the engine.

A thermal fuse is installed in each bottle which will melt and release the contents if the bottle is subjected to high temperatures. If a bottle is emptied in this way, a red blowout disk on the side of the fuselage will indicate thermal discharge. If the bottle is discharged by normal operation of the system a yellow disk, similarly mounted, will be blown out.

E. Smoke And Toxic Gas Detection Systems

A smoke detection system monitors certain areas of the aircraft for the presence of smoke, which is indicative of a fire condition. A smoke detection system is used where the type of fire anticipated is expected to generate a substantial amount of smoke before temperature changes are sufficient to activate a heat detection system.

The presence of carbon monoxide gas (CO), or nitrous oxides are dangerous to flight crews and passengers. Their presence may indicate a leak or failure of exhaust components, heaters, or may indicate a fire condition. Detection of the presence of either or both of these gases could be the earliest warning of a dangerous situation.

1. Carbon Monoxide Detectors

Because of the great hazard to personnel, the detectors which indicate concentrations of carbon monoxide gas are generally located in aircraft cabins or cockpits.

Carbon monoxide is a colorless, odorless, tasteless, non-irritating gas. It is the by-product of incomplete combustion, and is found in varying degrees in all smoke and fumes from burning carbonaceous substances. Exceedingly small amounts of the gas are dangerous. A concentration of 0.02% (2 parts in 10,000) may produce headache, mental dullness, and physical loginess within a few hours.

Probably the simplest and least expensive indicator may be worn as a badge, or installed on the instrument panel or cockpit wall. It is a button using a tablet which changes from a normal tan color to progressively darker shades of gray to black. The transition time required is relative to the concentration of CO. At a concentration of 50 ppm (0.005%), the indication will be apparent within 15 to 30 minutes. A concentration of 100 ppm (0.01%) will change the color of the tablet to gray in 2-5 minutes, from tan to dark gray in 15 to 20 minutes.

There are several types of portable testers (sniffers) in use. One type has a replaceable indicator tube which contains yellow silica gel, impregnated with a complex silico-molybdate compound and is catalyzed using palladium sulfate.

During operation, a sample of air is drawn through the detector tube. When the air sample contains carbon monoxide, the yellow silica gel turns to a shade of green. The intensity of the green color is proportional to the concentration of the carbon monoxide in the air sample at the time and location of the test.

2. Smoke Detectors

To be reliable, smoke detectors must be maintained so that smoke in a compartment will be indicated as soon as it begins to accumulate. Smoke detector louvers, vents, and ducts must not be obstructed. Smoke detection instruments are classified by method of detection.

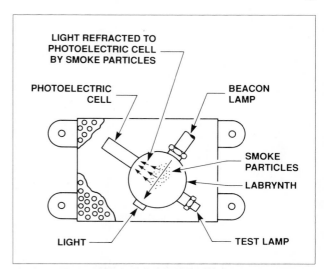

Figure 9-9. Photoelectric smoke detector.

a. Light Refraction Type

This type of detector consists of a photoelectric cell, a beacon lamp, and a light trap, all mounted in a labyrinth. Air samples are drawn through the detector unit. An accumulation of 10% smoke in the air causes the photoelectric cell to conduct electric current. Figure 9-9 shows the details of the smoke detector and indicates how the smoke particles refract the light to the photoelectric cell. When activated by smoke, the detector supplies a signal to the smoke detector amplifier. The amplifier signal activates a warning bell and light.

A test switch (figure 9-10) permits checking the operation of the smoke detector. Closing the switch connects 28 vdc to the test relay. When the test relay is energized, voltage is applied through the beacon lamp and test lamp, in series, to ground. An indication will be observed only if the beacon and test lamp, the photoelectric cell, the smoke detector amplifiers, and associated circuits are operable.

b. Ionization Type

Ionization type smoke detectors use a small amount of radioactive material to ionize some of the oxygen and nitrogen molecules in the air sample drawn into the detector cell. These ions

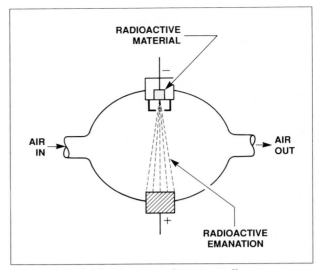

Figure 9-11. Ionization-type detector cell.

permit a small current to flow through the detector circuit. This cell is illustrated in figure 9-11.

If smoke is present in the air sample being drawn through the detector, small particles of the smoke will attach themselves to the oxygen and nitrogen ions, reducing the electrical current flow in the test circuit. If the current flow falls below a preset value, the alarm circuit will activate visual and aural cockpit alarms.

c. Solid-State Type

Solid-state smoke detection systems operate by comparing signals from two detecting elements. One will be located in the area being monitored, and the other exposed to outside air.

The detecting elements consist of a heating coil encased in a coating of semiconductor material. Carbon monoxide or nitrous oxides, if present, will be absorbed into this coating and will change the current-carrying ability of the detector. These sensors are connected into a type of bridge circuit so that when both elements are conducting evenly, the bridge will be balanced, and no warning signal will be present. If the element in the area being monitored is subjected to CO gas or nitrous oxides, an unbalanced condition will be created across the bridge and the warning circuit will illuminate the cockpit warning lamp.

F. Typical Multi-Engine Fire Protection System

The fire protection system used on the Boeing 727 jet transport is typical of those found on most of the high-performance jet aircraft of today.

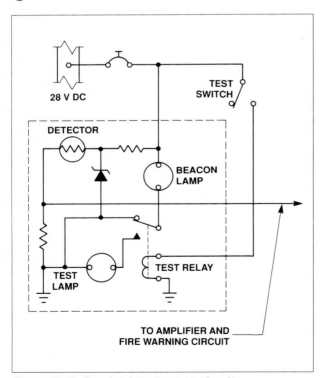

Figure 9-10. Smoke detector test circuit.

9-12

370

1. Operation Of System

The engine compartments are monitored by the fire detection sensors, and if a fire is sensed, a red light inside the engine fire switch illuminates, and the fire alarm bell rings. These lights and switches are located on the fire control panel above the main instrument panel (see figure 9-12).

The controls for the fire detection and extinguishing system are on the copilot's side of the instrument panel. They consist of the fire alarm bell disable switch, the fire detection system test switch, and the detector inop test switch. The fire alarm bell disable switch silences the fire alarm bell when it has been started by a fire indication in the engines or in one of the wheel wells. The fire detection system test switch checks the continuity of the detectors and the operation of the warning system. The detector inop test switch tests the circuits that activate the "Detector Inop" lights and, if the systems are functioning properly, will momentarily illuminate the "Detector Inop" lights.

When the warning light comes on, the pilot pulls the appropriate engine fire switch. This arms the fire extinguisher bottle discharge switch, disconnects the generator field relay, and shuts off the fuel to the engine, the hydraulic fluid to the pump, and the engine bleed air. It also deactivates the engine-driven hydraulic pump low-pressure lights.

When the fire switch is pulled, the bottle discharge switch is uncovered. If the pilot determines that a fire does actually exist in the engine compartment, the extinguishing agent can be released by depressing the bottle discharge switch and holding it for one second. This will discharge one of the HRD bottles into the engine compartment.

If the fire warning light does not go out within thirty seconds, indicating that the fire has been extinguished, the pilot can move the bottle transfer switch to its other position to select the second bottle of extinguishing agent, and again push the bottle discharge switch. When the fire extinguisher bottles have been discharged, or when their pressure is low, the appropriate bottle discharge light will come on.

2. System Components

In figure 9-13, we see the complete fire extinguishing system for the powerplant areas of the Boeing 727. The system is protected by two high-rate-of-discharge bottles of fire extinguishing agent, and these bottles are sealed with a metal seal. When the fire switch is pulled, the bottle discharge circuit is armed, and as soon as the bottle discharge switch is pressed, an explosive powder charge is ignited with an electric squib. The charge blows a knife into the seat and empties the contents of the bottle into the fire manifold. The extinguishing agent will flow to the engine appropriate to the switch being activated.

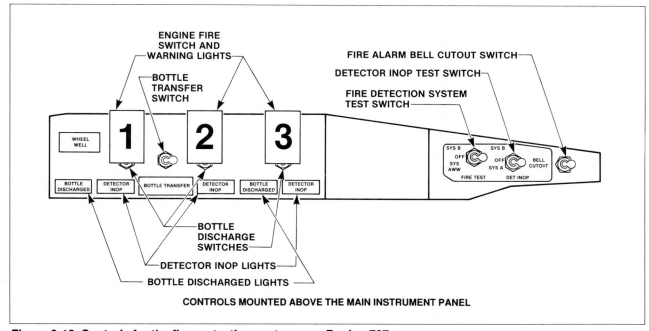

Figure 9-12. Controls for the fire protection system on a Boeing 727.

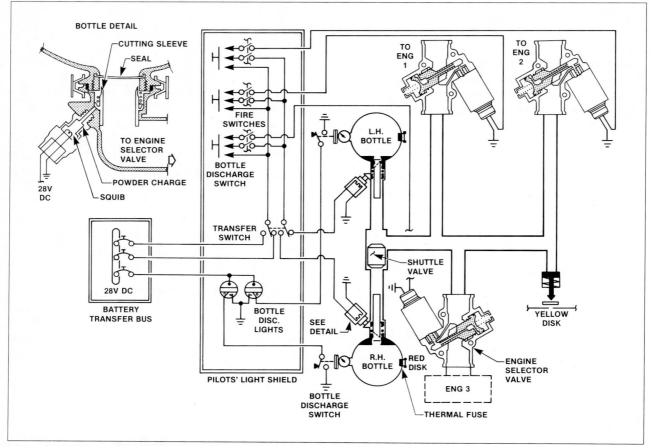

Figure 9-13. Fire extinguishing system for a Boeing 727.

Each of the two agent bottles have a gauge to indicate the pressure of the contents, and an electrical pressure switch is mounted on each bottle to activate a bottle discharge light on the instrument panel then the pressure on the agent bottle is below limits.

Each bottle has a thermal fuse that will melt and release the contents if the bottle is subjected to high temperatures. If a bottle is emptied in this way, a red blowout disk on the side of the fuselage is ruptured. This disk can be seen by crew members on a walk-around inspection. If the bottles are discharged by normal operation, a yellow disk similarly located will be blown out.

G. Fire Detection System Maintenance Practices

Fire detector sensing elements are located in many high-activity areas around aircraft engines. Their location, together with their small size, increases the chances of damage to the sensing elements during maintenance. The installation of the sensing elements inside the aircraft cowl

panels provides some measure of protection not afforded elements attached directly to the engine. On the other hand, the removal and re-installation of cowl panels can easily cause abrasion or structural defects to the elements.

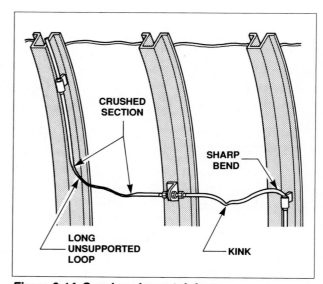

Figure 9-14. Sensing element defects.

1. Inspection

A well rounded inspection and maintenance program for all types of fire detection systems should include the following visual checks. These procedures are provided as examples and should not be used to replace approved local maintenance directives or the applicable manufacturer's instructions.

Sensing elements should be inspected for:

(1) Cracked or broken sections caused by crushing or squeezing between inspection plates, cowl panels, or engine components.

(2) Abrasion caused by rubbing of element on cowling, accessories, or structural members.

(3) Pieces of safety wire or other metal particles which may short the spot detector terminals.

(4) Condition of rubber grommets in mounting clamps, which may be softened from exposure to oils, or hardened from excessive heat.

(5) Dents and kinks in sensing element sections. Limits on the element diameter, acceptable dents or kinks, and degree of smoothness of tubing contour are specified by manufacturers. No attempt should be made to straighten any acceptable dent or kink, since stresses may be set up that could cause tubing failure. (See illustration of kinked tubing in figure 9-14.)

(6) Nuts at the end of the sensing elements (figure 9-15) should be inspected for tightness and safety wire. Loose nuts should be retorqued to the value specified by the manufacturer's instructions. Some types of sensing element connection joints require the use of copper crush gaskets. These should be replaced any time a connection is separated.

(7) If shielded flexible leads are used, they should be inspected for fraying of the outer braid. The braided sheath is made up of many fine metal strands woven into a protective covering surrounding the inner insulated wire. Continuous bending of the cable or rough treatment can break these fine wires, especially those near the connectors.

(8) Sensing element routing and clamping should be inspected carefully (figure 9-16). Long, unsupported sections may permit excessive vibration that can cause breakage. The distance between the clamps on straight runs, usually about 8 to 10 inches, is specified by each manufacturer. At end connectors, the first support clamp usually is located about 4 to 6 inches from the end connector fittings. In most cases, a straight run of 1 inch is maintained from all connectors before a bend is started, and an optimum bend radius of 3 inches normally is adhered to.

(9) Interference between a cowl brace and a sensing element can cause rubbing (figure 9-16). This interference may cause wear and short the sensing element.

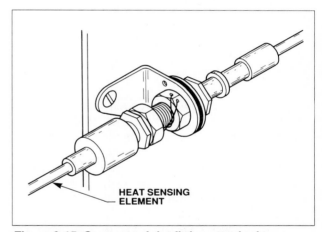

Figure 9-15. Connector joint fitting attached to structure.

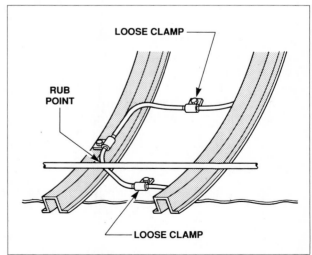

Figure 9-16. Rubbing interference.

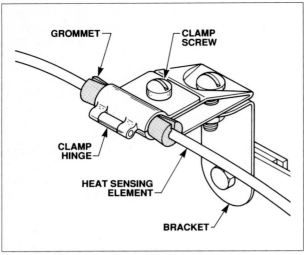

Figure 9-17. Typical fire detector loop clamp.

(10) Grommets should be installed on the sensing element so that both ends are centered on its clamp. The split end of the grommet should face the outside of the nearest bend. Clamps and grommets (figure 9-17) should fit the element snugly.

(11) Thermocouple detector mounting brackets should be repaired or replaced when cracked, corroded, or damaged. When replacing a thermocouple detector, note which wire is connected to the identified plus (+) terminal of the defective unit and connect the replacement in the same way.

(12) Test the fire detection system for proper operation by turning on the power supply and placing the fire detection test switch in the "TEST" position. The red warning

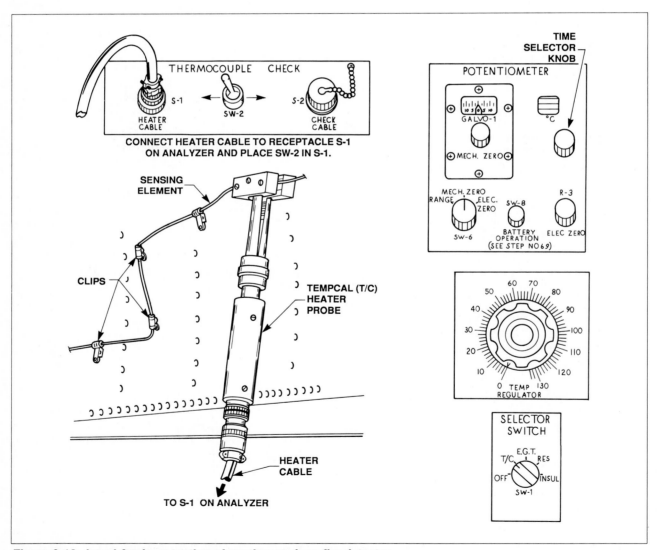

Figure 9-18. Jetcal Analyzer testing of continuous loop fire detector.

light should flash on within the time period established for the system. On some aircraft an audible alarm will also sound.

The Jetcal Analyzer unit may be used to test certain continuous loop detection systems. Figure 9-18 shows the unit being used to test a fire detection system. The heater probe is used to apply a known heat value to the sensing element of the continuous loop system. The heat value displays on the potentiometer of the Jetcal control panel. When the alarm temperature is reached, the cockpit warning light will illuminate. If the light illuminates before the prescribe temperature setting, the entire loop should be inspected for dents, kinks or other damage that could reduce the normal spacing between the power lead and ground potential of the loop.

2. Troubleshooting

The following troubleshooting procedures represent the most common difficulties encountered in engine fire detection systems.

(1) Intermittent alarms are most often caused by an intermittent short in the detector system wiring. Such shorts may be caused by a loose wire which occasionally touches a nearby terminal, a frayed wire brushing against a structure, or a sensing element which has rubbed against a structural member long enough to wear through the insulation. Intermittent faults can often best be located by moving wires to recreate the short.

(2) Fire alarms and warning lights can occur when no engine fire or overheat condition exists. Such false alarms can most easily be located by disconnecting the engine sensing loop from the aircraft wiring. If the false alarm continues, a short must exist between the loop connections and the control unit. If, however, the false alarm ceases when the engine sensing loop is disconnected, the fault is in the disconnected sensing loop. The loop should be examined for areas which have been bent into contact with hot parts of the engine. If no bent element can be found, the shorted section can be located by isolating and disconnecting elements consecutively around the entire loop.

(3) Kinks and sharp bends in the sensing element can cause an internal wire to short intermittently to the outer tubing. The fault can be located by checking the sensing element with a megohmmeter (megger) while tapping the element in the suspected area to produce the short.

(4) Moisture in the detection system seldom causes false fire alarm. If, however, moisture does cause an alarm, the warning will persist until the contamination is removed or boils away and the resistance of the loop returns to its normal value.

(5) Failure to obtain an alarm signal when the test switch is actuated may be caused by a defective test switch or control unit, the lack of electrical power, inoperative indicator light, or an opening in the sensing element or connecting wiring. When the test switch fails to provide an alarm, the continuity of a two-wire sensing loop can be determined by opening the loop and measuring the resistance. In a single-wire, continuous-loop system, the center conductor should be grounded.

H. Fire Extinguishing Systems Maintenance Practices

Regular maintenance of fire extinguisher systems typically includes such items as inspection and servicing of fire extinguisher bottles (containers), removal and re-installation of cartridge and discharge valves, testing of discharge tubing for leakage, and electrical wiring continuity tests. The following paragraphs contain details of some of the most typical maintenance procedures, and are included to provide an understanding of the operations involved.

Fire extinguisher system maintenance procedures vary widely according to the design and construction of the particular unit being serviced. The detailed procedures outlined by the airframe or system manufacturer should always be followed when performing maintenance.

1. Container Pressure Check

A pressure check of fire extinguisher containers is made periodically to determine that the pressure is between the minimum and maximum limits prescribed by the manufacturer. Changes of pressure with ambient temperature must also fall within prescribed limits. The graph shown in figure 9-19 is typical of the pressure/temperature curve graphs that provide maximum and minimum gauge readings. If the pressure does not fall within the graph limits, the extinguisher container should be replaced.

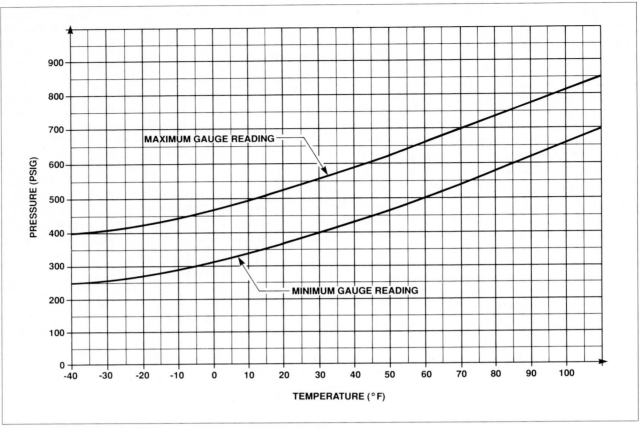

Figure 9-19. Fire extinguisher container pressure/temperature curve.

2. Discharge Cartridges

The service life of fire extinguisher discharge cartridges is calculated from the manufacturer's date stamp, which is normally placed on the face of the cartridge. The manufacturer's service life is usually recommended in terms of hours below a predetermined temperature limit. Many cartridges are available with a service life of approximately 5,000 hours. To determine the unexpired service life of a discharge cartridge, it is necessary to remove the electrical leads and discharge hose from the plug body, which can then be removed from the extinguisher container.

Care must be taken in the replacement of cartridges and discharge valves. Most new extinguisher containers are supplied with their cartridge and discharge valve disassembled. Before installation on the aircraft, the cartridge must be properly assembled into the discharge valve and the valve connected to the container. This is usually accomplished by means of a swivel nut that tightens against a packing ring gasket as illustrated in figure 9-20.

If a cartridge is removed from a discharge valve for any reason, it should not be used in another discharge valve assembly, since the distance the contact point protrudes may vary with each unit. Continuity might not exist if a plug is used, which had been indented with a long contact point, were installed in a discharge valve with a shorter contact point.

When actually performing maintenance, always refer to the applicable maintenance manuals and other related publications pertaining to a particular aircraft.

3. Agent Containers

Halogenated hydrocarbon extinguishing agents are stored in steel spherical containers. There are four sizes in common use today, ranging from 224 cu. in. (small) to 945 cu. in. (large). The large containers weigh about 33 pounds. The small spheres (figure 9-21) have two openings, one for the bonnet assembly (sometimes called an operating head), and the other for the fusible safety plug. The larger containers are usually equipped with two firing bonnets and a two-way check valve, as shown in figure 9-22.

The containers are charged with dry nitrogen in addition to a specified weight of the extinguishing agent. The nitrogen charge provides sufficient pressure for complete discharge of the agent. The bonnet assembly contains an electrically ignited powder cartridge which breaks the disk, allowing the extinguishing agent to be forced out of the sphere by the nitrogen charge.

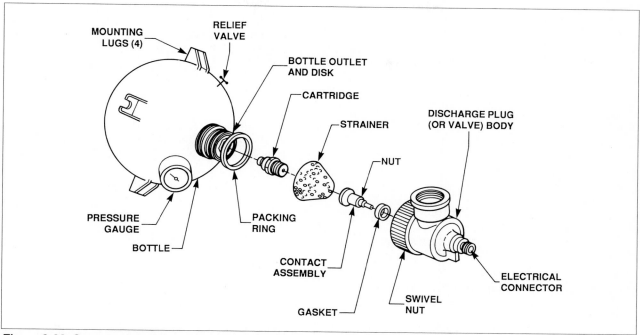

Figure 9-20. Components of a typical fire extinguisher container.

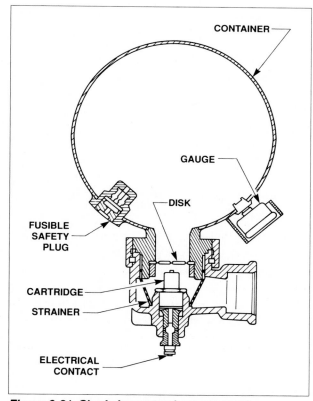

Figure 9-21. Single bonnet sphere assembly.

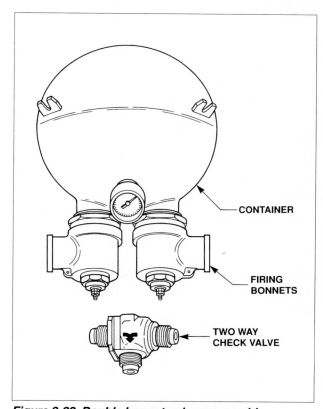

Figure 9-22. Double bonnet sphere assembly.

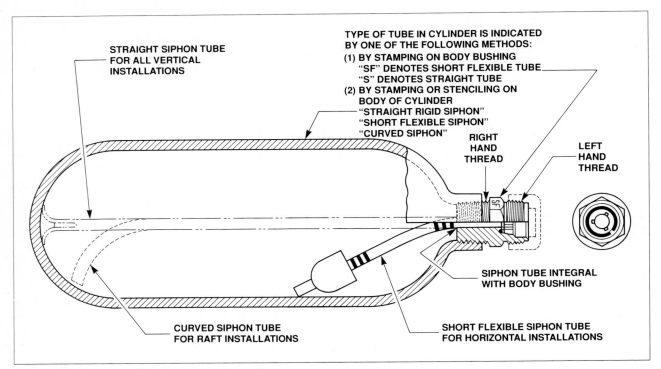

TYPE OF TUBE IN CYLINDER IS INDICATED
BY ONE OF THE FOLLOWING METHODS:
(1) BY STAMPING ON BODY BUSHING
    "SF" DENOTES SHORT FLEXIBLE TUBE
    "S" DENOTES STRAIGHT TUBE
(2) BY STAMPING OR STENCILING ON
    BODY OF CYLINDER
    "STRAIGHT RIGID SIPHON"
    "SHORT FLEXIBLE SIPHON"
    "CURVED SIPHON"

STRAIGHT SIPHON TUBE
FOR ALL VERTICAL
INSTALLATIONS

RIGHT
HAND
THREAD

LEFT
HAND
THREAD

SIPHON TUBE INTEGRAL
WITH BODY BUSHING

CURVED SIPHON TUBE
FOR RAFT INSTALLATIONS

SHORT FLEXIBLE SIPHON TUBE
FOR HORIZONTAL INSTALLATIONS

Figure 9-23. Typical CO₂ cylinder construction.

A single bonnet sphere assembly is shown disassembled in figure 9-20. The function of the parts shown, other than those describe previously are as follows: (1) the strainer prevents pieces of the broken disk from entering the system, (2) the fusible safety plug melts and releases the liquid when the temperature is between 208° and 220°F, and (3) the gauge shows the pressure in the container.

The gauge on the container should be checked for an indication of the specified pressure as given in the applicable aircraft maintenance manual. In addition, make certain that the indicator glass is unbroken and that the bottle is securely mounted.

Carbon dioxide cylinders come in various sizes, are made of stainless steel, and are wrapped with steel wire to make them shatterproof. The normal storage pressure of the gas ranges from 700 to 1,000 psi. However, the state of charge of the cylinder is determined by the weight of the CO_2.

The cylinder does not have to be protected against cold weather, because the freezing point of carbon dioxide is minus 110°F. However, it can discharge prematurely in hot climates. To prevent this, manufacturers put in a charge of dry nitrogen, at about 200 psi before they fill the cylinder with carbon dioxide. When treated in this manner, most CO_2 cylinders are protected against premature discharge up to 160°F. The nitrogen also provides additional pressure during normal release of the agent at low temperatures, during cold weather.

Carbon dioxide cylinders are equipped internally with one of three types of siphon tubes, as shown in figure 9-23. Aircraft fire extinguishers have either the straight rigid, or the short flexible siphon tube installed. The tube is used to make certain that the CO_2 is transmitted to the discharge nozzle in the liquid state. The type of siphon tube installed in the cylinder will dictate the necessary mounting position.

Almost all types of fire extinguisher containers require re-weighing at frequent intervals to determine the state of charge. In addition to the weight check, the containers must be hydrostatically tested, usually at five-year intervals.

Chapter X
Propellers

A. Basic Propeller Principles

Throughout the development of controlled flight as we know it, every aircraft required some kind of device to convert engine power to a usable form of thrust. With few exceptions, nearly all of the early practical aircraft designs used propellers to create this thrust. During the latter part of the 19th century, many unusual and innovative designs for propellers made their debut on the early flying machines. These ranged from simple fabric-covered wooden paddles to elaborate multi-bladed wire-braced designs.

As the science of aeronautics progressed, propeller designs improved from flat boards which merely pushed air backward, to airfoil shapes. These airfoils produce lift, as do wings, to pull the aircraft forward by aerodynamic action. By the time the Wright brothers began their first powered flights, propeller design had evolved into the standard two-bladed style similar in appearance to those used on today's modern light aircraft.

As aircraft designs improved, propellers were developed which used thinner airfoil sections and had greater strength. Because of its structural strength, these improvements brought the aluminum alloy propeller into wide usage. The advantage of being able to change the propeller blade angle in flight led to wide acceptance of the two-position propeller and, later, the constant-speed propeller system.

Today, propeller designs continue to be improved by the use of new airfoil shapes, composite materials, and multi-blade configurations.

Some recent improvements include the use of laminar flow symmetrical airfoils, composite materials, and gull wing propeller designs.

The Federal Aviation Administration has furnished guidelines regarding propeller system design, and the maintenance required for propeller systems. These are given to us in the Federal Aviation Regulations, the FAR's.

FAR 23, "Airworthiness Standards: Normal, Utility, and Acrobatic Aircraft," and FAR, Part 25, "Airworthiness Standards, Transport Category Aircraft," outline the requirements for propellers and their control systems for aircraft certification. Part 43 of the FAR's defines the different classes of maintenance for the propeller system and the minimum requirements for 100-hour and annual inspections.

1. Nomenclature

Before starting any discussion about propellers, it is necessary to define some basic terms to avoid confusion and misunderstanding.

A *propeller* is a rotating airfoil that consists of two or more blades attached to a central hub which is mounted on the engine crankshaft. The function of the propeller is to convert engine horsepower to useful thrust. Propeller blades have a leading edge, trailing edge, a tip, a shank, a face, and a back as shown in figures 10-1 and 10-2.

A term that will be used throughout our study of propellers is *blade angle*. This is the angle between the propeller's plane of rotation, and the chord line of the propeller airfoil.

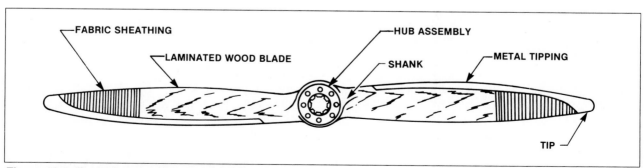

Figure 10-1. Typical wood aircraft propeller.

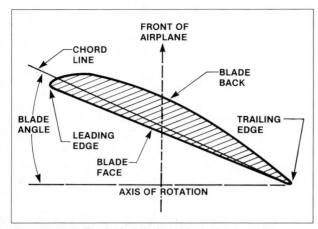

Figure 10-2. Typical airfoil section of a propeller.

Blade station is a reference position on a blade that is a specified distance from the center of the hub.

Pitch is the distance, in inches, that a propeller section will move forward in one revolution.

Pitch distribution is the gradual twist in the propeller blade from shank to tip.

2. Propeller Theory

As a propeller rotates, it produces lift and causes an aircraft to move forward. The amount of lift

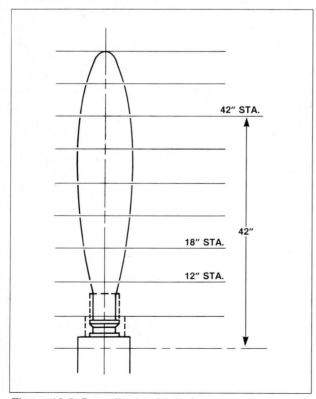

Figure 10-3. Propeller blade stations.

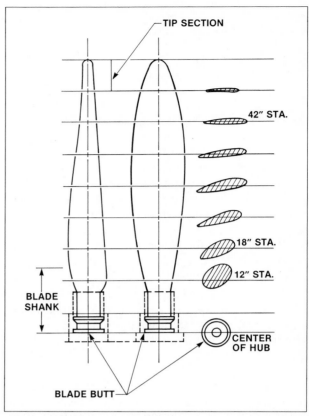

Figure 10-4. Pitch distribution in a typical aircraft propeller.

produced depends on variables such as engine RPM, propeller airfoil shape, and aircraft speed.

a. Propeller Lift And Angle Of Attack

Because a propeller blade is a rotating airfoil, it produces lift by aerodynamic action and pulls an aircraft forward. The amount of lift produced depends on the airfoil shape, RPM, and angle of attack of the propeller blade sections. Before discussing ways of varying the amount of lift produced by a propeller blade, we must understand some of the propeller design characteristics.

Starting from the centerline of the hub of a propeller, each blade can be marked off in one inch segments known as blade stations. If the blade angle is measured at each of these stations, the blade angle nearest the center of the propeller will be highest, with the blade angle decreasing toward the tip. This decrease in blade angle from the hub to the tip is called pitch distribution. A cross section of each blade station will show that low-speed airfoils are used near the hub and high speed airfoils toward the tip. The pitch distribution and the change in airfoil shape along the length of the blade are necessary, because each section moves through the air at a different velocity, with the slowest speeds near the hub and the highest speeds near the tip.

To illustrate the difference in the speed of airfoil sections at a fixed RPM, consider the three blade stations indicated on the propeller seen in figure 10-5. If the propeller is rotating at 1800 RPM, the 18-inch station will travel 9.42 feet per revolution (192.7 miles per hour), while the 36-inch station will travel 18.84 feet per revolution or 385.4 miles per hour. And the 48-inch station will move 25.13 feet per revolution, or 514 miles per hour. The airfoil that gives the best lift at 193 miles per hour is inefficient at 514 MPH. Thus, the airfoil is changed gradually throughout the length of the blade as we see in figure 10-4.

A look at one blade section will illustrate how the angle of attack on the blade of a fixed-pitch propeller changes with different flight conditions. The angle of attack is the angle between the airfoil chord line and the relative wind, and the direction of the relative wind is the resultant of

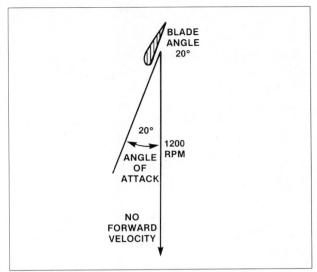

Figure 10-6. With no forward velocity, the angle of attack of a propeller blade is the same as the blade angle.

the combined velocities of rotational speed (RPM) and airspeed.

If the aircraft is stationary with no wind flowing past it, and the engine is turning at 1200 RPM, the propeller blade angle of 20 degrees at the 20-inch station will have an angle of attack of 20 degrees. This is because the direction of the relative wind is opposite to the movement of the propeller.

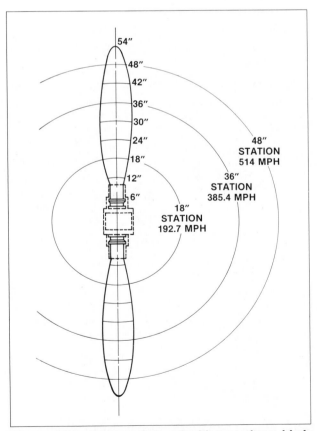

Figure 10-5. Comparative velocities at three blade stations of a typical propeller.

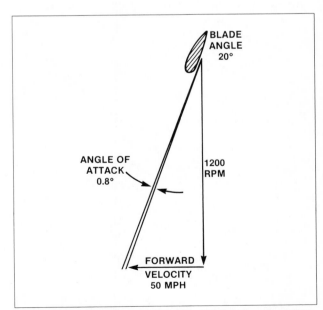

Figure 10-7. As the forward velocity of the aircraft increases, the angle of attack of the propeller blade decreases.

When this airplane is moving forward at 50 miles per hour, the relative wind now causes an angle of attack of 0.8 degrees.

Now if we increase the propeller speed to 1500 RPM, the relative wind will cause the angle of attack to be 4.4 degrees.

The most effective angle of attack is between two and four degrees, and any angle above 15 degrees

is ineffective because of the possibility of a stall. Fixed-pitch propellers may be selected to give this two- to four-degree angle of attack at either climb or cruise airspeeds and RPM, depending upon the desired flight characteristics.

b. Forces Acting On The Propeller

When a propeller rotates, many forces interact and cause tension, twisting, and bending stresses within the propeller.

1) Centrifugal Force

The force which causes the greatest stress on a propeller is centrifugal force. Centrifugal force can best be described as the force which tries to pull the blades out of the hub. The amount of stress created by centrifugal force may be greater than 7,500 times the weight of the propeller blade.

2) Thrust Bending Force

Thrust bending force attempts to bend the propeller blades forward at the tips, because the lift toward the tip of the blade flexes the thin blade sections forward. Thrust bending force opposes centrifugal force to some degree.

3) Torque Bending Force

Torque bending forces try to bend the propeller blade back in the direction opposite the direction of rotation.

4) Aerodynamic Twisting Moment

Aerodynamic twisting moment tries to twist a blade to a higher angle. This force is produced

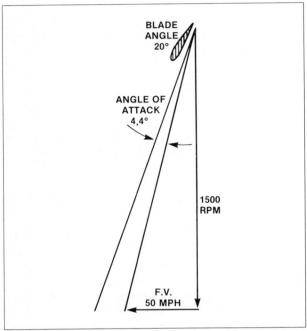

Figure 10-8. As the engine RPM increases for a given forward velocity, the angle of attack increases.

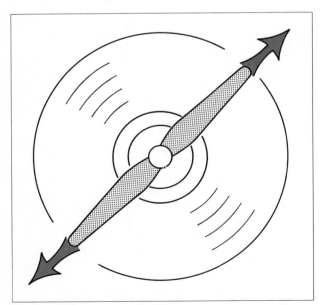

Figure 10-9. Centrifugal force tries to pull the propeller blades out of the hub.

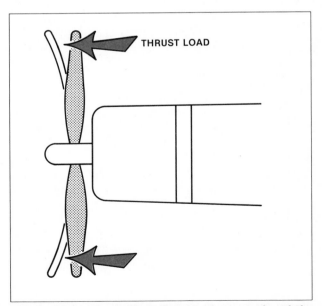

Figure 10-10. Thrust bending forces try to bend the propeller blade tips forward.

because the axis of rotation of the blade is at the midpoint of the chord line, while the center of the lift of the blade is forward of this axis. This force tries to increase the blade angle. Aerodynamic twisting moment is used in some designs to help feather the propeller.

5) Centrifugal Twisting Moment

Centrifugal twisting moment tries to decrease the blade angle, and opposes aerodynamic twisting moment. This tendency to decrease the blade angle is produced since all the parts of a rotating propeller try to move in the same plane of rotation as the blade centerline. This force is greater than the aerodynamic twisting moment at operational RPM and is used in some designs to decrease the blade angle.

6) Vibrational Force And Critical Range

When a propeller produces thrust, aerodynamic and mechanical forces are present which cause the blade to vibrate. If this is not compensated for in the design, this vibration may cause excessive flexing and work-hardening of the metal and may even result in sections of the propeller blade breaking off in flight.

Aerodynamic forces cause vibrations at the tip of a blade where the effects of transonic speeds cause buffeting and vibration.

Mechanical vibrations are caused by the power pulses in a piston engine and are considered to be more destructive in their effect than aerodynamic vibration. These power pulses cause a propeller blade to vibrate and set up standing wave patterns that cause metal fatigue and failure. The location and number of stress points change with different RPM settings, but the most critical location for these stress concentrations is about six inches in from the tip of the blades.

Most airframe-engine-propeller combinations have eliminated the detrimental effects of these vibrational stresses by careful design, but some combinations are sensitive to certain RPM's, and this critical range is indicated on the tachometer by a red arc. The engine should not be operated in the critical range except as necessary to pass through it to set a higher or lower RPM. If the engine is operated in the critical range, there is a possibility of structural failure in the aircraft because of the vibrational stresses set up.

c. Propeller Pitch

The *geometric pitch* of a propeller is defined as the distance, in inches, that a propeller will move

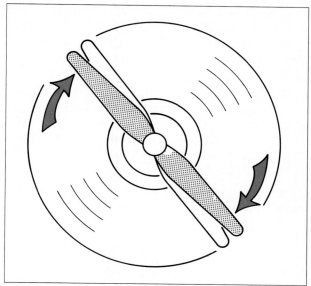

Figure 10-11. Torque bending forces try to bend the blade in the plane of rotation opposite the direction of rotation.

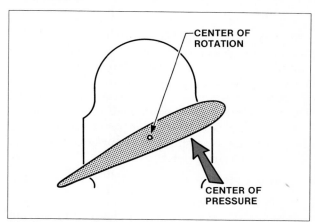

Figure 10-12. The aerodynamic twisting moment tries to increase the blade angle.

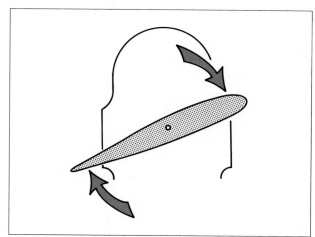

Figure 10-13. The centrifugal twisting moment tries to decrease the blade angle.

forward in one revolution, and this is based on the propeller blade angle at the 75% blade station. Geometric pitch is theoretical because it does not take into account any losses due to inefficiency.

Effective pitch is the distance the aircraft actually moves forward in one revolution of the propeller. It may vary from zero, when the aircraft is stationary on the ground, to about 90% of the geometric pitch during the most efficient flight conditions.

The difference between geometric pitch and effective pitch is called *slip*.

If a propeller has a pitch of 50 inches, in theory, it should move forward 50 inches in one revolution. But, if the aircraft actually moves forward only 35 inches in one revolution, the effective pitch is 35 inches and the propeller is 70% efficient.

3. Types Of Propellers

There are various types or classes of propellers, the simplest of which are the fixed-pitch and ground-adjustable propellers. The complexity of propeller systems increases from these simpler forms to the feathering and reversing propeller systems used on turboprop aircraft. The brief descriptions presented here are only to acquaint you with the basic types. No attempt has been made to include all propeller systems that may be encountered.

a. Fixed Pitch

Fixed-pitch propellers are simple propellers whose blade angle cannot be changed in normal operation. They are usually made of wood or aluminum alloy and are usually found on light, single-engine airplanes.

Fixed-pitch propellers are designed for best efficiency at one rotational and forward speed. They are designed to fit a set of conditions of both airplane and engine speeds. Any change in these conditions will reduced the efficiency of both the propeller and the engine.

b. Ground Adjustable

Ground-adjustable propellers are similar to fixed-pitch propellers in that their blade angles cannot be changed in flight, but the propeller is made so that the blade angles can be changed on the ground. The pitch, or blade angle, can be adjusted to give the desired flight characteristics, that is, low blade angle if the airplane is used for operation from short airstrips or high blade angle if high-speed cruise flight is of most importance. This type of propeller was widely used on aircraft built between the 1920's and the 1940's.

A ground-adjustable propeller is designed so that its blades can be rotated in the hub to change the blade angles. The hub is made in two halves that must be separated slightly to loosen the blades so they can be rotated. And the hub is held together with clamps or bolts to prevent the blades from rotating during operation.

The propeller blades may be of wood, aluminum, or steel with shoulders machined on to the root to hold the blades in the hub against the centrifugal operating loads.

The hub of the propeller is made of aluminum or steel, with the two halves machined as a matching pair. Grooves in the hub mate with the shoulders on the blades. When steel blades are

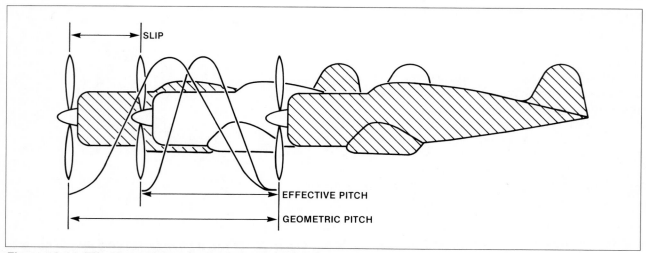

SLIP

EFFECTIVE PITCH

GEOMETRIC PITCH

Figure 10-14. Effective and geometric pitch of a propeller.

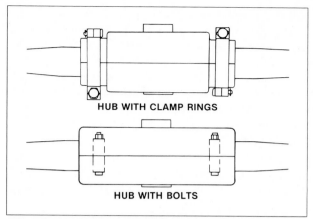

Figure 10-15. Typical propeller hubs for ground adjustable propellers.

used, the hub is usually held together with bolts. When wood or aluminum alloy blades are used, the hub halves are held together with bolts or clamp rings.

c. Controllable Pitch

The *controllable pitch propeller* permits a change in blade pitch, while the propeller is rotating. This permits the propeller to assume a blade angle that will give the best performance for the particular flight conditions. The number of pitch positions may be limited, as with a two-position controllable propeller; or the pitch may be adjusted to any angle between the minimum and maximum pitch settings of a given propeller.

The use of a controllable pitch propeller makes it possible to attain the desired engine RPM for a particular flight condition. As an airfoil is moved through the air, it produces two forces, lift and drag. Increasing propeller blade angle increases the angle of attack and produces more lift and drag; this action increases the horsepower required to turn the propeller at a given RPM. Since the engine is still producing the same horsepower, the propeller slows down. If the blade angle is decreased, the propeller speeds up. Thus, the engine RPM can be controlled by increasing or decreasing blade angle.

d. Automatic

In automatic propeller systems, the control adjusts pitch without attention by the operator, to maintain a specific preset engine RPM. For example, if engine speed increases, the controls automatically increase blade angle until the desired RPM has been re-established. A good automatic control system will respond to such small variations of RPM that, for all practical

purposes, a constant RPM will be maintained. Automatic propellers are usually termed *constant speed propellers*.

Additional refinements, such as pitch reversal and feathering features, are included on some propeller systems to improve still further their operational characteristics.

e. Reverse-Pitch

Reversing propeller systems are refinements of the constant-speed feathering systems. The propeller blades can be rotated to a negative angle to produce reverse thrust. This forces air forward instead of backwards, and permits a shorter landing roll and improved ground maneuvering.

f. Feathering Propellers

Most multi-engine aircraft are equipped with *feathering propellers*. These are constant-speed propeller systems which also have the capability of being feathered. When a propeller is feathered, its blades are rotated so they present their leading edge to the wind, eliminating the drag associated with a windmilling propeller. Feathering propellers must be used on multi-engine aircraft to reduce propeller drag during engine out operations.

4. Classifications Of Propellers

a. Tractor

Tractor propellers are those mounted on the upstream end of a drive shaft in front of the supporting structure. Most aircraft are equipped with this type of propeller. A major advantage of the tractor prop is that lower stresses are induced in the propeller as it rotates in relatively undisturbed air.

b. Pusher

Pusher propellers are those mounted on the downstream end of a drive shaft behind the supporting structure. As with tractor-type installations, pusher props may be constructed as either fixed- or variable-pitch propellers. Seaplanes and amphibious aircraft have used pusher propellers more than other types of aircraft.

On land planes, where propeller-to-ground clearance usually is less than propeller-to-water clearance of seaplanes, pusher propellers are subject to more damage than tractor propellers. Rocks, gravel, and small objects, dislodged by wheels, quite often may be thrown or drawn into a pusher propeller. Similarly, planes with pusher propellers are apt to encounter prop damage from water spray thrown up by the hull during landing or takeoff from water. Consequently, the pusher propeller quite often is mounted above and behind the wings to prevent such damage.

B. Propellers Used On Light Aircraft

Light aircraft may use either fixed-pitch or constant speed propellers, with design and materials depending upon the age of the aircraft, and its normal operating speed range.

1. Fixed Pitch

Fixed pitch propellers are found on small training and utility type aircraft, and may be either of wooden construction on older aircraft, or aluminum on the newer planes.

a. Wooden

Wooden propellers are often found on older single-engine airplanes. Most have a natural wood finish, although some may be found having a black or gray plastic coating. These coated blades are referred to as "armor coated".

These propellers are made of several layers of wood bonded together with a waterproof resin glue. Except for very few instances, they are nowadays made of birch. Each layer of a propeller is normally of the same thickness and type of wood, with a minimum of five layers of wood being used. When the planks of wood are glued together, they form what is called a propeller blank.

During fabrication, the blank is roughed to shape and is allowed to set for a week or so to allow the moisture to be distributed equally through all of the layers.

The white, as the rough-shaped blank is called, is finished to the exact airfoil and pitch dimensions required for the desired performance characteristics, and during this process, the center bore and bolt holes are drilled.

At this stage of its manufacture, the tip fabric, if used, is applied to the propeller. Cotton fabric is glued to the last 12 to 15 inches of the propeller blade, where it reinforces the thin sections of the tip. The fabric is doped to prevent

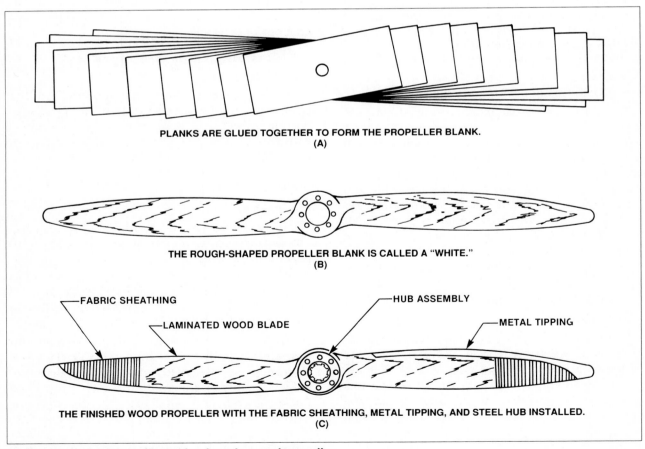

PLANKS ARE GLUED TOGETHER TO FORM THE PROPELLER BLANK.
(A)

THE ROUGH-SHAPED PROPELLER BLANK IS CALLED A "WHITE."
(B)

FABRIC SHEATHING — HUB ASSEMBLY — LAMINATED WOOD BLADE — METAL TIPPING

THE FINISHED WOOD PROPELLER WITH THE FABRIC SHEATHING, METAL TIPPING, AND STEEL HUB INSTALLED.
(C)

Figure 10-16. Stages in the production of a wood propeller.

deterioration by weather and by the rays of the sun. The propeller is then finished with clear varnish to protect the wood surface.

Monel, brass, or stainless steel tipping is applied to the leading edge of the propeller to prevent damage from small stones during ground operations. The metal is shaped to the leading edge contour and is attached to the blade with countersunk screws in the thick blade sections and with copper rivets in the thin sections near the tip. The screws and rivets are safetied into place with solder.

Three number 60 holes are drilled ³⁄₁₆-inch deep into the tip of each blade to release moisture from the propeller and allow the wood to breathe.

Wooden blades for controllable-pitch propellers are constructed in the same manner as fixed-pitch propellers, except that the shank of the blade is held in a metal sleeve with lag screws.

b. Aluminum Alloy

Aluminum propellers are the most widely used type of propellers in aviation. They are more desirable than wood propellers because thinner, more efficient airfoils may be used without sacrificing structural strength. Better engine cooling is also achieved by carrying the airfoil sections close to the hub and directing more air over the engine. These propellers require much less maintenance than wood propellers, thereby reducing the operating cost.

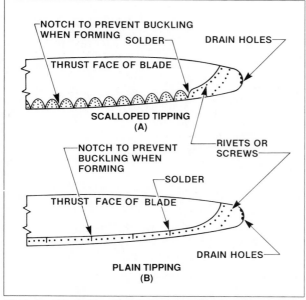

Figure 10-17. Types of metal tipping applied to a wood propeller.

High strength aluminum alloy forgings are used in the manufacture of propellers, and they are finished to the desired airfoil shape by machine and manual grinding. The final pitch is set by twisting the blades to the desired angles. As the propeller is being finished by grinding, its balance is checked and adjusted by removing metal from the tip of the blade to adjust horizontal balance and from the boss or leading and trailing edges of the blades to adjust vertical balance. Some propeller designs have their horizontal balance adjusted by placing lead wool in balance holes near the boss, and their vertical balance corrected by attaching balance weights to the side of the boss.

Once the propeller is ground to the desired contours and the balance is adjusted, the surfaces are finished by anodizing and painting.

Two propeller designation systems are discussed here, so the technician will be able to recognize the systems and understand the difference in propeller designs by their designation. The McCauley and Sensenich systems are representative of those presently in use.

1) McCauley Designation System

A McCauley propeller designated as 1B90/CM7246 has a basic design designation of 1B90. The CM component of the designation indicates the type of crankshaft the propeller will fit, its blade tip contour, and the adapter used, and provides other information pertaining to a specific aircraft installation. The 72 indicates the diameter of the propeller in inches, and the 46 indicates the pitch of the propeller at the 75% station.

2) Sensenich Designation System

The Sensenich designation 76DM6S5-2-54 indicates a propeller with a designed diameter of 76 inches. The D designates the blade design, and the M6 indicates the hub design and mounting information, such as bolt hole size, dowel pin location, etc. The S5 designates the thickness of the spacer to be used when the propeller is installed. The 2 indicates that the diameter has been reduced two inches from the designed diameter, meaning that the propeller has an actual diameter of 74 inches. The 54 designates the pitch in inches, at the 75% station.

In either designation system, a change in pitch will be indicated by the pitch stamping on the hub being restamped to indicate the new pitch setting.

Other propeller manufacturers use designation systems that are similar to the McCauley or the Sensenich system.

2. Constant Speed

Because of the long service life of aircraft and their related systems, a variety of constant speed propeller systems may be encountered in the field. The two presented here are representative of those in common used today. In all cases, consult the appropriate manufacturer's service information before installing, or performing any maintenance on, a propeller.

a. McCauley

The McCauley constant-speed propeller system is one of the more popular constant-speed systems for light and medium size general aviation airplanes. This is the system used on most of the Cessna aircraft that require constant-speed propellers. It is also used on many other aircraft designs.

1) The Propellers

Two series of propellers are currently being produced by McCauley, the threaded series and the threadless series. The threaded series propellers use a retention nut which screws into the propeller hub and holds the blades in the hub. The threadless design is the more modern of the two, and has the advantages of simplified manufacture and decreased overhaul time.

McCauley propellers use oil pressure on an internal piston to cause an increase in the blade angle, and this opposes a spring inside the hub which is used to decrease the blade angle. The movement of the piston is transmitted by blade actuating links to the blade actuating pins that are located on the butt of the blades. All of the pitch changing mechanism is enclosed inside the hub.

The propeller blades, hub, and piston are made of aluminum. The propeller cylinder, blade actuating pins, piston rod, and spring are all made of steel, plated with chrome or cadmium, and the actuating links are made of a phenolic material.

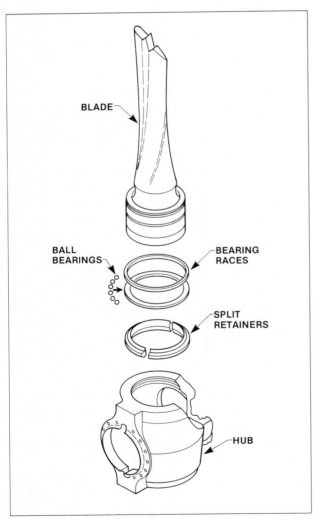

Figure 10-18. McCauley propeller with the threadless blades.

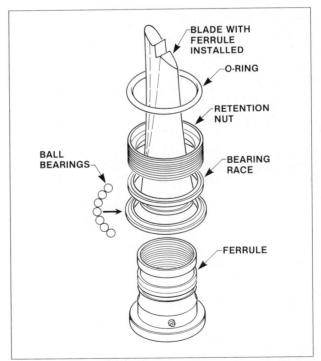

Figure 10-19. Threaded series of McCauley propeller blades.

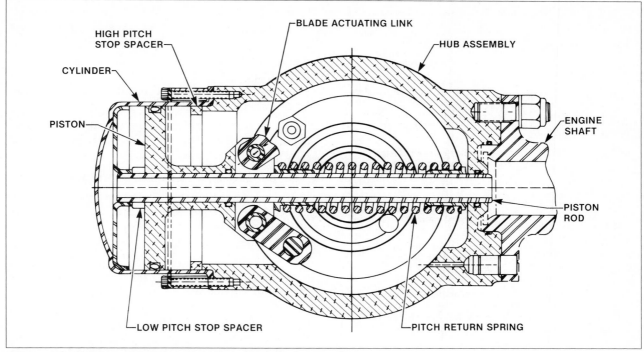

Figure 10-20. Pitch change mechanism in a McCauley propeller.

The hollow piston rod through the center of the hub is used as an oil passage to direct oil from the engine crankshaft to the propeller piston. The pitch return spring is located around the piston rod and is compressed between the piston and the rear inside surface of the hub. O-ring seals are used to seal between the piston and the cylinder, the piston and the piston rod, and the piston rod and the hub.

All operating components of the propeller are lubricated at overhaul and receive no additional lubrication during operation.

Certain models of McCauley propellers have been modified to allow for an ongoing dye-penetrant type of inspection. The hub breather holes are sealed and the hub is partially filled with engine oil colored with a red dye. The red dye in the oil makes the location of cracks readily apparent and indicates that the propeller should be removed from service.

The McCauley propeller designation system is broken down as we see in figure 10-21. The most important parts of the designation for the technician are the dowel pin location, the C-number, and the modification or change letter after the C-number. The modification and change designation indicates the compliance with required or recommended alterations.

The blade designation is included with the propeller designation when determining which propeller will fit a specific aircraft. For example: a C203 propeller will fit a Cessna 180J aircraft, but the land-plane version requires a 90DCA-8 blade of 82-inches diameter, while the seaplane version requires a 90DCA-2 blade of 88-inches diameter.

McCauley serial numbers on the propeller hub indicate the year in which the hub was manufactured.

2) Installation And Adjustment

McCauley constant-speed propellers are found only on flanged crankshafts and are installed following the basic procedures for fixed-pitch flanged shaft installations. Before the propeller is placed on the crankshaft, the O-ring in the rear of the hub is lubricated with a light coat of engine oil. When placing the propeller on the flange, take care to protect this O-ring from being damaged. The bolts or nuts should be torqued following a torquing sequence. Safety them as appropriate, and be sure to use new fiber lock nuts, if applicable.

When the propeller and governor are installed, the cockpit control is rigged for the proper cushion. Check the system for the proper operation on the ground, correcting adjustments and

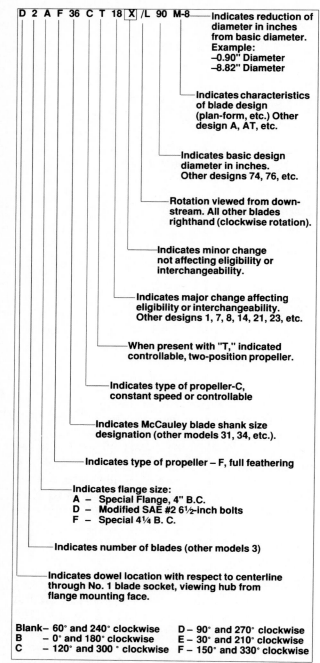

D 2 A F 36 C T 18 [X] /L 90 M-8

— Indicates reduction of diameter in inches from basic diameter. Example: −0.90" Diameter −8.82" Diameter

— Indicates characteristics of blade design (plan-form, etc.) Other design A, AT, etc.

— Indicates basic design diameter in inches. Other designs 74, 76, etc.

— Rotation viewed from downstream. All other blades righthand (clockwise rotation).

— Indicates minor change not affecting eligibility or interchangeability.

— Indicates major change affecting eligibility or interchangeability. Other designs 1, 7, 8, 14, 21, 23, etc.

— When present with "T," indicated controllable, two-position propeller.

— Indicates type of propeller–C, constant speed or controllable

— Indicates McCauley blade shank size designation (other models 31, 34, etc.).

— Indicates type of propeller – F, full feathering

— Indicates flange size:
A – Special Flange, 4" B.C.
D – Modified SAE #2 6½-inch bolts
F – Special 4¼ B. C.

— Indicates number of blades (other models 3)

— Indicates dowel location with respect to centerline through No. 1 blade socket, viewing hub from flange mounting face.

Blank– 60° and 240° clockwise   D – 90° and 270° clockwise
B – 0° and 180° clockwise   E – 30° and 210° clockwise
C – 120° and 300° clockwise   F – 150° and 330° clockwise

Figure 10-21. McCauley propeller designation system.

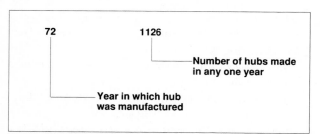

72   1126

— Number of hubs made in any one year

— Year in which hub was manufactured

Figure 10-22. McCauley propeller and governor serial numbering system.

rigging as necessary to obtain the correct maximum RPM, the correct response to the cockpit control movement, and correct cushion. It should be noted that some systems cannot reach their rated RPM on the ground. A test flight should now be performed to check the operation and to check for oil leaks.

Install the propeller spinners and spacers in accordance with the applicable aircraft service manual.

3) Inspection, Maintenance And Repair

The propeller should be inspected for surface defects on the blades and hub areas, security of the blades in the hub, proper safety installation, oil leaks, and security of mounting bolts and nuts.

Oil found coming from the hub breather holes indicates a defective internal O-ring. The piston-to-cylinder O-ring is often the cause of this leak. On some models, this can be replaced by a technician following the procedures outlined in the propeller or aircraft service manual. On other models, the propeller will have to be returned to a repair facility. If other seals are the cause of the leak, they will have to be replaced by a repair facility.

A dye-penetrant inspection of the blade retention areas of the hub and of the blade shanks is advisable at each 100-hour and annual inspections, but be sure to remove all of the residue after the inspection, as some of the substances used are corrosive.

b. Hartzell

The Hartzell constant-speed propeller systems are used in modern general aviation airplanes and share the market with McCauley. Hartzell systems are used extensively on Piper aircraft and on many other designs.

1) The Propellers

Hartzell produces two styles of constant-speed propellers: a steel hub propeller and a "Compact" model. Steel hub propellers are identified by their exposed operating mechanism, while Compact models have the pitch changing mechanism inside the hub assembly.

Some models of the steel hub propellers use oil pressure to decrease blade angle and the centrifugal force on the counterweights to increase blade angle. Other models of the steel hub propellers have no counterweights and use centrifugal twisting moment to decrease the blade angle and oil pressure to increase blade angle.

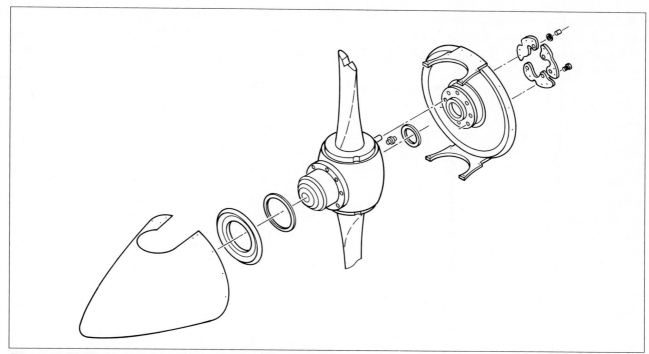

Figure 10-23. McCauley constant-speed propeller installation.

Hartzell steel hub propellers (figure 10-25) use a steel spider as the central component. Bearing assemblies and aluminum blades are placed on the spider arms and are held in place by two-piece steel clamps. A steel cylinder is screwed onto the front of the spider and an aluminum piston is placed over the cylinder. The piston is connected to the blade clamps by steel link rods.

During operation, oil pressure is directed to the propeller piston through the engine crankshaft where it causes a change in blade angle. Counterweight models use oil pressure to decrease the blade angle, and centrifugal force on the counterweights increases the angle. Non-counterweighted models use oil pressure to increase the blade angle and centrifugal twisting moment to decrease the angle.

Some steel hub propellers are made so they will mount on flanged crankshafts, and others mount on splined shafts. Compact designs are normally used only with flanged crankshafts.

Hartzell Compact propellers use aluminum blades mounted in an aluminum hub. This propeller is illustrated in figure 10-26. The hub is held together with bolts and contains the pitch changing mechanism of the propeller. This mechanism consists of a piston, piston rod, and actuating links.

The Compact propeller uses governor oil pressure to increase blade angle and the centrifugal twisting moment acting on the propeller blades to decrease blade angle.

The Hartzell propeller designation system is the same for steel hub and Compact propeller models, as we see in the sample designations in figure 10-27.

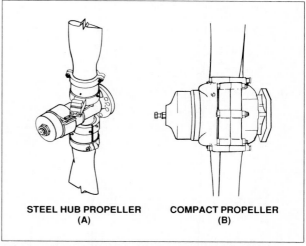

STEEL HUB PROPELLER (A)   COMPACT PROPELLER (B)

Figure 10-24. Hartzell constant-speed propellers.

2) Installation And Adjustments

Hartzell propellers are installed following the same basic practices as those used with the McCauley propellers.

The steel hub propellers can be adjusted for the desired low blade angle by loosening the hub clamps and rotating the blades in the clamps until the desired blade angle is obtained. Then clamps are retorqued and safetied. This also changes the high blade angle, since the range between high and low blade angle is fixed by the range of the piston movement.

The low pitch setting of the Compact propellers can be adjusted by loosening the lock nut on the adjusting screw on the hub cylinder and rotating the screw in to increase the low blade angle, or out to decrease the angle. When the desired angle is set, retighten the lock nut.

When changing the blade angles, always refer to the aircraft specifications and the propeller manufacturer's manual for instructions about specific propeller models.

3) Inspection, Maintenance And Repair

The Hartzell constant-speed propeller system requires basically the same inspection, maintenance, and repair as for systems previously discussed. However, special care should be taken when lubricating the propeller blades to prevent damage to the blade seals.

Before lubricating a blade, remove one of the two zerk fittings for the blade and grease the blade through the remaining zerk fitting. This

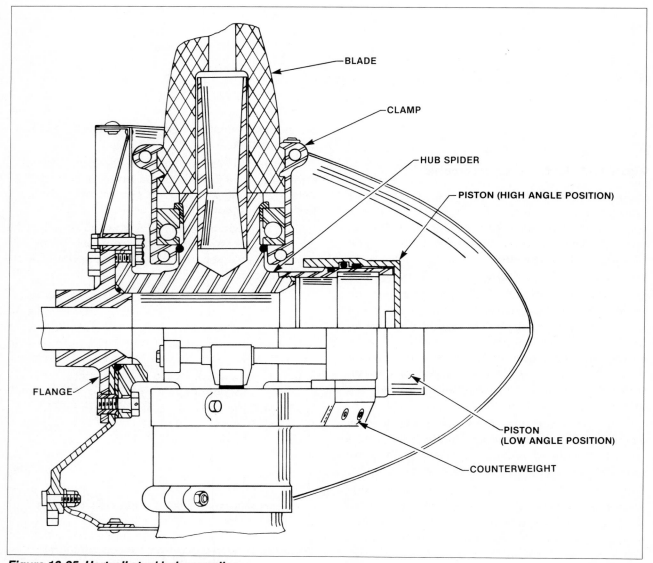

BLADE

CLAMP

HUB SPIDER

PISTON (HIGH ANGLE POSITION)

FLANGE

PISTON (LOW ANGLE POSITION)

COUNTERWEIGHT

Figure 10-25. Hartzell steel hub propeller.

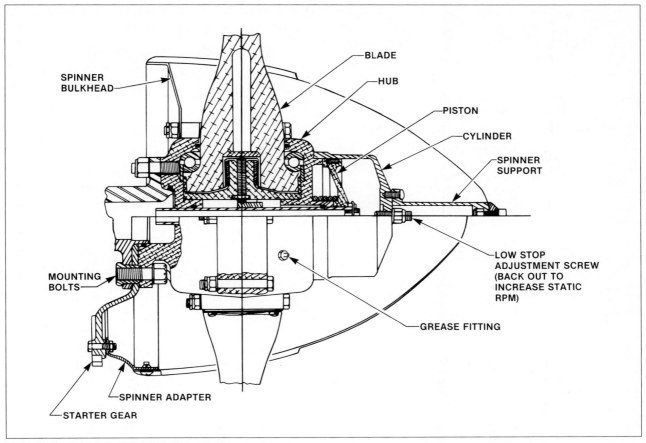

Figure 10-26. Hartzell Compact propeller.

will prevent any pressure building up in the blade grease chamber and prevent damage to the blade seals. Some propeller models are serviced until grease comes out of the hole of the removed fitting. Other models require less grease, so check the service manual before lubricating the propeller. After lubrication, reinstall the zerk fitting, replace the protective cap, and safety it.

A grease leak is readily noticeable, and the cause should be determined and corrected as soon as possible. The most common causes of grease leakage are loose or missing zerk fittings, defective zerk fittings, loose blade clamps, defective blade clamp seals, and over-lubrication of the blades.

If the zerk fitting is loose, missing, or defective, it should be tightened or replaced as appropriate. Loose blade clamps should be torqued to the specified value for the particular model of propeller and resafetied. Be sure to check to make certain that the blade angle is not changed after retorquing.

C. Feathering Type Propellers

Feathering propellers are used on most modern multi-engine airplanes. The primary purpose of a feathering propeller is to eliminate the drag created by a windmilling propeller when an engine fails.

Feathering propeller systems are constant-speed systems with the additional capability of being able to feather the blades. This means that the blades can be rotated to an approximate 90 degree blade angle. The constant-speed controls and operations we have discussed in previous sections apply to the feathering propeller system, but the cockpit propeller control lever incorporates an additional range of movement to allow the propeller to feather, or else a separate cockpit control may be used to operate the feathering mechanism.

Feathering functions are independent of the constant-speed operation and can override the constant-speed operation to feather the propeller at any time. The engine does not have to be developing power, and in some systems the engine does not even have to be rotating for the propeller to feather. In short, propellers are feathered by forces which are totally independent of engine operation.

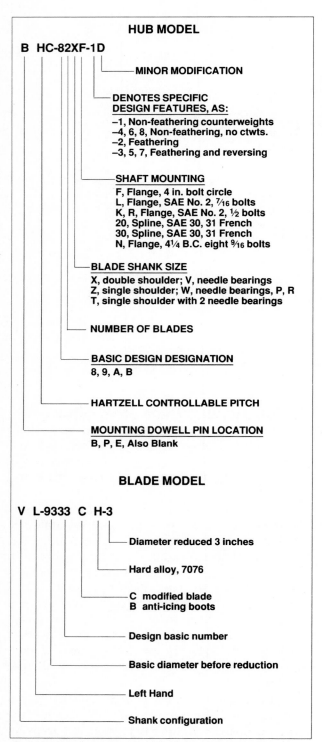

HUB MODEL

B HC-82XF-1D

— **MINOR MODIFICATION**

— **DENOTES SPECIFIC DESIGN FEATURES, AS:**
–1, Non-feathering counterweights
–4, 6, 8, Non-feathering, no ctwts.
–2, Feathering
–3, 5, 7, Feathering and reversing

— **SHAFT MOUNTING**
F, Flange, 4 in. bolt circle
L, Flange, SAE No. 2, $7/16$ bolts
K, R, Flange, SAE No. 2, $1/2$ bolts
20, Spline, SAE 30, 31 French
30, Spline, SAE 30, 31 French
N, Flange, $4\frac{1}{4}$ B.C. eight $9/16$ bolts

— **BLADE SHANK SIZE**
X, double shoulder; V, needle bearings
Z, single shoulder; W, needle bearings, P, R
T, single shoulder with 2 needle bearings

— **NUMBER OF BLADES**

— **BASIC DESIGN DESIGNATION**
8, 9, A, B

— **HARTZELL CONTROLLABLE PITCH**

— **MOUNTING DOWELL PIN LOCATION**
B, P, E, Also Blank

BLADE MODEL

V L-9333 C H-3

— Diameter reduced 3 inches

— Hard alloy, 7076

— C modified blade
B anti-icing boots

— Design basic number

— Basic diameter before reduction

— Left Hand

— Shank configuration

Figure 10-27. Hartzell propeller and blade designation system.

It should be noted that when the propeller is feathered, the engine stops rotating.

1. Hartzell Compact Propellers

Hartzell feathering systems are used on twin-engine aircraft manufactured by several different companies.

a. Propellers

Both Compact and steel hub propeller designs are used for Hartzell feathering propellers.

Compact designs use governor oil pressure to decrease the blade angle. Air pressure in the propeller cylinder and counterweights and springs on some models are used to feather the propeller. A latch stop (called the automatic high pitch stop by Hartzell) is located inside the cylinder to hold the blades in a low blade angle when the engine is stopped on the ground. The latch mechanism is composed of springs and locking pins.

b. Governors

Hartzell feathering systems may use either Hartzell or Woodward governors for operation. The governors may incorporate an internal mechanism with a lift rod and accumulator oil passages as well as valves. Or, they may have an external adapter which contains a shutoff valve linked to the governor control arm to control the accumulator operation.

c. System Operation

The constant-speed operation of the Hartzell feathering propellers is the same as for the con-

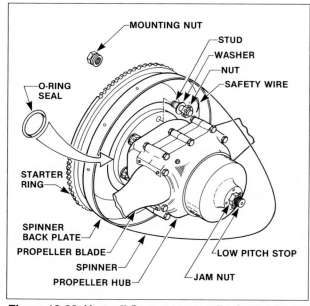

Figure 10-28. Hartzell Compact propeller installation.

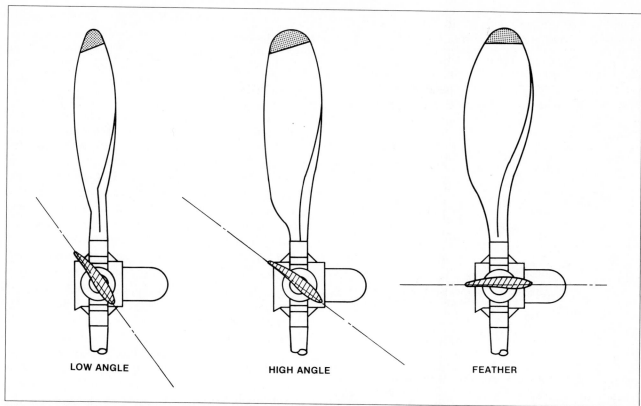

LOW ANGLE   HIGH ANGLE   FEATHER

Figure 10-29. *When a propeller is feathered, its blades are turned to an angle of approximately 90 degrees to the plane of propeller rotation.*

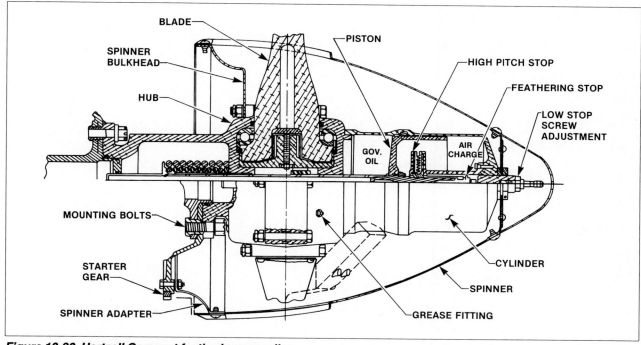

Figure 10-30. *Hartzell Compact feathering propeller.*

stant-speed models, except for the change in direction of oil flow in some models.

The feathering propellers utilize oil pressure from the governor to move the blades into low pitch (high RPM). The centrifugal twisting moment of the blades also tends to move the blades into low pitch. Opposing these two forces is a force produced by compressed air trapped between the cylinder head and the piston, which tends to move the blades into high pitch in the absence of governor oil pressure.

Feathering is accomplished by moving the cockpit control full aft. The governor pilot valve is raised by the lift rod and releases oil from the propeller. With the oil pressure released, the Compact models will go to feather by the force of the air pressure in the cylinder. The time necessary to feather depends upon the size of the oil passages back through the engine and governor, and the air pressure carried in the cylinder. The blades are held in feather by air pressure.

When unfeathering the propeller in flight, the system relies on engine rotation by the starter to initiate the unfeathering operation unless an accumulator is used. If an accumulator is installed in the system and the cockpit control is moved forward (out of the "feather" position) a check valve will be opened in the governor and allow the oil pressure from the accumulator to flow to the propeller cylinder and force the blades to a lower angle.

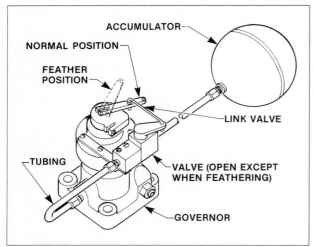

Figure 10-31. Propeller governor with an external accumulator adapter to aid in unfeathering the propeller in flight.

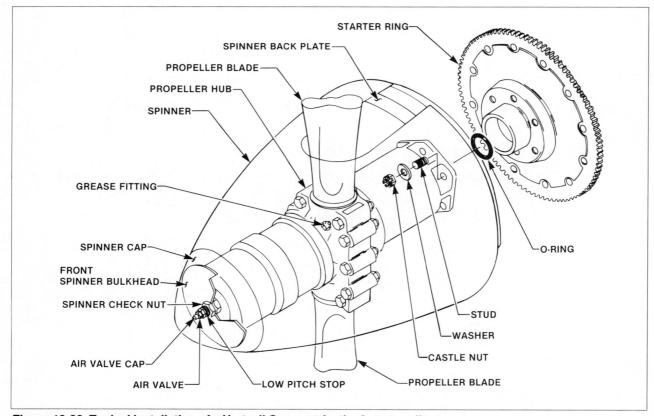

Figure 10-32. Typical installation of a Hartzell Compact feathering propeller.

When shutting the engine down after flight, the propeller cockpit control should be placed in full forward position while the engine is idling. This causes the spring in the latch mechanism to force the lock pin into a low-pitch lock position and to engage when the engine is shut down and the blades attempt to rotate toward feather.

d. System Maintenance

Installation and adjustment of the propellers are the same as for the constant-speed models. If the blades are feathered, they can be rotated to the latch angle by placing a blade paddle on each blade and rotating the blades simultaneously to the latch angle. The air pressure in the Compact model propellers should be checked and serviced as necessary with the propeller at the latch angle.

Governor installation and adjustment is the same as for a constant-speed governor.

Accumulators are installed in accordance with the aircraft maintenance manual and are serviced with dry air or nitrogen to the value specified in the aircraft maintenance manual.

The inspection, maintenance, and repair of the Hartzell feathering propeller system are the same as described for other constant-speed and feathering systems. The Compact propeller air pressure should be checked at each 100-hour and annual inspection.

If the air charge is too low in the Compact propeller, it may not feather or respond properly to constant-speed operation, and it may have a tendency to over-speed or surge. If the air charge is too great, the system may not reach full RPM and may feather when the engine is shutdown on the ground.

2. Hamilton-Standard Hydromatic Propellers

The Hamilton-Standard feathering system is used on many medium and large reciprocating engine transports. The Hamilton-Standard design goes by the trade name of Hydromatic, indicating that the principal operating forces are oil pressure.

a. Propellers

The Hamilton-Standard Hydromatic propeller is made up of three major assemblies: the hub or barrel assembly, the dome assembly, and the distributor valve.

The barrel assembly contains the spider, blades, blade gear segments, barrel halves, and necessary support blocks, spacers, and bearings. Front and rear cones, a retaining nut, and a lock ring are used to install the barrel assembly on the splined crankshaft.

The dome assembly contains the pitch changing mechanism of the propeller and includes the dome shell, a piston, a rotating cam, a stationary cam, and two blade angle stop rings. The dome shell acts as the cylinder for the propeller piston.

The distributor valve is used to direct oil from the crankshaft to the inboard and outboard side of the piston and is shifted during unfeathering to reverse the oil passages to the piston.

b. Governors

The feathering Hydromatic governor includes all of the basic governor components discussed for constant-speed governors. And, in addition, the Hydromatic governor contains a high-pressure transfer valve which is used to block the governor constant-speed mechanism out of the propeller control system when the propeller is feathered or unfeathered.

A pressure cut-out switch is located on the side of the governor and is used to automatically stop the feathering operation.

c. Feathering System Components

The cockpit control for the feathering system is a push button approximately 1-1/4 inches in diameter, and is used to feather and unfeather the propeller. The feathering button incorporates a holding coil to electrically hold the button in after it is pushed.

An electrically operated feathering pump is used to supply oil under high pressure of about 600 psi to the propeller when the feathering system is actuated. The pump takes its oil from the engine oil supply tank, at a level below the standpipe feeding the engine lubrication system.

d. Principles Of Operation

The Hydromatic propeller uses governor oil pressure on one side of the propeller piston, opposed by engine oil pressure on the other side of the piston. Depending on the model of the propeller, governor oil pressure may be directed to the outboard side or inboard side of the piston.

For discussion purposes, consider that governor oil pressure is on the inboard side of the propeller piston and engine oil pressure is on the outboard side of the piston.

The Hydromatic propeller does not use any springs or counterweights for operation. The fixed force is the engine oil pressure, which is about 60 psi. And the governor oil pressure (200 or 300 psi, depending on the system) is controlled by the pilot valve during constant-speed operation.

e. Over/Underspeed Operations

When the system is in an over-speed condition, the pilot valve in the governor is raised and governor oil pressure flows to the inboard (rear) side of the propeller piston via the crankshaft transfer bearing and the distributor valve. The increase in pressure on the inboard side of the piston forces the piston outboard (forward). As the piston moves outboard, it rotates, following the slot in the stationary cam, and this causes the rotating cam to rotate. As the rotating cam turns, the gears on the bottom of the cam, which

mesh with the gears on the blade segment and rotate the blade to a higher blade angle. With this increase in blade angle, the system RPM slows down and the governor returns to the on-speed condition. The oil in the outboard side of the piston is forced back into the engine lubrication system.

When the system is under speed, the pilot valve is lowered, and the governor oil pressure in the inboard side of the piston is released. This causes engine oil pressure on the outboard side of the piston to force the piston inboard. As the piston moves inboard, the rotation created by the piston and the cams causes the blades to rotate to a lower blade angle, allowing system RPM to increase to the on-speed condition.

f. Feathering

To feather the propeller, the feather button in the cockpit is pushed. When this is done, electri-

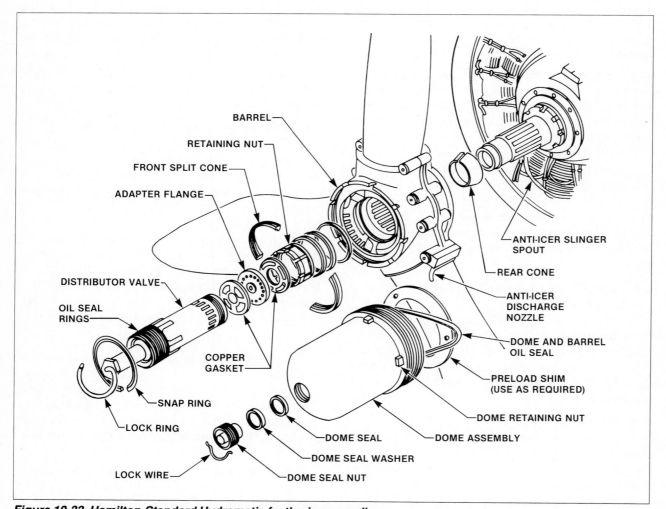

Figure 10-33. Hamilton-Standard Hydromatic feathering propeller.

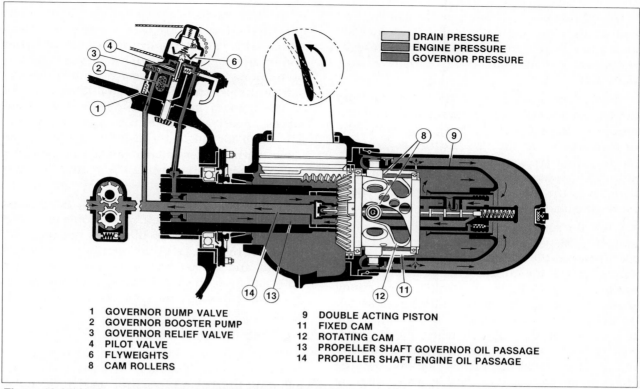

DRAIN PRESSURE
ENGINE PRESSURE
GOVERNOR PRESSURE

1	GOVERNOR DUMP VALVE	9	DOUBLE ACTING PISTON
2	GOVERNOR BOOSTER PUMP	11	FIXED CAM
3	GOVERNOR RELIEF VALVE	12	ROTATING CAM
4	PILOT VALVE	13	PROPELLER SHAFT GOVERNOR OIL PASSAGE
6	FLYWEIGHTS	14	PROPELLER SHAFT ENGINE OIL PASSAGE
8	CAM ROLLERS		

Figure 10-34. Hydromatic propeller installation in an over-speed condition.

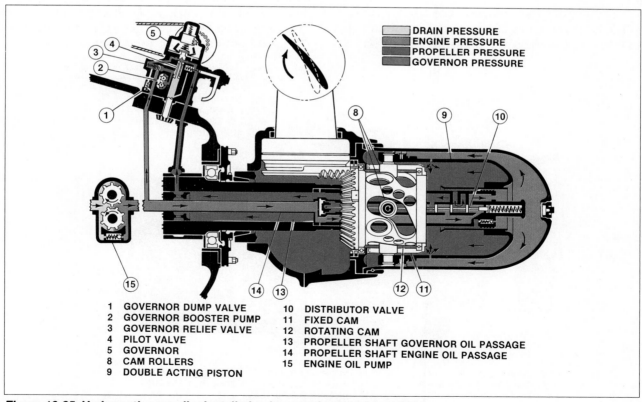

DRAIN PRESSURE
ENGINE PRESSURE
PROPELLER PRESSURE
GOVERNOR PRESSURE

1	GOVERNOR DUMP VALVE	10	DISTRIBUTOR VALVE
2	GOVERNOR BOOSTER PUMP	11	FIXED CAM
3	GOVERNOR RELIEF VALVE	12	ROTATING CAM
4	PILOT VALVE	13	PROPELLER SHAFT GOVERNOR OIL PASSAGE
5	GOVERNOR	14	PROPELLER SHAFT ENGINE OIL PASSAGE
8	CAM ROLLERS	15	ENGINE OIL PUMP
9	DOUBLE ACTING PISTON		

Figure 10-35. Hydromatic propeller installation in an under speed condition.

cal contacts close and energize the holding coil which holds the feather button in. Another set of feather button electrical contacts close at the same time and cause the feathering relay to close.

The feathering relay completes the circuit from the battery to the auxiliary pump, and the high-pressure oil generated by the pump shifts the high-pressure transfer valve in the governor to block the governor constant-speed components out of the system. This high-pressure oil is then directed to the inboard side of the piston, and it moves the blades toward the feather angle.

When the rotating cam contacts the high-pitch stop, the piston stops moving and the blades have reached the feather angle. Since the piston cannot move any further, the pressure in the system starts to build rapidly. This increasing pressure is sensed by the pressure cutout switch on the governor, and it breaks the circuit to the feather button holding coil when the pressure reaches about 650 psi. This releases the feather relay and shuts off the auxiliary pump. With the engine stopped and the propeller in feather, all oil pressures drop to zero. The blades are held in their full-feather position by aerodynamic forces.

To unfeather the propeller, the feather button is pushed and held in to prevent the button popping back out when the pressure cutout switch opens. The auxiliary pump starts building pressure above the setting of the pressure cutout switch. This causes the distributor valve to shift and reverse the flow of oil to the piston. Auxiliary pump pressure is then directed to the outboard side of the piston, and engine oil lines are open to the inboard side of the piston. The piston moves inboard and causes the blades to rotate to a lower blade angle through the action of the cams. With this lower blade angle, the propeller starts to windmill, allowing the engine to be re-started.

At this point, the feather button is released and the system will return to constant-speed operation. If the feather button is not released, the dome relief valve in the distributor valve will off-seat and release excess oil pressure (above 750 psi) from the outboard side of the piston after the rotating cam contacts the low blade angle stop.

g. System Maintenance

The installation of a Hydromatic propeller requires the barrel assembly to be installed first, following the basic procedure used to install a fixed-pitch propeller on a splined crankshaft. A hoist is required for most Hydromatic propellers because of their size and weight, and special tools are necessary to tighten the retaining nut. The standard checks for proper cone seating and

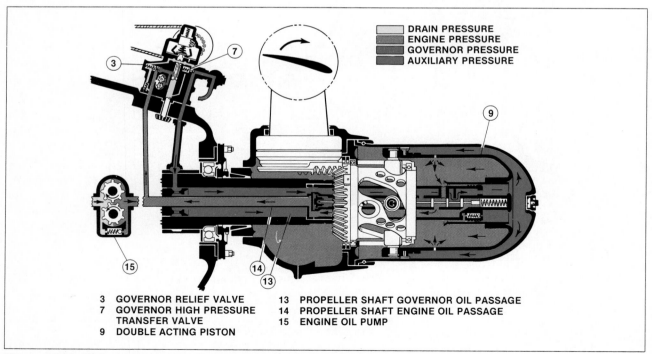

	DRAIN PRESSURE
	ENGINE PRESSURE
	GOVERNOR PRESSURE
	AUXILIARY PRESSURE

3	GOVERNOR RELIEF VALVE	13	PROPELLER SHAFT GOVERNOR OIL PASSAGE
7	GOVERNOR HIGH PRESSURE TRANSFER VALVE	14	PROPELLER SHAFT ENGINE OIL PASSAGE
9	DOUBLE ACTING PISTON	15	ENGINE OIL PUMP

Figure 10-36. Hydromatic propeller installation being unfeathered.

spline wear are made when installing the barrel assembly.

The distributor valve gasket and distributor valve are installed in the crankshaft. The distributor valve is carefully screwed into the internal threads on the crankshaft, and it is then torqued to the value specified for the particular installation. The distributor valve and retaining nut are now safetied to the crankshaft with a special lock ring.

The dome assembly is prepared for installation on the barrel assembly. The pitch stop rings must first be installed so that the propeller will have the proper blade angle range. Refer to the appropriate service manual to set these rings.

Turn the rotating cam until the lugs on the high-pitch stop ring contact the dome stop lugs. This sets the dome in its feather position.

Rotate the blades in the barrel until the scales on the blade shanks indicate that each of the blades are in their feather position. Install the dome shim on the dome shelf in the barrel, and place the base gasket on the bottom of the dome. Install the dome on the barrel, following the procedure recommended by the manufacturer for the particular model of propeller. Torque and safety the dome and install and safety the dome plug.

Check the track of the propeller and the low- and high-blade angles of each blade.

The governor is installed and rigged in the same manner as those used with Hamilton-Standard counterweight propellers. The only additional steps required are to connect the electrical plug to the pressure cutout switch and attach the oil line from the auxiliary pump.

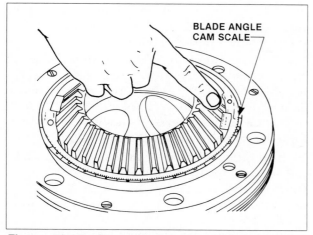

Figure 10-37. Stop rings inside the dome of a Hydromatic propeller.

If an electric head is used on the governor, governor rigging is simplified, since the electrical plug for the head needs only to be connected and the high and low RPM limit switches set.

The propellers and governors are inspected and repaired in accordance with the procedures discussed in the previous sections of this text. The inspection primarily involves assuring proper operation, checking for oil leaks, and inspecting the external oil lines for signs of deterioration or abrasion.

Oil leaks in the propeller are normally caused by a faulty gasket or a loose nut or bolt. If oil covers all of the propeller, the dome plug is leaking. If oil appears on the barrel immediately behind the dome, the dome gasket is leaking or the dome nut is loose. The dome plug seal and the dome-to-barrel seal can be replaced in the field, and the nuts should be torqued and safetied.

If oil comes from the blade shank area or from between the barrel halves, the hub bolts may be loose or the gaskets may be defective. If no irregularities are found, the bolts may be retorqued, but the gaskets must be replaced by an overhaul facility.

The propeller is lubricated by engine operating oil and it needs no other lubrication.

Troubleshooting procedures and solutions discussed for other systems are generally applicable to the feathering Hydromatic system.

If the propeller fails to respond to the cockpit propeller control lever, but can be feathered and unfeathered, the cause is most likely a failure of the governor or governor control system.

If the propeller fails to feather, check the system for electrical faults or for open wiring to the electrical components.

If the propeller fails to unfeather after feathering normally, the distributor valve is not shifting.

If the propeller feathers and immediately unfeathers, the problem may be a shorted line from the holding coil to the pressure cutout switch or a defective pressure cutout switch. The same thing will happen if the feather button is shorted internally.

Sluggish movement of the propeller may be the result of a buildup of sludge in the propeller dome or a worn out piston-to-dome seal inside the dome.

Erratic or jerky operation of the propeller is an indication of the wrong preload shim being used between the dome and the barrel assemblies, and the dome will have to be removed and the proper shim installed.

D. Hydraulic Governors

As we have seen in the above description of how various propeller systems operate, the constant-speed function is controlled by a balance of two forces. One of these forces is always governor oil pressure. The flyweight-type hydraulic governor is really a very simple and reliable mechanism. We will examine here three of the basic types used on aircraft propeller systems.

1. Hamilton-Standard Governors

The Hamilton-Standard propeller governor is divided into three parts: the head, the body, and the base.

The head of the governor contains the flyweights and flyweight cup, the speeder spring, a speeder rack and pinion mechanism, and a control pulley. Cast on the side of the head is a flange for the pulley adjustment stop screw. Some head designs incorporate a balance spring above the speeder rack to set the governor to cruise RPM if the control cable breaks.

The body of the governor contains the propeller oil flow control mechanism, which is composed of the pilot valve, oil passages, and the pressure relief valve which is set for 180 to 200 psi.

The base contains the governor boost pump, the mounting surface for installation on the engine, and oil passages which direct engine oil to the pump and return oil from the propeller to the engine sump.

The head, body, and base are held together with studs and nuts. The governor drive shaft extends below the base to mate with the engine drive gear. The drive shaft passes up through the base where it drives the oil pump, through the body where it has oil ports so oil can flow to and from the propeller, and into the head, where it is attached to the flyweight cup and rotates the flyweights.

The governor designation system indicates the design of the head, body, and base used on a particular governor. For a governor model 1A3-B2H, the basic design of the head is indicated by the 1 with minor modifications to the head design indicated by the B following the dash. The body design is A with minor modification, 2. The base is a 3 altered by and H minor modification.

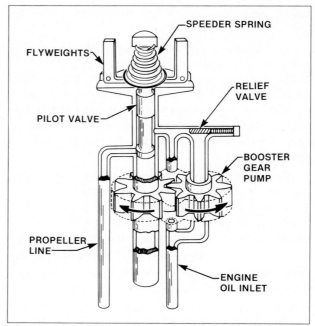

Figure 10-38. Basic configuration of a typical propeller governor.

The propeller governor is an RPM sensing device which responds to a change in system RPM by directing oil to or releasing oil from the propeller to change the blade angle and return the system RPM to the original value. The governor may be set up for a specific RPM by the cockpit propeller control.

The basic governor contains a drive shaft which is connected to the engine drive train, and it rotates at a speed that is proportional to the engine RPM. An oil pump drive gear is mounted on the drive shaft, and it meshes with an oil pump idler gear. These gears take oil at engine oil system pressure and boost it to the propeller operating pressure. Excess pressure built up by the booster pump is returned to the inlet side of the pump by a pressure relief valve.

The boosted oil is routed through passages in the governor to a pilot valve which fits in the center of the hollow drive shaft. This pilot valve can be moved up and down in the drive shaft, and it directs oil through ports in the drive shaft to or from the propeller to vary the blade angle.

The position of the pilot valve is determined by the action of the flyweights attached to the end of the drive shaft. The flyweights are designed to tilt outward when the RPM increases and inward when RPM decreases. When the flyweights tilt outward, they raise the pilot valve, and when they tilt inward, the pilot valve is lowered. The

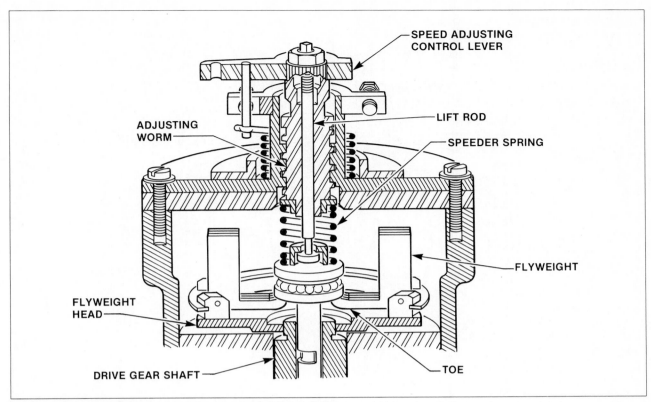

Figure 10-39. Propeller governor in the on-speed condition.

movement of the pilot valve in response to changes in RPM directs oil flow to adjust the blade angle to maintain the selected RPM.

The action of the flyweights is opposed by a speeder spring located above the flyweights and adjusted by the pilot through a control cable, pulley, and speeder rack. When a higher RPM is desired, the cockpit control is moved forward to compress the speeder spring. This increased speeder spring compression tilts the flyweights inward and the pilot valve is lowered. This causes the blade angle to decrease, and the RPM will increase until the centrifugal force on the flyweights overcomes the force of the speeder spring and returns the pilot valve to the neutral position.

The opposite action occurs if the cockpit control is moved aft. When the speeder spring compression is reduced, the flyweights tilt outward, the pilot valve is raised, and the blade angle increases until the engine slows down and the centrifugal force on the flyweights decreases. The pilot valve returns to its neutral position.

Whenever the flyweights tilt outward and the pilot valve is raised, the governor is said to be in an over-speed condition, with the RPM higher than the governor speeder spring setting calls for. When the flyweights tilt inward, the governor is in an under-speed condition, with the RPM lower than the speeder spring setting calls for. When the RPM is the same as the governor setting is calling for, the governor is in its on-speed condition.

The same governing action of the flyweights and pilot valve occurs with changing flight conditions. If the aircraft is in a cruise condition and the pilot begins a climb, airspeed will decrease and cause an increase in the angle of attack of the propeller blades. This increase produces more drag, and the RPM decreases. The governor senses this decrease in RPM by the reduced centrifugal force on the flyweights, and they tilt inward, lowering the pilot valve and producing an under-speed condition. When the pilot valve is lowered, the blade angle is reduced and the RPM increases to its original value. The system returns to the on-speed condition.

If the aircraft is placed in a dive from cruising flight, an over-speed condition is created, and the governor will cause an increase in blade angle to return the system to the on-speed condition.

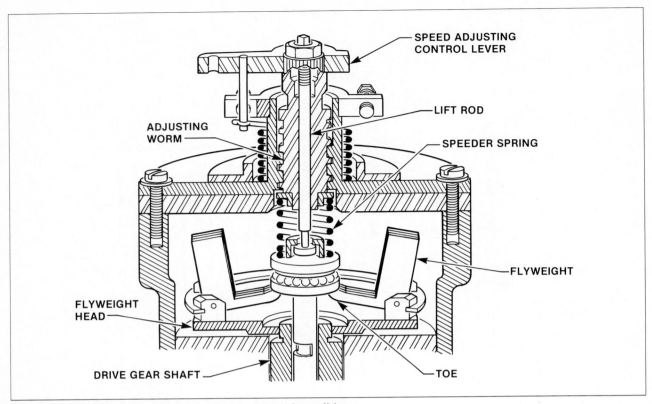

Figure 10-40. Propeller governor in the over-speed condition.

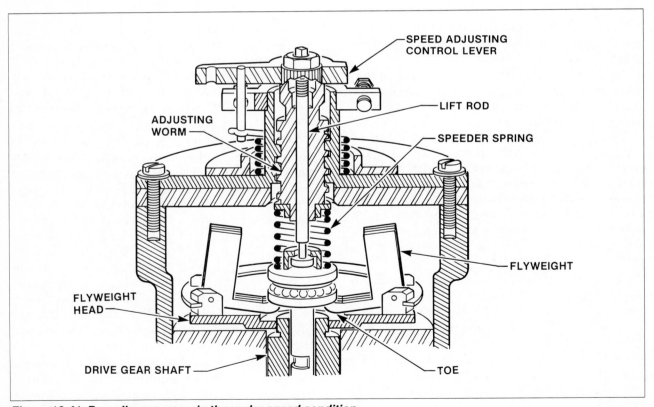

Figure 10-41. Propeller governor in the under speed condition.

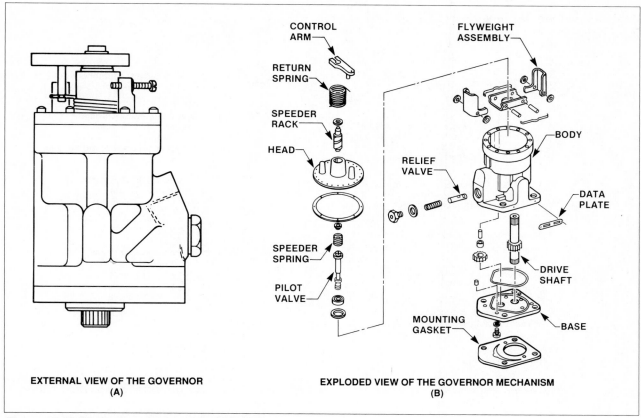

Figure 10-42. McCauley constant-speed governor.

A change in throttle setting will have the same effect as placing the aircraft in a climb or dive. Increasing the throttle will cause an increase in the blade angle to prevent an RPM increase. Retarding the throttle will result in a decrease in blade angle.

2. McCauley Governors

McCauley governors use the same principles of operation as the Hamilton-Standard governors, except that oil is released from the propeller to decrease blade angle, directly opposite from the oil flow in the Hamilton-Standard system. The governor relief valve is set for an oil pressure of about 290 psi. The governor control lever is spring loaded to the high RPM setting. The over-all construction of the governor is simpler than the Hamilton-Standard governor, being lighter and smaller, and all governors incorporate a high RPM stop, while some governors also use an adjustable low RPM stop.

The governor is installed using the procedure covered in the section on the Hamilton-Standard constant-speed governor. The McCauley governor uses a control arm instead of a pulley to connect

the governor control shaft to the cockpit control cable. The push-pull cockpit control is adjustable in length through a limited range by an adjustable rod end, and the governor high RPM limit can be adjusted by the set screw on the head of the governor, with one turn of the screw changing the RPM by 17, 20, or 25 RPM,

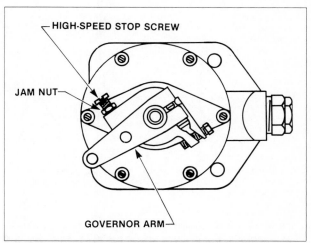

Figure 10-43. High-RPM stop screw adjustment on a McCauley propeller governor.

depending upon the engine gear ratio and the governor.

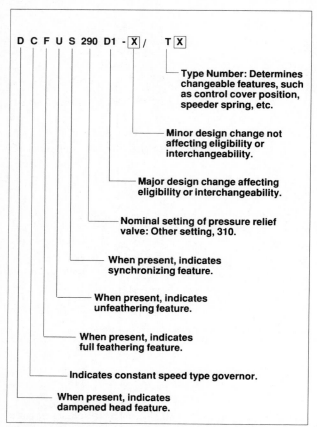

Figure 10-44. McCauley governor designation system.

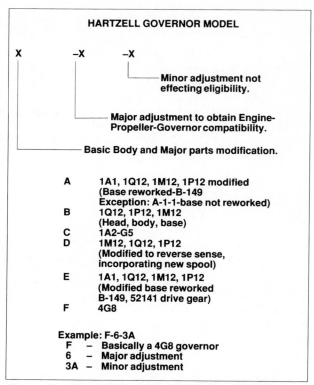

Figure 10-46. Hartzell governor designation system.

3. Hartzell Governors

Hartzell governors may be reworked Hamilton-Standard governors or Woodward governors. The Hartzell governor designation system is shown in figure 10-45.

The governors are installed and adjusted in the same way we have discussed for the McCauley system.

E. Propeller Synchronization Systems

The propeller synchronization system is used to set all propellers at exactly the same RPM, thereby eliminating excess noise and vibration. It is used for all flight operations except takeoff and landing.

1. Master Motor Synchronization

An early type, which may still be found on some operating aircraft, consists of a synchronizer master unit, four alternators, a tachometer, engine RPM master control levers, switches and wiring. These components automatically control the speed of each engine and synchronize all engines at any desired RPM.

A synchronizer master unit incorporates a master motor which mechanically drives four

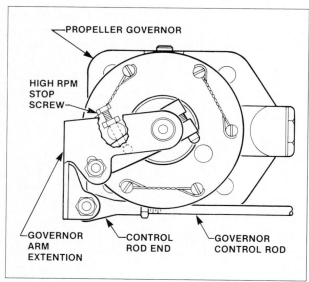

Figure 10-45. The amount of travel of a propeller governor control arm may be regulated by the amount the governor control rod is screwed into the control rod end.

contactor units; each contactor unit is electrically connected to an alternator. The alternator is a small three-phase, alternating current generator driven by an accessory drive of the engine. The frequency of the voltage produced by the generators is directly proportional to the speed of the engine. In automatic operation, the desired engine RPM may be set by manually adjusting the RPM control lever until a master tachometer on the instrument panel indicates the desired RPM. Any difference in RPM between an engine and the master motor will cause the corresponding contactor unit to operate the pitch-change mechanism of the propeller until the engine is on-speed.

2. One Engine Master Control System

Synchronizer systems are also installed in light twin-engine aircraft. Typically, such systems consist of a special propeller governor on the left-hand engine, a slave governor on the right-hand engine and an actuator in the right-hand engine nacelle.

A frequency generator built into the propeller governor generates a signal that is proportional to the RPM of the engine. A comparison circuit in the control box compares the RPM signal from the slave engine to the RPM signal from the master engine and sends a correcting signal to the slave engine governor control mechanism.

The comparison unit has a limited range of operation, and the slave engine must be within about 100 RPM of the master engine for synchronization to occur.

3. Synchrophasing

Synchrophasing is a refinement of synchronization which allows the pilot to set the angular difference in the plane of rotation between the blades of the slave engines and the blades of the master. Synchrophasing is used to reduce the noise and vibration created by the engines and propellers, and the synchrophase angle can be varied by the pilot to adjust for different flight conditions and still achieve a minimum noise level.

A pulse generator is keyed to the same blade of each propeller blade number one, for example and a signal is generated to determine if both number one blades are in the same relative position at any given instant. By comparison of the signals from the two engines, a signal is sent to the governor of the slave engine to cause it to establish the phase angle selected by the pilot.

A propeller manual phase control in the cockpit allows the pilot to select the phase angle which produces the minimum vibration and noise.

F. Propeller Ice Control Systems

As aircraft use has become a more vital part of our transportation system, the necessity to fly in

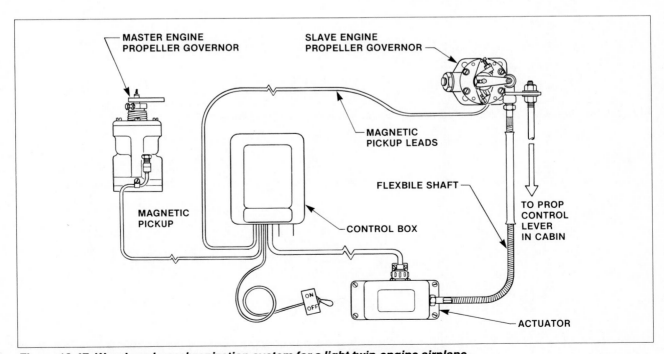

Figure 10-47. Woodward synchronization system for a light twin-engine airplane.

nearly all weather conditions has brought about the development of systems permitting the aircraft to operate safely in these adverse environments.

1. Effects Of Propeller Icing

Ice formation on a propeller blade, in effect, produces a distorted blade airfoil section which causes loss in propeller efficiency. Generally, ice

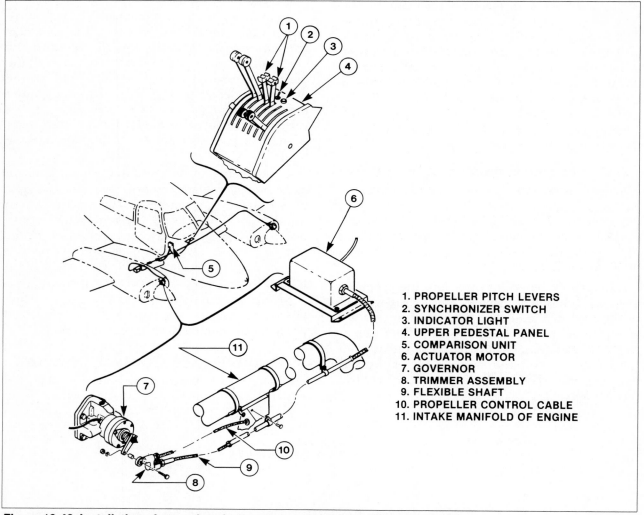

1. PROPELLER PITCH LEVERS
2. SYNCHRONIZER SWITCH
3. INDICATOR LIGHT
4. UPPER PEDESTAL PANEL
5. COMPARISON UNIT
6. ACTUATOR MOTOR
7. GOVERNOR
8. TRIMMER ASSEMBLY
9. FLEXIBLE SHAFT
10. PROPELLER CONTROL CABLE
11. INTAKE MANIFOLD OF ENGINE

Figure 10-48. Installation of a synchronization system in a light twin-engine airplane.

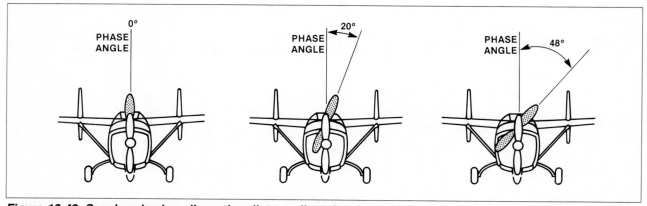

Figure 10-49. Synchrophasing allows the pilot to adjust the phase angle between the propellers on the various engines to reduce the noise, and keep vibration to a minimum.

collects unsymmetrically on a propeller blade and produces propeller unbalance and destructive vibration.

2. Fluid Systems

A typical fluid system (figure 10-51) includes a tank to hold a supply of anti-icing fluid. This fluid is forced to each propeller by a pump. The control system permits variation in the pumping rate so that the quantity of fluid delivered to a propeller can be varied, depending on the

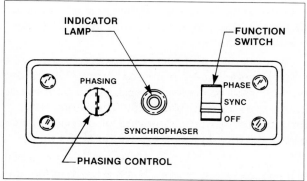

Figure 10-50. Synchrophasing control panel for a light twin-engine airplane.

severity of the icing. Fluid is transferred from a stationary nozzle on the engine nose case into a circular U-shaped channel (slinger-ring) mounted on the rear of the propeller assembly. The fluid under pressure of centrifugal force is transferred through nozzles to each blade shank.

Because airflow around a blade shank tends to disperse anti-icing fluids to areas on which ice does not collect in large quantities, feed shoes, or boots, are installed on the blade leading edge. These feed shoes are a narrow strip of rubber, extending from the blade shank to a blade station that is approximately 75% of the propeller radius. The feed shoes are molded with several parallel open channels in which fluid will flow from the blade shank toward the blade tip by centrifugal force. The fluid flows laterally from the channels, over the leading edge of the blade.

Isopropyl alcohol is used in some anti-icing systems because of its availability and low cost. Phosphate compounds are comparable to isopropyl alcohol in anti-icing performance and have the advantage of reduced flammability. However, phosphate compounds are comparatively expensive and, consequently, are not widely used.

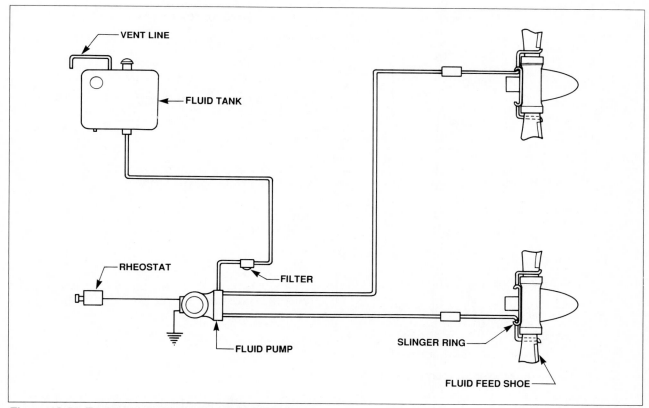

Figure 10-51. Typical propeller fluid anti-icing system.

3. Electric Deicing Systems

An electrical propeller icing control system (figure 10-52) consists basically of an electrical energy source, a resistance heating element, system controls, and necessary wiring. The heating elements are mounted internally or externally on the propeller spinner and blades. Electrical power from the aircraft system is transferred to the propeller hub through electrical leads, which terminate in slip rings and brushes. Flexible connectors are used to transfer power from the hub to the blade elements.

Icing control is accomplished by converting electrical energy to heat energy in the heating element. Balanced ice removal from all blades must be obtained as nearly as possible if excessive vibration is to be avoided. To obtain balanced ice removal, variation of heating current in the blade elements is controlled so that similar heating effects are obtained in opposite blades.

Electrical deicing systems are usually designed for intermittent application of power to the heating elements to remove ice after formation but before excessive accumulation. Proper control of heating intervals aids in preventing run-back,

since heat is applied just long enough to melt the ice face in contact with the blade.

If heat supplied to an icing surface is more than that required to melt just the inner ice face, but insufficient to evaporate all the water formed, water will run back over the unheated surface and freeze. Run-back of this nature causes ice formation on uncontrolled icing areas of the blade or surface.

Cycling timers are used to energize the heating element circuits for periods of 15 to 30 seconds, with a complete cycle time of 2 minutes. A cycling timer is an electric motor driven contactor which controls power contactors in separate sections of the circuit.

Controls for propeller electrical deicing systems include on-off switches, ammeters in the circuits, and protective devices, such as current limiters or circuit breakers. The ammeters or loadmeters permit monitoring of individual circuit currents and reflect operation of the timer.

To prevent element overheating, the propeller deicing system is generally used only when the propellers are rotating, and for short periods of time during ground run-up.

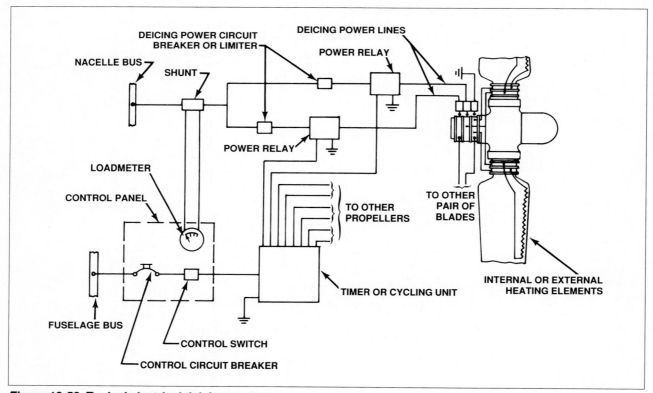

Figure 10-52. Typical electrical deicing system.

G. Propeller Inspection And Maintenance

1. Propeller Maintenance Regulations

a. Authorized Maintenance Personnel

The inspection, adjustment, installation, and minor repair of a propeller and its related parts and appliances on the engine are the responsibility of the powerplant technician. The powerplant technician may also perform the 100-hour inspection of the propeller and its related components.

A propeller repairman may perform or supervise the major overhaul and repair of propellers and related parts and appliances for which he is certificated, but the repair and overhaul must be performed in connection with the operation of a certificated repair station or, within limits, by the holder of a commercial operator or air carrier certificate.

An A&P technician who holds an Inspection Authorization may perform the annual inspection of a propeller, but he may not approve for return to service major repairs and alterations to propellers or their related parts and appliances. Only an appropriately rated facility, such as a propeller repair station, may return a propeller or accessory to service after a major repair or alteration.

b. Preventive Maintenance

The following are types of preventive maintenance that may be associated with propellers and their systems: replacing defective safety wiring or cotter keys; lubrication not requiring disassembly other than removal of nonstructural items such as cover plates, cowlings, and fairings; applying preservative or protective material (paint, wax, etc.) to components when no disassembly is required and where the coating is not prohibited or contrary to good practice.

c. Major Alterations And Repairs

The following are major propeller alterations when not authorized in the FAA propeller specifications: a change to the blade or hub design, a change in the governor or control design, installation of a governor or feathering system, installation of a propeller deicing system, installation of parts not approved for the propeller.

Propeller major repairs are classified as any repair to or straightening of steel blades; repairing or machining of steel hubs; shortening of blades; retipping of wood propellers; replacement of outer laminations on fixed-pitch wood propellers; repairing elongated bolt holes in the hub of fixed-pitch wood propeller; inlay work on wood blades; repairs to composition blades; replacement of tip fabric; replacement of plastic covering; repair of propeller governors; overhaul of controllable-pitch propellers; repairs to deep dents, cuts, scars, nicks, etc., and straightening of aluminum blades; the repair or replacement of internal blade elements.

Major repairs and alterations to propellers and control devices are normally performed by the manufacturer or a certified repair station.

When a propeller or control device is overhauled by a repair facility, a maintenance release tag must be attached to the item to certify that the item is approved for return to service. This tag takes the place of a FAA Form 337 and should be included in the maintenance record.

2. Propeller Inspection

When performing a 100-hour or annual inspection, Appendix D of FAR 43 specifies that the following areas relating to propellers and their controls must be inspected: engine controls for defects, improper travel, and improper safety; lines, hoses, and clamps for leaks, improper condition, and looseness; accessories for apparent defects in security of mounting; all systems for improper installation, poor general condition, defects, and insecure attachment; propeller assembly for cracks, nicks, binds, and oil leakage; bolts for improper torquing and lack of safetying; anti-icing devices for improper operation and obvious defects; control mechanisms for improper operation, insecure mounting, and restricted travel.

These inspection are the minimum required by regulation, and you should always refer to the manufacturer's manuals for specific inspection procedures.

a. Inspection, Maintenance And Repair Of Wooden Propellers

Wooden propellers have many components and require a close inspection of each part to assure proper operation and to prevent failures.

Defects that may occur in the wood include separation of laminations, dents or bruises on the surface especially on the face of the blade, scars across the blade surface, broken sections, warping, and worn or oversize center bore and bolt holes.

Separated laminations are not repairable unless they occur in the outside lamination of fixed-pitch propellers. Delamination of the outer layers may be repaired by a repair station certified for this work.

Inspect dents, bruises, and scars on the blade surfaces with a magnifying glass while flexing the blade to expose any cracks. Some cracks may be repaired by an inlay at a propeller repair facility.

Small cracks parallel to the grain may be repaired by working resin glue into the crack. When the glue is dry, sand the area and refinish with varnish. Small cuts are treated in the same manner.

Broken sections may be repaired by a repair facility, depending on the location and severity of the break.

Check the tip fabric for cracks or bubbles in the material, chipping of the paint, and wrinkles that appear when the tip is twisted or flexed.

If the tip fabric has surface defects of three quarters of an inch or less, and it does not indicate a breakdown in the wood structure, the defect may be filled with several coats of lacquer until the defect blends in with the fabric surface. Defects larger than three-quarters of an inch should be referred to a repair facility.

When inspecting the metal tipping, look for looseness or slipping, loose screws or rivets, cracks in the solder joints, damage to the metal surface, and cracks in the metal, especially on the leading edge.

Cracks in the solder joint near the blade tip may be indications of wood deterioration. Inspect the area closely while flexing the blade tip. If no defects are found, the joint may be resoldered, but inspect the area closely at each opportunity for evidence of recurrence.

On a controllable-pitch blade made of wood, check the metal sleeve and the wood next to the sleeve for cracks. This may indicate loose or broken lag screws and should be referred to an overhaul facility for correction.

If the varnish should begin to chip or peel, sand the surface lightly to feather in the edges of the irregularity and then apply a fresh coat of varnish to the area.

The following defects are not repairable and are reasons for considering a propeller unairworthy: a crack or deep cut across the grain; a split blade; separated laminations, except for the out-

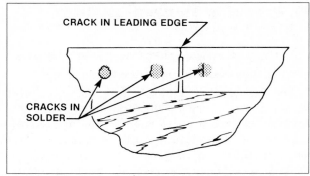

Figure 10-53. Inspection of metal tipping. Check for cracks in the solder that is used to safety the screw heads.

side laminations of a fixed-pitch propeller; unused screw or rivet holes; any appreciable warp; an appreciable portion of wood missing; cracks, cuts, or damage to the metal sleeve of a changeable-pitch propeller; an oversized crankshaft bore in a fixed-pitch propeller; cracks between crankshaft hole and bolt holes; cracked internal laminations; and excessively elongated bolt holes.

When a wood propeller is stored, place it in a horizontal position to keep the moisture evenly distributed throughout the wood. The storage area should be cool, dark, dry, and well ventilated. Do not wrap the propeller in any material that will seal off the propeller from the surrounding airflow, or the wood will rot.

b. Inspection, Maintenance And Repair Of Aluminum Alloy Blades

As we have mentioned, an advantage of aluminum propellers is the low cost of maintenance. This is because of their one-piece construction and the hardness of the metal from which the propellers are made. However, when damage does occur, it is usually critical and may result in blade failure. For this reason, the blades must be carefully inspected and any damage must be repaired before further flight.

Before inspecting a propeller, clean it with a solution of mild soap and water to remove all of the dirt, grease, and grass stains. Then inspect the blades for pitting, nicks, dents, cracks, and corrosion, especially on the leading edges and face. A four-power magnifying glass will aid in these inspections, and dye-penetrant inspection should be performed when cracks are suspected.

A majority of the surface defects that occur on the blades can be repaired by the powerplant technician. Defects on the leading and trailing edge of a blade may be dressed out by using round and half-round files. The repair should blend in smoothly with the edge and should not leave any sharp edges or angles. The approximate maximum allowable size of a repaired edge defect is ⅛-inch deep and no more than 1-½ inches in length. Repairs to the face and back of a blade are performed with a spoon-like riffle file which is used to dish out the damaged area. The maximum allowable repair size of a surface defect is ¹⁄₁₆-inch deep, ⅜-inch wide, and 1 inch long. All repairs are finished by polishing with very fine sandpaper, moving the paper in a direc-

tion parallel to the length of the blade, and then treating the surface with Alodine, paint, or some other appropriate protective coating.

Inspect the hub boss for damage and corrosion inside the center bore and on the surfaces which mount on the crankshaft. The bolt holes should be inspected for damage, security and dimensions.

Light corrosion in the boss can be cleaned with sandpaper and then painted or treated to prevent the recurrence of corrosion. Propellers with damage, dimensional wear, or heavy corrosion in the boss area should be referred to a repair station for appropriate repairs.

Damage in the shank area of a propeller blade should be referred to an overhaul facility for corrective action. Since all forces acting on the propeller are concentrated on the shank, any damage in this area is critical.

If a blade has been bent, measure the angle of the bend and the blade station of the bend center and, by using the proper chart, determine the repairability of the blade. To make this decision, find the center of the bend, and measure from the center of the hub to determine the blade station of the bend center. Next, mark the blade one inch on each side of the center of the bend and

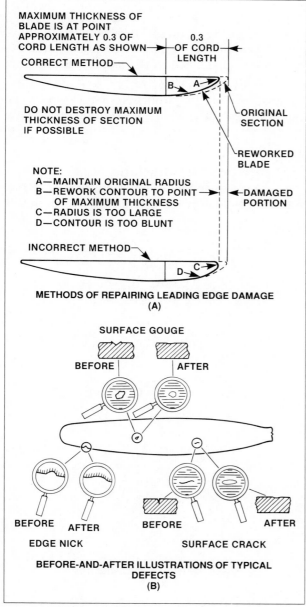

Figure 10-54. Allowable repairs to a metal propeller blade.

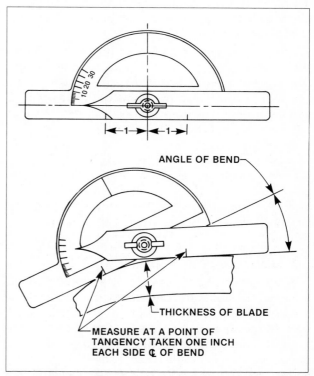

Figure 10-55. Method of measuring a propeller blade bend using a protractor.

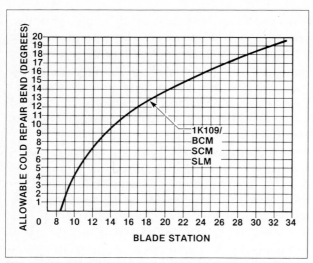

Figure 10-56. Typical chart for determining the allowable amount of bend in a metal propeller blade.

measure the degree of bend by using a protractor similar to the one in figure 10-55. Be sure the protractor is tangent to the one-inch lines when measuring the angle. Use the chart approved by the propeller manufacturer, similar to the one seen in figure 10-56, to determine if the bend is repairable. When reading the chart, any bend above the graph line is not repairable. If the proper chart is not available, take the measurements and contact an overhaul facility for a decision before sending the propeller to them for straightening.

After the propeller has been repaired, repaint the surfaces if they were painted originally. Paint the face of each blade with one coat of zinc chromate primer and two coats of flat black lacquer from the six-inch station to the tip. The back of the blade should have the last four inches of the tip painted with one coat of zinc chromate primer and two coats of a high visibility color such as red, yellow, or orange. The color scheme on the back of the blade on some aircraft differs from that described here, so the original color scheme may be duplicated if desired.

3. Vibration

When powerplant vibration is encountered, it is sometimes difficult to determine whether it is the result of engine vibration or propeller vibration. In most cases the cause of the vibration can be determined by observing the propeller hub, dome, or spinner while the engine is running within a 1,200 to 1,500 RPM range. Observe the hub or spinner and determine whether or not the

propeller hub rotates on an absolutely horizontal plane. If the propeller hub appears to swing in a slight orbit, the vibration will normally be caused by the propeller. If the propeller hub does not appear to rotate in an orbit, the difficulty will probably be caused by engine vibration.

When propeller vibration is the reason for excessive powerplant vibration, the difficulty will usually be caused by a propeller blade unbalance, propeller blades not tracking, or variation in propeller blade angle settings. Check propeller blade tracking and then the low-pitch blade-angle setting to determine if they are the cause of the vibration.

If both the propeller tracking and low blade-angle setting are incorrect, the propeller is statically or dynamically unbalanced and should be replaced or rebalanced by the manufacturer.

In recent years electronic equipment for dynamic balance of propeller installations has come into common use. This equipment allows for very accurate balancing, and the reduction of vibration.

4. Propeller Installations

The method used to attach the propeller to the engine crankshaft will vary with the design of the

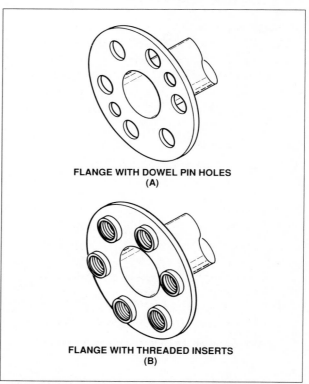

Figure 10-57. Typical crankshaft flanges for mounting a propeller.

crankshaft. Basically there are three types of crankshafts used on aircraft engines: (1) the flanged crankshaft, (2) the tapered crankshaft, and (3) the splined crankshaft. We will address the installation procedures for all three types, but, as with all other maintenance, the manufacturer's maintenance instructions should be followed for each particular installation.

a. Flanged Shaft Installation

Flanged propeller shafts are used on most horizontally opposed and some turboprop engines. The front of the crankshaft is formed into a flange four to eight inches across and perpendicular to the crankshaft centerline. Mounting bolt holes and dowel pin holes are machined into the flange and, on some flanges, threaded inserts are pressed into the bolt holes.

1) Preparation For Installation

Before installing the propeller, inspect the flange for corrosion, nicks, burrs, and other surface defects. Any defects found should be repaired in accordance with the engine manufacturer's recommendations. Light corrosion can be removed with very fine sandpaper, and if a bent flange is suspected, a run-out inspection should be performed. The bolt holes and threaded inserts should be clean and in good condition.

When the flange area is clean and smooth, apply a light coat of oil or anti-seize compound to prevent corrosion and make removal of the propeller easy.

Inspect the mounting surface of the propeller and prepare it in the same way as you did the flange.

The attaching bolts should be in good condition and inspected for cracks with either a dye penetrant or magnetic particle inspection process. Washers and nuts should also be inspected, and new fiber lock nuts used if they are required in the installation.

2) Installation

The propeller is now ready to mount on the crankshaft. If dowel pins are used, the propeller will fit on the shaft in only one position, but if there is no dowel, install the propeller in the position specified in the aircraft or engine maintenance manual, as propeller position is critical for maximum engine life in some installations. If no position is specified on a four-cylinder horizontally opposed engine, the propeller should be installed so that the blades are at the 10 o'clock and 4 o'clock positions when the engine is

Figure 10-58. When installing a propeller on a four-cylinder horizontally opposed engine, one of the blades should come to a rest at the ten o'clock position.

stopped. This reduces vibration in many instances and puts the propeller in position for hand propping the engine. Other engine configurations, if not doweled, are not normally affected by installation position.

The bolts, washers, and nuts are installed next, according to the particular installation. Tighten all of the bolts slightly, then use an alternating torquing sequence to tighten the bolts to the desired value, which is usually 35 foot-pounds or higher for metal propellers and about 25 foot-pounds for wood propellers.

When a "skull cap" spinner is used, the mounting bracket is installed with two of the propeller mounting bolts. And if a full spinner

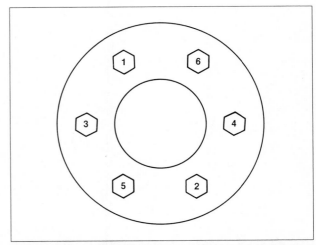

Figure 10-59. Typical torque sequence for tightening propeller retaining bolts.

is used, a rear bulkhead is slipped on the flange before the propeller is installed, and a front bulkhead is installed, on the front of the boss before the bolts are slipped through the boss. After the bolts are tightened and safetied, the spinner is installed with machine screws through the spinner into nut plates on the bulkheads.

When a wood propeller is installed, a faceplate is normally placed on the front of the propeller boss before installing the bolts. This faceplate distributes the compression load of the bolts over the entire surface of the boss.

After the bolts are installed and properly torqued, the propeller is tracked and safetied.

b. Tapered Shaft Installations

Tapered shaft crankshafts are found on older model engines of low horsepower. This type of crankshaft requires a hub to adapt the propeller to the shaft.

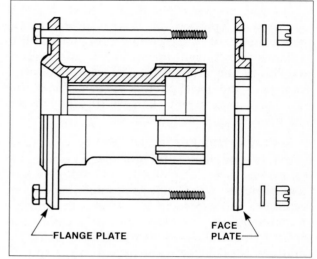

Figure 10-62. Propeller hub used to mount a wood propeller on a tapered or splined-shaft engine.

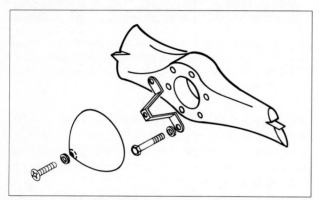

Figure 10-60. Skull-cap-type spinner installation.

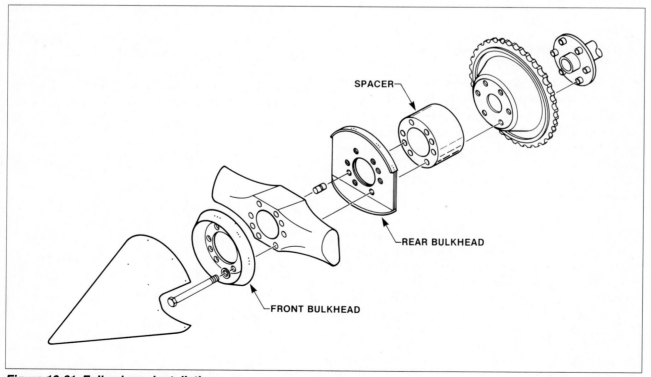

Figure 10-61. Full spinner installation.

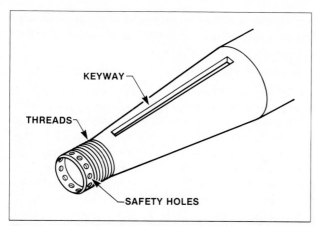

Figure 10-63. Tapered shaft used on some of the smaller aircraft engines.

1) Preinstallation Checks

Before installing the propeller, carefully inspect the taper of the shaft for corrosion, thread condition, cracks, and wear in the areas of the keyway. The keyway is critical, since cracks can develop in the corners of the keyway and result in the crankshaft breaking. A dye-penetrant inspection of the keyway area is advisable each time the propeller is removed.

If surface irregularities are found, dress or polish out the defects as the engine manufacturer recommends.

Inspect the hub components and mounting hardware for wear, cracks, corrosion, and warpage. Inspect the hub and bolts with dye penetrant or magnetic particle inspection methods, and correct any defects that are found.

The fit of the hub on the crankshaft should be checked by the use of a transfer ink such as Prussian Blue. The Prussian Blue is applied in a thin, even coating on the tapered area of the crankshaft. Then, with the key installed in the keyway, install the hub on the shaft and tighten the retaining nut to the recommended installation torque. Remove the hub and note the amount of dye transferred from the crankshaft to the hub.

The dye transfer should indicate that there is a minimum contact area of 70%. If less than 70% contact area is indicated, the hub and crankshaft should be checked for surface irregularities such as dirt, wear, and corrosion. The surfaces may be lapped to fit by removing the key from the crankshaft and lapping the hub to the crankshaft, using a fine-grit polishing compound, until a minimum of 70% contact area

is achieved. (Check the engine manufacturer's instructions for specific information about this lapping procedure.)

This inspection and corrective action may be done with the propeller installed on the hub, and when sufficient contact area is obtained, clean the hub and shaft of the dye and polishing compound.

2) Installation

Apply a very light coat of oil or anti-seize compound to the crankshaft, making sure that the key is installed properly, and then place the propeller and hub assembly on the shaft. Be sure that the threads on the shaft and nut are clean and dry, then install the retaining nut and torque the nut to the proper value. Install the puller snap ring and track and safety the propeller.

3) Removal

To remove the propeller from the tapered shaft, remove the safety and back the retaining nut off with a bar to pull the propeller from the shaft. A snap ring is installed inside the hub so the retaining nut can act as a puller to loosen the hub from the shaft as the nut is unscrewed. If no snap ring is installed, hub removal may be very difficult.

c. Splined Shaft Installations

Splined crankshafts are found on most radial engines and some horizontally opposed, in-line, and even turboprop engines. The splined shaft has grooves and splines of equal dimensions, and a master, or double-width, spline so that a hub will fit on the shaft in only one position.

1) Preinstallation Checks

Inspect the crankshaft for cracks, surface defects, and corrosion, and repair any defects in

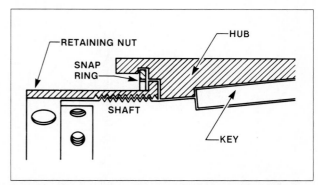

Figure 10-64. The snap ring is installed inside the hub of a propeller mounted on a splined or tapered shaft to aid in pulling the propeller from the shaft.

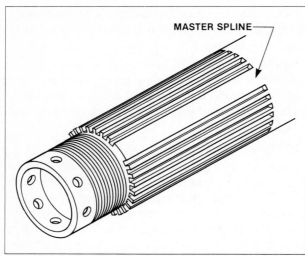

Figure 10-65. Splined propeller shaft showing the master spline.

accordance with the engine manufacturer's instructions.

Inspect the splines on the crankshaft and on the hub for wear by using a "go no-go" gauge which is 0.002-inch larger than the maximum space allowed between the splines. The crankshaft or spline is serviceable if the gauge cannot be inserted between the splines for more than 20% of the spline length. If it will go in more than 20% of the way, the hub or the crankshaft is worn excessively and should be replaced.

The cones that are used to center the hub on the crankshaft should be inspected for general condition. The rear cone is made of bronze and is split to allow flexibility during installation and to assure a tight fit when it is installed. The front

cone is made in two pieces and is a matched set. The two halves are marked with a serial number to identify the mates in a set.

2) Trial Installation

Slip the rear cone and, in some installations, a bronze spacer on the crankshaft, and push them all the way back on the shaft. Apply a thin coat of Prussian Blue to the rear cone, and slide the hub on the shaft, taking care to align the hub on the master spline. Push the hub back against the rear cone. Coat the front cone halves with Prussian Blue and place them around the lip of the retaining nut. Install the nut in the hub and tighten it to the proper torque.

Remove the retaining nut and the front cone and note the amount of Prussian Blue transferred to the hub. A minimum of 70% contact is required. Remove the hub from the crankshaft and note the transfer of dye from the rear cone. Again, a minimum of 70% contact is required. If contact is insufficient, lap the hub to the cones, using special lapping fixtures.

If no dye is transferred from the rear cone during the transfer check, a condition known as rear cone bottoming exists. This happens when the apex, or point, of the rear cone contacts the land on the rear seat of the hub before the hub can seat on the rear cone. Correct rear cone bottoming by removing up to 1/16-inch from the apex of the cone with sandpaper on a surface plate.

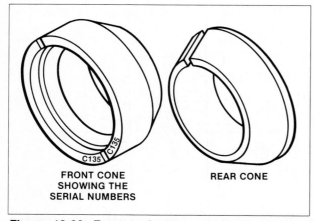

FRONT CONE
SHOWING THE
SERIAL NUMBERS

REAR CONE

Figure 10-66. Front and rear cone for mounting a propeller on a splined propeller shaft.

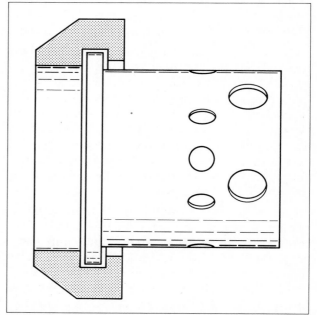

Figure 10-67. Propeller retaining nut and the front cone used to secure a propeller to a splined shaft.

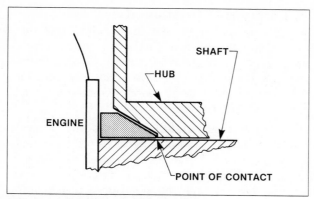
Figure 10-68. Rear cone bottoming.

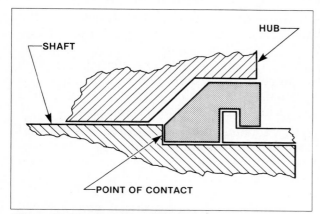
Figure 10-69. Front cone bottoming.

Front cone bottoming occurs when the apex of the front cone bottoms on the splines of the crankshaft before it seats on the hub. Front cone bottoming is indicated when the hub is loose on the shaft after the retaining nut has been torqued and there is no transfer of Prussian Blue to the front hub seat. Correct front cone bottoming by using a spacer of no more than 1/8-inch thickness behind the rear cone. This moves the hub forward so that the front cone can seat properly.

3) Installation

Install the propeller on the hub in the same manner as is used for a tapered shaft installation. The position of the propeller on the hub in relation to the master spline is critical. Some installations require that one blade align with the master spline while other installations require that the blades be perpendicular to the master spline position; so be sure to consult the engine maintenance manual for the requirements of a particular installation.

Once the propeller is mounted on the hub, coat the crankshaft with oil or an anti-seize com-

pound and slide the propeller and hub assembly in place on the shaft. Install and torque the front cone and install the retaining nut. Track the propeller and then safety the installation.

Propeller removal is done in the same way as is done with a tapered shaft installation.

5. Blade Tracking

Once the propeller is installed and torqued, check the track. The track of the propeller is defined as the path which the tips of the blades follow as they rotate with the aircraft stationary. For light aircraft with propellers of up to approximately six feet in diameter, metal propellers can be out of track no more than 1/16-inch, and the track of a wood propeller may not be out more than 1/8-inch.

Before the propeller can be tracked, the aircraft must be made stationary by cocking the wheels so that the aircraft will not move. Next, place a fixed reference point within 1/4-inch of the propeller arc. This may be done by placing a

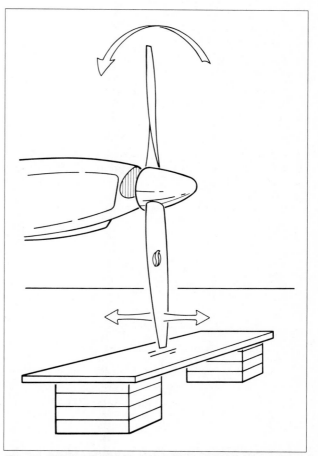
Figure 10-70. Method of tracking a propeller, using a reference board.

board on blocks under the propeller arc and taping a piece of paper to the board so the track of each blade can be marked. Rotate the propeller by hand until one blade is pointing down at the paper, and mark this position on the paper. Now turn the propeller so that the track of the next blade can be marked on the paper, and repeat this for each blade. The maximum difference in track for all of the blades should not exceed the limits mentioned above.

If the propeller track is off more than is allowed, the reason should be determined, and the condition corrected. Probably the easiest item to check is the propeller torque. If all bolts are properly torqued, it will probably be necessary to remove the propeller, inspect for dirt or damage, and check the crankshaft for alignment.

6. Safetying The Propeller

Once a propeller is properly tracked and torqued, it can be safetied. There is no one correct way to safety a propeller installation because of the many different types of installations, and for this reason only the more commonly used safeties will be discussed.

A flanged shaft installation has the largest variety of safety methods because of its many variations. If the flange has threaded inserts installed, the propeller is held on by bolts screwed into the inserts. The bolt heads are drilled and safetied with 0.041-inch stainless steel safety wire, using standard safety wire procedures.

If threaded inserts are not pressed into the flange, bolts and nuts are used. Some installations use fiber lock nuts which require no safetying, but the nuts should be replaced each time the propeller is removed. Other installations use castellated nuts and drilled bolts and the nuts are safetied to the bolts with cotter pins.

The retaining nuts for tapered and splined shaft installations are safetied in the same way. A clevis pin is installed through the safety holes in the retaining nut and crankshaft. Position this pin with the head toward the center of the crankshaft so that the centrifugal force will hold the pin in the hole.

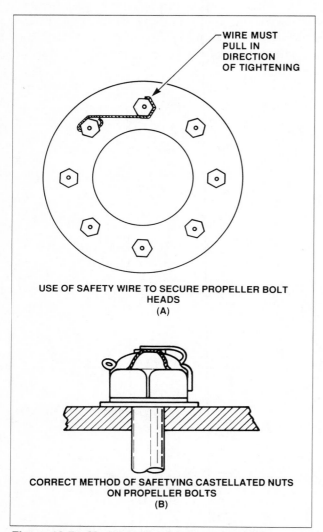

USE OF SAFETY WIRE TO SECURE PROPELLER BOLT HEADS
(A)

CORRECT METHOD OF SAFETYING CASTELLATED NUTS ON PROPELLER BOLTS
(B)

Figure 10-71. Methods of safetying a propeller.

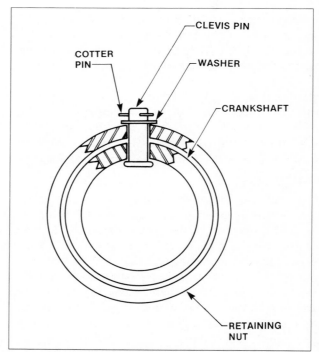

Figure 10-72. Method of safetying a retaining nut on tapered or splined propeller shaft.

7. Checking And Adjusting Blade Angle

The universal propeller protractor can be used to check propeller blade angles when the propeller is on a balancing stand or installed on the engine. Figure 10-73 shows the parts and adjustments of a universal propeller protractor.

The frame of the protractor is made of aluminum alloy, and three sides of it are ninety degrees to each other. A bubble spirit level is mounted on one corner of the front of the frame, and this level swings out to indicate when the protractor is level. A moveable ring is located inside the frame and is used to set the zero reference angle for blade-angle measurements. The ring is engraved with vernier index marks, which allow readings as small as one-tenth of a degree. A center disk is engraved with a degree scale from zero to 180 degrees, both positive and negative, and it contains a spirit level to indicate when the disk is level.

When using the propeller protractor and before measuring the angle of a propeller blade, determine the reference blade station from the aircraft manufacturer's maintenance manual, and mark this reference station on the blade with chalk or with a grease pencil.

The next step is to establish the reference plane from the engine crankshaft centerline, rather than the airframe attitude, because some engines are canted in the aircraft. To zero the protractor, loosen the ring-to-frame lock, align the zeros on the disk and the ring, and then engage the disk-to-ring lock. Place one edge of the protractor on a flat surface on the propeller hub that is parallel to, or perpendicular to, the crankshaft centerline and turn the ring adjuster until the spirit level in the center of the disk is level. The corner level should also be leveled. Now, tighten the ring-to-frame lock, and release the disk-to-frame lock. The protractor is now aligned with the engine crankshaft.

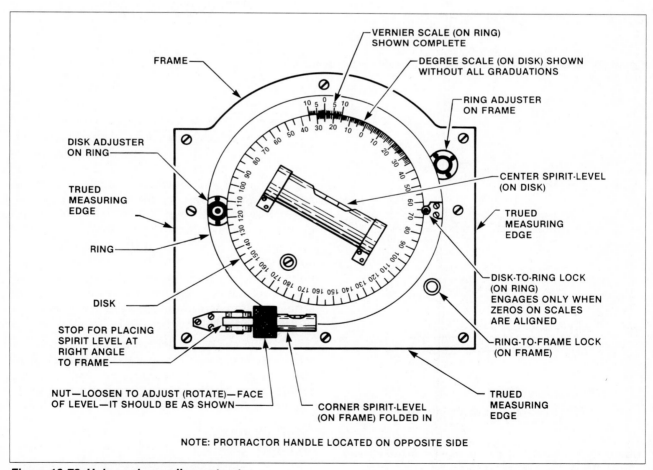

Figure 10-73. Universal propeller protractor.

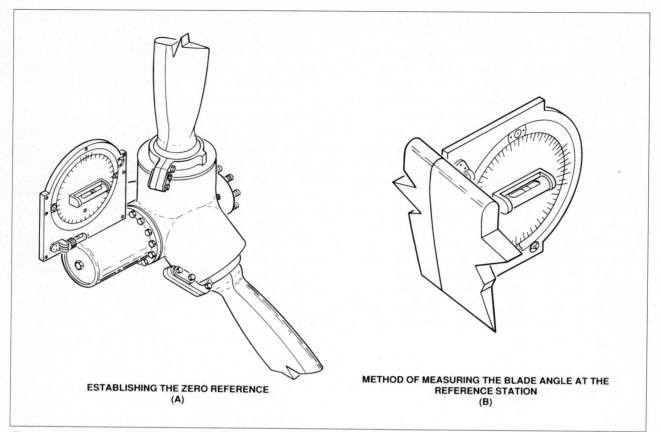

ESTABLISHING THE ZERO REFERENCE
(A)

METHOD OF MEASURING THE BLADE ANGLE AT THE
REFERENCE STATION
(B)

Figure 10-74. Correct method of using a propeller protractor.

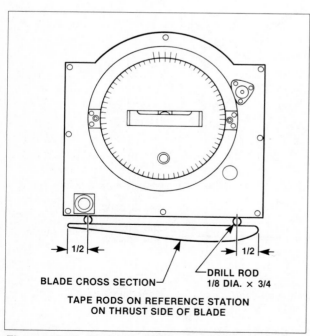

1/2 ← → 1/2 ←

BLADE CROSS SECTION

DRILL ROD
1/8 DIA. × 3/4

TAPE RODS ON REFERENCE STATION
ON THRUST SIDE OF BLADE

Figure 10-75. Method of correcting for blade curva-
ture when using a universal propeller protractor.

Place one blade of the propeller horizontal and move out to the reference station marked on the face of the blade to measure the blade angle. Stand on the same side of the airplane, facing in the same direction, as when you established the zero with the protractor, otherwise the measurement will be incorrect. Place the edge of the protractor on the face of the blade at the reference station and turn the disk adjuster until the spirit level centers. Now read the blade angle, using the zero line on the ring as the index. Tenths of degrees can be read from the vernier scale. Rotate each blade to the same horizontal position, and measure the angle.

If the face of the propeller blade is curved, use masking tape to attach a piece of 1/8-inch drill rod, 1/2-inch from the leading and trailing edges and measure the angle with the protractor resting on the rods.

8. Balancing

Propeller unbalance, which is a source of vibration in an aircraft, may be either static or dynamic.

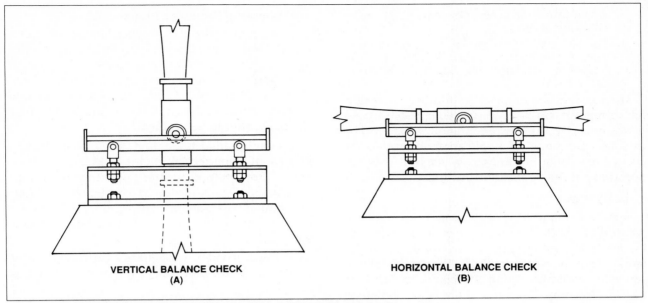

VERTICAL BALANCE CHECK
(A)

HORIZONTAL BALANCE CHECK
(B)

Figure 10-76. Positions of two-bladed propeller during balance check.

a. Static

Propeller static unbalance occurs when the center of gravity of the propeller does not coincide with the axis of rotation.

Static balancing can be done by the suspension method or by the knife-edge method. In the suspension method, the propeller or part is hung by a cord, and any unbalance is determined by the eccentricity between a disk firmly attached to the cord and a cylinder attached to the assembly or part being tested. The suspension method is used less frequently that the simpler, and more accurate knife-edge method.

The knife-edge test stand (figure 10-76) has two hardened steel edges mounted to allow the free rotation of an assembled propeller between them. The knife-edge test stand must be located in a room or area that is free from any air motion, and preferably removed from any source of heavy vibration.

During a propeller static balance check, all blades must be at the same angle. Before conducting the balance check, inspect to see that each blade has been set at the same blade angle.

The standard method of checking propeller assembly balance involves the following sequence of operations:

(1) Insert a bushing in the engine shaft hole of the propeller.

(2) Insert a mandrel or arbor through the bushing.

(3) Place the propeller assembly so that the ends of the arbor are supported upon the balance stand knife-edges. The propeller must be free to rotate.

If the propeller is properly balanced, statically, it will remain in any position in which it is placed. Check two-bladed propeller assemblies for balance, first with the blades in a vertical position and then with the blades in a horizontal position (figure 10-76). Repeat the vertical position check with the blade positions reversed; that is, with the blade which was checked in the downward position placed in the upward position.

Check a three-bladed propeller assembly with each blade in a downward vertical position, as shown in figure 10-77.

Unless otherwise specified by the manufacturer, an acceptable balance check requires that the propeller assembly have no tendency to rotate in any of the positions previously described. If the propeller balances perfectly in all described positions, it should also balance perfectly in all intermediate positions. When necessary, check for balance in intermediate positions to verify the check in the originally described positions.

When a propeller assembly is checked for static balance and there is a definite tendency of the assembly to rotate, certain corrections to remove the unbalance are allowed.

(1) The addition of permanent fixed weights at acceptable locations when the total weight

of the propeller assembly or parts is under allowable limits.

(2) The removal of weight at acceptable locations when the total weight of the propeller assembly or parts is equal to the allowable limit.

The location for removal or addition of weight for propeller unbalance correction has been determined by the propeller manufacturer. The method and point of application of unbalance corrections must be checked to see that they are according to the applicable drawings.

b. Dynamic

Dynamic unbalance results when the center of gravity of similar propeller elements, such as blades or counterweights, down not follow in the same plane of rotation. Since the length of the propeller assembly along the engine crankshaft is short in comparison to its diameter, and since the blades are secured to the hub so that they lie in the same plane perpendicular to the running axis, the dynamic unbalance resulting from improper mass distribution is negligible, provided the track tolerance requirements are met.

Dynamic balance checks are now being done with the propeller, spinner, and related equipment installed on the aircraft, and the engine running. Electronic equipment may be used to locate unbalance and determine the amount of weight required to correct the condition.

Another type of propeller unbalance, aerodynamic unbalance, results when the thrust (or pull) of the blades is unequal. This type of unbalance can be largely eliminated by checking blade contour and blade-angle setting.

9. Servicing Propellers

Propeller servicing includes cleaning, lubricating and replenishing operating oil supplies.

a. Cleaning Propeller Blades

Aluminum and steel propeller blades and hubs usually are cleaned by washing the blades with a suitable cleaning solvent, using a brush or cloth. Acid or caustic materials should not be used. Power buffers, steel wool, steel brushes, or any other tool or substance that may scratch or mar the blade should be avoided.

If a high polish is desired, a number of good grades of commercial metal polish are available. After completing the polishing operation, all traces of polish should be removed. When the blades are clean, they should be coated with a clean film of engine oil or suitable equivalent.

To clean wooden propellers, warm water and a mild soap can be used, together with brushes or cloth.

If a propeller has been subjected to salt water, it should be flushed with fresh water until all traces of salt have been removed. This should be accomplished as soon as possible after the salt water has splashed on the propeller, regardless of whether the propeller parts are aluminum alloy, steel, or wood. After flushing, all parts should be dried thoroughly, and metal parts should be coated with clean engine oil or a suitable equivalent.

b. Propeller Lubrication

Propeller lubrication procedures, with oil and greases specifications, are usually published in the manufacturer's instructions. Experience indicates that water sometimes gets into the propeller blade bearing assembly on some models of propellers. For this reason the propeller manufacturer's greasing schedule must be followed to ensure proper lubrication of moving parts.

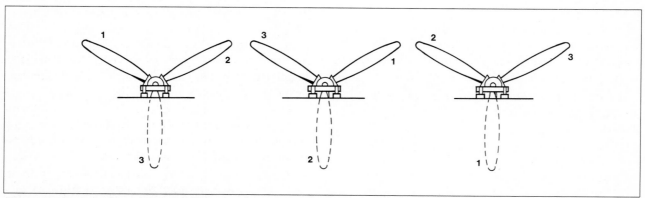

Figure 10-77. Positions of three-bladed propeller during balance check.

10. Cockpit Controls And Instruments

a. Control Rigging

The propeller controls must be rigged so that an increase in RPM is obtained by moving the controls forward, and a decrease in RPM is caused by moving the controls aft. The throttles must be arranged so that forward thrust is increased by forward movement of the control, and reverse thrust is increased by aft movement of the throttle.

Cockpit powerplant controls must be arranged to prevent confusion as to which engine they control. Newer aircraft will incorporate controls that are distinguished by their shape and color. We see these shapes in figure 10-78.

b. Cockpit Instruments

An aircraft with a fixed-pitch propeller uses the tachometer to indicate the throttle setting, with the RPM increasing as the throttle is advanced and decreasing as the throttle is retarded. A constant-speed system uses a manifold pressure gauge to indicate the throttle setting, and the tachometer is used to indicate the setting of the propeller control. However, there is some interaction between the propeller control and the manifold pressure gauge when changing the RPM and holding the throttle setting fixed.

The throttle directly controls horsepower, so with a fixed throttle setting, the horsepower output of the engine is constant. For example, assume an engine is producing 200 brake horsepower at 23 inches of mercury manifold pressure and 2300 RPM. If the propeller control is advanced to 2400 RPM, the manifold pressure must decrease to some lower value; for example, 22 inches of mercury. If the RPM is reduced to 2200 RPM, the manifold pressure may increase to 24 inches. By these two examples we can see that when the RPM is adjusted, a change in manifold pressure will occur. The amount of change will vary, of course, with different en-

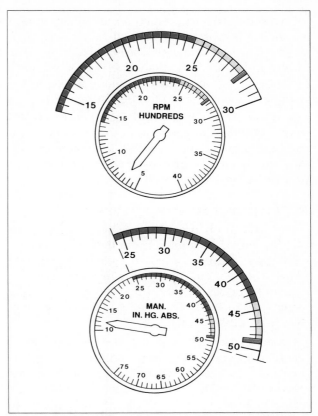

Figure 10-79. Typical range marking for power-plant instruments.

gines and under different conditions, but if the throttle is not moved, the horsepower output does not change.

It is important to note that an engine can be seriously damaged by excessive manifold pressure for a given RPM, and the aircraft flight manual must always be considered when operating an aircraft engine.

With a fixed propeller control setting, the manifold pressure can be changed with the throttle. The RPM, however, will remain constant because the governor will adjust the blade angle to maintain a constant RPM.

When changing power settings, take care to prevent damage to the engine by creating too high a manifold pressure for a given RPM. When power is to be increased, it is best to increase the RPM to the desired setting and then advance the throttle to the desired manifold pressure. When decreasing power, pull the throttle back until the manifold pressure is about one inch below the desired setting and then reduce the RPM with the propeller governor control, and the manifold pressure will increase to the desired value.

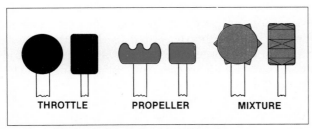

Figure 10-78. Powerplant control knobs.

Cockpit instruments such as tachometers and manifold pressure gauges must be marked with a green arc to indicate the normal operating range, a yellow arc for takeoff and precautionary range, a red arc for critical vibration range, and a red radial line for maximum operating limit.

Part of the conformity check during annual/100-hour inspections is to determine that the markings on the aircraft's instruments conform to the limits printed on the aircraft Type Certificate Data Sheet.

H. Turboprop Propellers

The turboprop propeller is operated by a gas turbine engine through a reduction gear assembly. It has proved to be an extremely efficient power source. Turboprop engines are used on aircraft ranging in size from large four-engine transports to relatively small single-engine business and utility aircraft.

Because the engine and propeller must work together to produce the required thrust for a turboprop installation, there are a few unique relationships. The turboprop fuel control and the propeller governor are connected and operate in coordination with each other. The power lever directs a signal from the cockpit to the fuel control for a specific amount of power from the engine. The fuel control and the propeller governor together establish the correct combination of RPM, fuel flow, and propeller blade angle to provide the desired power.

The propeller control system is divided into two types of control: one for flight and one for ground operation. For flight, the propeller blade angle and fuel flow for any given power setting are governed automatically according to a predetermined schedule. This is known as the alpha range. Below the "flight idle" power lever position, the coordinated RPM blade angle schedule becomes incapable of handling the engine efficiently. Here the ground handling range, referred to as the beta range, in encountered. In the beta range of the throttle quadrant, the propeller blade angle is governed by the propeller governor, but is controlled by the power lever position. When the power lever is moved below the start position, the propeller pitch is reversed to provide reverse thrust for rapid deceleration of the aircraft after landing.

1. Reduction Gear Assembly

The reduction gear assembly may be integral with the engine power unit, or it may be separately located and driven by the power unit through an extension shaft. The reduction gear assembly may incorporate sensors for the NTS (negative torque signal), TSS (thrust sensitive signal), and a propeller brake.

The negative torque signal control system provides a signal which increases propeller blade angle to limit negative shaft torque.

If a power loss occurs during takeoff, the thrust sensitive signal increases propeller blade angle and causes the propeller to feather, automatically.

The propeller brake is designed to prevent the propeller from windmilling when it is feathered in flight, and to decrease the time for the propeller to come to a complete stop after engine shutdown.

2. Turbo-Propeller Assemblies

In this section of the text, we will discuss the Hartzell reversing propellers used with the Garrett AiResearch TPE-331, and the Pratt and Whitney of Canada PT6 engines.

a. Hartzell Reversing Propeller System Used On TPE-331

The Hartzell propeller on the TPE-331 is used on aircraft such as the Mitsubishi MU-2, the Short Skyvan, and the Aero Commander 690.

The TPE-331 engine is a fixed turbine engine that produces more than 600 horsepower when the engine is turning at about 40,000 RPM. A reduction gear assembly on the front of the engine couples the engine drive shaft to the propeller drive shaft and reduces the engine speed to about 2200 RPM at the propeller drive shaft.

The engine gear ratio and the method of mounting the reduction gearing to the engine varies with the installation. Some engines have the propeller drive shaft below the engine centerline, and other installations have the propeller above the engine centerline.

1) Propeller

The propeller commonly used on the TPE-331 is a three- or four-bladed Hartzell steel hub reversing propeller. The propeller is spring-loaded and counterweighted to the feather position and uses engine oil pressurized by the governor to decrease the blade angle. The propeller is flange-mounted on the drive shaft, and it locks in a flat angle of about two degrees when the engine is shut down on the ground. This prevents excessive strain on the engine starter when the engine is being started.

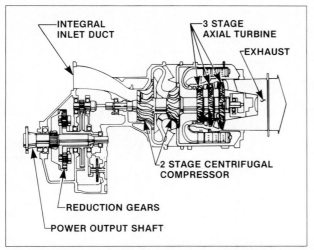

Figure 10-80. Cutaway view of a Garrett-AiResearch TPE-331 turboprop engine.

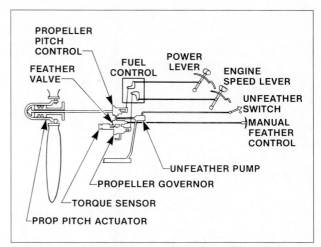

Figure 10-82. System components located on the gear reduction assembly of a TPE-331 engine.

The propeller is constructed similar to the feathering steel hub designs. The principal additional component is the beta tube, which passes through the center of the propeller and serves as an oil passage and follow-up device during propeller operation.

The same designation system is used for the reversing Hartzell propellers as is used for Hartzell feathering and constant-speed propellers.

The cockpit controls for the TPE-331 turboprop installation include a power lever which controls the horsepower output of the engine, a speed lever which controls system RPM, a feather handle, and an unfeathering switch.

The power lever is similar to the reciprocating engine throttle in that it controls system horsepower. During ground operation, the power lever directly controls the propeller blade angle by positioning the propeller pitch control unit, and during flight operations, the power lever directly controls the engine fuel control unit.

The speed lever is similar to the propeller control lever in a reciprocating engine system in that it controls the system RPM. During ground operation, the speed lever adjusts the underspeed governor on the fuel control unit to vary the fuel flow and maintain a fixed RPM as the blade angle is changed by the power lever. During flight operations, the speed lever sets the RPM on the propeller governor which varies the blade angles when the engine power is changed with the power lever or when flight operations change to keep the RPM constant.

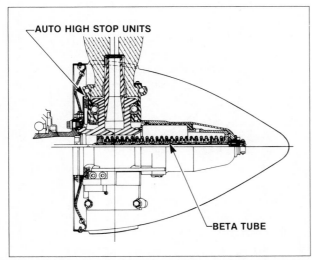

Figure 10-81. Hartzell propeller used on a TPE-331 engine.

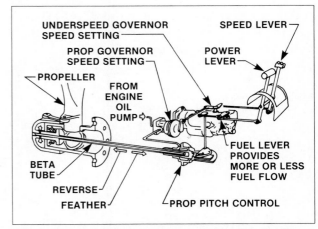

Figure 10-83. Control system for a TPE-331 engine.

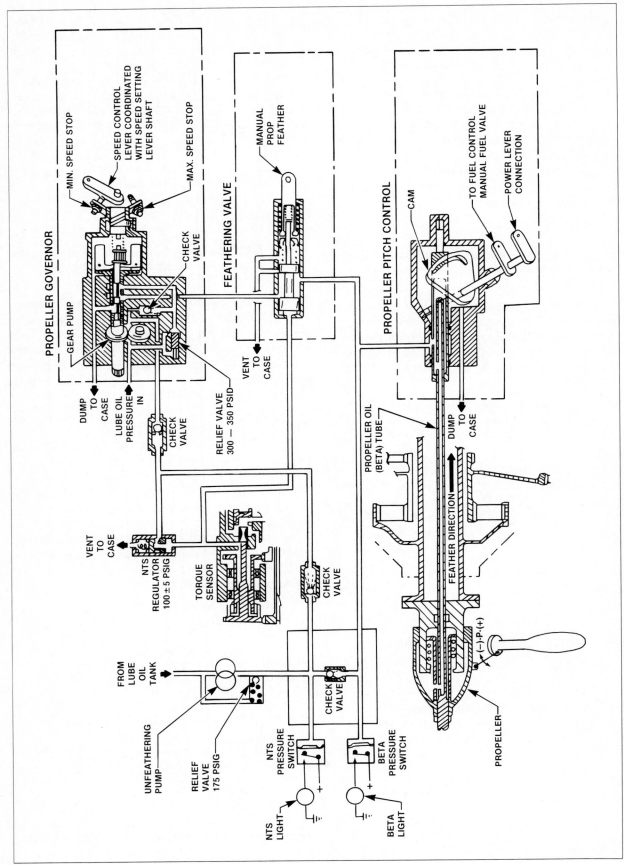

Figure 10-84. Schematic of the propeller control system for a TPE-331 engine.

PROPELLER GOVERNOR

MIN. SPEED STOP

SPEED CONTROL LEVER COORDINATED WITH SPEED SETTING LEVER SHAFT

MAX. SPEED STOP

CHECK VALVE

GEAR PUMP

DUMP TO CASE

LUBE OIL PRESSURE IN

CHECK VALVE

RELIEF VALVE 300 — 350 PSID

VENT TO CASE

NTS REGULATOR 100 ± 5 PSIG

TORQUE SENSOR

CHECK VALVE

FROM LUBE OIL TANK

UNFEATHERING PUMP

RELIEF VALVE 175 PSIG

CHECK VALVE

NTS PRESSURE SWITCH

BETA PRESSURE SWITCH

NTS LIGHT

BETA LIGHT

FEATHERING VALVE

MANUAL PROP FEATHER

VENT TO CASE

PROPELLER PITCH CONTROL

CAM

TO FUEL CONTROL MANUAL FUEL VALVE

POWER LEVER CONNECTION

PROPELLER OIL (BETA) TUBE

DUMP TO CASE

FEATHER DIRECTION

(−)-P-(+)

PROPELLER

Many aircraft use a feather handle connected to the feathering valve on the engine. Other aircraft connect the feathering valve to the speed lever so that full aft movement of the lever will cause the propeller to feather. When the feathering valve is moved by the cockpit control, oil is released from the propeller and the propeller feathers.

An unfeathering switch is used to control the electric unfeathering pump to unfeather the propeller.

2) System Operation

The two basic operating modes of the TPE-331 system are the Beta mode, meaning any ground operation including start, taxi, and reverse operation, and the Alpha mode, which is any

flight operation from takeoff to landing. Typically, Beta mode includes operation from 65% to 95% RPM, and Alpha mode includes operation from 95% to 100% of system rated RPM.

When the engine is started, the power lever is set at the ground idle position and the speed lever is in the start position. When the engine starts, the propeller latches are retract by reversing the propeller with the power levers, and the propeller moves to a zero degree blade angle as the propeller pitch control is positioned by the power lever over the Beta tube. The Beta tube is attached to the propeller piston, and it moves forward with the piston as the propeller moves to the low blade angle. The propeller blade angle stops changing when the Beta tube moves for-

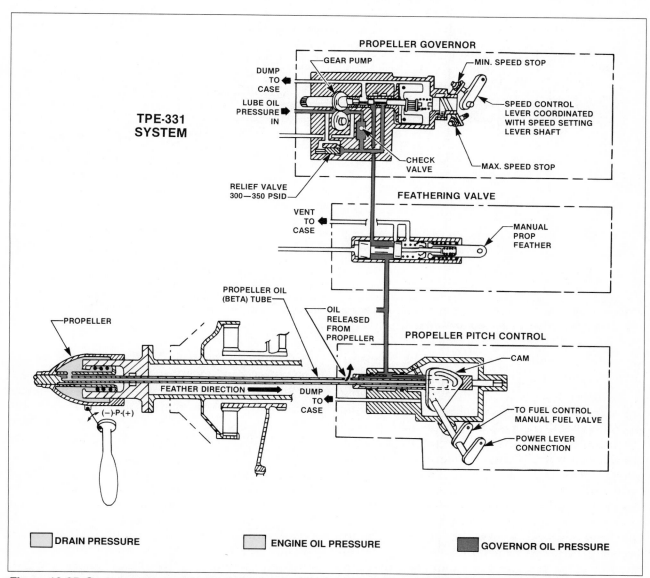

Figure 10-85. System components positioned to increase the propeller blade angle in the Beta mode.

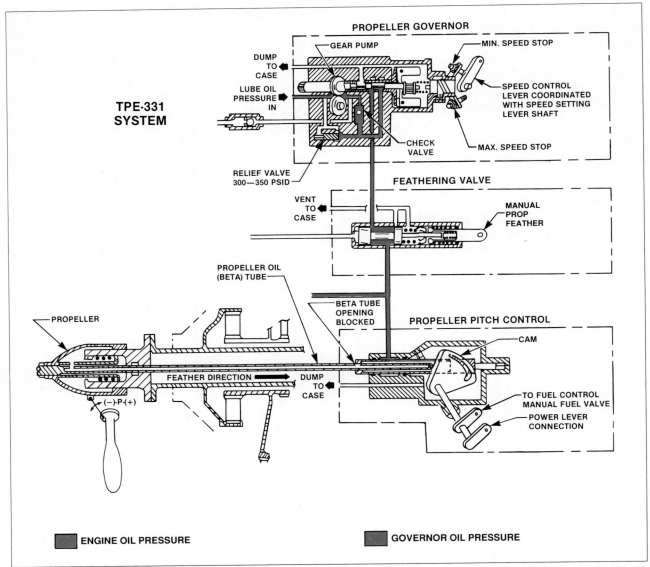

PROPELLER GOVERNOR

GEAR PUMP

MIN. SPEED STOP

DUMP TO CASE

LUBE OIL PRESSURE IN

SPEED CONTROL LEVER COORDINATED WITH SPEED SETTING LEVER SHAFT

TPE-331 SYSTEM

CHECK VALVE

MAX. SPEED STOP

RELIEF VALVE 300—350 PSID

FEATHERING VALVE

VENT TO CASE

MANUAL PROP FEATHER

PROPELLER OIL (BETA) TUBE

BETA TUBE OPENING BLOCKED

PROPELLER PITCH CONTROL

PROPELLER

CAM

FEATHER DIRECTION

DUMP TO CASE

(-)-P-(+)

TO FUEL CONTROL MANUAL FUEL VALVE

POWER LEVER CONNECTION

ENGINE OIL PRESSURE

GOVERNOR OIL PRESSURE

Figure 10-86. The Beta tube stops propeller blade angle change in the Beta mode by moving to the neutral position in the propeller pitch control unit.

ward to the neutral position in the propeller pitch control.

The speed lever is used to set the desired RPM through the underspeed governor during ground operation, and the power lever is used to vary the blade angle to cause the aircraft to move forward or rearward. If the power lever is moved forward, the propeller pitch control moves rearward, so that the oil ports on the end of the Beta tube are open to the gear reduction case and the oil in the propeller is forced out by the springs and counterweights. As the blade angle increases, the propeller piston moves inward until the Beta tube returns to its neutral position in the propeller pitch control unit. This causes a

proportional response of the propeller to the power lever movement.

With the increase in blade angle, the engine will start to slow down, but the underspeed governor, which is set by the speed lever, will adjust the fuel flow to the engine to maintain the selected RPM.

If the power lever is moved rearward, the propeller pitch control moves forward over the Beta tube, and governor oil pressure flows out to the propeller piston and causes a decrease in blade angle. As the piston moves outward, the Beta tube moves with it and returns to the neutral position as the blade angle changes. With this lower blade angle, the engine RPM will try to change, but the underspeed governor will reduce the fuel flow to maintain the selected RPM.

In the Alpha mode of operation, flight operation, the speed lever is moved to a high RPM setting of between 95% to 100%, and the power lever is moved to the flight idle position. When this is done, the underspeed governor is fully opened and no longer affects system operation. RPM control is now accomplished through the propeller governor.

When the power lever is moved to flight idle, the propeller pitch control moves forward so that the Beta tube is fully in the propeller pitch control and it no longer functions to adjust the blade angle. The power lever now controls the fuel flow through the engine fuel control unit.

With a fixed power lever setting in the Alpha mode, the propeller governor is adjusted by the speed lever to set the system RPM in the same manner as for any constant-speed system.

With a fixed speed lever setting in the Alpha mode, the power lever adjusts the fuel control unit to control the amount of fuel delivered to the engine. When the power lever is moved forward, fuel flow will increase and the propeller blade angle will be increased by the propeller governor to absorb the increased engine power and maintain the set RPM. When the power lever is moved aft, fuel flow will decrease and the propeller blade angle will decrease by the action of the propeller governor to maintain the selected RPM.

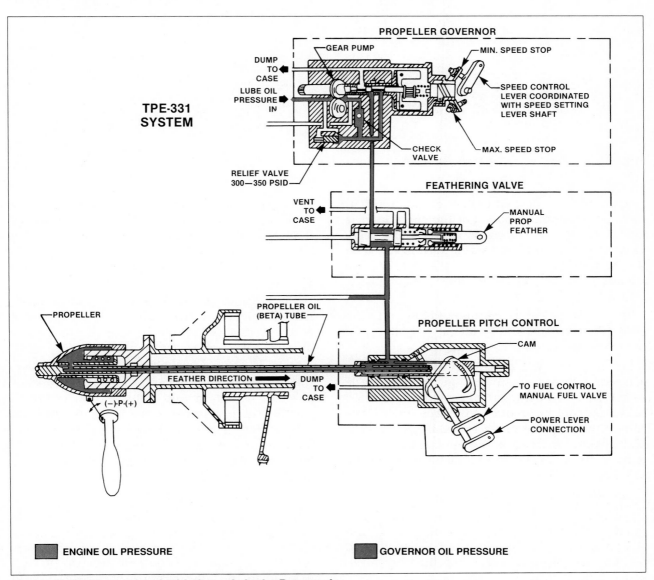

Figure 10-87. Decreasing the blade angle in the Beta mode.

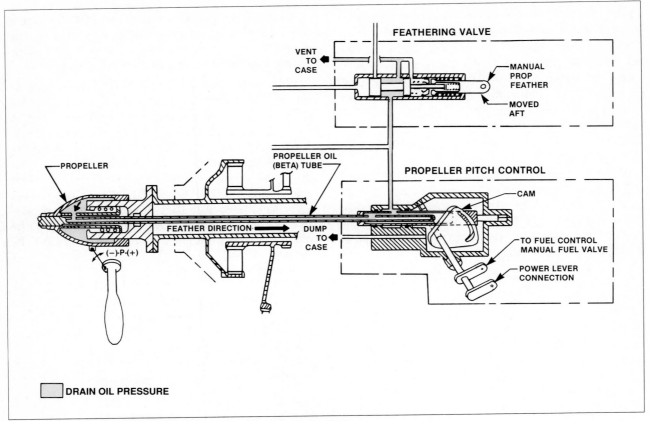

Figure 10-88. Feathering the propeller by the cockpit controls.

Whenever it is desired to feather the propeller, the feather handle is pulled or the speed lever is moved full aft, depending on the aircraft design. This action shifts the feathering valve, located on the rear of the gear reduction assembly, and releases the oil pressure from the propeller, returning the oil to the engine sump.

The springs and counterweights on the propeller force the oil out of the propeller, and the blades go into the feather angle.

To unfeather the propeller, the electric unfeathering pump is turned on with a toggle switch in the cockpit, and oil pressure is directed to the propeller to reduce the blade angle. This causes the propeller to start windmilling in flight and an air start can be accomplished. On the ground, the propeller can be unfeathered in the same manner before starting the engine.

3) Installation And Adjustment

The propeller is installed following the basic procedure used for the installation of other flange-shaft propellers. The Beta tube is installed through the propeller piston after the propeller is installed, and is bolted to the forward part of the piston.

To adjust the reverse blade angle, the Beta tube is adjusted in or out of the piston to set the neutral position on the propeller pitch control unit. This angle must be adjusted according to the aircraft service manual during propeller installation.

The propeller governor, propeller pitch control, feather valve, and fuel control unit are mounted on the engine gear reduction assembly in accordance with the engine service manual.

The interconnection between the speed lever, the underspeed governor, and the propeller governor is rigged and adjusted according to the manual pertaining to the particular aircraft and engine model used. The same holds true for the interconnection between the power lever, the fuel control unit, and the propeller pitch control.

4) System Maintenance

Inspect and repair the propeller following the basic procedures set forth for other versions of the Hartzell steel hub propeller. Take care when removing or installing the Beta tube to prevent damage to the tube surface. The Beta tube is trued for roundness and is machined to close tolerances.

Inspect the propeller control units for leaks, security, and damage. Check the linkages between these units for freedom of movement, security, and damage. Replace any defective seals, adjust rigging, and secure all nuts and bolts as appropriate for the installation. Use the engine or aircraft maintenance manuals for specific instructions concerning each aircraft model.

Basic troubleshooting procedures as have been previously discussed apply to the Hartzell reversing propeller system. If the proper propeller response is not occurring, and there is no obvious defect, check the system for proper rigging.

In the Beta mode, if the RPM is not constant, investigate the underspeed governor on the fuel control unit. If the blade angle does not respond properly to power lever movement, check the propeller pitch control.

In the Alpha mode, if the RPM is not constant, check the propeller governor. If power does not change smoothly, check the fuel control unit.

b. Hartzell Reversing Propeller System On The Pratt & Whitney Of Canada PT6 Engine

The Hartzell propeller on the PT6 engine is used on the Piper Cheyenne, DeHavilland Twin Otter, and most models of the Beechcraft King Air series.

The PT6 engine is a free-turbine turboprop engine that produces more than 600 horsepower at 38,000 RPM. A geared reduction mechanism couples the engine power turbine to the propeller drive shaft with the propeller rotating at 2200 RPM at 100% RPM. The free-turbine design means that the power turbine is not mechanically connected to the engine compressor, but rather is air coupled. The hot gases generated by the gas generator section of the engine flow through the power turbine wheel and cause the power turbine and the propeller to rotate.

Another turbine section is mechanically linked to the compressor section and is used to drive the compressor. It is possible, during engine start, for the compressor and its turbine to be rotating while the propeller and the power turbine do not move. During engine start, the power turbine will eventually reach the speed of the

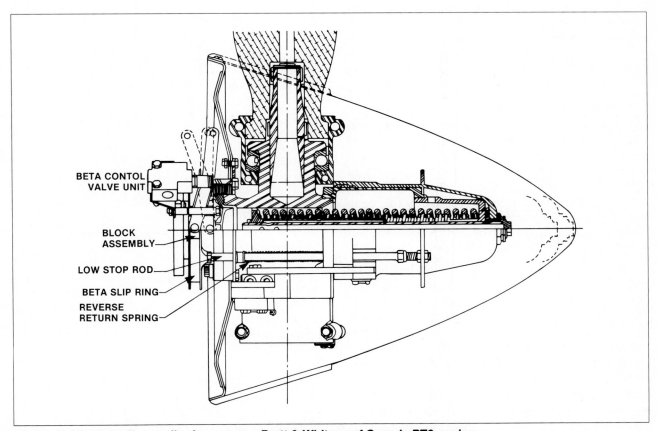

BETA CONTOL VALVE UNIT

BLOCK ASSEMBLY

LOW STOP ROD

BETA SLIP RING

REVERSE RETURN SPRING

Figure 10-89. Hartzell propeller for use on a Pratt & Whitney of Canada PT6 engine.

compressor, but the starter motor is not under a load from the propeller and the power turbine during engine start. For this reason, the propeller can be shut down in feather and does not need a low blade angle latch mechanism for engine starting.

1) Propeller

The propeller commonly used with the PT6 is a three- or four-bladed Hartzell steel hub reversing propeller. The propeller is flange-mounted on the engine and is spring-loaded and counterweighted to the feather position, with oil pressure being used to decrease the blade angle. A Beta slip ring assembly on the rear of the propeller serves as a follow-up mechanism in giving proportional propeller response to control inputs in the Beta mode.

2) Governor

The propeller governor used with the PT6 is basically the same as other governors discussed for constant-speed operation. It uses a speeder spring and flyweights to control a pilot valve which directs oil flow to and from the propeller. A lift rod is incorporated in the governor to allow the propeller to feather.

For beta mode operation, the governor contains a beta control valve operated by the power lever linkage, and it directs oil pressure generated by the governor boost pump to the propeller, or else it relieves oil from the propeller to change the blade angle.

3) System Components

A propeller over-speed governor is mounted on the gear reduction assembly and it releases oil from the propeller whenever the propeller RPM exceeds 100%. The release of oil pressure results in a higher blade angle and a reduction in RPM. The over-speed governor is adjusted by the overhaul facility, and it cannot be adjusted in flight. There are no cockpit controls to this governor except for a test mode in some aircraft.

A power turbine governor is installed on the gear reduction assembly as a safety backup in case the other propeller governing devices should fail. If the power turbine speed reaches about 105%, the power turbine governor will reduce the fuel flow to the engine. The power turbine governor is not controllable from the cockpit.

The engine fuel control unit is mounted on the rear of the engine and is linked through a cam assembly to the Beta control valve on the

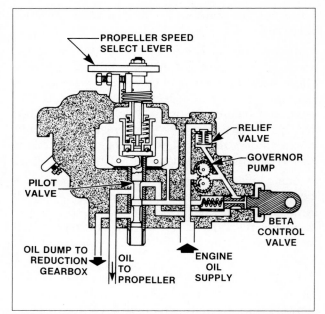

Figure 10-90. Propeller governor for use on a PT6 installation.

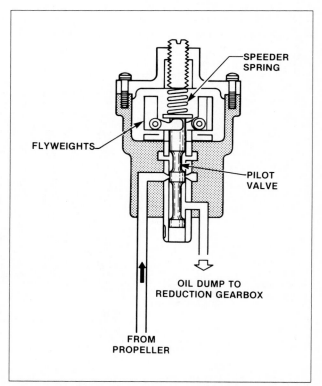

Figure 10-91. Over-speed governor for use on a PT6 installation.

propeller governor and also to the Beta slip ring on the propeller. This interconnection with the fuel control unit is used during Beta mode operation.

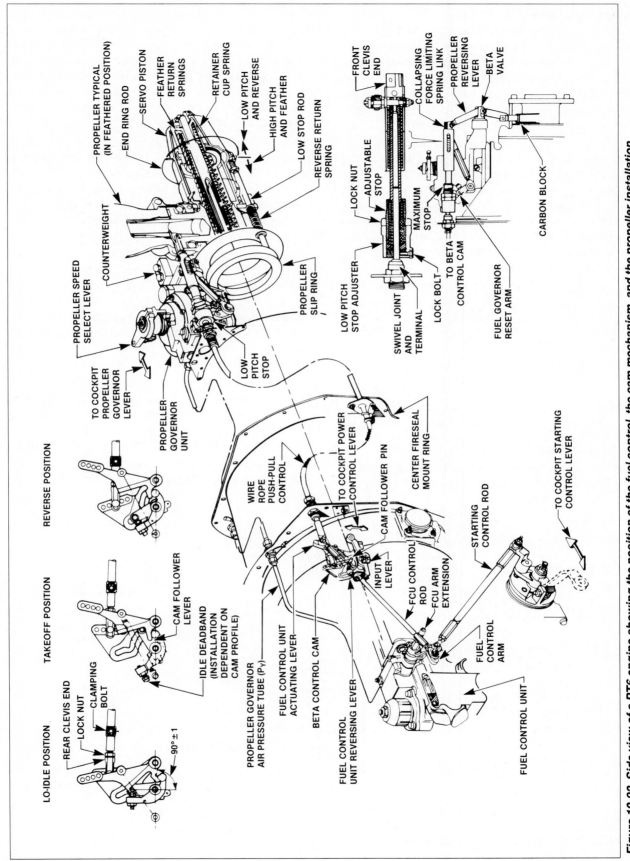

LO-IDLE POSITION   TAKEOFF POSITION   REVERSE POSITION

REAR CLEVIS END
CLAMPING BOLT
LOCK NUT
90° ± 1

CAM FOLLOWER LEVER

IDLE DEADBAND (INSTALLATION DEPENDENT ON CAM PROFILE)

PROPELLER GOVERNOR AIR PRESSURE TUBE (P$_\gamma$)

FUEL CONTROL UNIT ACTUATING LEVER

BETA CONTROL CAM

FUEL CONTROL UNIT REVERSING LEVER

INPUT LEVER

FCU CONTROL ROD

FCU ARM EXTENSION

FUEL CONTROL ARM

FUEL CONTROL UNIT

CAM FOLLOWER PIN

CENTER FIRESEAL MOUNT RING

STARTING CONTROL ROD

TO COCKPIT STARTING CONTROL LEVER

TO COCKPIT POWER CONTROL LEVER

WIRE ROPE PUSH-PULL CONTROL

PROPELLER GOVERNOR UNIT

TO COCKPIT PROPELLER GOVERNOR LEVER

PROPELLER SPEED SELECT LEVER

COUNTERWEIGHT

PROPELLER TYPICAL (IN FEATHERED POSITION)

END RING ROD

SERVO PISTON

FEATHER RETURN SPRINGS

RETAINER CUP SPRING

LOW PITCH AND REVERSE

HIGH PITCH AND FEATHER

LOW STOP ROD

REVERSE RETURN SPRING

PROPELLER SLIP RING

LOW PITCH STOP

FRONT CLEVIS END

COLLAPSING FORCE LIMITING SPRING LINK

PROPELLER REVERSING LEVER

BETA VALVE

LOCK NUT

ADJUSTABLE STOP

MAXIMUM STOP

LOW PITCH STOP ADJUSTER

SWIVEL JOINT AND TERMINAL

LOCK BOLT

TO BETA CONTROL CAM

FUEL GOVERNOR RESET ARM

CARBON BLOCK

Figure 10-92. Side view of a PT6 engine showing the position of the fuel control, the cam mechanism, and the propeller installation.

435

10-57

4) Cockpit Controls

The cockpit controls for the PT6 turboprop installation consist of a power lever controlling engine power output in all modes and propeller blade angle in the Beta mode. There is also a propeller control lever which adjusts the system RPM when in the Alpha mode, and a fuel cutoff lever which turns the fuel at the on or off fuel control.

The power lever is linked to the cam assembly on the side of the engine and, from there, rearward to the fuel control unit and forward to the propeller governor Beta control valve. The power lever adjusts both engine fuel flow and propeller blade angle when operating in the Beta mode which is reverse to flight idle. But in the Alpha mode, the lever controls only fuel flow to the engine.

The propeller control lever adjusts system RPM in the Alpha mode through conventional governor operation. Full aft movement of the lever raises the lift rod in the governor and causes the propeller to feather.

The fuel cut-off lever turns the fuel to the engine on and off at the engine fuel control unit. Some designs have an intermediate position, called lo-idle, to limit system power while operating on the ground.

5) System Operation

Beta mode operation is generally in the range of 50 to 85% RPM. In this range, the power lever is used to control both fuel flow and propeller blade angle. When the power lever is moved forward, the cam assembly on the side of the engine causes the fuel flow to the engine to increase. At the same time, the linkage to the propeller governor moves the Beta control valve forward out of the governor body, and oil pressure in the propeller is released.

As the propeller cylinder moves rearward in response to the loss of oil, the slip ring on the rear of the cylinder moves rearward and, through the carbon block and linkage, returns the Beta control valve to a neutral position. This gives a proportional movement to the propeller.

When the power lever is moved rearward, fuel flow is reduced and the Beta control valve moves into the governor body, directing oil pressure to the propeller to decrease the blade angle. And as the propeller cylinder moves forward, the Beta control valve returns to its neutral position by the action of the slip ring, carbon block, and linkage. This again gives a proportional response.

If the power lever is moved aft of the zero thrust position, fuel flow will increase and the blade angle goes negative to allow a variable reverse thrust. This change in fuel flow is caused by the cam mechanism on the side of the engine.

During operation in the Beta mode, the propeller governor constant-speed mechanism is

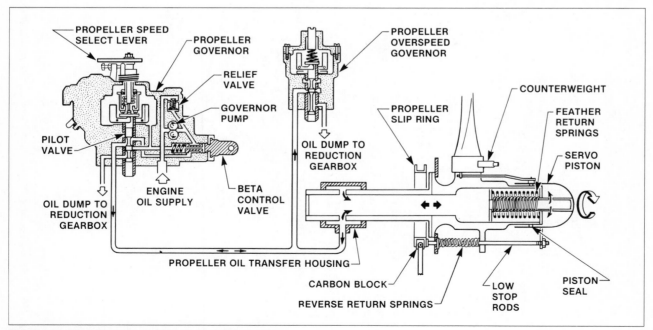

Figure 10-93. PT6 propeller system configuration.

underspeed and the pilot valve is lowered. The governor oil pump supplies the oil pressure for propeller operation in the Beta mode.

In the Alpha mode, the system RPM is high enough for the propeller governor to operate, and the system is in a constant-speed mode of operation. When the power lever is moved forward, more fuel flows to the engine to increase the horsepower, and the propeller governor causes an increase in propeller blade angle to absorb the power increase and maintain the selected system RPM. If the power lever is moved aft, the blade angle will be decreased by the governor to maintain the selected RPM.

To feather the propeller, move the propeller control lever full aft. This raises the pilot valve in the governor by a lift rod, and releases all of the oil pressure in the propeller. The springs and counterweights in the propeller will take it to feather.

To unfeather the propeller, start the engine. As it begins to rotate, the power turbine will rotate, and the governor or Beta control valve will take the propeller to the selected blade angle or governor RPM setting. When the engine is restarted, the engine will be started before the propeller is rotating at the same proportional speed because of the free-turbine characteristic of the engine.

If the propeller RPM should exceed 100%, the propeller over-speed governor will raise its pilot valve and release oil from the propeller to increase blade angle and prevent over-speeding of the propeller. The over-speed governor is automatic and is not controllable in flight.

The power turbine governor prevents excessive over-speeding of the propeller by reducing fuel flow to the engine at approximately 105% RPM. This governor is not controllable in flight and is automatic in operation.

6) System Installation And Maintenance

When installing the propeller, follow the basic procedures for flanged-shaft installations. The slip ring and carbon block arrangement must be installed following the procedures in the aircraft service manual for the specific model involved.

Adjust the governors and rig them with the fuel control unit and the cam mechanism, according to the appropriate maintenance manual.

The comments for the TPE-331 installation are applicable to the PT6 installation.

Basic troubleshooting procedures, as have been previously discussed, are applicable to the Hartzell reversing system. If you do not get the proper propeller response, check the system for proper rigging before investigating individual units unless the defect is obvious.

In Beta mode operation, the interconnection should be checked between the power lever, the cam mechanism, the fuel control unit, the Beta control valve on the propeller governor, and the Beta slip ring.

In the Alpha mode, the propeller governor and linkage to it from the propeller control lever and the cam mechanism should be checked.

If the system RPM is too low, the fault may be with the adjustment of the propeller over-speed governor or the power turbine governor. These components are not involved in the control linkage rigging, but do not forget them.

3. Blade Cuffs

A blade cuff is a metal, wood, or plastic structure designed for attachment to the shank end of the blade, with an outer surface that will transform the round shank into an airfoil section. The cuff is designed primarily to increase the flow of cooling air to the engine nacelle.

The cuffs are attached to the blades by mechanical clamping devices or by using bonding materials. Rubber-base adhesives and epoxy adhesives generally are used as bonding agents. Organic adhesives may cause corrosion, which results from moisture entrapment between the inner cuff surface and the outer shank surface.

Index